Proceedings of the International Symposium on

TRANSPORT PROCESSES IN STATISTICAL MECHANICS

Proceedings of the International Symposium on

TRANSPORT PROCESSES IN STATISTICAL MECHANICS

Held in Brussels, August 27-31, 1956

Sponsored by
THE INTERNATIONAL UNION OF PURE AND APPLIED PHYSICS
INSTITUTS SOLVAY (*Université Libre, Brussels*)
and EUROPEAN OFFICE, AIR RESEARCH AND DEVELOPMENT COMMAND,
UNITED STATES AIR FORCE (*Brussels*)

Editor: I. PRIGOGINE
Professor of Physical Chemistry and of Theoretical Physics
Université Libre, Brussels, Belgium

1958

INTERSCIENCE PUBLISHERS, INC., NEW YORK
INTERSCIENCE PUBLISHERS LTD., LONDON

Library of Congress Catalog Card Number 58-9936

Interscience Publishers, Inc.
250 Fifth Avenue, New York, N. Y.

For Great Britain and Northern Ireland:

Interscience Publishers Ltd.
88/90 Chancery Lane, London, W.C. 2, England

PRINTED IN THE NETHERLANDS

BY LATE HOITSEMA BROTHERS, GRONINGEN

FOREWORD

The problem of irreversible processes is one of the most fascinating in theoretical physics and chemistry.

While in other fields, such as valency theory or equilibrium processes, the basic theory is known and the difficulties are of a more purely-mathematical character, in the field of irreversible processes there is no agreement at present about the basic concepts and the basic methods that have to be used.

As Professor Uhlenbeck once observed, statistical mechanics is a slowly growing subject in which short periods of rapid development are followed by longer periods of stagnation. Today, it seems as though we are in one of the periods of rapid development.

It is hoped that the proceedings of this conference will give an idea of recent trends in this wide field from the point of view of both theoretical and experimental research.

The division of parts in this volume corresponds to the needs of the organization of the conference and not always to logical order. Nevertheless, theoretical papers appear in Parts I through XII, and experimental work appears in Parts XIII and XIV.

I wish to thank the authorities of the Université Libre de Bruxelles, the Instituts Solvay, the Air Research and Development Command U. S. A. F., and the International Union of Pure and Applied Physics whose generous support has made this Symposium possible.

I also wish to express my gratitude to all my co-workers who helped organize the Symposium.

October, 1957

I. PRIGOGINE
Faculte des Sciences, Université Libre,
Brussels, Belgium

CONTENTS

Part I

Part II

Part III

Part IV

Part V

Part VI

Part VII

Part VIII

Part IX

Part X

Part XI

Part XII

Part XIII

Part XIV

PART I

THE STATISTICAL MECHANICAL BASIS OF THE BOLTZMANN EQUATION

JOHN G. KIRKWOOD, *Sterling Chemistry Laboratory, Yale University, New Haven, Connecticut*

JOHN ROSS, *Metcalf Chemical Laboratories, Brown University, Providence, Rhode Island*

The statistical mechanical basis of the Maxwell-Boltzmann integro-differential equation of transport has been the subject of a number of recent investigations.[1–5] In the analysis of Kirkwood,[2] the Boltzmann equation is derived in the limit of zero density from the first principles of statistical mechanics for a coarse-grained single particle distribution function in μ-space, the coarse-grained function being defined as an average over an interval of time τ long relative to the representative duration of a binary collision.[6] It is the purpose of the present article to refine the derivation of Kirkwood by means of a more precise formulation of the binary collision mechanism, depending upon the use of phase space transformation functions. More detailed attention is given to the spatial dependence of the distribution functions and to the conditions for the existence of the integral of the pair correlation function in the collision term. The formalism based upon the phase space transformation functions will be applied in a future investigation to the generalization of the Boltzmann equation to higher densities and to the development of cluster expansions of the distribution functions.

We shall denote by $f^{(N)}(\mathbf{R}, \mathbf{p}; t)$ the probability density in phase space in a statistical ensemble of identical systems of N molecules. This function satisfies the Liouville equation,

$$\frac{\partial f^{(N)}}{\partial t} + \sum_{j=1}^{N} \left\{ \frac{\mathbf{p}_j}{m_j} \cdot \nabla_{\mathbf{R}_j} f^{(N)} + (\mathbf{X}_j + \mathbf{F}_j) \cdot \nabla_{\mathbf{p}_j} f^{(N)} \right\} = 0, \tag{1}$$

subject to arbitrary initial conditions.

The external forces on particle j are designated by $\mathbf{X}_j$ and the intermolecular forces by $\mathbf{F}_j$; the latter are assumed to be decomposable into central symmetric pair forces,

$$\mathbf{F}_j = \sum_{j \neq i = 1}^{N} \mathbf{F}_{ij}(|\mathbf{R}_j - \mathbf{R}_i|). \tag{2}$$

Integration of the distribution function $f^{(N)}$ over the coordinates and momenta of a subset of the N particles yields a reduced distribution function for the remaining set of particles. Integration of any distribution function over an interval of time τ leads to a time-smoothed function defined as

$$\bar{f}^{(n)}(\mathbf{r}, \mathbf{p}; t) = \frac{1}{\tau} \int_0^\tau f^{(n)}(\mathbf{r}, \mathbf{p}; t+s)\, ds. \tag{3}$$

Thus the equation for the time-smoothed singlet distribution function, in terms of which the derived Boltzmann equation will be expressed, is obtained from Eq. (1) by integration over the phase space of the complementary set of $N-1$ molecules,

$$\begin{aligned} &\frac{\partial \bar{f}^{(1)}}{\partial t} + \frac{\mathbf{p}_1}{m_1} \cdot \nabla_{\mathbf{R}_1} \bar{f}^{(1)} + \mathbf{X}_1 \cdot \nabla_{\mathbf{p}_1} \bar{f}^{(1)} \\ &\quad = -\frac{(N-1)}{\tau} \int_0^\tau \cdots \int \mathbf{F}_{12} \cdot \nabla_{\mathbf{p}_1} f^{(2)}(\mathbf{R}_1 \mathbf{R}_2 \mathbf{p}_1 \mathbf{p}_2; t+s)\, d\mathbf{R}_2 d\mathbf{p}_2 ds. \end{aligned} \tag{4}$$

Before proceeding with the further development of Eq. (4) we turn to a consideration of phase space transformation functions.* The integral equation

$$f^{(N)}(\mathbf{Rp}; t+s) = \int \cdots \int K^{(N)}(\mathbf{Rp}|\mathbf{R}'\mathbf{p}'; s) f^{(N)}(\mathbf{R}'\mathbf{p}'; t)\, d\mathbf{R}' d\mathbf{p}' \tag{5}$$

defines the transformation function $K^{(N)}$, which is a conditional probability density of finding the N-particle system at $[\mathbf{R}, \mathbf{p}]$ in phase space at time $(t+s)$ if the system was at $[\mathbf{R}'\ \mathbf{p}']$ at time t. $K^{(N)}$ obeys Liouville's equation

$$\frac{\partial K^{(N)}}{\partial s} + \sum_{j=1}^{N} \left\{ \frac{\mathbf{p}_j}{m_j} \cdot \nabla_{\mathbf{R}_j} K^{(N)} + (\mathbf{X}_j + \mathbf{F}_j) \cdot \nabla_{\mathbf{p}_j} K^{(N)} \right\} = 0 \tag{6}$$

* These functions have been discussed by J. E. Moyal, *Proc. Cambridge Phil. Soc.*, **45**, 99 (1949), in connection with quantum statistical problems. The theory has been further developed by J. Ross and J. G. Kirkwood, *J. Chem. Phys.*, **22**, 1094 (1954), and applied to a derivation of the analog of the Boltzmann equation of transport for quantum mechanical systems. For an application of these functions in classical statistical mechanics see J. Ross, *J. Chem. Phys.*, **24**, 375 (1956), "Contribution to the Theory of Brownian Motion."

with the initial condition

$$K^{(N)}(\mathbf{Rp}|\mathbf{R}'\mathbf{p}';\,0)=\prod_{j=1}^{N}\delta(\mathbf{R}_j-\mathbf{R}_j')\,\delta(\mathbf{p}_j-\mathbf{p}_j'). \tag{7}$$

The formal solution of Eq. (6) for the transformation function can be expressed as follows

$$K^{(N)}(\mathbf{Rp}|\mathbf{R}'\mathbf{p}';\,s)=\prod_{j=1}^{N}\delta[\mathbf{R}_j-\mathbf{R}_j'-\Delta\mathbf{R}_j(s)]\,\delta[\mathbf{p}_j-\mathbf{p}_j'-\Delta\mathbf{p}_j(s)]$$

where $\Delta\mathbf{R}_j(s)$ and $\Delta\mathbf{p}_j(s)$ are the changes in coordinates and momenta of particle j determined from a solution of the equation of motion of the N-particle system.

Reduced transformation functions can be formed from the defining Eq. (5) by integration. Consider first the reduced distribution $f^{(n)}(\mathbf{r},\mathbf{p};\,t+s)$ which is given by the expression,

$$f^{(n)}(\mathbf{r},\mathbf{p};\,t+s)=\int\cdots\int f^{(N)}(\mathbf{rpQP};\,t+s)\,d\mathbf{P}d\mathbf{Q}, \tag{8}$$

where $[\mathbf{r},\mathbf{p}]$ are the phase space coordinates of the subset of n particles and $[\mathbf{Q},\mathbf{P}]$ the coordinates of the remaining set. The two functions $f^{(n)}$ and $f^{(N)}$ are also related by the equation

$$f^{(N)}(\mathbf{rpQP};\,t+s)=f^{(n)}(\mathbf{rp};\,t+s)\,f^{(n|N-n)}(\mathbf{rp}|\mathbf{QP};\,t+s), \tag{9}$$

which defines the relative probability density $f^{(n|N-n)}$. Substitution of Eq. (5) into Eq. (8) shows that the reduced transformation function $K^{(n)}$ which fulfills the relation

$$f^{(n)}(\mathbf{rp};\,t+s)=\int\cdots\int K^{(n)}(\mathbf{rp}|\mathbf{r}'\mathbf{p}';\,s)\,f^{(n)}(\mathbf{r}'\mathbf{p}';\,t)\,d\mathbf{r}'d\mathbf{p}' \tag{10}$$

is given by

$$\begin{aligned}K^{(n)}(\mathbf{rp}|\mathbf{r}'\mathbf{p}';\,s)=\int\cdots\int &K^{(N)}(\mathbf{rpQP}|\mathbf{r}'\mathbf{p}'\mathbf{Q}'\mathbf{P}';\,s)\\ &\times f^{(n|N-n)}(\mathbf{r}'\mathbf{p}'|\mathbf{Q}'\mathbf{P}';\,t)\,d\mathbf{P}\,d\mathbf{Q}\,d\mathbf{P}'d\mathbf{Q}'.\end{aligned} \tag{11}$$

We return now to Eq. (4) to introduce the pair transformation function

$$\begin{aligned}&\frac{\partial\bar{f}^{(1)}}{\partial t}+\frac{\mathbf{p}_1}{m_1}\cdot\nabla_{\mathbf{R}_1}\bar{f}^{(1)}+\mathbf{X}_1\cdot\nabla_{\mathbf{p}_1}\bar{f}^{(1)}\\ &=-\frac{(N-1)}{\tau}\int_0^{\tau}\cdots\int\mathbf{F}_{12}\cdot\nabla_{\mathbf{p}_1}K^{(2)}(s)f^{(2)}(t)\,d\mathbf{R}_2d\mathbf{p}_2ds\,d\mathbf{R}_1'\,d\mathbf{R}_2'd\mathbf{p}_1'd\mathbf{p}_2'\end{aligned} \tag{12}$$

and relate the pair distribution function to singlet distribution functions by the equation

$$f^{(2)}(\mathbf{R}_1'\mathbf{R}_2'\mathbf{p}_1'\mathbf{p}_2';t) = g(\mathbf{R}_1'\mathbf{R}_2'\mathbf{p}_1'\mathbf{p}_2';t)\,f^{(1)}(\mathbf{R}_1'\mathbf{p}_1';t)\,f^{(1)}(\mathbf{R}_2'\mathbf{p}_2';t), \quad (13)$$

which defines the pair correlation function g, so that we obtain

$$\frac{\partial \bar{f}^{(1)}}{\partial t} + \frac{\mathbf{p}_1}{m_1}\cdot\nabla_{\mathbf{R}_1}\bar{f}^{(1)} + \mathbf{X}_1\cdot\nabla_{\mathbf{p}_1}\bar{f}^{(1)} = (N-1)\left[\Omega+\frac{\Theta}{\tau}\right], \quad (14)$$

where

$$\Omega = -\frac{1}{\tau}\int_0^\tau\cdots\int \mathbf{F}_{12}\cdot\nabla_{\mathbf{p}_1}K^{(2)}(s)f^{(1)}(t)f^{(1)}(t)\,d\mathbf{R}_2 d\mathbf{p}_2 ds\, d\mathbf{R}_1' d\mathbf{R}_2' d\mathbf{p}_1' d\mathbf{p}_2',$$

$$\Theta = +\int_0^\tau\cdots\int \mathbf{F}_{12}\cdot\nabla_{\mathbf{p}_1}K^{(2)}(s)\left\{[1-g^{(2)}(t)]\,f^{(1)}(t)\,f^{(1)}(t)\right\} \times d\mathbf{R}_2\, d\mathbf{p}_2\, ds\, d\mathbf{R}_1' d\mathbf{R}_2' d\mathbf{p}_1' d\mathbf{p}_2'. \quad (15)$$

We require that the correlation integral, which is the integral of the deviation of the pair correlation function from unity over relative configuration space, be finite at a given initial time and denote this condition a part of the assumption of molecular chaos. Furthermore, it can be shown in the limit of zero density that if the correlation integral is finite at one time it will remain finite at future times. Thus the contribution of the term (Θ/τ) can be made as small as desired for sufficiently large τ.

The integro-differential equation satisfied by $K^{(2)}$ is derived from Liouville's equation for $K^{(N)}$ by multiplication of that equation by $f^{(2|N-2)}(\mathbf{R}_1'\mathbf{R}_2'\mathbf{p}_1'\mathbf{p}_2'|\mathbf{P}'\mathbf{Q}';t)$ from the right and integration over $d\mathbf{P}\,d\mathbf{Q}\,d\mathbf{P}'d\mathbf{Q}'$; this leads to

$$\frac{\partial K^{(2)}}{\partial s} + \frac{\mathbf{p}_1}{m_1}\cdot\nabla_{\mathbf{R}_1}K^{(2)} + \frac{\mathbf{p}_2}{m_2}\cdot\nabla_{\mathbf{R}_2}K^{(2)} + (\mathbf{X}_1+\mathbf{F}_{12})\cdot\nabla_{\mathbf{p}_1}K^{(2)} + (\mathbf{X}_2+\mathbf{F}_{21})\cdot\nabla_{\mathbf{p}_2}K^{(2)}$$
$$= -\sum_{j=3}^{N}\int\cdots\int[\mathbf{F}_{1j}\cdot\nabla_{\mathbf{p}_1}+\mathbf{F}_{2j}\cdot\nabla_{\mathbf{p}_2}]K^{(N)}(s)f^{(2|N-2)}(\mathbf{R}_1'\mathbf{R}_2'\mathbf{p}_1'\mathbf{p}_2'|\mathbf{Q}'\mathbf{P}';t)\,d\mathbf{P}d\mathbf{Q}d\mathbf{P}'d\mathbf{Q}' \quad (16)$$

where $d\mathbf{P} = d\mathbf{p}_3\cdots d\mathbf{p}_N$, $d\mathbf{Q} = d\mathbf{R}_3\cdots d\mathbf{R}_N$, etc. Eq. (13) is applicable to a description of the behavior of two particles in a system at arbitrary density. In the limit of zero density the triple collision terms on the right-hand side of Eq. (16) obviously vanish and $K^{(2)}$ approaches

$K_0^{(2)}$ which obeys the equation

$$\frac{\partial K_0^{(2)}}{\partial s}+\frac{\mathbf{p}_1}{m_1}\cdot\nabla_{\mathbf{R}_1}K_0^{(2)}+\frac{\mathbf{p}_2}{m_2}\cdot\nabla_{\mathbf{R}_2}K_0^{(2)}+(\mathbf{X}_1+\mathbf{F}_{12})\cdot\nabla_{\mathbf{p}_1}K_0^{(2)} +(\mathbf{X}_2+\mathbf{F}_{21})\cdot\nabla_{\mathbf{p}_2}K_0^{(2)}=0. \tag{17}$$

The solution for $K_0^{(2)}$ is determined with the additional approximation that the external forces are sufficiently slowly varying so as not to affect significantly a binary encounter. With this simplification $K_0^{(2)}$ becomes

$$K_0^{(2)}(\mathbf{R}_1\mathbf{p}_1\mathbf{R}_2\mathbf{p}_2|\mathbf{R}_1'\mathbf{p}_1'\mathbf{R}_2'\mathbf{p}_2';s) = \delta[\mathbf{R}_1-\mathbf{R}_1'-\Delta\mathbf{R}_1(s)]\,\delta[\mathbf{R}_2-\mathbf{R}_2'-\Delta\mathbf{R}_2(s)]\,\delta[\mathbf{p}_1-\mathbf{p}_1'-\Delta\mathbf{p}_1(s)]\,\delta[\mathbf{p}_2-\mathbf{p}_2'-\Delta\mathbf{p}_2(s)], \tag{18}$$

where now $\Delta\mathbf{p}_1$, $\Delta\mathbf{p}_2$, $\Delta\mathbf{R}_1$, and $\Delta\mathbf{R}_2$ are the increments, in the time interval s, in the momenta and radius vectors of a pair of molecules undergoing a binary collision with initial coordinates $\mathbf{p}_1'\mathbf{R}_1'\mathbf{p}_2'\mathbf{R}_2'$. We take Eqs. (17) and (18) to be the analytic formulation of the binary collision mechanism in the limit of zero density.

Substitution of Eq. (17) into the function Ω Eq. (15), leads to

$$\Omega=\frac{1}{\tau}\int\cdots\int_0^\tau\left\{\frac{\partial K_0^{(2)}}{\partial s}+\frac{\mathbf{p}_1}{m_1}\cdot\nabla_{\mathbf{R}_1}K_0^{(2)}+\frac{\mathbf{p}_2}{m_2}\cdot\nabla_{\mathbf{R}_2}K_0^{(2)}\right\} \times f^{(1)}(\mathbf{R}_1'\mathbf{p}_1';t)\,f^{(1)}(\mathbf{R}_2'\mathbf{p}_2';t)\,d\mathbf{R}_2\,d\mathbf{p}_2\,ds\,d\mathbf{R}_1'\,d\mathbf{R}_2'\,d\mathbf{p}_1'\,d\mathbf{p}_2', \tag{19}$$

which, with the aid of Eq. (18) can be altered to read

$$\Omega=\frac{1}{\tau}\int\cdots\int_0^\tau\{\delta(\mathbf{R}_1-\mathbf{R}_1'-\Delta\mathbf{R}_1)\delta(\mathbf{R}_2-\mathbf{R}_2'-\Delta\mathbf{R}_2) \frac{\partial}{\partial s}[\delta(\mathbf{p}_1-\mathbf{p}_1'-\Delta\mathbf{p}_1)\delta(\mathbf{p}_2-\mathbf{p}_2'-\Delta\mathbf{p}_2)]\} \times f^{(1)}(\mathbf{R}_1'\mathbf{p}_1';t)\,f^{(1)}(\mathbf{R}_2'\mathbf{p}_2';t)\,d\mathbf{R}_2\,d\mathbf{p}_2\,ds\,d\mathbf{R}_1'\,d\mathbf{R}_2'\,d\mathbf{p}_1'\,d\mathbf{p}_2'. \tag{20}$$

We denote the difference between this last expression and

$$\Omega'=\frac{1}{\tau}\int_0^\tau\cdots\int\{\delta(\mathbf{R}_1-\mathbf{R}_1')\delta(\mathbf{R}_2-\mathbf{R}_2')\frac{\partial}{\partial s}[\delta(\mathbf{p}_1-\mathbf{p}_1'-\Delta\mathbf{p}_1)\delta(\mathbf{p}_2-\mathbf{p}_2'-\Delta\mathbf{p}_2)] \times f^{(1)}(\mathbf{R}_1'\mathbf{p}_1';t)\,f^{(1)}(\mathbf{R}_1'\mathbf{p}_2';t)\,d\mathbf{R}_2\,d\mathbf{p}_2\,ds\,d\mathbf{R}_1'\,d\mathbf{R}_2'\,d\mathbf{p}_1'\,d\mathbf{p}_2' \tag{21}$$

by $(\Delta\Omega|\tau)$, i.e., $\Omega=\Omega'+(\Delta\Omega|\tau)$. The expansion of the δ-functions in

Taylor series leads to the following expression for $[\varDelta\varOmega|\tau]$ to first order in configuration space gradients

$$\frac{\varDelta\varOmega}{\tau} = -\frac{1}{\tau^2}\int\cdots\int_0^\tau \{\delta(\mathbf{R}_1-\mathbf{R}_1')[\varDelta\mathbf{R}_2\cdot\nabla_{\mathbf{R}_2}\delta(\mathbf{R}_2-\mathbf{R}_2')-\delta(\mathbf{R}_2-\mathbf{R}_2')\mathbf{R}'\cdot\nabla_{\mathbf{R}_1}']$$
$$+\delta(\mathbf{R}_2-\mathbf{R}_2')\varDelta\mathbf{R}_1\cdot\nabla_{\mathbf{R}_1}\delta(\mathbf{R}_1-\mathbf{R}_1')\}$$
$$\times\left\{\frac{\partial}{\partial s}[\delta(\mathbf{p}_1-\mathbf{p}_1'-\varDelta\mathbf{p}_1)\delta(\mathbf{p}_2-\mathbf{p}_2'-\varDelta\mathbf{p}_2)]\right\}$$
$$f^{(1)}(\mathbf{R}_1'\mathbf{p}_1';t)f^{(1)}(\mathbf{R}_1'\mathbf{p}_2';t)\,d\mathbf{R}_2\,d\mathbf{p}_2\,ds\,d\mathbf{R}_1'\,d\mathbf{R}_2'\,d\mathbf{p}_1'\,d\mathbf{p}_2'.$$

The term $[\varDelta\varOmega|\tau]$ is independent of τ for sufficiently large values of τ and therefore is in general a constituent of the Boltzmann equation. An estimate of the average extent of $\varDelta\mathbf{R}(s)$ yields a distance L_τ which is much larger than the range of the intermolecular forces but much smaller than the mean free path. If the application of the equation of transport is restricted to systems in which the distribution functions and therefore the macroscopic properties do not vary significantly over a distance L_τ, then the term $[\varDelta\varOmega|\tau]$ becomes a small correction which is usually neglected.

The integration over s, $\mathbf{R}_1'$, $\mathbf{R}_2'$ in Eq. (21) is simple and $\varOmega'$ becomes

$$\varOmega' = \int\cdots\int\frac{1}{\tau}\{\delta[\mathbf{p}_1-\mathbf{p}_1'-\varDelta\mathbf{p}_1(\tau)]\delta[\mathbf{p}_2-\mathbf{p}_2'-\varDelta\mathbf{p}_2(\tau)]-\delta[\mathbf{p}_1-\mathbf{p}_1']\delta[\mathbf{p}_2-\mathbf{p}_2']\}$$
$$\times f^{(1)}(\mathbf{R}_1\mathbf{p}_1';t)f^{(1)}(\mathbf{R}_1\mathbf{p}_2';t)\,d\mathbf{R}\,d\mathbf{p}_2\,d\mathbf{p}_1'\,d\mathbf{p}_2', \qquad (22)$$

where $d\mathbf{R}_2$ has been replaced by $d\mathbf{R}$, $\mathbf{R} = \mathbf{R}_2-\mathbf{R}_1$. At this point the remainder of the derivation is identical with that of Kirkwood and will be outlined only briefly. The integration over the relative configuration space is accomplished in a cylindrical coordinate system (z, b, ε) with origin on molecule 1 and z-axis antiparallel to the initial relative momentum vector. The regions of this relative Lagrange configuration space for which complete collisions occur in the interval τ consist of filaments of volume

$$\frac{\mathbf{p}_{12}}{m_{12}}\tau b\,db\,d\varepsilon,$$

where $\mathbf{p}_{12}$ is the magnitude of the initial relative momentum and m_{12} is the reduced mass. Incomplete collisions or motion in multiply periodic orbits arise from regions of relative configuration space of finite volume elements independent of τ so that their contribution becomes inconsequential for sufficiently large τ. For all other regions of relative configuration space the bracket in Eq. (21) vanishes since the increments in momenta of particles 1 and 2 are zero. These considerations and use of Eqs. (14) and (22) lead to an expression which, upon additional time smoothing, finally yields the Boltzmann equation,

$$\begin{aligned}&\frac{\partial \bar{f}^{(1)}}{\partial t}+\frac{\mathbf{p}_1}{m_1}\cdot\nabla_{\mathbf{R}_1}\bar{f}^{(1)}+\mathbf{X}_1\cdot\nabla_{\mathbf{p}_1}\bar{f}^{(1)}\\&=(N-1)\int\cdots\int\frac{\mathbf{p}_{12}}{m_{12}}\{\bar{f}^{(1)}[\mathbf{R}_1,\mathbf{p}_1-\Delta\mathbf{p}_1;t]\bar{f}^{(1)}[\mathbf{R}_1,\mathbf{p}_2-\Delta\mathbf{p}_2;t]\\&\qquad-\bar{f}^{(1)}(\mathbf{R}_1\mathbf{p}_1;t)\bar{f}^{(1)}(\mathbf{R}_1\mathbf{p}_2;t)\}\,bd\,bd\,\varepsilon d\,\mathbf{p}_2,\end{aligned}\tag{23}$$

provided the function $\overline{f^{(1)}f^{(1)}}$ can be replaced by $\bar{f}^{(1)}\bar{f}^{(1)}$, a procedure which can be justified for distributions close to equilibrium.

One of the authors (J. R.) wishes to acknowledge that this work was supported in part by a grant from the National Science Foundation.

References

(1) J. Yvon, *Actualités Scientifiques et Industrielles,* Hermann, Paris, 1935.
(2) J. G. Kirkwood, *J. Chem. Phys.*, **15**, 72 (1947).
(3) M. Born and H. S. Green, *A General Kinetic Theory of Liquids,* Cambridge Univ. Press, London, 1949.
(4) N. Bogolyubov, *J. Phys. (U. S. S. R.)*, **10**, 265 (1946).
(5) H. L. Frisch, *J. Chem. Phys.*, **22**, 1713 (1954).
(6) J. G. Kirkwood, *J. Chem. Phys.*, **14**, 180 (1946).
(7) S. Chapman and T. G. Cowling, *The Mathematical Theory of Non-Uniform Gases,* Cambridge Univ. Press, London, 1952.

STATISTICAL MECHANICS AND THE BOLTZMANN EQUATION

MELVILLE S. GREEN, *National Bureau of Standards, Washington, D.C.*

The statistical theory of bulk matter has always had two parts. The part usually called statistical mechanics is applicable to a very wide range of material systems in all states of aggregation but is almost entirely limited to the explanation of the static, equilibirum, time-independent properties of matter. On the other hand, the part usually called the kinetic theory of gases, while narrowly limited to dilute gases, is capable of dealing with the dynamic, nonequilibirum, time-dependent behavior of matter and in particular with the transport properties whose theory is the subject of this colloquium. The basic difference in method between these two parts is, of course, that the population, in the statistician's sense, of statistical mechanics is a fictitious ensemble of identical systems of many molecules while that of kinetic theory is the assembly of the actual molecules of the gas. The information contained in the ensemble of statistical mechanics is in a certain sense complete, and it is not at all surprising that the distribution function of the ensemble propagates itself in an entirely predictable way according to a first-order differential equation in time, the Liouville equation. It is, however, very surprising indeed that the distribution function of the assembly in kinetic theory also propagates itself predictably according to such an equation, the Boltzmann equation. My purpose today is to discuss some recent work which places kinetic theory and the Boltzmann equation[1] in the framework of statistical mechanics and at the same time extends and generalizes the method so as to apply to moderately compressed gases.

It is widely recognized that the Boltzmann equation and its solution is the first step in an approximation scheme appropriate to small concentrations. Indeed the concept of collision on which the Boltzmann equation is based has meaning only if the time that a molecule spends in interaction with others is small compared to the time spent in free rectilinear motion. It is perhaps not so widely recognized that the Boltzmann equation is valid only if there is substantial spatial uniformity over regions containing a large number of molecules. That this is so, however, is clear from the heuristic derivation of the Boltzmann equation of which an essential feature is the computation of the expected number of collisions of certain types which occur in a defined region of space. If the fluctuations from the expected value are to be negligible, the number in the defined region must be large, while in order to compute the expected number at all the distribution of the molecules must be homogeneous throughout the region. It should be noted, however, that the diameter of a region containing a large number of molecules may be small compared to a mean free path so that for the validity of the Boltzmann equation, there is no need for spatial uniformity over a mean free path. Thus the Boltzmann equation should be valid for shock and other phenomena of large Knudsen number although the methods needed to solve it must certainly change with the Knudsen number.

In order to avoid complications which are not essential to the question at hand I suppose that we are dealing with a gas of a large number of molecules contained in a large volume which is in a spatially uniform but nonequilibrium state. Eventually I shall wish to assume that the gas is dilute, that is to say that only a small fraction of the total volume is occupied by molecules. I also wish to assume that there are no correlations among the positions and momenta of molecules separated by a macroscopic distance. This last assumption can be expressed in terms of the distribution functions $f_n(1 \cdots n)$ of the positions and moments of particles (abbreviated in the symbol $(1 \cdots n)$) in the form:

$$f_{n+h}(1 \cdots n, n+1 \cdots n+h) \rightarrow f_n(1 \cdots n) f_h(n+1 \cdots n+h) \qquad (1)$$

if the groups of molecules $1 \cdots n$ and $n+1 \cdots n+h$ are separated far enough and will therefore be called the product condition. It cannot be strictly true for a finite system because the constancy of the number of particles or of the energy requires a constant correlation between all particles of the order of the reciprocal of their number. The product condition is the more valid the larger the system.

The product condition is a statistical hypotheses about the distribution of the system and it is easy to imagine distributions which do not satisfy it. It has, however, this advantage over similar hypotheses (the "Stosszahl ansatz" or the superposition principle), that in the limit of an infinite system, if it is true at one time it is true at all others as a consequence of the equations of motion.

There have been in the past several proposals about how the Boltzmann equation is to be fitted into the framework of statistical mechanics. One such proposal which has much to recommend it but which turns out not to be correct reasons from the fact that a self-contained equation for the single particle distribution is certainly not valid for liquids. Since there is a continuity of state between a liquid or a dense gas and a dilute gas, a self-contained equation for $f_{(1)}$ is not rigorously valid for a dilute gas except in the lowest order of approximation in power series in the density. As soon as we go to the next order of approximation we must have, instead of a single self-contained equation for f_1, a pair of simultaneous equations for f_1, and f_2 and to the next order, a triple of simultaneous equations for f_1, f_2, and f_3 and so on.

A quite different proposal was made by Bogolyubov in 1946.[2–4] According to this proposal a single self-contained equation for f_1 is valid to all orders of the concentration. However, the equation for f_1 appropriate to a finite concentration contains in addition to the usual binary collision contribution to this rate of change of f_1 contributions from triple and higher order collisions. It is almost a corollary of the existence of a self-contained equation for f_1 that the pair and all higher distribution functions are determined by f_1, i.e., that all distribution functions are functionals of f_1. Bogolyubov gave a scheme for developing these functionals as well as the collisional contribution to the rate of change of f_1 in power series in the concentration. In order to explain the fact that a self-contained equation for f_1 is not valid for dense gases and liquids, it is probably necessary to assume that these series are asymptotic rather than convergent.

Bogolyubov was well aware that physical situations can be arbitrarily set up in which the higher order distribution functions are not determined by f_1 through a functional relationship. He assumed that such situations are short-lived and quickly go over into situations in which the functional relation obtains in the very short time of duration of a single collision. The work that I wish to report on more particularly today confirms Bogolyubov's ideas in general and detail by a rather different method. Before I give a few of the details of this work, however, I would like to mention one more point about the relation between kinetic theory and statistical mechanical methods. In this point of view, suggested by Uhlenbeck[5] and much developed by Siegert[6] and Kac,[7] attention is directed toward a division of momentum space into cells and to the many-dimensional random variable consisting of the occupation numbers of these cells. According to this point of view, at low densities the temporal sequence of the occupation number random variable is a Markoff process and is governed by an equation of the Chapman-Kolmogonoff type which has been called the *master equation*. The fact that the future value f_1, which is essentially the expectation value of the occupation number of a cell divided by the cell volume, develops from its present value according to a self-contained equation is a reflection of the fact that the future distribution of the occupation numbers develops from its present value according to the master equation, and of the fact that, when the number of particles is large, fluctuations of the occupation numbers from their expectation values are very small. There are several advantages in connecting the Boltzmann equation to statistical mechanics via the master equation, one of the most important being that the master equation is linear. Approaches which attempt to derive the Boltzmann equation directly are not in contradiction to the approach via the master equation but merely represent the first term in expansion in reciprocal powers of the number of particles.

It will not be possible here to give the details of the solution for the distribution function in powers of the concentration which are unfortunately very complicated (those interested are referred to a publication shortly to appear in *Journal of Chemical Physics*[1]). I will, however, describe the general character of the solution and then illustrate some of its properties through an explicit discussion of the first few terms of the series for the singlet and pair distribution functions. It turns out to be convenient to work with a sequence of functions which have been used very often in the equilibrium theory of imperfect gases, the Ursell-Mayer or cluster functions $g_n(1 \cdots n)$. This sequence contains the same information as the sequence of distribution functions but instead of the product condition has the property that each g_n is zero unless all n molecules are clustered together in one compact group. The first two of these functions are

$$\begin{aligned} cg_1(1) &= f_1(1), \\ c^2g_2(1, 2) &= f_1(1, 2) - f_1(1)f_1(2). \end{aligned} \tag{2}$$

The Ursell-Mayer function g_n is given as a power series in the concentration the rth term of which can be computed as soon as the dynamic equations of motion of groups of molecules up to size $n+r$ can be solved. To uniquely specify a solution the initial values of all the Ursell-Mayer functions must be known. However, the rth term of the series has an asymptotic form which is a polynomial of order r in the time. It is the asymptotic form for g, which obeys a self-contained equation, the modified Boltzmann equation, while the asymptotic form of the higher order Ursell-Mayer functions are functions of the asymptotic form for g_1. To specify the asymptotic solution for all times only the initial value of g_1 need be specified. It must be emphasized that, although the asymptotic form is valid for all large times, the particular series expansion which is given for it is valid only for times much smaller than the mean free time.

Let us look in detail at the first two terms of the series for $g_1(1)$ and the first term of the series for $g_2(1, 2)$. These are expressed in terms of two arbitrary functions, $\xi_1(1)$ which may be considered to be in the zeroth order in the concentration the initial value of $c^{-1}f_1(1)$, and $\xi_2(1, 2)$ which may be considered the zeroth order approximation to $c^{-2}f_2(1, 2)$. $\xi_2(1, 2)$ obeys the product condition

$$\xi_2(1, 2) \to \xi_1(1)\xi_1(2), \tag{3}$$

when molecules 1 and 2 are far apart. We will also need to know the solution of the dynamic equations of group of two isolated molecules. We will indicate by the symbols $1'_t$, $2'_t$ the positions and moments at time t of molecules 1 and 2, respectively, considered as functions of their initial positions and moments. Then

$$\begin{aligned} g_1(1, t) &= \xi_1(1)+c\int(\xi_2(1'_{-t}, 2'_{-t})-\xi_1(1)\xi_1(2))d(2)+\cdots, \\ g_2(1, 2t) &= \xi_2(1'_{-t}, 2'_{-t})-\xi_1(1)\xi_1(2)+\cdots. \end{aligned} \tag{4}$$

The qualitative behavior of g_1 and g_2 can in the present order or approximation be understood in terms of the properties of the function which appears as the integrand in the second term in g_1 and as the first term in g_2. When t is zero this function is zero outside some bounded region of the space of relative configurations of the two molecules. Inside this region it represents the initial correlation of the two molecules. Let us now consider the asymptotic form of this function for some large time t (less than the mean free time) and in particular its dependence on relative configuration for fixed value of the momenta of the two molecules. The important point to realize is that configurations in which the two molecules were originally close together and in which there was some correlation between them have separated a distance equal to the relative velocity times t. On the other hand configurations in which the two molecules are now close together have come from distant regions in which the two molecules are not correlated at all and for which ξ_2 can be represented as a product of ξ_1's. For these configurations we may represent $g_2(1, 2)$ as

$$\xi_1(p_1')\xi_2(p_2')-\xi_1(p_1)\xi_1(p_2), \tag{5}$$

where p_1', p_2' are the moments in the indefinite past of molecules 1 and 2 considered as a function of their initial relative positions and momenta. This asymptotic form is a functional of ξ_1. It is different from zero in a quasi-cylindrical region surrounding the origin and the positive ray in the direction of the relative velocity and is valid along this ray until points which have come from the originally correlated region are reached. Beyond these points the function is again zero. When we insert this expression in the second term in the expansion for $g_{(1)}$, the major contribution comes from the cylindrical portion which grows in length in proportion to the time. The integral is thus proportional to the time, and the proportionality constant is a functional of the single particle distribution function and is indeed simply the Boltzmann collision integral.

I want to emphasize two points resulting from this analysis. The first is that the change in the single particle distribution function is essentially determined by the initial value of this function itself while the the asymptotic form of the pair distribution depends on the single particle distribution function except for certain separated configurations. These two properties of the solutions which have been discussed for times small compared to the mean free time can be shown to be valid for all times. The calculations which lead to this result are too long to be presented here. But we may discuss a few of the points which arise in this analysis. Like the second term in the equation for g_1, the general term of the series solution is an integral over an integrand which differs from zero only for configurations which are so to speak connected by collisions which occur at some time between 0 and $-t$. Among these configurations are a subclass (to be described as "connected τ")

which are connected by collisions which take place between 0 and $-\tau$, where τ is some fixed time much longer than a collision time, but still much shorter than a mean free time. If t is long enough none of the configurations which were correlated at $t = 0$ belong to this subclass. The integration may be carried out first over all configurations which are not connected. The analysis then contains no further reference to the correlated configurations. The resulting series sum very conveniently to show that for configurations which are connected τ the Ursell-Mayer functions are functionals of g_1. That g_1 satisfies a generalized Boltzmann equation is a consequence of this.

To sum up we may say that, although the equations for the distribution functions have many solutions corresponding to arbitrary specifications of the initial values of all the distribution functions, the memory of these initial conditions are lost except for widely separated points which are of no significance for most properties of the system. The time for initial correlations to be scattered in such a harmless way depends on the magnitude of the initial regions of correlations. While this time may be large for some initial conditions we may expect that it is usually of the order of magnitude of the duration of a collision.

This work was sponsored by the United States Air Force through the Office of Scientific Research of the Air Research and Development Command.

References

(1) M. S. Green, *J. Chem. Phys.*, **25,** 836 (1956).
(2) N. N. Bogolyubov, *J. of Phys.* (*U. S. S. R*), **10**, 265 (1946).
(3) N. N. Bogolyubov, *Problems of Dynamical Theory in Statistical Physics*, Moscow, 1946.
(4) G. E. Uhlenbeck, *Lecture Notes, Higgins Lectures*, Princeton, 1954.
(5) A. Nordsieck, W. E. Lamb, Jr., and G. E. Uhlenbeck, *Physica*, **7**, 344 (1940).
(6) A. J. F. Siegert, *Phys. Rev.*, **76**, 1708 (1949).
(7) M. Kac, *Proceedings of the Third Berkeley Symposium on Mathematical Statistics and Probability*, University of California Press, Berkeley, 1956, pp. 171—197.

STATISTICAL MECHANICAL FOUNDATIONS OF THE BOLTZMANN EQUATION

R. BROUT,* *Faculté des Sciences, Université Libre de Bruxelles, Belgium*

PART I

This report constitutes an attempt to find the necessary and sufficient conditions to prove the validity of the Boltzmann equation from the principles of classical mechanics.

We shall restrict ourselves to binary collisions, but the general development points the way to the higher order collisions.

Our technique shall be to work from the full Liouville equation in phase space

$$\partial\varrho(\mathbf{v}_1 \cdots \mathbf{v}_N \mathbf{r}_1 \cdots \mathbf{r}_N)/\partial t + [H, \varrho] = 0 \tag{1.1}$$

to the "master" equation[1,2] which is in some sense a contraction of (1.1) over all $\mathbf{r}_i$. This equation in the binary collision approximation is

$$\begin{aligned}\frac{\partial\varrho(\mathbf{v}_1 \cdots \mathbf{v}_N)}{\partial t} &\\ = \sum_{1\leq i<j\leq N} \int \frac{\mathrm{d}\Omega_{ij}|\mathbf{v}_i-\mathbf{v}_j|\sigma(\theta_{ij})}{V}&[\varrho(\mathbf{v}_1\cdots\mathbf{v}'_i\cdots\mathbf{v}'_j\cdots\mathbf{v}_N)-\varrho(\mathbf{v}_1\cdots\mathbf{v}_N)]\\ \equiv \Omega\varrho(\mathbf{v}_1\cdots\mathbf{v}_N)&\end{aligned} \tag{1.2}$$

$\mathbf{v}_i, \mathbf{v}_j$ = the velocities of molecules i and j, respectively

$H = \sum \frac{m\mathbf{v}_i^2}{2} + \sum_{1\leq i<j\leq N} V_{ij}$

V_{ij} = intermolecular potential between i and j

$\sigma(\theta_{ij})$ = scattering cross-section as function of the scattering angle

$\mathrm{d}\Omega_{ij}$ = element of solid angle

$\mathbf{v}'_i, \mathbf{v}'_j$ = velocities of molecules i and j after scattering through angle θ_{ij} given $\mathbf{v}_i$ and $\mathbf{v}_j$ initially.

Eqs. (1.1) and (1.2) are completely different in character, the first

* Present address: Cornell University, Ithaca, N.Y.

containing the operator $[H, \varrho]$ which is unitary in character. The second contains the operator Ω which is self-adjoint. The first operator has only imaginary eigenvalues corresponding to reversible behavior. The second has real negative eigenvalues corresponding to relaxation times and irreversible behavior. It is far from obvious that (1.1) can under some circumstances imply (1.2). We shall prove this to be the case under the following necessary and sufficient conditions.

A. Mechanical Conditions

(1) It is assumed that V_{ij} has a finite radius of interaction. For two molecules within this radius a collision is said to be taking place. Out of this radius there is no collision.

(2) The system is taken to be very large. In fact rigorous results only hold in the strict limit $N \to \infty$. This hypothesis is essential in that it reduces the existence of correlation propagating cycles to probability zero. If molecule 1 collides with 2, their velocities are correlated by virtue of the collision. If 1 then collides with 3 and recollides with 2, one can show that this event is not correctly described by Eq. (1.2). It is only by explicit neglect of such terms in the general theory that (1.2) holds. This neglect is valid for infinite systems only. One may say that a sufficiently large system allows for "random" mixing of the available energy among all degrees of freedom.

(3) *Double Time Scale.* Condition (1) leads to a definition of a collision time. If R is the range of the force, then $\tau_{\text{collision}} = R/|\mathbf{v}_i - \mathbf{v}_j|$. We shall confine ourselves to the solution of (1.1) for $t \gg \tau_{\text{collision}}$. A mathematical way to do this and at the same time to restrict oneself to binary collisions is to notice that the relaxation time is proportional to $1/c$. Hence if one takes a dilute system $(c \to 0)$ for times long enough $(t \to \infty)$ such that $(ct) \to$ const., then we satisfy $t \gg \tau_{\text{collision}}$ and secure binary collisions only. Hypothesis (3) is essentially that such times exist.

B. Statistical Conditions

The passage from (1.1) to (1.2) involves an integration over all r_i. This is not trivial. In the theory of weakly coupled systems it has been shown that only that component of ϱ which is phase-independent (here the phase is $\mathbf{r}_i$) obeys an irreversible equation.[3] This has its analog in the present problem. Here it must be assumed that the correlation length is finite at the initial time. That is $\varrho(\mathbf{v}_1 \cdots \mathbf{v}_N, \mathbf{r}_1 \cdots \mathbf{r}_N)$ is independent of $(\mathbf{r}_i - \mathbf{r}_j)$ if $|\mathbf{r}_i - \mathbf{r}_j| > R_1$, where R_1 is thought of as some microscopic distance of the order of the range of force. This assumption is essentially an assumption of randomness in configuration space. It is equivalent in some sense to a "Stosszahl ansatz." It is a necessary and sufficient condition in order to derive (1.2) from (1.1) Ordered distributions do not work.

PART II

We shall briefly indicate how these assumptions lead to the derivation of (1.2). Details will be found elsewhere.[4]

If no collision takes place in the interval $0 \leqq t_1 \leqq t$, then the solution of the Liouville equation is $\varrho(\mathbf{v}_1 \cdots \mathbf{v}_N, \mathbf{r}_1 - \mathbf{v}_1 t \cdots \mathbf{r}_N - \mathbf{v}_N t; 0)$. If a collision takes place between molecules 1 and 2, then the solution of the Liouville equation is

$$\varrho(\mathbf{v}_1 \cdots \mathbf{v}_N, \mathbf{r}_1 \cdots \mathbf{r}_N; t) = \varrho(\mathbf{v}_1', \mathbf{v}_2', \mathbf{v}_3, \cdots, \mathbf{v}_N; \mathbf{r}_1', \mathbf{r}_2', \mathbf{r}_3 - \mathbf{v}_3 t \cdots \mathbf{r}_N - \mathbf{v}_N t), \quad (2.1)$$

where $\mathbf{v}_1', \mathbf{v}_2', \mathbf{r}_1', \mathbf{r}_2'$ are the velocities and positions of 1 and 2 before collision such that they give $\mathbf{r}_1, \mathbf{r}_2, \mathbf{v}_1, \mathbf{v}_2$ after collision. They are, of course, unique as determined by the equations of motion. It is also possible to write (2.1) as [we define $\varrho(1', 2', 3, \cdots,)$ as the solution of the Liouville equation if only 1 and 2 collide in this time]

$$\varrho(t) = \varrho(1, \cdots, N) + [\varrho(1', 2', \cdots N) - \varrho(1, \cdots, N)]. \quad (2.2)$$

If three molecules interact in the interval $0 \leqq t_1 \leqq t$, we may write the solution as $\varrho(1', 2', 3', \cdots, N)$ or alternatively

$$\begin{aligned} \varrho(t) = {} & \varrho(1, \cdots, N) + [\varrho(1', 2', \cdots, N) - \varrho(1, \cdots, N)] \\ & + [\varrho(1', 2, 3', \cdots, N) - \varrho(1, \cdots, N)] + [\varrho(1, 2', 3', \cdots, N) - \varrho(1, \cdots, N)] \\ & + [\varrho(1', 2', 3', \cdots, N) - \varrho(1', 2', 3, \cdots, N) - \varrho(1, 2', 3', \cdots, N) \\ & - \varrho(1', 2, 3', \cdots, N) + 2\varrho(1, \cdots, N)]. \end{aligned} \quad (2.3)$$

This process may be continued indefinitely.

Finally we write

$$\varrho(t) = \varrho(1, \cdots, N) + \sum_{1 \leqq i < j \leqq N} [\varrho(1, \cdots, i', \cdots, j', \cdots, N) - \varrho(1, \cdots, N)] + \cdots. \quad (2.4)$$

For the explicit statement of the expansion, see ref. 4. In Eq. (2.4) we define $(1, \cdots, N)$ as the solution of the Liouville equation for the problem in which no molecules interact, $\varrho(1, \cdots, i', \cdots, j', \cdots, N)$ the solution in which only i and j interact, etc.

We now integrate (2.4) over all configurations. The second term gives a contribution only from those $\mathbf{r}_i$ and $\mathbf{r}_j$ which were initially in the collision cylinder $\int d\Omega_{ij}|\mathbf{v}_i-\mathbf{v}_j|t\sigma(\theta_{ij})$, where, for given θ_{ij}, $\mathbf{v}_i'$, $\mathbf{v}_j'$ are determined by the laws of a collision. In the time interval discussed in assumption A(3) using the statistical hypothesis B, the contribution to (2.4) by integration over all $\mathbf{r}_i$.

$$
\begin{aligned}
&\varrho(\mathbf{v}_1 \cdots \mathbf{v}_N; t) \\
&= \varrho(\mathbf{v}_1 \cdots \mathbf{v}_N; 0) + t \sum_{i<j} \int \frac{d\Omega_{ij}\sigma(\theta_{ij})|\mathbf{v}_i-\mathbf{v}_j|}{V} [\varrho(\mathbf{v}_1, \ldots, \mathbf{v}_i', \cdots, \mathbf{v}_j', \cdots, \mathbf{v}_N; 0) \\
&\quad - \varrho(\mathbf{v}_1 \cdots \mathbf{v}_N; 0)] + \cdots \qquad (2.5) \\
&\equiv \varrho(\mathbf{v}_1 \cdots \mathbf{v}_N; 0) + t\Omega\varrho(0) + \cdots
\end{aligned}
$$

where we have neglected terms of $0(cR^3)$ which do not contain the time (this is the contribution from molecules in the course of collision around $t_1 \simeq 0$ and $t_1 \simeq t$). This requires hypothesis A(3). The higher order terms may be dealt with in a similar manner. Using hypotheses A(2) and (3) it may then be shown that they can be regrouped to give

$$\varrho(t) = \sum_n \frac{(t\Omega)^n}{n!} \varrho(0).$$

Differentiation then leads to (1.2).

This work was sponsored by the Air Research and Development Command, USAF, through the European Office.

References

(1) M. Kac, *Proceedings of the Third Berkeley Symposium on Mathematical Statistics and Probability*, University of California Press, Berkeley, 1956, p. 171.
(2) G. Uhlenbeck, *Notes on Statistical Mechanics of Irreversible Processes*, Les Houches, 1955.
(3) R. Brout and I. Prigogine, *Physica*, **22**, 621 (1956).
(4) R. Brout, *Physica*, **22**, 509 (1956).

Discussion I

J. G. Kirkwood (*to M. Green*): Professor Kirkwood asked Dr. Green to make his statement about his product condition more precise.

M. Green: I must confess to an imprecision of my statement of the product condition. Kirkwood's statement that the Ursell-Mayer functions should be integrable is actually necessary for the existence of the power series solution.

R. Brout: In order to examine time-smoothing, let us look at the asymptotic expansions derived by either M. Green or R. Brout, and compare them with the time-smoothed equation of Professor Kirkwood. The asymptotic expansions are of the type

$$f(v; t+s) = f(v, t) + s\Omega f(v, t) + \frac{s^2}{2!}\Omega^2 f(v, t) + \cdots, \tag{1}$$

where Ω is the Boltzmann collision operator. Eq. (1) is also rewritten

$$\frac{f(v; t+s) - f(v, t)}{s} = \Omega f(v, t) + \frac{s}{2!}\Omega^2 f(v, t) + \cdots. \tag{2}$$

The time-smoothed equation is

$$\frac{f(v, t+s) - f(v, t)}{s} = \Omega \overline{f(v, t)} + 0(s, s^2, \cdots), \tag{3}$$

where $\overline{f(v, t)}$ is the average of f between t and $t+s$. One may also write $\overline{f(v, t)} = f(v, t) + 0(s, s^2, \cdots)$. In this argument one sees that the time-smoothed equation corresponds to the first term in the asymptotic expansion (2).

In our opinion the demonstration on the basis of time-smoothing is a *short-time* demonstration in which repeated assumption of molecular chaos must be made. If this latter can be proved rigorously to be the case by an independent calculation, as has been claimed by Professor Kirkwood, the two demonstrations are absolutely equivalent. The difficulty in the choice between an asymptotic time limit and a time-smoothed equation is purely semantic.

J. G. Kirkwood, *Comments on the papers of M. Green and R. Brout*: The analysis of Ross and Kirkwood clearly demonstrates that the time-averages singlet distribution function satisfies the Boltzmann equation in an infinite system as a consequence of the Liouville equation and the strong product condition. In their opinion only a coarse-grained function can satisfy the Boltzmann equation. Adequate coarse-graining, equivalent to that of time-smoothing, may perhaps be achieved by the asymptotic time-limiting operation employed by both Green and Brout, but this remains to be proved in detail. In any case, it is clear that the fine-grained distribution function cannot satisfy the Boltzmann equation.

D. K. C. MacDonald: I would be grateful for a specific definition of the "Boltzmann equation" as it is being used in the present context.

G. Uhlenbeck (*to D. K. C. MacDonald*): We mean by the Boltzmann equation the equation used in the kinetic theory of gases for the distribution function f of the molecules, that is

$$\frac{\partial f}{\partial t} + v_\alpha \frac{\partial f}{\partial x_\alpha} + a_\alpha \frac{\partial f}{\partial v_\alpha} = \int d\mathbf{v}_1 \int d\Omega\, g I(g, \theta)\, [f'f_1' - ff_1],$$

where a_α = acceleration due to outside forces and $g = |\mathbf{v} - \mathbf{v}_1|$, $I(g, \theta)$ = differential cross-section for a collision $(\mathbf{v}, \mathbf{v}_1) \rightarrow (\mathbf{v}', \mathbf{v}_1')$. Collision time is the average time that two molecules are in each force field.

J. L. Lebowitz: Forgetting for a moment the question of time-smoothing I would like to mention some points and ask a question. As is well known there are two types of reversibility: (1) Poincaré cycle which is taken care of by making the system infinite, $N \rightarrow \infty$; (2) time reversibility of the basic laws of motion — if all the velocities are reversed the system will retrace its motion. Making the system infinite does not change this at all. For example, suppose we start a system at t_0 with all the molecules confined to one-half of the container. At time t_1 there will be some uniformization of density and let us say at time t_r the system will have reached equilibrium. Now if we reverse all the velocities at t_1 then the system will go back toward its original state of t_0. Obviously we cannot permit an initial condition which corresponds to the state of the system at t_1 but with all velocities reversed. Experimentally, of course, we could never create such a situation specifically excluded by the conditions of Ross-Kirkwood, Green, etc.

M. Green (*to J. L. Lebowitz*): I wish to speak to Dr. Lebowitz in reference to my derivation. First, in my derivation, I speak of an asymptotic solution for large times. There is an analytically different asymptotic form for positive and negative times. Second, I assume a very limited class of initial correlation situations; this determines which asymptotic form is followed.

L. Van Hove: On every important new element has been discussed by M. Green concerning the Boltzmann equation: its extension to higher order in the density. The central point in this extension is that the *n*-particle distribution functions are determined by the knowledge of the one-particle distribution. I want to ask how much of this very important point is established?

G. Uhlenbeck: So far as I know, only Dr. Green has attempted to prove this point in an asymptotic sense (that is for $t \gg$ collision time) up to the order $1/v^2$ (that is, triple collisions included) in the density. Of course, Bogolyubov *postulates* the dependence of f_n on f_1 in what may be called the kinetic stage.

H. Wergeland: The steps of a statistical nature to arrive at the Boltzmann equation from the Liouville equation should be as few as possible, preferably just one. The derivation of Kirkwood and Ross, attractive as it is, seems however to be committed two such steps; if I interpret the equations on the slides correctly, it employs a phase-averaging over the molecules we want to ignore. In addition there is a coarse-graining in time which is not objectionable although one would be still happier to see the task accomplished, for example, by a phase-averaging alone.

G. Uhlenbeck: I think the difference between the derivation of Kirkwood-Ross and the derivation of Brout and of Green is just that the first use, besides statistical assumption about the initial state, an additional time-smoothing. I agree that it would be best if *only* probabilistic assumptions would be made about the initial state. But the situation is certainly not yet quite settled.

J. E. Mayer: I would like to make a comment about the assumption corresponding to the lack of long-range order in the initial distribution. This assumption has been given in two forms, one by Ross as an integrability assumption, and the other by Green as a product assumption. Briefly, these can be stated in terms of the cluster functions, $g^{(n)}$ $(1, 2, \ldots, n)$. The first assumption is that these functions, if integrated over the coordinates of $n-1$ molecules, are finite. The second assumption is that the functions approach zero in value if any pair distance becomes sufficiently large. Neither of these assumptions necessarily implies the other. In the first case the integral may be finite due to an oscillatory character of the function at large distance. In the second case the function may indeed approach zero, but not sufficiently rapidly to assure integrability.

I would like to suggest that on intuitive grounds one may argue that the "product condition," namely that $g^{(n)}$ goes to zero for any large pair distance, is likely to be required in addition to integrability. The basis of this argument is as follows. One knows that there exist initial distributions for which the system will move further from equilibrium with increasing time, namely any one obtained from a distribution which is approaching equilibrium by reversing the sign of the time t. Now such distributions are presumably, and indeed almost certainly, characterized by abnormal correlations at large distances, namely by cluster functions $g^{(n)}$ $(1, 2, \ldots, n)$, which do not approach zero at large pair distances. On the other hand, it would seem probable, and probably even certain, that in these distributions the cluster functions have precisely the oscillatory character at large pair distance values that leaves them integrable.

R. Eisenschitz: Since there exist — apart from the energy — no time-independent integrals of the mechanical equations the steady nonequilibrium state requires time-smoothing.

H. L. Frisch: In reference to Professor Uhlenbeck's remark, it appears of interest to consider not only the types of initial conditions but also the structure of the Hamiltonian of a particular system under consideration. Thus we know there do exist pathological systems whose velocity distribution cannot be approximated easily for any time by solutions of the appropriate Boltzmann equation. To give but one example, consider a one-dimensional gas of identical rigid sphere molecules (ball-bearing gas) even with an infinite number of molecules. The initial velocity distribution remains unchanged, i.e., does not vary in time. In so far as we discuss only the velocity distribution, this does represent a permanent nonequilibrium steady state of a physical system.

H. B. Callen: I would like to request the explicit restoration of the Liouville equation as a physical assumption rather than an axiom. As a matter of fundamental principle, no system can be rigourously isolated, and no system has a rigorously definite Hamiltonian. Each system is coupled to all the universe by its existence in a "vacuum bath" of zero-point oscillations, virtual pairs, etc., and by physical walls. The Liouville equation must therefore contain additional stochastic terms which we here neglected. I believe that the causes of irreversible behavior treated in this session *usually* dominate the effects to which I allude. However, in the various "pathological cases" in which certain initial conditions are ostensibly propagated forever, the external perturbations dominate and destroy the alleged exceptional behavior. It is the external perturbations which underlie the fluctuation-dissipation theorem. Their neglect in the Liouville equation is a drastic simplification.

D. Massignon: Is the Kirkwood and Ross method valid very near a wall? The Boltzmann equation may not be quite correct. Is it possible to derive a correction to it by that method? That might be physically interesting for very dilute gases.

J. L. Lebowitz: I want to comment on the remark of Professor Mayer that both the separability of the distribution and the integrability of $(1-g^{(n)})$ are necessary to exclude the peculiar distributions I talked of earlier (i.e., reversed velocities) which do not proceed in the direction of equilibrium. I wonder if even both assumptions together insure the exclusion of those distributions. These assumptions are not really altered perhaps when the velocities are reversed.

R. Brout: The initial condition corresponding to the derivation of the master equation is necessary and sufficient. This is best shown in weakly coupled systems (see the lecture by Prigogine and Brout at this conference).

F. P. Buff: It might be advantageous to consider the integrability condition as the convergence of partial density fluctuations.

G. Uhlenbeck: I would like to conclude this discussion with the remark that the real test of these developments will come if they are extended to dense systems where we *do not* know the answer (in contrast to the usual Boltzmann equation). Only Bogolyubov has at present given a recipe for such a generalization. It will be of great interest to see whether the methods of Kirkwood-Ross, Green, and Brout will lead to the same results. At present, as Ehrenfest would say, nothing certain is known.

PART II

IRREVERSIBLE PROCESSES IN WEAKLY COUPLED SYSTEMS

I. PRIGOGINE and R. BROUT,* *Faculté des Sciences, Université Libre de Bruxelles, Belgium*

I. INTRODUCTION

The simplest situation in which we may expect an irreversible approach toward the equilibrium distribution corresponds to a class of Hamiltonians which may be called "weakly coupled systems." In such systems the Hamiltonian is the sum of individual Hamiltonians referring to the different "components" of the system (molecules, normal modes . . .) plus a perturbation energy which couples together the components. This perturbation energy is assumed to be so small that it does not appear in the equilibrium properties of the system, but it plays a decisive role in the approach of the system toward thermodynamic equilibrium.

We shall summarize here the results we obtained recently in the study of such systems.[1] In this case, as we shall show, it is really possible to go far beyond the classical ideas based on a Boltzmann equation or a Fokker-Planck equation.

Our method is based on a new method for the solution of the Liouville equation; we shall describe it briefly in Section II.

II. THE LIOUVILLE EQUATION

The Liouville equation for the density in phase space $\varrho(p, q, t)$, is

$$\partial\varrho/\partial t = [H, \varrho], \tag{2.1}$$

where $[H, \varrho]$ is the Poisson bracket of ϱ with the Hamiltonian. We shall write this in the form

$$i(\partial\varrho/\partial t) = L\varrho, \tag{2.2}$$

where, as it may be easily verified, L is a self-adjoint differential operator in phase space. Let us introduce its eigenfunctions $\varphi_k(p, q)$ and its eigenvalues λ_k

$$L\varphi_k = \lambda_k \varphi_k . \tag{2.3}$$

* Present address: Cornell University, Ithaca, N. Y.

The solution of the Liouville equation then takes the form

$$\varrho(p, q, t) = \sum_k c_k e^{-i\lambda_k t} \varphi_k(p, q). \tag{2.4}$$

These relations have a simple and compact form if angle-action variables are used as a special choice of the canonical variables q, p. This may be done so long as we neglect the coupling term in the Hamiltonian which is then the sum of independent contributions

$$H = \sum H_i. \tag{2.5}$$

Each of the H_i is then expressed in terms of the action variables J_i and the Liouville operator L becomes

$$L = -i \sum_k \frac{\partial H_k}{\partial J_k} \frac{\partial}{\partial \alpha_k} = -i \sum_k \nu_k \frac{\partial}{\partial \alpha_k}, \tag{2.6}$$

where α_k are the angle variables and $\nu_k(J_k)$ the characteristic frequencies. The eigenfunctions and the eigenvalues of the operator (2.6) are well known from quantum mechanics and (2.4) takes the explicit form (for N degrees of freedom)

$$\varrho(J_1 \cdots J_N, \alpha_1 \cdots \alpha_N, t) = \sum_{\{n\}} \varrho_{\{n\}}(J_1 \cdots J_N; 0)\, e^{i\Sigma n_k(\alpha_k - \omega_k t)}, \tag{2.7}$$

where $\omega_i = 2\pi\nu_i$ and $\{n\}$ represents any set of integers $n_1 \cdots n_N$. The coefficients $\varrho_{\{n\}}(J_1 \cdots J_N, 0)$ are calculated using the orthogonality of the eigenfunctions $e^{i\Sigma n_k \alpha_k}$ by

$$\varrho_{\{n\}}(J_1 \cdots J_N, 0) = \frac{1}{(2\pi)^{N/2}} \int_0^{2\pi} \int_0^{2\pi} \varrho(J_1 \cdots J_N, \alpha_1 \cdots \alpha_N, 0)\, e^{-i\Sigma n_k \alpha_k} d\alpha_1 \cdots d\alpha_N \tag{2.8}$$

The relation (2.7) represents the solution of the Liouville equation for systems formed by noninteracting components for which the Hamiltonian is given by (2.6). Let us now introduce a weak coupling between the components and write the Hamiltonian in the form

$$H = \sum_k H(J_k) + \lambda V(J_1 \cdots J_N, \alpha_1 \cdots \alpha_N), \tag{2.9}$$

where it is convenient to introduce the coupling parameter λ. As long as λ is small we may distinguish two time scales in the evolution of the system: a short time scale related to the large term $\sum H_k$ in (2.9) and a long time scale related to λV. In other words, the small perturbation will introduce slow changes in the evolution of the system, and it becomes possible to use a perturbation technique.

We shall therefore write the solution of the Liouville equation for the Hamiltonian (2.9) in the form similar to (2.7)

$$\varrho(J_1 \cdots J_N, \alpha_1 \cdots \alpha_N, t) = \sum_{[\{n\}} \varrho_{\{n\}}(J_1 \cdots J_N; t) \exp [i \sum_k n_k(\alpha_k - \omega_k t)]. \tag{2.10}$$

But now the factors $\varrho_{\{n\}}(J_1 \cdots J_N, t)$ are considered to be functions of time in accordance with the well-known method of variation of constants used in quantum mechanics.

The Liouville equation corresponding to (2.9) may be written in the form

$$i(\partial\varrho/\partial t) = (L+\lambda\delta L)\varrho, \tag{2.11}$$

where $\delta L \cdot \varrho$ is the supplementary term due to the coupling in (2.9).

Let us write for the perturbation

$$V = \sum_{\{n\}} V_{\{n\}}(J)\, e^{i\Sigma n_i \alpha_i}, \tag{2.12}$$

where we may suppose

$$V_{\{0\}}(J) = 0 \tag{2.13}$$

since this term may be added to H_0. Then the operator δL has the form

$$\delta L = \sum_{\{n\}} e^{i\Sigma n_k \alpha_k} \sum_k \left[\frac{\partial V_{\{n\}}}{\partial J_k} \frac{\partial}{\partial \alpha_k} - i n_k V_{\{n\}} \frac{\partial}{\partial J_k} \right]. \tag{2.14}$$

Let us replace ϱ by its value (2.10) in (2.11). We then obtain for $\varrho_{\{n\}}(J_1 \cdots J_N, t)$ the set of equations

$$\frac{\partial}{\partial t} \varrho_{\{n\}}(J_1 \cdots J_N, t) = \lambda \sum_{\{n'\}} e^{+i\Sigma n_i \omega_i t} \langle\{n\}|\delta L|\{n'\}\rangle\, e^{-i\Sigma n'_i \omega_i t} \varrho_{\{n'\}}(J_1 \cdots J_N, t). \tag{2.15}$$

We have introduced here the "matrix element" of δL

$$\langle\{n\}|\delta L|\{n'\}\rangle = \int d\alpha_1 \cdots d\alpha_N\, e^{-i\Sigma n_i \alpha_i} \delta L\, e^{i\Sigma n'_i \alpha_i}. \tag{2.16}$$

As seen from (2.15) the matrix elements (2.16) are operators acting on the action variables $J_1 \cdots J_N$.

Before we proceed further we shall now consider the conditions on the perturbation we have to postulate to obtain an irreversible evolution of the system toward thermodynamic equilibrium.

III. THE INTERACTION ENERGY

We now have to require that the perturbation energy V satisfies two kind of conditions to insure an irreversible approach of the system toward thermodynamic equilibrium.

In the absence of the perturbation every action J_k or any function of the action variables is an invariant of motion. The perturbation V must be such that all these invariants of motion are destroyed. Moreover it must be impossible to define new invariants which, for $\lambda \to 0$, in (2.9) would reduce to the old invariants. These conditions have been established by Poincaré[2] and may be summarized as follows:

For each degree of freedom l it must be possible to find a nonvanishing set of integers $m_1 \cdots m_N$ such that the resonance condition

$$m_1 \nu_1 + m_2 \nu_2 \cdots + m_N \nu_N = 0 \qquad (\text{with } m_l \neq 0) \tag{3.1}$$

is satisfied and such that the corresponding Fourier coefficient of the perturbation

$$V_{m_1 m_2 \ldots m_N} \neq 0 \tag{3.2}$$

does not vanish.

If at resonance the perturbation does not vanish we may indeed expect persistent and cumulative effects which will bring the system toward thermodynamic equilibrium.

This Poincaré condition plays a basic role in our theory.

The second condition refers to the number of degrees of freedom of the system. In view of the basic reversibility of the equation of motion which is clearly expressed in Poincaré's well-known recurrence theorem we may only expect irreversible behavior over times much shorter than the Poincaré recurrence time.

Now this time increases rapidly with the number of degrees of freedom of the system.* In order to present an irreversible behavior over long periods of time we have to consider systems of a large number of degrees of freedom. The simplest procedure is then to consider the limit of a system which presents an infinite number of degrees of freedom.

As has been observed by Van Hove[3] this can be expressed by an interesting property of the perturbation energy. The formulation of

* See the interesting discussion remark (p. 362) of Dr. Frisch at this meeting.

this property in classical mechanics is the following.[1] The diagonal elements of

$$\sum_{\{n''\}} V_{\{n-n''\}} V_{\{n''-n'\}} = V^2_{\{n-n'\}} \tag{3.3}$$

which correspond to $\{n\} = \{n'\}$ are at least by a factor N larger than the nondiagonal elements of V^2. The same singularity may also appear for higher powers of V.

The two conditions we have considered until now are independent of any assumption about the magnitude of the coupling constant λ. Therefore a theory of irreversible process independent of any assumption about λ should be possible.* We shall, however, consider here as in our original publication[1] the simplest case for which λ is considered to be very small, while the time t over which the dissipation process occurs is very large such that $\lambda^2 t$ is finite.

Let us now go back to equations (2.15).

IV. SOLUTION OF THE LIOUVILLE EQUATION

Using the condition on the interaction energy we have summarized in Section III, Eqs. (2.15) take a remarkable simple diagonal form

$$\partial \varrho_{\{n\}}/\partial t = \lambda^2 \Omega_{\{n\}}\, \varrho_{\{n\}}, \tag{4.1}$$

where $\Omega_{\{n\}}$ is a second-order differential operator.† As an example, we shall write these equations for the case of a slightly anharmonic crystal. In this case retaining only three phonon processes the perturbation has the form

$$V = \sum V_{kk'k''}\, e^{i(\alpha_k+\alpha_{k'}+\alpha_{k''})}. \tag{4.2}$$

(4.1) takes then the form[7]

$$\frac{\partial \varrho_{\{n\}}}{\partial t} = \sum_{kk'k''} C_{kk'k''} \left(\omega_k \frac{\partial}{\partial E_k} + \omega_{k'} \frac{\partial}{\partial E_{k'}} + \omega_{k''} \frac{\partial}{\partial E_{k''}}\right) (E_k E_{k'} E_{k''}/\omega_k^2 \omega_{k'}^2 \omega_{k''}^2) \left(\omega_k \frac{\partial}{\partial E_k} + \omega_{k'} \frac{\partial}{\partial E_{k'}} + \omega_{k''} \frac{\partial}{\partial E_{k''}}\right) \varrho_{\{n\}} \tag{4.3}$$

$$-C_{kk'k''} E_k E_{k'} E_{k''}/\omega_k^2 \omega_{k'}^2 \omega_{k''}^2 (r_k \omega_k/2E_k + r_{k'}\omega_{k'}/2E_{k'} + r_{k''}\omega_{k''}(2E_{k''})^2 \varrho_{\{n\}}$$

* See the paper of Van Hove at this conference; a method for arbitrary order in λ in the case of classical mechanics will be soon published by one of us (I.P.).

† For details of the calculations see our paper.[1] In this paper we used an iteration method. One of us (I.P.) has since derived these equations by two other, more compact, methods which will be published shortly.

with

$$C_{kk'k''} = \pi \frac{|V_{kk'k''}|^2}{\omega_k^2 \omega_{k'}^2 \omega_{k''}^2}. \tag{4.4}$$

The summation in (4.2) extends only to frequencies satisfying the resonance condition

$$\omega_k + \omega_{k'} + \omega_{k''} = 0. \tag{4.5}$$

For $\{n\} = 0$, (4.2) reduces to an equation first proposed by Peierls[4] on the basis of Fokker-Planck type reasoning. For $\{n\} \neq 0$, such equations were not known. Similar equations may be written down for other types of weakly coupled systems (i.e., gases with weak collisions).*

Let us now discuss the physical significance of these equations.

V. THE MASTER EQUATION

The simplest case corresponds to the situation in which initially the distribution is already phase-independent. Then all functions $\varrho_{\{n\}}$ initially vanish by virtue of (2.8), and because of the diagonal character of (4.1) this remains so at every moment. The persistence of phase independence is a consequence of weak coupling. If finite values of λ are considered, the equilibrium distribution would include phase correlations.

The physical meaning of phase independence is independence of spatial coordinates, that is, homogeneity in coordinate space. The whole distribution function then reduces to the simple Fourier coefficient $\varrho_{\{0\}}$, which satisfies the self-adjoint second-order differential equation (4.1) for ($\{n\} = 0$). It is easily shown by calculating the moments that this equation describes a Fokker-Planck type of diffusion process in the space of all action variables.[1]

This kind of equation has been called the "master equation" by Uhlenbeck, Siegert, and Kac because, once it is postulated, it is easy to deduce the usual forms of the theory of irreversible processes by specifying the initial conditions. Indeed if we assume *initially*

$$\varrho_{\{n\}}(J_1 \cdots J_N, 0) = \prod_{i=1}^{N} \varphi_i(J_i, 0), \tag{5.1}$$

* See the communication by R. Balescu at this conference.

it may be shown that this factorization holds *at every time* and one obtains for φ the Boltzmann equation corresponding to weakly coupled systems (cf. ref. 5).

If one assumes the more special distribution in which all components except m are in equilibrium

$$\varrho_{\{0\}}(J_1 \cdots J_N, 0) = \prod_{i=1}^{N} \varphi^0(J_i)\varphi_m(J_m) \tag{5.2}$$

(the φ^0 are equilibrium distributions) then one derives from the master equation a Fokker-Planck equation for the distribution function $\varphi_m(J_m)$.

Because of the self-adjoint character of (4.1) for $\{n\} = 0$, $\varrho_{\{0\}}$ satisfies an H-theorem.

Summarizing, we may say that the method we have followed permits us to deduce easily the existence of dissipative processes of the Markoff type for a single of the Fourier coefficients of the distribution function in its expansion in terms of the eigenfunctions of the unperturbed Liouville operator.

VI. DISSIPATION AND MOTION

Let us now consider the general case of phase-dependent distribution functions and write (2.10) in the form

$$\begin{aligned}\varrho(J_1 \cdots J_{N_1}, \alpha_1 \cdots \alpha_N, t) \\ = \varrho_{\{0\}}(J_1 \cdots J_N, t) + \sum_{\{n\} \neq \{0\}} \varrho_{\{n\}}(J_1 \cdots J_N, t) \exp[i \textstyle\sum n_k(\alpha_k - \omega_k t)].\end{aligned} \tag{6.1}$$

The time appears here in two different ways: first, in the rapidly varying exponentials and then in the slowly varying functions $\varrho_{\{n\}}$. If we neglect the time-dependence of the $\varrho_{\{n\}}$ for $\{n\} \neq 0$ the change of the distribution function ϱ is represented as the *sum* of the dissipative process due to the change of $\varrho_{\{0\}}$ and the unitary processes due to the unperturbed Hamiltonian $\sum H_k$. This is the approximation used in the Boltzmann equation where the flow process and the collision integral are added. This assumption is also used in Kramers'[6] extension of the Fokker-Planck equation to the whole phase space.

However, in reality $\varrho_{\{n\}}(J_1 \cdots J_N, t)$ (with $\{n\} \neq 0$) also change with time. This then gives rise to a modification of the initial phase relations by the interaction energy. For example, in a crystal the anharmonic forces give rise not only to the dissipative terms describing the change of $\varrho_{\{0\}}$ but also to a modification of the propagation of the phonons. This interference of motion and dissipation is precisely described by the time-dependence of $\varrho_{\{n\}}$ for $\{n\} \neq 0$.

The domain of validity of the classical concepts in the theory of irreversible processes is therefore limited to the approximation in which the $\varrho_{\{n\}}$ (with $\{n\} \neq 0$) may be treated as constants. This is certainly incorrect for strong gradients or rapidly varying external forces.

Summarizing, we may say that the time evolution of the distribution functions as represented in (6.1) has been separated into three groups of terms each of which has a simple physical meaning. This is expressed in the following scheme:

Liouville equation

↙ ↓ ↘

purely dissipative term

$$\frac{\partial \varrho_{\{0\}}}{\partial t}$$

unperturbed mechanical motion

$$\sum_{\{n\}\neq 0} \varrho_{\{n\}}(J_1 \cdots J_N, 0)\, e^{i\Sigma n_k(\alpha_k - \omega_k t)}$$

interference

between dissipation and motion

$$\sum_{\{n\}=0} [(\varrho_{\{n\}}(J_1 \cdots J_N, t) - \varrho_{\{n\}}(J_1 \cdots J_N, 0)]\, e^{i\Sigma n_k(\alpha_k - \omega_k t)}.$$

It seems very plausible that these considerations open wide possibilities for the field of irreversible process. The main limitation in this method is the condition of weak coupling, but this is closely related to a good choice of variables and to the definition of good collective variables.

This work was sponsered by the Air Research and Development Command, USAF, through the European Office.

References

(1) R. Brout and I. Prigogine, *Physica*, **22**, 621 (1956).

(2) H. Poincaré, *Méthodes nouvelles de mécanique céleste*, Gauthier-Villars, Paris, 1892.

(3) L. Van Hove, *Physica*, **21**, 518 (1955).

(4) R. Peierls, *Ann. Physik*, **3**, 1055 (1929).

(5) R. Brout and I. Prigogine, *Physica*, **22**, 35 (1956).

(6) H. A. Kramers, *Physica*, **7**, 284 (1940).

(7) cf. I. Prigogine and J. Philippot, *Physica*, **23**, 569 (1957).

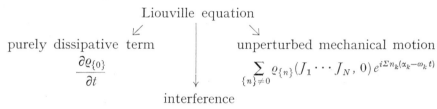

GRAVITATIONAL FORCES AND DYNAMIC FRICTION

R. BALESCU, *Faculté des Sciences, Université Libre de Bruxelles, Belgium*

The master equation derived by Brout and Prigogine[1] for classical weakly coupled systems is very convenient in studying irreversible processes. We shall illustrate its use for gases with long-range interactions between the particles. For more details we refer to our recent publication.[4]

An example of this kind is provided by a stellar "globular cluster." As is well known in stellar dynamics, such a system can adequately be described as a gas of point stars interacting through gravitational forces. We shall now show that, as a result of the interactions, any incident star will be systematically decelerated in the direction of its motion, a phenomenon known as *dynamic friction.*[2] We shall calculate this effect by evaluating the quantity $\overline{d\mathbf{v}_0/dt}$.

Let us first stress the peculiar nature of gravitational forces: due to their long range, close collisions between stars are exceedingly rare; each star is moving along a smooth trajectory which suffers slight deviations as a result of stellar encounters. The interaction potential is therefore, almost everywhere, very small with respect to the kinetic energy so that all the fundamental ideas contained in Brout and Prigogine's theory apply to this case.

The Hamiltonian of an isolated globular cluster may be written as

$$H = \sum \frac{p_i^2}{2m} - Gm^2 \sum_{i\neq j} \frac{1}{r_{ij}} = \sum \frac{p_i^2}{2m} - 4\pi G m^2 \frac{1}{(2\pi)^{3/2}} \sum_{i\neq j} \int d\mathbf{k} \, \frac{1}{k^2} e^{i\mathbf{k}\cdot(\mathbf{r}_i - \mathbf{r}_j)}, \quad (1)$$

where G is the gravitational constant, and m a suitable average mass of the stars (we neglect in this approximation a dispersion of the stellar masses).

With this Hamiltonian, the master equation takes the form

$$\frac{\partial \varrho}{\partial t} = \frac{A}{\gamma} \sum_{i<j} \int d\mathbf{k} \, \frac{1}{k^4} \mathbf{k} \cdot \left(\frac{\partial}{\partial \mathbf{v}_i} - \frac{\partial}{\partial \mathbf{v}_j} \right) \delta[\mathbf{k}\cdot(\mathbf{v}_i - \mathbf{v}_j)] \mathbf{k} \cdot \left(\frac{\partial}{\partial \mathbf{v}_i} - \frac{\partial}{\partial \mathbf{v}_j} \right) \varrho \quad (2)$$

with $A = 2G^2m^2$ and $\gamma =$ volume of the system.

We now calculate the time derivative of the average velocity of a peculiar star, hereafter denoted by the index 0. We shall make the following assumptions: (a) the distribution function $\varrho(\mathbf{v}_0, \mathbf{v}_1, \cdots, \mathbf{v}_N, t)$ is factorized, and (b) the distribution functions of the "field stars" depend only upon the absolute value, v, of the velocity (i.e., the distribution of the cluster is spherically symmetrical).

With these assumptions

$$\varrho(\mathbf{v}_0, \mathbf{v}_1, \cdots, \mathbf{v}_N, t) = \varphi(\mathbf{v}_0, t) \prod_{i=1}^{N} f(\mathbf{v}_i, t). \tag{3}$$

Introducing this form into (1), multiplying both sides of (1) by $\mathbf{v}_0$ and integrating over the velocities, we are left, after an integration by parts, with:

$$\begin{aligned} -\frac{1}{nA}\overline{\frac{d\mathbf{v}_0}{dt}} = & \int d\mathbf{v}_0 \int d\mathbf{v}\, f(v) \int d\mathbf{k}\, \frac{\mathbf{k}}{k^4}\, \delta(\mathbf{k}\cdot\mathbf{V})\,\mathbf{k}\cdot\frac{\partial\varphi}{\partial\mathbf{v}_0} \\ & - \int d\mathbf{v}_0 \varphi(\mathbf{v}_0) \int d\mathbf{v}\, \frac{1}{v}\frac{\partial f}{\partial v} \int d\mathbf{k}\, \frac{\mathbf{k}}{k^4}\, \delta(\mathbf{k}\cdot\mathbf{V})\,\mathbf{k}\cdot\mathbf{v}_0, \end{aligned} \tag{4}$$

where $\mathbf{V} = \mathbf{v}_0 - \mathbf{v}$, is the relative velocity of the two stars suffering an encounter, and n is the number density of the cluster.

In order to perform the integration over $\mathbf{k}$, it is convenient to take a reference system with the z-axis along $\mathbf{V}$. The x-component of the first integral is

$$\int d\mathbf{k}\, \frac{k_x}{k^4}\mathbf{k}\cdot\frac{\partial\varphi}{\partial\mathbf{v}_0}\delta(\mathbf{k}\cdot\mathbf{V}) = \pi\frac{\partial\varphi}{\partial v_{0x}}\int dk\int d\theta\, \sin^3\theta\,\delta(kV\cos\theta) = \frac{\partial\varphi}{\partial v_{0x}}\frac{\pi}{V}\int\frac{dk}{k}. \tag{5}$$

The integral (5) diverges at both limits: it is necessary to introduce two cut offs. Their exact value is not important because of the logarithmic character of the divergence, and therefore the following arguments are sufficient to fix their order of magnitude.

(1) *Divergence for* $k \to 0$: It corresponds to a long-distance divergence. Let us recall that (1) is essentially a binary collision equation. Now, due to the long range of gravitational forces, if the star 0 is sufficiently far from any of the field stars, it will undergo small forces of the same order of magnitude from a great number of the latter, so that very distant encounters are actually multiple encounters. In other words, at such distances the system has a *collective behavior*. However, as the potential energy is assumed to be small compared to the kinetic

energy, such collective effects may be neglected, by introducing a cut off k_D equal to the inverse of the "Debye length" of the system as defined by Pines and Bohm.[3]

Now a numerical evaluation of this quantity shows that the Debye length of typical globular clusters is of the order of R_0, the average distance between the stars. Thus the upper cut off will be put equal to $k_D = 1/R_0$.

(2) *Divergence for* $k \to \infty$: It is a short-range divergence. This situation corresponds to the close collisions of an ordinary gas; Eq. (1) does not apply to this case because in a close collision the potential is very large. However, as we pointed out at the beginning, such collisions are very rare and one can neglect them by introducing a cut off which we take equal to $k_\infty = (GM/V^2)^{-1}$. Physically, at this distance the potential energy is twice the kinetic energy, and two stars at distances shorter than this actually form a *binary star*, one revolving around the other: there is no longer true scattering, instead one star is trapped by the other's field.

With these arguments, the integral (5) becomes

$$\frac{\partial \varphi}{\partial v_{0x}} \frac{\pi}{V} \ln qV^2, \qquad \text{with } q = R_0/Gm.$$

The other integrals in (4) may be performed in the same manner. The subsequent integration over $\mathbf{v}$ is performed in a reference system having the z-axis along $\mathbf{v}_0$. We shall not give further details here (see Balescu[4]), but quote the result in first approximation

$$\overline{\frac{d\mathbf{v}_0}{dt}} = -\int d\mathbf{v}_0 \varphi(\mathbf{v}_0)\eta(\mathbf{v}_0)\mathbf{v}_0 = -\overline{\eta(v_0)\mathbf{v}_0}, \tag{6}$$

thus exhibiting the coefficient of dynamic friction

$$\eta(v_0) = 16\pi^2 nA \ln q\overline{v_0^2} \cdot \frac{1}{v_0^3}\int_0^{v_0} dv\, v^2 f(v). \tag{7}$$

One immediately sees from this formula that $\eta > 0$, corresponding to a systematic deceleration. This formula was first obtained by Chandrasekhar.[2]

The research reported in this publication has been made possible through the support and sponsorship of the Air Research and Development Command, USAF.

References

(1) R. Brout and I. Prigogine, *Physica,* **22**, 621 (1956).
(2) S. Chandrasekhar, *Astrophys. J.*, **97**, 255 (1943).
(3) D. Pines and D. Bohm, *Phys. Rev.*, **85**, 338 (1952).
(4) R. Balescu, *Bull. classe sci. Acad. roy. Belg.*, **43**, 179 (1957).

Discussion II

J. G. Kirkwood, *Comment on the paper of I. Prigogine and R. Brout*: J. Ross has derived the Chandrasekhar equation, a generalization of the Fokker-Planck equation for phase space, by means of a perturbation method from the Liouville equation. This was done using distribution functions coarse-grained in time and the formalism of phase space transformation functions.

H. N. V. Temperley (*to R. Balescu*): What happens to a star that is initially at rest?

R. Balescu (*to H. N. V. Temperley*): The dynamic friction is of course an average effect. A star initially at rest acquires a finite velocity through a fluctuation and then undergoes a deceleration on the average.

E. Montroll asked R. Balescu what happens if one considers a star in an external field.

R. Brout (*to E. Montroll*): When there is an external field, the definition of the angles must be modified. For example, if the system of stars is in a net gravitational field, the angle variables are no longer the positions r_i, but far more complex, and the master equation correspondingly so.

M. Green (*to I. Prigogine*): Cannot the theory of weakly coupled system be generalized to include not merely unperturbed Hamiltonians H_0 which are sums of partial Hamiltonians H_i but also those which have an arbitrary set of integrals of motion? The distribution function of these integrals, of course, would be a mathematical object to which attention would be directed.

I. Prigogine (*to M. Green*): Yes, I think so.

G. Uhlenbeck: I would like to urge Mr. Prigogine to try to calculate the heat conductivity of a solid in terms of the anharmonicity and therefore to obtain a definite relation between the heat conductivity and the heat expansion of the solid, which could be tested. It seems that he now has the method at hand. It would solve an old problem.

D. K. C. MacDonald (*to G. Uhlenbeck*): Professor Uhlenbeck has remarked that it would now be good if we could relate thermal conductivity quantitatively to anharmonicity, and make experimental comparison. This is undoubtedly precisely what experimental laboratories such as ours are most anxious to see. The difficulty, as I will also mention in my paper tomorrow, appears to be that, in Professor Uhlenbeck's own words, "nothing is known theoretically with certainty." Peierls, in his latest book, points out that at high temperatures the thermal conductivity (of an insulator) probably falls with a law somewhere between $1/T$ and $1/T^2$ and himself admits that this may seem "rather a poor return" for so long a theoretical discussion. However, there is now available a considerable body of quite reliable experimental data (Berman, White and Woods, Wilks, *et al.*) on solids such as diamonds, sapphire, and the solid inert gases, and it is interesting that two independently derived semiquantitative expressions for thermal conductivity at high temperatures (Leibfried-Schlömann, Dugdale-MacDonald) agree rather well with one another and interpret the experimental data rather usefully.

L. Van Hove: It might be interesting to compare the thermal expansion of a crystal, an equilibrium property, with a nonequilibrium property less intricate, than thermal conduction, namely the finite mean free path of individual phonons. When one excites, in a crystal in thermal equilibrium, an additional phonon, it has a finite mean free path corresponding to an imaginary part of its frequency as well as a real shift in frequency, both due to the anharmonic forces and both temperature-dependent. It is remarkable that inelastic scattering of very slow neutrons by crystals is, with the present experimental accuracy, not far from making a measurement of these effects possible.

R. Brout: A surprising case in which perhaps a weakly coupled system has validity where the contrary might be expected is to be found in the Bridgman formula for thermal conductivity in liquids (Balescu, 1956). Here the thermal conductivity is expressed in terms of the velocity of sound and the lattice distance combined in such a way that the mean free path of the phonons is of the order of the lattice distance. This suggests that an H_0 exists which is an ensemble of phonons with certain effective frequencies.

J. L. Lebowitz: To come back to the question of smoothing of the distribution function there obviously will always have to be some kind of coarse-graining since, according to the Liouville theorem, the entropy defined as $-k \int f_N \ln f_N \, dX_N$ is invariant in time and defining the entropy as $-k \int f_1 \ln f_1 \, dX_1$ will not change this if, as was ascertained, the distribution function remains a product if it was initially a product. It is for this reason that Professor Prigogine defined entropy in terms of averages over phases.

R. Eisenschitz: The velocity of sound and molecular distances should affect the thermal conductivity of liquids by determining some characteristic correlation time. They are not directly connected with the mechanism of heat transmission.

J. Ross: Although the Fokker-Planck equation and the formulation of the friction coefficient as an autocorrelation function of forces is not strictly applicable to liquids because a perturbation solution is not very applicable, these equations do provide an approximation for the transport coefficients as recent experiments have shown.

J. L. Lebowitz (*to I. Prigogine*): What you have done then is to show that a coarse-grained entropy as defined, for example, by Tolman does indeed increase for $t \to \infty$ (forgetting about the Poincaré cycle since $N \to \infty$). This is the classical form of what Van Hove has shown quantum mechanically. Tolman of course was never able to show this without assuming random phasing, not only initially but over and over again.

M. S. Green: I would like to comment on I. Prigogine's discussion of the type irreversibility which exists in an infinite linear harmonic chain. I think that a similar situation exists in an infinite spatially uniform gas or liquid. It is certainly an open question whether the infinite Born-Green-Kirkwood-Yvon hierarchy has irreversibility in it and whether an H-theorem is valid. I do not have the answer to this question but I believe that I have a valid expression for the entropy of such a system in terms of the reduced distribution functions. The time behavior which I conjecture very tentatively about such an entropy expression is not that it always increases but rather it increases monotonically after a time that depends on the initial conditions.

H. C. Longuet-Higgins: Would Professor Green agree that although, of course, the integral $-k \int f^{(N)} \ln f^{(N)} d\tau$ is invariant in time, nevertheless the entropy production, defined in terms of lower order distribution functions, need not vanish even if the system is isolated? One might therefore speak of the information contained in $f^{(N)}$ flowing from the lower distribution functions to those of higher orders, which are inaccessible to observations.

R. Brout: This is contrary to what Professor Prigogine and I have proved. The master equation is an equation of evolution of all N-generalized momenta and not of particular degrees of freedom.

N. G. van Kampen: May I put the argument of Professor Longuet-Higgins in the following, somewhat more general, way? The macroscopic state of a system is defined by the values of certain macroscopically observable quantities. The initial state is macroscopically defined by the initial values of these same quantities. This is only very incomplete information concerning the initial microscopic state. During the evolution this information is carried over to unobservable microscopic quantities and becomes, therefore, useless. In the case that the determination of the above-mentioned macroscopic observables is equivalent to the determination of the distribution function $f^{(1)}$, this formulation coincides with that of Longuet-Higgins.

H. C. Longuet-Higgins (*to N. G. van Kampen*): I quite agree with Dr. van Kampen in his general statement. I actually had in mind the transport of energy momentum, and matter in gases and liquids, where, of course, the observable fluxes are determined by $f^{(2)}$ as well as by $f^{(1)}$.

J. E. Mayer: I wish to call attention to the calculations by Ulam and Fermi. The system treated by Ulam and Fermi had the built-in characteristic that energy could flow only from the first mode, initially excited, into the second, and thence to the third, etc. It was then not followed in time long enough for the energy to have reached, in appreciable amounts, the last or highest mode. The remarkable behavior observed was that, after a certain period (not by any means the Poincaré period but much shorter), practically all of the energy, perhaps 98%, returned to the first mode.

PART III

LE PRINCIPE DE LOCALISATION

J. YVON, *C. E. N. de Saclay, Gif sur Yvette, Seine et Oise, France*

Résumé

Rappel de la définition régressive de la matrice densité relative à une seule particule μ_1, de la matrice densité relative à deux particules μ_{12} dans un système macroscopique. Propriétés "locales" de μ_1. Corrélation à grande distance. Propriétés locales de μ_{12}. La méthode progressive déduit μ_{12} de μ_1. Les idées de cette note pourraient conduire à un "principe de localisation."

I. CALCULS RÉGRESSIFS

Considérons un système quantique fermé constitué de très nombreuses particules suffisamment approchées. C'est un système macroscopique. Pour fixer les idées et limiter la discussion, supposons que toutes les particules sont identiques et indestructibles. Cette dernière limitation est certainement une perte sérieuse de généralité, un système où se créent ou s'annihilent des particules pose des problèmes plus fondamentaux.

L'état du système est défini à chaque instant par une matrice densité — le terme de matrice évoque une représentation particulière et je préfère celui d'opérateur densité.

Cet opérateur, μ, défini pour N particules est infiniment trop compliqué pour être commode à manipuler. Des grandeurs plus modestes s'obtiennent en prenant la trace partielle de l'opérateur global:

$$1 = T_{12\cdots N}\mu, \tag{1}$$

$$\mu_1 = NT_{23\cdots N}\mu, \tag{2}$$

$$\mu_{12} = N(N-1)T_{34\cdots N}\mu. \tag{3}$$

Ces calculs peuvent s'effectuer pas à pas:

$$N = T_1\mu_1, \tag{4}$$

$$(N-1)\mu_1 = T_2\mu_{12}, \tag{5}$$

$$(N-2)\mu_{12} = T_3\mu_{123}. \tag{6}$$

Pour évaluer la plupart des grandeurs intéressantes du point de vue macroscopique, il suffit de connaître μ_1 et μ_{12}.

Cette suite d'opérations qui réduit pas à pas le nombre de degrés de liberté relatifs aux grandeurs manipulées a été qualifiée par I. Prigogine d'un terme expressif: ces opérations sont des opérations régressives.

II. LOCALISATION DE μ_1

Les états propres — en général fonction du temps — de l'opérateur μ_1, occupent tout l'espace offert au système.

Représentons l'opérateur μ_1 sous forme de matrice — continue — à l'aide des coordonnées spatiales (l'existence d'un spin complique un peu sans changer l'essentiel). On obtient la matrice

$$\mathfrak{M}_{\mathrm{I}}(x_1'\,;\,x_1''),$$

où x_1' et x_1'' sont deux points quelconques du volume occupé par le système.

On peut prendre comme variables indépendantes $x_1 = (x_1'+x_1'')/2$ et $X = x_1''-x_1'$. Un fait, sinon absolument général, du moins très général est que $\mathfrak{M}_{\mathrm{I}}$ tend très rapidement vers zéro quand $r_1 = |x_1''-x_1'|$ augmente. Il s'agit ici de distances microscopiques. On peut donc parler de la "valeur" de $\mathfrak{M}_{\mathrm{I}}$ et partant de μ_1 dans telle ou telle région de l'espace.

III. MÉTHODES D'APPROXIMATION

Les calculs régressifs conduisent à un formalisme intéressant, mais ils n'apportent rien d'original par eux-mêmes.

Toutefois ils suggèrent des méthodes d'approximation.

Il est tout d'abord naturel de penser qu'il n'existe aucune corrélation entre deux particules situées en des points x_1 et x_2 éloignés (au sens microscopique). Ceci se traduit par la relation:

$$\mu_{12} \approx \mu_1\mu_2. \tag{1}$$

En fait le principe d'indiscernabilité des particules de même nature oblige à introduire ici un facteur de symétrie. Désignons par P_{12} l'opérateur qui permute les particules 1 et 2, par ε un nombre égal à $+1$ pour les bosons et à -1 pour les fermions. Il faut écrire:

$$\mu_{12} \approx (1+\varepsilon P_{12})\mu_1\mu_2. \tag{2}$$

Dégageant, même quand les particules sont proches, le même facteur de symétrie, nous écrirons en général

$$\mu_{12} = (1+\varepsilon P_{12})C_{12}. \tag{3}$$

La matrice — composantes d'espace — qui correspond à C_{12} soit:

$$C_{\mathrm{II}}(x'_1, x'_2; x''_1, x''_2),$$

subit aussi très généralement un effet de localisation. Elle s'annule quand soit r_1 soit r_2 sont microscopiquement grands. Ce résultat a d'abord été mis en évidence par Wigner ainsi que le résultat analogue qui concerne μ_1 dans le cas des électrons libres en équilibre.

IV. MÉTHODE PROGRESSIVE ET PRINCIPE DE LOCALISATION

Grace à la formule II, (2) μ_{12} est connu lorsque la distance $r_{12} = |x_2-x_1|$ est grande. Il s'agit de le déterminer pour les faibles distances. Supposons connu μ_1 dans une certaine région de l'espace. Je crois qu'on peut affirmer que μ_{12}, dans cette région là, est entièrement défini par μ_1. Le problème de la détermination de μ_{12} en fonction de μ_1, et ensuite de μ_{123}, est le problème fondamental. Il a été abordé sérieusement dans le cas des systèmes classiques en équilibre. Il est résolu intuitivement dans le cas des gaz classiques hors d'équilibre par l'hypothèse du chaos moléculaire. Il reste à l'approfondir dans les différents domaines présentés par la physique quantique. En opposition avec la définition régressive de μ_1, μ_{12}, etc. cette méthode de recherche peut être appelée une méthode progressive.

En régime variable, μ_1 défini en tout point x_1, et peut être sur un petit intervalle de temps, définit ipso facto les conditions initiales. De μ_1 on doit déduire une valeur instantanée de μ_{12}, laquelle à son tour gouverne l'évolution de μ_1. En général μ_1 définition des conditions initiales ne sera pas absolument arbitraire, souvent cet opérateur ne devra pas trop s'écarter de sa valeur à l'équilibre.

Il est clair que, dans cette voie, la connaissance des fonctions d'onde à N particules n'est pas recherchée, qu'elle est d'ailleurs inutile.

Cette localisation de μ_1 et de μ_{12}, cette détermination de point en point de μ_{12} en fonction de μ_1 sont d'un caractère très contraire à la dilution des particules par la fonction d'onde. Ces propriétés appartiennent aux systèmes suffisamment denses constitués de nombreuses particules. J'imagine que lorsque ces propriétés auront été davantage mises en valeur, on pourra parler d'un principe de localisation. Je me permets du moins d'employer aujourd'hui le mot de principe pour attirer de mon mieux l'attention sur les idées que je viens de résumer. Ces idées ne sont qu'une modernisation et adaptation aux problèmes quantiques du théorème de causalité macroscopique énoncé autrefois par Hilbert et rappelé par Uhlenbeck dans des lectures à l'Université de Princeton (1954).

THE STATISTICAL MECHANICS OF THE STEADY STATE

H. N. V. TEMPERLEY, *Atomic Weapons Research Establishment, Aldermaston, Berkshire, England*

Abstract

It is shown that the Fowler-Darwin definitions of the temperature and chemical potential can be extended in a natural way to cover nonequilibrium but steady assemblies. The concept of equilibrium is replaced by the more general one of "compatibility," and it becomes possible to show that the quantities defined statistically reduce to suitable averages over the assembly of the locally measured quantities. The usual restrictions to small departures from equilibrium are unnecessary. A simple problem (flow of gas in a tube) is discussed from the new point of view.

I. INTRODUCTION

A large number of workers have remarked on the difficulty of giving accurate *thermodynamic definitions* of quantities such as temperature and pressure and entropy for an assembly that is not in true equilibrium. This has had the effect of restricting the application of "irreversible thermodynamics" to assemblies that depart only slightly from equilibrium, although it is still experimentally possible to make accurate measurements of temperatures and pressures in assemblies that are very far from equilibrium, provided that conditions are steady for a long enough time for the measurement to be made. We shall show in this paper that the Fowler-Darwin formalism of statistical mechanics can be extended in a natural way to apply not only to an assembly in equilibrium but to an assembly in a steady state. By this we mean an assembly, such as gas or liquid flowing through a pipe, subject to the proviso that macroscopic conditions at any one point are effectively constant in time. This excludes phenomena like turbulence or cavitation, but includes a very large class of phenomena which can be made macroscopically steady by a proper choice of the boundary conditions, for example a shock front can be held in a tube at constant position and strength if the flow rates are adjusted properly.

It is well known that Schrödinger's time-independent wave equation can be used to handle steady-state problems such as the impact of a stream of particles on a potential barrier, or the steady flow of electrons in a metal under a constant electric field, and that nothing in such treatments requires, as a matter of *principle,* that the assembly should be "nearly" in static equilibrium. (In a practical problem, it may be necessary to resort to perturbation theory in order to obtain numerical results, and this may impose such a condition in practice, but the wave functions and energy levels for the more general problem undoubtedly exist.) We are tacitly assuming that we are employing one of the standard devices, such as imposing periodic boundary conditions, or supposing our flow to take place in a large torus, which permits steady flow into and out of any given small volume, and yet enables us to specify a definite spectrum of energy levels for the whole assembly. In these circumstances we shall show that natural, and mutually consistent, definitions can be given of the "local" temperature of a small region and of the "temperature" of the whole assembly; similar remarks apply to quantities like pressure. These definitions are based solely on statistical mechanics and make no explicit reference to heat engines, but become identical with the accepted definitions when applied to an assembly in equilibrium. There is no question of a *difference* between "statistical" and "thermodynamic" temperatures, since we do not know how to define the latter for a nonequilibrium assembly. What we do have to recognize is that an assembly in a steady state requires *more* macroscopic parameters to describe it than does a similar assembly in equilibrium.

II. THE TYPE OF ASSEMBLY STUDIED

To fix our ideas, suppose that our assembly is enclosed in a toroidal vessel, not necessarily of uniform cross-section. We are not restricting ourselves to the case of small interactions, so the Schrödinger equation will be a many-body one, containing terms representing the mutual interactions of the particles, and the effect of external fields of force. Some such field, for example an electric field, may have to be applied periodically to part of the assembly in order to maintain the steady motion, and it will also be necessary to withdraw heat from the assembly in order to maintain its energy content constant. In a moment we shall describe an idealized mechanism that is capable of being used as a pump or as a manometer or as a thermometer, and of introducing or withdrawing heat at any point. We may, in principle, suppose the assembly, made up of N molecules together with these auxiliary devices, to be described by a single Schrödinger equation. It will be necessary to ensure that the periods associated with these "pumping," "cooling," and "measuring" devices are very small compared with the "time of making an observation," or conditions would not be "steady." We confine ourselves to Newtonian liquids and gases in order to avoid complications arising from a nonisotropic pressure.

Our idealized "measuring instrument" is extremely simple, yet is capable of measuring both pressure and temperature. We may suppose that small side tubes are let into our torus at various points along its length, each of them closed by a piston backed by a spring. First of all, let us suppose that the only coupling between one such device and the rest of the assembly is through the collision of molecules with the piston. The spring will be compressed to an average extent that measures the "pressure" in the assembly at the point. Furthermore, it will oscillate about this mean position as the result of the collisions, and the mean energy associated with these oscillations, the Brownian movement, is a measure of the "temperature" of the assembly at that point, which can be measured in principle if we measured the mean-square displacement of the piston over a reasonable number of periods. Now let us suppose that we increase the amplitude of the oscillations of the piston by supplying energy to it mechanically or electrically. This extra energy will be imparted to the molecules colliding with the piston, which thus becomes a source of heat. We could equally well make a heat "sink" by connecting the piston to a dashpot or to an electromagnetic brake, that is, by coupling it in some way to some assembly of lower temperature than the one we are studying. Even more simply, we could endow our otherwise closed assembly with one or more "windows" through which radiation can escape.

Thus we conclude that it is possible to construct an assembly which is not in equilibrium, and yet has an energy content and other observable properties that are constant in time. Such an assembly would be continually absorbing mechanical or electrical energy and rejecting an equivalent quantity of heat, but the entire assembly, consisting of the gas or liquid, the vessel that contains it, and the devices necessary to maintain the circulation, could, in principle, be described by a single Schrödinger equation of many-body type.

Another, slightly different, type of steady-state assembly is often considered in the literature. Instead of considering a complete torus, we might fix our attention on a short length of it, and suppose that our substance is being fed in and out by means of two pistons outside the volume actually considered, matters being arranged in such a way that the mean number of molecules and the energy content of the particular portion of the tube we are considering remain constant. This is the assembly that is usually used in the textbook discussion of the Joule-Thomson effect. Here again, if interactions between the molecules are neglected, the molecules, traveling through the volume considered with various energies and speeds, could be described by Schrödinger's equation, using the "traveling wave" type of solution. If interactions are important, we should have to go over to the many-body Schrödinger equation. As the driving pistons are outside the assembly considered we do not have to incorporate them into its wave equation, but, as with the former type of assembly, we should want to consider pistons in side tubes as an idealized means of measuring "local" pressures and temperatures. The coupling of the latter pistons to the assembly via molecular collisions means that they have to be incorporated into the Schrödinger equation.

III. THE CONCEPT OF "COMPATIBILITY" OF STEADY-STATE ASSEMBLIES

The reasoning of thermodynamics and statistical mechanics is based very largely on the concept of equilibrium between two different assemblies, that is, nothing happens to the macroscopic properties of two such assemblies if we permit exchanges of energy or matter, or both, between them. In other words, in certain circumstances we can bring them into intimate contact, or even incorporate them with one another, without any changes in pressure, temperature, etc. Now it is physically obvious that pairs of steady-state assemblies also exist with an analogous property, and it is this property that we define as *compatibility*. Like all new concepts, it is best understood by means of examples.

(*a*) Two streams of gas, flowing in two tubes of a heat exchanger, will be compatible and no macroscopic exchange of heat will occur if their temperatures are the same all along the dividing wall. If, further, their pressures and densities are also the same all along the wall and the streams are chemically alike, the streams are compatible and will not affect one another macroscopically even if the dividing wall is *porous*. Finally, if their tangential velocities are made to agree, the two streams are compatible even if there is no dividing wall at all.

(*b*) Two samples of gas, with pressures, temperatures, and stream velocities corresponding to two stages in the history of a sample of gas undergoing a Joule-Thomson expansion, or some other steady-state process, would be said to be compatible. This is because either or both samples could be incorporated into a certain steady assembly without any change in the observable properties, provided that we chose the appropriate region of that assembly for each sample. In each case we could add the sample to the assembly provided that the temperature, pressure, stream velocity, etc., of the small sample agreed with the *locally measured* values of these quantities for the assembly.

(*c*) Consider an assembly such as a gas conducting heat. We might divide it up into small samples by planes along and perpendicular to the heat flow. We could imagine the assembly built up of these small samples which could, in principle, be added one by one without disturbing the temperatures or gradients in the rest of the assembly. Although two such neighboring samples may have slightly different local properties, they are compatible. Some of their properties must agree, for example the temperature and heat flux along their common boundary, but others, such as their mean measured temperatures, will be different. Yet, if they are brought together in the proper way, no changes in either set of properties take place.

Just as we begin thermodynamics with the argument that two assemblies in equilibrium must have some properties in common, so we now assert that the same must be true of compatible assemblies, apart altogether from any boundary conditions imposed, e.g., by continuity considerations. We shall show that it is possible to define a temperature and entropy for the whole of a steady assembly, and that these quantities correspond to appropriate averages over the locally measured values of these quantities. The "local" measurements could consist of observations on pistons in side tubes (see Section II), or the use of more practical thermometers and manometers.

IV. THE STATISTICAL MECHANICS OF THE STEADY STATE

In equilibrium, we work with two main types of ideal assembly, the completely closed assembly whose total energy and total number of molecules are held fixed, and the open assembly which is permitted to exchange energy and matter with heat baths and reservoirs. We have seen above that, in the steady-state case, we can define analogs of these two types of assembly. The open assembly corresponds to the case in which we fix our attention on a particular length of tube, through which gas is being driven steadily. The energy and number of molecules in the assembly fluctuate about mean values as the result of interchanges with neighboring portions of the gas which are compatible with it. The analog of the closed equilibrium assembly is the rather more elaborate assembly, also described above, in which we can assert that the energy and number of molecules remain constant, but we cannot close it off completely from its surroundings on account of the necessity of supplying mechanical energy to maintain it in steady motion and of withdrawing a corresponding quantity of heat.

As in the equilibrium case, we suppose that our assembly, when it contains N molecules, has $g(N, E_r)$ energy levels each of total energy E_r. Thus, we are *not* restricting ourselves to small interactions between molecules, but we imagine that we have solved the many-body wave equation. The energy E_r refers to the discrete or continuous spectrum of eigenvalues appropriate to the *whole* assembly, consistent with whatever boundary conditions we may impose. We have already pointed out that many other sets of conditions besides the rigid walls appropriate to an equilibrium problem can be handled by the wave equation. We also need consideration of the way in which these numbers of levels vary with N in order to be able to handle the "open" assembly. We also make the convention that the E_r's are to include the entire kinetic energy, including that of any bulk motion, of the gas or liquid in the assembly, but that we specify separately the kinetic and potential energies of the small pistons and springs that we are coupling into the assembly as measuring instruments. We are keeping the discussion quite general, so that we are assuming implicitly that we only list energy levels corresponding to wave functions with the correct symmetry properties and that any factors resulting from spin degeneracy are incorporated into $g(N, E_r)$.

Now, just as in equilibrium theory, we can define a "grand partition function" by the equation:

$$f(\lambda, \theta) = \sum_{N} \sum_{E_r} \lambda^N \theta^{E_r} g(N, E_r) \tag{1}$$

which equation can nearly always be asymptotically inverted to read

$$\log g(N, E) \approx \log f - N \log \lambda - E \log \theta \tag{2}$$

with

$$\lambda \frac{\partial}{\partial \lambda} (\log f) = N \text{ and } \theta \frac{\partial}{\partial \theta} (\log f) = E.$$

These functions can certainly be *defined* for a steady assembly; we now have to *interpret* them. Now, a completely isolated assembly, for which N and E are fixed is, at any given instant, equally likely to be found in any one of the $g(N, E)$ complexions of given N and E. We have, in equilibrium theory, to discuss the interaction of at least two assemblies in order to be able to define the concept of temperature. If, in our generalized theory, we permit two assemblies to share the same stock of *energy*, we can conclude, just as in the true equilibrium case, that matters will adjust themselves so that $g_1(N_2, E_2) \times g_2(N_2, E_2)$ is a maximum subject to $E_1 + E_2 =$ constant. If matter is also allowed to pass from one to the other it will do so if the product $g_1 \cdot g_2$ is thereby increased. If, however, the two assemblies are compatible in the sense described above, no changes in the macroscopic properties will occur when they are brought together. This gives us the natural extension to steady assemblies of the principle of increase of entropy for equilibrium assemblies, and we can take over the whole of Fowler's argument[1] to show that two assemblies which are allowed to share energies are described by the same θ in their partition functions, and that if they are allowed to share matter they are described by the same λ. (We cannot yet identify these quantities with temperatures or partial potentials because the pressures and temperatures vary from point to point in a steady assembly.) For the moment, all that we assert is that these quantities each represent some common property of two compatible assemblies, two assemblies being defined as compatible if there exists a third steady assembly into which both of the assemblies considered can be incorporated without any changes in their macroscopically measurable properties.

We now show that, if an assembly is described by a partition function such as (1), we can arrive at a satisfactory definition of the local pressure at each point. Consider what happens to the assembly if we alter, by a small distance dx, the position of the piston in one of the side tubes, which tube we suppose to communicate with the assembly at a distance y along the main tube. The result of the displacement is a slight change in the volume of the assembly and a corresponding shifting of all the energy levels. If we knew for certain that the assembly was occupying a certain level, r, of the energy E_r the change in the energy of that level would exactly balance the work needed to compress the spring through dx, so that we should have

$$P_1 = -\frac{1}{a}\frac{\partial E_r}{\partial x_1},$$

where a is the cross-section of the side tube. Actually, the assembly is almost equally likely to be found in a very large number of different levels of nearly the same energy, so that we have

$$P_1 = -\frac{1}{a}\left[\frac{\partial E_r}{\partial x_1}\right]_{\text{Av}}, \tag{3}$$

where the averaging has, just as in the equilibrium case, to be performed on the basis that a level of total energy E_r is occupied by a total of N molecules with a probability proportional to $\theta^{E_r}\lambda^N$, that is

$$P_1 = -\frac{1}{a}\sum_N\sum_r\left(\frac{\partial E_r}{\partial x_1}\right)\theta^{E_r}\lambda^N \Big/ \sum_N\sum_r \theta^{E_r}\lambda^N = -\frac{1}{a\log\theta}\frac{\partial(\log f)}{\partial x_1}, \tag{4}$$

a similar formula applying to all points of the assembly. This is a natural generalization of the formula

$$P = -\frac{1}{\log\theta}\frac{\partial(\log f)}{\partial V}$$

applying to an equilibrium assembly (in which the pressure is uniform, so that it does not matter in what way the deformation of volume is supposed to take place). Thus, in the steady assembly, the single pair of "force" and "displacement" variables (P, V) characteristic of an equilibrium assembly is replaced by a whole set of pairs of such variables, one pair for each point along the tube containing the assembly.

We may also interpret Eq. (4) slightly differently. It describes what happens if a small volume adx_1 is removed from the side tube and incorporated with the main assembly, the result being that the quantity $-\log f/\log \theta$ is increased by $P_1 adx_1$. Now we can always, in principle, consider an assembly as being built up step by step out of small elements, provided that this can be done in such a way as to avoid changing the measured properties of the part of the assembly that is already there, that is provided that the portions added at each stage are *compatible* with the rest of the assembly. Thus, we might build up our assembly, consisting of gas flowing through a tube, by injecting at each point gas at the appropriate pressure, velocity, and density, the walls of the vessel expanding sideways at the appropriate rate at each point. If this is done properly, all parts of the assembly could be described by the same values of θ and λ throughout the process (by the argument already outlined, two compatible assemblies can be brought together without change in $g_1 \cdot g_2$). (We have restricted ourselves to cases in which the pressure is known to be isotropic as a matter of observational fact. Generalization of this work to the case in which the stresses have to be represented by a tensor is almost certainly possible.)

On this basis we conclude that $-\log f/\log \theta$ is an additive quantity for compatible assemblies, in other words that

$$-\frac{\log f}{\log \theta} = \int P(y)\, A(y)\, dy, \tag{5}$$

where the integration is to be taken over the assembly, $P(y)$ being the pressure at a point y along the tube and $A(y)$ the corresponding cross-section. This is to be compared with the formula obtained by Fowler[2] for an equilibrium assembly

$$-\frac{\log f}{\log \theta} = \Sigma_s X_s x_s, \tag{6}$$

where the summation is over all relevant pairs of "force" and "displacement" variables, which sum reduces simply to PV if pressure is the only force variable. Comparison of (5) and (6) suggests that we can define a "statistical temperature," by means of the variable θ, for a steady assembly as well as for an equilibrium one. We can also define, if we wish, a mean pressure $\bar{P}$ for the whole assembly by writing

$$\bar{P}V = -\log f/\log \theta, \tag{7}$$

and Eq. (5) then shows that $\bar{P}$ represents the measured pressures averaged in a natural way over the whole assembly.

Other standard formulae can be generalized in a natural way. Once it is realized that log f is additive for two compatible assemblies we can apply the equations

$$E = \theta \frac{\partial (\log f)}{\partial \theta} \quad \text{and} \quad N = \lambda \frac{\partial (\log f)}{\partial \lambda}$$

to a *portion* of our assembly quite as well as to the whole of it, the function replacing log f in these formulae being obtained by restricting the integration in Eq. (5) to any portion of the assembly, whereupon the above two formulae lead to the common sense result that, if we want the mean number of molecules likely to be found in the assembly between y and $y+dy$, we must write

$$N(y)dy = \lambda \frac{\partial}{\partial \lambda} \left(\partial \frac{(\log f)}{\partial y} \right) dy, \tag{8}$$

and similarly

$$E(y)dy = \theta \frac{\partial}{\partial \theta} \left(\partial \frac{(\log f)}{\partial y} \right) dy \tag{9}$$

for the mean total kinetic and potential energy residing between these two planes.

These considerations, together with the Eqs. (5) to (7), lead us to look for a connection between the parameter θ and the measured *local* temperatures, the additivity of log f suggesting the existence of a result similar to that found from (5) and (7) for the pressures.

We can deduce the form of the expression for local temperature by a different argument, and we shall arrive at the expected relation between θ and an average over the local temperatures. Consider Eqs. (3) and (4) for the local pressure. This derivation is based on the argument that, if our assembly were definitely known to be in energy level E_r, there would be a definitely known mean compression of the spring of the piston at station 1, and at all other stations where we had inserted side tubes. This follows directly from the fact that there is supposed to be a definite coupling between the pistons and the rest of the assembly, so that the motions of them, and of the assembly, are described by the same many-body Schrödinger equation.

The *mean-square* displacement of piston 1 is also fixed if the assembly is definitely known to be occupying the level E_r. If the assembly is occupying other levels in turn, each level is associated with a certain mean-square displacement of piston 1, and the mean-square displacement that we shall actually observe will be an appropriate average over all the levels of the assembly, of the same type as (3) and (4). In the language of statistical mechanics, we say that piston 1 is trembling about its mean displacement because it is coupled with the rest of the assembly. (The corresponding kinetic energy varies for the different levels.) In the language of kinetic theory, we say that this trembling is caused by bombardment of the piston by neighboring molecules, and that the mean-square amplitude is a measure of the local "temperature." Clearly there is no reason to expect that the "readings" shown by two pistons in different parts of the assembly should be the same, nor is there reason to expect pressures to be uniform in a nonequilibrium assembly. On the other hand, a quantity such as θ, determining the distribution over all the levels, is a property of the assembly as a whole, while the "local" temperatures refer to particular places and are statistical averages over all the accessible levels. Our central problem is to relate these two quite distinct definitions of temperature, but before we can do this we must determine the averaging process by which "local" temperatures are defined.

We can determine this quantity by analogy with (3). The quantity $dx_1(\partial E_r/\partial x_1)$ may be thought of as the change in the energy level E_r that would be brought about by applying on external force to piston 1 which changed its equilibrium position by dx_1. Equally, we could think of it as the change that results from injecting an *additional* volume adx_1 of matter into the side tube. (This extra material would have to be compatible with that already present, which implies that its pressure and temperature would have to be P_1 and T_1.) We can conclude that these two slightly different operations must have the same effect on the energy levels from the undoubted experimental fact that "spring" or Bourdon and "liquid" or U-tube type manometers give results that are consistent with one another. We now examine the effect of introducing a small additional quantity of *energy* at station 1. This could be done in various ways, e.g. by increasing the amplitude of vibrations of the piston or by allowing radiation to enter. If the assembly were definitely known to be in energy level E_r, we should have, by conservation of energy, that the change in E_r would be $(\partial E_r/\partial s_1)ds_1$ and that the total addition of heat or energy at station 1 would be vT_1ds_1. Here T_1 and s_1 are the locally measured values of temperature and entropy per unit volume in side tube 1 of volume v_1. We have already defined the local temperature T_1 (see above), and we defer for a moment definition of s_1 the local entropy per unit volume. We postulate a formula of the type

$$T_1 = \frac{1}{v_1}\left[\frac{\partial E_r}{\partial s_1}\right]_{\text{Av}} = \frac{1}{v_1}\sum_N \sum_r \left(\frac{\partial E_r}{\partial s_1}\right) \theta^{E_r}\lambda^N \Big/ \sum_N \sum_r \theta^{E_r}\lambda^N \tag{10}$$

to allow for the fact that the assembly may be found in a large number of different levels. We may not write this relationship simply as

$$T_1 = \frac{1}{v_1 \log \theta} \frac{\partial (\log f)}{\partial s_1},$$

because the introduction of a small quantity of energy into the assembly not only changes the levels E_r, but also, in general, changes the probability of occupation of each level, that is we must allow for the effect of small consequential changes in θ and λ. From (2) it is plain that (10) is equivalent to

$$T_1 = \frac{1}{v_1 \log \theta} \frac{\partial}{\partial s_1} (\log f - N \log \lambda - E \log \theta) \tag{11}$$

because then the coefficients of $\partial\lambda/\partial s_1$ and $\partial\theta/\partial s_1$ vanish by (2).

If the assembly is such that the local entropy and temperature are functions of y only, that is, if we may consider them to be the same over any cross-section perpendicular to y (we shall return to this point later), we may arrive at a formula analogous to (5) by integrating (11) over the entire assembly, the entropy content of the region between y and $y+dy$ being simply $A(y)S(y)dy$, where $S(y)$ is the entropy content per unit volume at y (which is equal to s_1 at station 1). Then

$$TS = \int A(y)\, T(y)\, S(y)\, dy. \tag{12}$$

We can carry through an exactly similar discussion for the other selector variable, λ, by imagining a process in which extra molecules are added to the assembly at station 1, in such a way that the statistical temperature θ is unaltered. By considering the quantity $[\partial E_r/\partial N_1]_{\text{Av}}$, we arrive at the result for the "Helmholtz free energy" in a very similar fashion

$$F = T \int \frac{\mu(y) A(y) \varrho(y)}{m T(y)} dy, \tag{13}$$

where $\mu(y)$ is the measured value of the chemical potential at station y and $\varrho(y)$ is the local density, and m is the mass of one molecule.

We must now consider how to define the local entropy content per unit volume s_1 or $S(y)$. Our extension of statistical mechanics calls for a close relationship between this quantity, the local temperature T_1 and the energy changes caused by feeding a given quantity of heat into the assembly along side tube 1, but we have still to show that we can consistently give a definition equivalent to the "equilibrium" one in terms of specific heats. Now, we defined T_1 in terms of the Brownian motion of a piston in side tube 1, but we could equally well have defined it by saying that a further small assembly could be used as a local thermometer. That is to say that, if it were initially in equilibrium at the temperature T_1, it could be brought into thermal contact with side tube 1, without suffering any net gain or loss of heat. That is, it would be compatible with the main assembly. Now suppose that, instead of the thermometer, we introduce into the assembly, along side tube 1, a small mass of material that is initially in equilibrium at the local temperature and density. Again, no net interchange of energy or matter with the rest of the assembly will occur, so that it is plain that the energy added to the assembly in this way is determined by the *equilibrium* heat capacity of the small additional mass, that is that we can safely define entropy content in the side tubes in terms of *equilibrium* heat capacities. Equations (12) and (13) then show that, if we extend our definition of local entropy from each side tube to regions of the main assembly in the same plane, we remain consistent with the statistical definition of the "entropy" of the whole assembly, the possibility of adding up entropies being equivalent to compatibility.

In making our definition of compatibility, it was understood that we should have to make restrictions on the possible ways in which two assemblies are going to be brought into contact. There is, therefore, no *general* principle that two assemblies that are compatible with the assembly are compatibile with one another, though more restricted statements of this type are possible in special cases. We find, for example, that there is a distinct difference between the concepts of compatibility between two assemblies that are to have only one very small region in common, and between two assemblies that are to make contact at two or more widely separated points, or over a region of finite size. Let us suppose that one of the steady-state assemblies is a nonequilibrium one, so that its local properties differ from point to point. Then, as we have seen, it is possible for a small assembly, originally in equilibrium, to be compatible with this one if it is brought into contact with it over one small region only, but, if contact occurs over a region large enough for a significant change in the local properties to occur, then compatibility is only possible if the second assembly is also a nonequilibrium one. Bound up with this is the fact that, although there is always a sense in which we can say that two spatially separated small portions of a steady assembly are described by the same θ, it does *not* follow from this that they have the same *local* temperature. None of the above work has envisaged such a process as bringing two spatially separated parts of a nonequilibrium assembly into contact, although this might be possible for an equilibrium one. A finite deformation of any assembly implies that all its energy levels are altered, and in general, this would change the relationship between θ and E. Again, if we attempted to separate off one small portion of an assembly in order to bring it near another portion, it would, once separated off, have to be described by a set of wave functions quite different from those describing the main assembly.

It is a trivial point that we cannot define *equilibrium* between two assemblies apart from some expressed or implied specification of the means by which they are to be coupled up (e.g. thermal contact, semipermeable membranes). The restrictions on the definition of compatibility are of the same type. They are, in practice, more complicated simply because we require a more elaborate macroscopic description of a steady-state assembly, more parameters being involved than for an equilibrium one.

V. DISCUSSION

We have shown that, for a steady assembly, we can generalize the concepts of "statistical temperature" and "statistical partial potential" arrived at by an extension of the Fowler-Darwin treatment of the equilibrium assembly, and that these quantities can be expressed as appropriate averages over the locally measured properties of the assembly. There is one important proviso, for a steady streaming assembly such as a gas flowing through a tube. The measurements are supposed to take place in side tubes, which means that both the instruments and the material in immediate contact with them are at rest. In practice, measurements of pressure and temperature are nearly always carried out in this way, but there are also types of measurement, such as the use of a Rayleigh disc, that depend essentially on the local stream velocity. We have not considered the effect of this explicitly; what we are saying is that, even in a portion of the assembly where the stream velocity is appreciable, we can *define* such quantities as temperature and entropy by reference to a neighboring portion of the assembly that is at rest, but is compatible with the part that we are talking about. We assume always that conditions have settled down so that these two portions do not, in the long run, exchange matter or energy with one another even though they may be free to do so. Since there is, at present, no precise thermodynamic definition of temperature or entropy in part of an assembly in macroscopic motion, and since measurements are seldom, if ever, made with instruments "moving with the stream," it seems that there is no inconsistency in what we have done.

VI. TREATMENT OF A SIMPLE PROBLEM

We consider a perfect gas flowing in a rectangular tube of cross-section $Q \times R$, with a steady stream velocity v. We shall examine how the pressure varies with v if the density and temperature are kept constant. To calculate the pressure, we shall use formula (4), by fixing our attention on a short length of tube L, and examining the effect of varying the cross-section slightly by pushing one of the walls inwards. The wave functions appropriate to this problem are

$$\psi = e^{\pm ipx} \sin\left(\frac{q\pi y}{Q}\right) \sin\left(\frac{r\pi z}{R}\right) \tag{14}$$

where q and r are integers, but p may take any real value. We have now to consider how we must allocate our occupation numbers between states $+p$ and $-p$ to take account of the fact that the stream velocity of the whole assembly is known to be v, that is to say that the total x-momentum in the given portion of tube is $nLQRmv$ where $nLQR = Nm$ is the number of molecules in this portion. This problem was considered by Temperley[3] and by Zilsel.[4] Our occupation numbers have to be chosen in such a way that the momentum, as well as the energy, adds up to the correct value when we sum over all the levels. This is achieved by introducing another selector variable, or Lagrange multiplier, associated with the momentum in the same way that Θ is associated with energy, whose value is afterward determined in terms of v and turns out to be simply $\exp(-v/kT)$ per molecule.

Using this result, we find for the classical partition function per molecule

$$f = \int_{-\infty}^{+\infty} dp \sum_q \sum_r \exp\left[\frac{-h^2}{8\pi^2 mkT}\left(p^2 + \frac{\pi^2 q^2}{Q^2} + \frac{\pi^2 r^2}{R^2}\right) + \frac{hp}{2\pi}\frac{v}{kT}\right] \tag{15}$$

since $hp/2\pi$ is the momentum in the x-direction according to (14). Performing the integration over p, and replacing the summations over q and r by integrations in the usual way, we find, for an assembly of N molecules

$$N \log f = N\left(\text{constant} + \log(QR) + \frac{3}{2}\log T + \frac{mv^2}{2kT}\right). \tag{16}$$

Applying (4) to an assembly consisting of the molecules within a volume LQR, and allowing Q to vary, (4) becomes

$$\begin{aligned} P &= \frac{kT}{LR}\frac{\partial}{\partial Q}(N \log f) = \frac{kT}{LR}\left(\frac{N}{Q} + \frac{m}{2kT}\frac{d}{dQ}(Nv^2)\right) \\ &= nkT - \frac{nmv^2}{2} \end{aligned} \tag{17}$$

if N and v vary with Q but n, the number of atoms per unit volume and Nv, the flux in and out of the volume considered, are held constant during the change in Q. (17) is just Bernoulli's expression for the pressure. We are supposing that we make the measurement by letting the wall deform in such a way that the disturbance of the flow is very small, which is consistent with the above assumptions.

This process can be extended to quantum statistics without difficulty, and a similar treatment is possible for the many-body problem if we know the total energy and total momentum associated with each level of the whole assembly. The introduction of the extra selector variable enables us to decide the relative weights to be given to a given level and the level of equal energy but reversed momentum that are always weighted equally for an assembly in a closed vessel. Our treatment as it stands can be applied, e.g., to a vessel in the form of a sector of a cylinder or sphere, it being only necessary to fix our attention on a region cut off between radii R and $R+dR$, replace the functions (14) by the corresponding solutions in the cylindrical and spherical cases, and calculate the partition function as before under the restraint that we specify the total momentum along the bisector of the angle of the sector. (This is easily seen to lead to expressions equivalent to (16) and (17) in the limit of large radius.) The relationship between momentum and flux now varies with R, but this introduces no difficulty of principle, our general theory showing that any convenient portion of our vessel may be taken as our "open assembly" without introducing any inconsistency.

I should like to thank Professor G. S. Rushbrooke for helpful discussions and the Director, Atomic Weapons Research Establishment, for permission to publish this paper.

References

(1) R. H. Fowler, *Statistical Mechanics,* 2nd ed., Cambridge Univ. Press, London, 1936.
(2) R. H. Fowler, *Proc. Cambridge Phil. Soc.,* **34**, 382 (1938).
(3) H. N. V. Temperley, *Proc. Phys. Soc.* (*London*), A **65**, 490 (Appendix), (1952).
(4) P. R. Zilsel, *Phys. Rev.,* **92**, 1106 (1953).

Discussion III

R. Eisenschitz: The question raised by Professor Yvon whether to use x_1 and x_2 or x_1+x_2 and x_1-x_2 for a pair of particles becomes important when considering which type of coordinates are statistically independent.

M. Green asked Professor Yvon to explain the physical significance of the matrix $\mathfrak{M}(x_1', x_2'')$.

J. Yvon: La matrice densité $\mathfrak{M}(x_1', x_1'')$ concerne *une seule* particule envisagée en deux points différents. Les résultats évoqués par M. Green concernent la matrice densité à deux particules. $\mathfrak{M}(x_1', x_1')$ n'est pas autre chose que la densité *ordinaire*. Par contre, pour des fermions, $X = \mathfrak{M}(x_1', x_1'; x_1', x_1')$ est nul. C'est une conséquence de la formule $\mu_{12} = (1-P_{12})C_{12}$. Il n'y a pas de résultat général dans le cas des bosons.

PART IV

ON THERMAL CONDUCTION IN INSULATING SOLIDS

D. K. C. MACDONALD, *Division of Pure Physics, National Research Council, Sussex Drive, Ottawa, Canada*

Abstract

From the work of Debye and Peierls we are today satisfied that thermal resistivity in an insulating crystal free from physical and chemical defects arises from the anharmonic component of the interatomic potential. Nonetheless we still seem to be quite a long way from an adequate quantitative theory of heat conduction.

An analysis is given of the one-dimensional problem using classical particle-mechanics. Carrying the discussion to the quartic potential term does not yet appear on this model to lead to a finite thermal conductivity.

I. INTRODUCTORY SUMMARY

Debye[6] in 1914 made an approximate analysis of the thermal resistivity of an insulating solid on the assumption that the anharmonicity of lattice vibrations was the responsible factor; Schrödinger,[22] however, argued that the vital feature was the discrete atomic structure of the solid as opposed to a continuum.

Ornstein and Zernike[14] also considered the problem, but it is generally accepted that the most significant contribution following Debye has been that of Peierls[15] (see also ref. 17). He emphasized that the anharmonic component of the interatomic potential must be responsible for thermal resistivity in an ideal periodic crystal free from chemical or physical defects* and analyzed in some detail the anharmonic interaction of lattice waves, leading to a qualitative estimate of the "relaxation time." Peierls' analysis led him to conclude that only a certain very restricted class of anharmonic interactions between the normal modes would be fundamentally responsible for thermal resistance. These specialized interactions he called "Umklapp processes" and a detailed knowledge of the dispersion laws of the crystal would be necessary to predict their frequency of occurrence. Peierls deduced, in agreement with Debye's earlier conclusion, that at high tempera-

* And sufficiently large in dimensions that scattering of lattice waves at external boundaries plays no appreciable role.

tures ($T \gtrsim \theta$) the thermal resistance, W, would follow the law:

$$W \propto T \tag{1}$$

while for sufficiently low temperatures ($T \ll \theta$), Peierls predicted:

$$W \propto \exp\,(-\theta/\beta T), \qquad (\beta \approx 2). \tag{2}$$

The factor $\exp\,(-\theta/\beta T)$ represents the rapidly decaying frequency of occurrence of possible "Umklapp processes" as the temperature is reduced. It seems rather probable that Eq. (1) is essentially correct, and Eq. (2) fits some experimental data rather well (e.g. cf. refs. 2, 3, 23) although in other experiments (e.g. refs. 20, 21, 24, 25) no "Umklapp region" corresponding to (2) has been observed, at any rate as yet.

Since the work of Peierls, some efforts have been made[7, 10–13] (cf. also ref. 5) to derive more quantitative expressions for thermal resistance. The particular difficulty involved in evaluating Peierls' theory quantitatively lies in determining the possible "Umklapp processes" that can occur. In the case of a one-dimensional chain, Peierls concluded that interactions due to the first anharmonic (cubic) term in the interatomic potential could not provide appropriate "Umklapp processes" (of the so-called 3-phonon type) and hence could not contribute to a thermal resistance. On the other hand, Peierls argued that, if we include the next (quartic) term in the potential for the chain, "Umklapp processes" (in this case involving "4-phonon" interactions) can always occur which will therefore govern the thermal resistivity.

In a three-dimensional solid, on the other hand, Peierls originally assumed that the requirements of Umklapp processes could generally be met by the cubic anharmonic term. However, Pomeranchuk[18] and Herpin[8] maintain that in solids the cubic term will *not* provide finite conductivity and that in solids, too, one must include higher order anharmonic terms. In that case a higher power of T would then appear in Eq. (1) above (cf. also ref. 17). Bauer and Wu[1] suggested very recently that, if one relaxes strictly periodic boundary conditions, the cubic term will suffice for finite thermal conductivity.

We wish, therefore, in this paper to consider afresh the problem of thermal conduction in a one-dimensional chain. Our analysis is carried through on the basis of elementary classical particle dynamics, lattice waves only being introduced where necessary to evaluate the magnitude of expressions derived. The outcome of the analysis appears to throw some possible doubt on the validity of previous conclusions on this problem and on the adequacy of our present understanding of this field.

First, however, as an introduction to the principal problem, we want to mention briefly the problem of the calculation of *electrical* resistance in a solid arising from its thermal vibrations.

II. ELECTRICAL RESISTIVITY

The electric current density J is given by:

$$J = Nev, \tag{3}$$

where N is the electron density and v the average electron velocity. Hence

$$dJ/dt = Ne(dv/dt), \tag{4}$$

assuming that N is constant in time.

If we have an electric field $\mathscr{E}$ applied to the solid then dv/dt has two parts, the first due to the electromechanical acceleration $e\mathscr{E}/m^*$ of the field (where m^* is the effective electron mass) and the other term, say $(dv/dt)_{\text{coll}}$, arising from the "collisions" of the electrons with the vibrating lattice. If a steady state is achieved in this way so that $dJ/dt = 0$ we have from (4):

$$(Ne^2\mathscr{E}/m^*) + Ne(dv/dt)_{\text{coll}} = 0. \tag{5}$$

In calculating the second term, which represents the essentially irreversible part of the whole process, it is assumed that the lattice vibrations themselves remain in thermal equilibrium. This assumption, as Peierls[16] pointed out (cf. also ref. 26a), cannot be strictly true by very virtue of the fact that the directed momentum which the electrons are receiving from the electric field has to be imparted continuously to the lattice. With this assumption, which means in brief that the lattice "forgets" very rapidly so providing irreversibility, the second term in (5) can be expressed* as $-J/\tau$ where τ is the "relaxation time" (or alternatively we may write as the mean free path: $l = v\tau$: where v is the electron speed). Thus we now have:

$$J = Ne^2\tau\mathscr{E}/m^* \tag{6}$$

or

$$\sigma \equiv J/\mathscr{E} = Ne^2\tau/m^*.$$

It may be remarked here that the conductivity, σ, is governed essen-

* At least at "high" temperatures ($T \gtrsim \theta$); at low temperatures ($T \ll \theta$) the situation is analytically somewhat more complex (cf. e.g. ref. 26b).

tially by the two factors: m^*, introduced by the "mechanical" action of the "driving force," $\mathscr{E}$, and τ, arising from the *irreversible* part of the process.

III. THERMAL CONDUCTIVITY OF A CHAIN

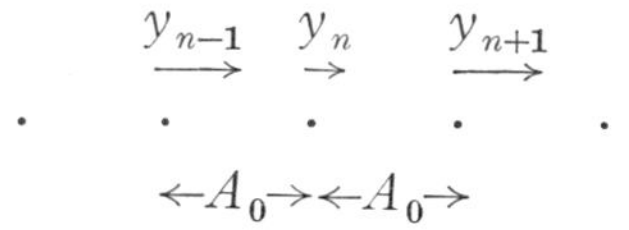

Figure 1

We consider a chain of atoms (Fig. 1) whose mutual spacing is Δ_0 in static equilibrium. The displacement of the nth atom at any instant from this position of equilibrium is y_n. We restrict ourselves to nearest neighbor interaction and assume that the potential energy, W, between the nth and $(n-1)$th atoms is given by:

$$W = \frac{\lambda}{2}(y_n - y_{n-1})^2 - \frac{\mu}{3}(y_n - y_{n-1})^3 + \frac{\nu}{4}(y_n - y_{n-1})^4. \tag{7}$$

Then at any instant, t, the energy flow from left to right, $\dot{\mathbf{E}}(t)$, is given by:

$$\dot{\mathbf{E}}(t) = \{-\lambda(y_n - y_{n-1}) + \mu(y_n - y_{n-1})^2 - \nu(y_n - y_{n-1})^3\}\{\dot{y}_n + \dot{y}_{n-1}\}.$$

Let us assume first $\nu = 0$. We write $\Delta y_n \equiv y_n - y_{n-1}$. Then:

$$(\partial/\partial t)\dot{\mathbf{E}}(t) = \{-\lambda\Delta\dot{y}_n + 2\mu\Delta y_n\Delta\dot{y}_n\}\{\dot{y}_n + \dot{y}_{n-1}\} + \{-\lambda\Delta y_n + \mu(\Delta y_n)^2\}\{\ddot{y}_n + \ddot{y}_{n-1}\}.$$

But

$$m\{\ddot{y}_n + \ddot{y}_{n-1}\} = \lambda\{\Delta y_{n+1} - \Delta y_{n-1}\} - \mu\{(\Delta y_{n+1})^2 - (\Delta y_{n-1})^2\},$$

and thus

$$\begin{aligned}\frac{\partial}{\partial t}\dot{\mathbf{E}}(t) = &-\frac{\lambda}{m}[\Delta(m\dot{y}_n^2) + \Delta\{\lambda(y_{n+1} - y_n)(y_n - y_{n-1})\}] \\ &+ 2\mu\Delta y_n\Delta\dot{y}_n^2 + \frac{\mu\lambda}{m}(y_{n+1} - y_{n-2})[\Delta\{(y_{n+1} - y_n)(y_n - y_{n-1})\}] \\ &- \frac{\mu^2}{m}\Delta\{(y_{n+1} - y_n)(y_n - y_{n-1})\}^2.\end{aligned} \tag{8}$$

If now we average both sides of Eq. (8) over a "long" time (i.e., significant for the experimental measurement of *heat* flow, where $\dot{H} = \overline{\dot{\mathbf{E}}(t)}$) then it is evident that in the steady state of heat conduction we must have $\overline{(\partial/\partial t)\dot{E}(t)} = 0$. The terms in the first bracket on the right-hand side of Eq. (8), which do not involve μ, represent then the "driving force" for the energy flow $\dot{\mathbf{E}}(t)$. The first term is immediately recognized quite generally as involving the gradient of the kinetic energy. The second term is evidently a quasi-potential energy gradient and to interpret this term in the "driving force" we may consider the form of these terms when we have harmonic waves in the chain. If we set

$$y_n(t) = \sum_i A_i \sin(\omega_i t + \phi_i - 2\pi n A_0/\tilde{\lambda}_i) + \sum_r B_r \sin(\omega_r t + \psi_r + 2\pi n A_0/\tilde{\lambda}_r), \quad (9)$$

where ω_i is the angular frequency, $\tilde{\lambda}_i$ is the corresponding wave length and ϕ_i, ψ_r are arbitrary phase angles, then the "driving force" for heat flow may be written

$$-(2\lambda/m) \sum_i \{\lambda \sin^2(\alpha_i/2)(1+\cos\alpha_i)\Delta(\overline{A_i^2}+\overline{B_i^2})\} \quad (10)$$

(where now for convenience we write $\alpha_i \equiv 2\pi A_0/\tilde{\lambda}_i$). In the case of long waves ($\alpha_i \to 0$) this reduces simply to

$$-(\lambda^2/m) \sum_i \alpha_i^2 \Delta(\overline{A_i^2}+\overline{B_i^2}). \quad (11)$$

The corresponding general expression for the average energy per particle is

$$E = 2\lambda \sum_i \sin^2(\alpha_i/2)(\overline{A_i^2}+\overline{B_i^2}) \quad (12)$$

and so for *long* waves evidently

$$(\partial\dot{H}/\partial t)_{\text{driv}} = -(2\lambda/m)\Delta E. \quad (12a)$$

However, as we approach the *short*-wave limit when $\tilde{\lambda}_i = 2A_0$ ($\therefore \alpha_i = \pi$), then (10) tends to zero, i.e., $(\partial\dot{H}/\partial t)_{\text{driv}} \to 0$ for short waves. We see thus that the "driving force" itself varies with wave length and this will of course already influence markedly the conductivity to be observed at different temperatures. This contribution may then be compared with the influence of effective electron mass, m^*, on electrical conductivity as mentioned above.

Before turning to consider the anharmonic terms we might point out that there is already perhaps some conceptual difficulty in using Eq. (9) to evaluate Eq. (8) (or more particularly the "potential energy" term), leading to Eq. (10) since, *strictly* speaking, we cannot have an energy gradient present if we restrict ourselves to purely harmonic waves. This might amount already to some implicit introduction of irreversibility by our very postulation that an energy gradient (which we interpret later as arising from a temperature gradient) can exist.

Turning then to the anharmonic terms we see that we should expect to find that we can express these in the form $-\overline{\dot{\mathbf{E}}(t)/\tau} \equiv -\dot{H}/\tau$ if we are to have heat conduction in the steady state (i.e., $\partial\dot{H}/\partial t = 0$). That is, writing the expression in (10) as $-f(\alpha_i)\Delta E$, we should then have

$$0 = \overline{-f(\alpha_i)\Delta E} - \dot{H}/\bar{\tau}, \tag{13a}$$

where $\overline{f(\alpha_i)\Delta E}$ and $\bar{\tau}$ signify averages over the excited lattice vibrations appropriate to the temperature considered. It is very probable that these averages would have to be treated together, i.e.,

$$\dot{H} = -\overline{\tau f(\alpha_i)\,\Delta E}. \tag{13b}$$

In the case of the one-dimensional chain considered we have:

$$\overline{-f(\alpha_i)\Delta E} = -\Delta 2\left(\frac{\lambda}{m}\right)^{3/2}\frac{\hbar}{\pi}\int_0^{\pi}\frac{(1+\cos\alpha_i)\cdot\sin(\alpha_i/2)\cdot d\alpha_i}{\left\{\exp\left(\frac{2\hbar}{kT}\left(\frac{\lambda}{m}\right)^{1/2}\sin\frac{\alpha_i}{2}\right)-1\right\}}. \tag{14}$$

At high temperatures ($T \gtrsim \theta$) where $\theta = (2\hbar/k)(\lambda/m)^{1/2}$ this yields

$$\begin{aligned}\overline{-f(\alpha_i)\Delta E} &= -\Delta\frac{\lambda}{m}kT \\ &\approx -\frac{\lambda k A_0}{m}\frac{\partial T}{\partial x}\end{aligned} \tag{15a}$$

and hence

$$\dot{H} = -(\lambda k A_0\bar{\tau}/m)\cdot(\partial T/\partial x). \tag{15b}$$

More generally we have:

$$\begin{aligned}\overline{-f(\alpha_i)\Delta E} &= -\Delta\frac{8\hbar}{\pi}\left(\frac{\lambda}{m}\right)^{3/2}\left(\frac{T}{\theta}\right)^2\int_0^{\theta/T}\frac{(1-(T/\theta)^2x^2)^{1/2}\,x\,dx}{\varepsilon^x-1} \\ &\approx -\Delta\frac{8\hbar}{\pi}\left(\frac{\lambda}{m}\right)^{3/2}\left(\frac{T}{\theta}\right)^2\int_0^{\infty}\frac{x\,dx}{\varepsilon^x-1}, \qquad \text{for } T \ll \theta\end{aligned}$$

$$\begin{aligned} &= -\frac{2h}{3}\left(\frac{\lambda}{m}\right)^{3/2} \Delta \left(\frac{T}{\theta}\right)^2 \\ &\approx -\frac{4\pi\lambda k A_0}{3m}\left(\frac{T}{\theta}\right)\frac{\partial T}{\partial x} \end{aligned} \tag{16a}$$

and hence in this case

$$\dot{H} = -\frac{4\pi\lambda k A_0 \tau}{3m}\left(\frac{T}{\theta}\right)\frac{\partial T}{\partial x}. \tag{16b}$$

In the three dimensional *analog* the corresponding expressions to (15a) would be:

$$-3\left(1-\frac{6}{\pi^2}\right)\frac{\lambda k A_0}{m}\frac{\partial T}{\partial x}, \qquad \text{for } T \gtrsim \theta. \tag{15c}$$

While at low temperatures we may write directly from (12a)

$$\left(\frac{\partial \dot{H}}{\partial t}\right)_{\text{driv}} \approx -\frac{2\lambda A_0}{m} c_{\text{at}} \frac{\partial T}{\partial x},$$

where c_{at} is the specific heat per atom.

When we consider the anharmonic terms it is clear that the sign of τ must not depend on the intrinsic sign of μ since the *direction* of heat flow is uniquely governed by the second law of thermodynamics, independently of any specific assumptions about the character of interatomic forces. If then we adopt the harmonic wave approximation in evaluating the terms in μ and $\mu\lambda$ in Eq. (8) (and also any subsequent anharmonic terms with odd powers of μ or ν) it follows directly that these must not contribute to the expected *relaxation* term, and this is also evident in detail if we substitute Eq. (9) in these terms in (8) and then take a time average. It appears in fact that the terms in μ and $\mu\lambda$ play the role of correction terms to the "driving force" which we may neglect in the case of small anharmonicity. We therefore turn our attention to the last term in (8), quadratic in μ. This is indeed of the correct *form* that might yield a term of the type $-\dot{H}/\tau$, but it is immediately evident that again in this approximation this term will *vanish* on taking a time average since it is a simple difference function (effectively of the form $\Phi(n)-\Phi(n-1)$), and this conclusion may again be readily confirmed by substitution of Eq. (9) in the approximate term. The term will of course vanish when averaged under *any* quasi-equilibrium description (not necessarily in terms of harmonic waves).

The adoption here of the harmonic approximation (or more generally, quasi-equilibrium approximation) to evaluate the anharmonic term(s) would appear to correspond to the assumption in the electrical conductivity problem that we can evaluate the electron *collision* term there by neglecting any disturbance of the thermodynamic equilibrium; it is in this way that the assumption of irreversibility would really enter the present problem since we are explicitly assuming that the anharmonic "damping" of the waves does not disturb significantly the over-all equilibrium. This is again conceptually somewhat unpleasing since we are after all trying to analyze on an "atomic" level a fundamental problem in irreversibility and in doing so are being led to introduce certain assumptions of irreversibility. However, we should be reasonably content with this procedure if it enabled us to emerge with a quantitative answer; a more adequate critical discussion of the details of irreversible heat flow would demand a detailed analysis of how, starting from the boundaries of the specimen in contact with thermal "baths," a temperature gradient is set up and maintained through the specimen (cf. also ref. 5). This of course in turn might lead us to ask exactly how a thermal bath *itself* can absorb irreversibly an energy flow while remaining in effective thermodynamic equilibrium. It appears to the writer that we are always led in the *final analysis* to ascribe irreversibility to the ultimately "open" character of a system which is conducting heat in a steady state; it is of course equivalent to talk of "infinitely large" heat baths.

The failure of the anharmonic term in μ^2 to yield a limiting heat flow in the linear chain might lead us to conclude that it would be necessary, as Peierls argued, to include higher order terms in the potential energy. However if we now consider the next anharmonic term in Eq. (8) (ignoring, as remarked earlier, those of odd powers in μ and ν) we find that it may be written simply:

$$-\frac{\nu^2}{m}\Delta\{(y_{n+1}-y_n)^3\cdot(y_n-y_{n-1})^3\}.$$

But this is once more a simple difference function which when time averaged, using the quasi-equilibrium approximation, must once more yield zero.* We consequently appear to have met with a serious difficulty

* This appears to be a quite general — and indeed perhaps somewhat trivial — result if, for example, we write $W = (\lambda/2)\,(y_n - y_{n-1})^2 + F(y_n - y_{n-1})$ where F is an arbitrary function representing the higher order terms in the potential energy.

in the analysis. If we try now to avoid these null results (predicting essentially infinite thermal conductivity) by going to a higher approximation in evaluating the anharmonic terms and including the gradient explicitly in them it appears that we can no longer then expect to arrive at an equation of the form:

$$\dot{H} \propto -\Delta E \quad (\text{i.e., } \propto -\partial T/\partial x), \quad (\text{cf. eq. } (13))$$

namely the law of heat conduction.

The other prediction of Peierls that essentially the term in μ^2 can yield finite thermal conductivity if we do not restrict ourselves to a *one*-dimensional chain may well be true (but cf. again refs. 8 and 18) although it is difficult for us to see on a two-dimensional particle model on the present type of analysis why this should essentially be so.

Born[4] in his discussion of the foundations of the Second Law argues that there is an essential difference between classical and quantum mechanics, an element of irreversibility being intrinsically involved in the latter. Other authors, however, maintain that this is not so and that in the high temperature region quantum mechanics is only used as a matter of convenience for the analysis of thermal conductivity. The failure of the foregoing particle mechanics analysis to yield a finite conductivity tempts one to ask whether a quantum mechanical description (with the consequent inclusion of the Uncertainty Principle) of the interatomic interaction may not perhaps be fundamentally indispensable for an adequate solution of the problem. It is interesting that Landé[11] has already argued emphatically that deterministic classical mechanics cannot lead validly to irreversibility.

On the other hand, it may be that we have not found the appropriate approximation for evaluating the anharmonic term(s) (see also Note added in proof following) which if found would then yield a quantitative result for the thermal resistivity.

IV. CONCLUSION

We have carried out this particle mechanics analysis of the problem because it seemed worth while to examine in this way the fundamental assumptions and difficulties involved. We do not of course deny that thermal resistivity exists! — nor that it is related to the anharmonic properties of the solid. It appears, however, that the approximations involved must yet be carefully examined if we are to arrive finally at a satisfactory answer.

Note added in proof:

If one discusses thermal conductivity in terms of normal vibrations of the lattice, then the irreversibility can be introduced by assuming that when a given mode decays toward equilibrium through the weak anharmonic interaction, the "environment" furnished by the *other* vibrational modes remains essentially undisturbed (cf. e.g. ref. 19). A particular difficulty presented by the foregoing particle mechanics discussion is to see where any similar additional hypothesis about the *particle* "environment" can be logically introduced into the analysis.

I am most grateful to Doctors J. S. Dugdale and T. H. K. Barron for much patient discussion on this rather vexing question. I should also like to thank Doctors T. Y. Wu and P. G. Klemens for reading the manuscript and for their comments.

References

(1) E. Bauer and T. Y. Wu, private communication, 1956.
(2) R. Berman, F. E. Simon, and J. Wilks, *Nature,* **168**, 277 (1951).
(3) R. Berman, *Adv. Phys.* (*Phil. Mag. Supp.*), **2**, 103 (1953).
(4) M. Born, *Ann. Physik,* **3**, 107 (1948).
(5) R. Brout and I. Prigogine, *Physica,* **22**, 263 (1956). (Also Prigogine and Brout, *Tech. Rep.* EOARDC-TN-54 (1955), Free Univ. Brussels.)
(6) P. Debye, *Vorträge über die kinetische Theorie,* Teubner, Leipzig, 1914.
(7) J. S. Dugdale and D. K. C. MacDonald, *Phys. Rev.* **98**, 1751 (1955).
(8) A. Herpin, *Ann. phys.*, **7**, 91 (1952).
(9) P. G. Klemens, *Proc. Roy. Soc.* (London), A **208**, 108 (1951).
(10) P. G. Klemens, *Handbuch der Physik,* Ed. Flügge; Springer, Leipzig, **14**, 59 (1956).
(11) A. Landé, *Scientific Papers presented to Max Born,* Oliver & Boyd, Edinburgh, 1953, p. 59.
(12) G. Leibfried, *Handbuch der Physik,* Ed. Flügge; Springer, Leipzig, **7**, Part 2, 290 (1955).
(13) G. Leibfried and E. Schlömann, *Nachr. Ges. Wiss. Göttingen, IIa,* **71** (1954).
(14) L. S. Ornstein and F. Zernike, *Proc. Roy. Acad. Amsterdam,* **19**, 1295 (1917).
(15) R. E. Peierls, *Ann. Physik,* **3**, 1055 (1929).
(16) R. E. Peierls, *Ann. Physik,* **12**, 154 (1932).
(17) R. E. Peierls, *Quantum Theory of Solids*, Clarendon Press, Oxford, 1955.
(18) I. Pomeranchuk, *J. Phys.* (*U.S.S.R.*), **4**, 259 (1941).
(19) I. Prigogine and R. Balescu, *Physica,* **23,** 555 (1957).
(20) H. M. Rosenberg, *Proc. Phys. Soc.* (*London*), A **67**, 837 (1954).
(21) H. M. Rosenberg, *Proc. Intern. Conf. Low Temps.*, p. 464, Annexe 1955—3 (*Suppl. Bull. inst. intern. Froid*).
(22) E. Schrödinger, *Ann. Physik,* **44**, 916 (1914).
(23) F. J. Webb and J. Wilks, *Phil. Mag.,* **44**, 663 (1953).
(24) G. K. White and S. B. Woods, *Can. J. Phys.,* **33**, 58 (1955).
(25) G. K. White and S. B. Woods, *Phys. Rev.,* **103,** 569 (1956).
(26) A. H. Wilson, *The Theory of Metals,* 2nd ed., Cambridge Univ. Press, 1953. (a) *Idem,* p. 296. (b) *Idem,* p. 277.

THE TRANSPORT OF ENERGY AND MATTER IN A DENSE TWO-COMPONENT MIXTURE OF HARD SPHERES

H. C. LONGUET-HIGGINS, J. A. POPLE, and J. P. VALLEAU,
Department of Theoretical Chemistry, University of Cambridge, England

Abstract

The matter and energy transport coefficients of a fluid composed of hard spheres, all of the same radius but of two different masses, are calculated by kinetic theory on the assumption that, for nonequilibrium states in which the concentrations of both components are uniform, the pair distribution function f_{AB} is given by

$$f_{AB}(\mathbf{r}_a, \mathbf{v}_a; \mathbf{r}_b, \mathbf{v}_b) = n^0_{AB}(\mathbf{r}_a, \mathbf{r}_b) f'_A(\mathbf{r}_a, \mathbf{v}_a) f'_B(\mathbf{r}_b, \mathbf{v}_b),$$

where n^0_{AB} is the equilibrium two-particle density function and $f'_A(\mathbf{r}_a, \mathbf{v}_a)$ is a Maxwellian velocity distribution determined by the mean velocity of species A and the temperature at the point $\mathbf{r}_a$. The mutual diffusion coefficient and the thermal diffusion ratio are found to be

$$D_{12} = \frac{a}{2\chi}\left(\frac{\pi kT}{2\mu_{12}}\right)^{1/2}, \quad k_1^T = \frac{\chi n_1 n_2 (m_1 - m_2)}{n^2(m_1 + m_2)},$$

where a is the particle radius, m_1 and m_2 the particle masses, μ_{12} the reduced mass $m_1 m_2/(m_1+m_2)$, n_1 and n_2 the particle concentrations, $n = n_1+n_2$, and $\chi = P/nkT - 1$.

The calculated transport coefficients are found to satisfy the reciprocal relations of Onsager, and the reasons for this are examined in detail.

I. INTRODUCTION

This paper presents an approximate statistical calculation of the matter and energy transport coefficients for a dense fluid mixture of hard spheres, in which the spheres are all of the same radius, but of two different masses. In systems of more than one component, as is well known, the processes of heat transfer and matter transfer are coupled, so that a consideration of one is inseparable from a consideration of the other. Furthermore, according to the theory originated by Onsager,[6] certain reciprocal relations should hold between the coupling coefficients, and these relations might or might not be verified by an exact statistical calculation, could such a calculation be carried out. On the other hand, there is no logical reason why an approximate statistical theory should lead to the Onsager relations, so we shall here calculate all the transport coefficients independently, obtaining explicit expressions for them in terms of thermodynamic properties.

The paper is divided into nine main sections. In Section II we transform the standard equations of irreversible thermodynamics into a form suitable for statistical discussion, and suggest that the matter flux and the temperature gradient be chosen as the variables determining the statistical characteristics of the mixture when the particle concentrations are uniform. In Section III we relate the heat and matter fluxes to the one- and two-particle distribution functions for nonequilibrium states, and Section IV describes a set of approximations to these distribution functions. In Sections V and VI two nonequilibrium states are examined in detail, and for each a calculation is performed on two of the thermodynamic observables; the results of these calculations are used in Section VII to obtain the four coefficients for heat and matter transport independently of one another. The Onsager relations are, somewhat unexpectedly, found to be satisfied. This leads to an inquiry whether the approximate distribution functions adopted in Section IV have any special significance; Sections VIII and IX are concerned with the answer to this question.

II. THE THERMODYNAMIC EQUATIONS FOR HEAT AND MATTER TRANSPORT

The thermodynamic theory of irreversible processes relates the fluxes of heat and matter in a nonequilibrium system to the gradients of temperature and chemical potential. If we consider a small region of a two-component fluid, and choose axes moving with the barycentric velocity, the mass fluxes $\mathbf{J}_1$, $\mathbf{J}_2$ of the two components will be related by the identity

$$\mathbf{J}_1+\mathbf{J}_2 = 0. \tag{2.1}$$

These mass fluxes and the heat flux $\mathbf{J}_0$ will in the neighborhood of equilibrium be linear functions of the conjugate variables[3]

$$\mathbf{X}_0 = -\frac{1}{T}\nabla T, \tag{2.2}$$

$$\mathbf{X}_1 = \mathbf{Y}_1-T\nabla\left(\frac{\mu_1}{T}\right), \tag{2.3}$$

$$\mathbf{X}_2 = \mathbf{Y}_2 - T\nabla\left(\frac{\mu_2}{T}\right), \tag{2.4}$$

where μ_1, μ_2 represent the local chemical potentials of the two components per unit mass, and $\mathbf{Y}_1$, $\mathbf{Y}_2$ are the external forces per unit mass acting upon them. The equations expressing these relations are

$$\mathbf{J}_0 = L_{00}\mathbf{X}_0 + L_{01}\,(\mathbf{X}_1 - \mathbf{X}_2) \tag{2.5}$$

$$\mathbf{J}_1 = L_{10}\mathbf{X}_0 + L_{11}(\mathbf{X}_1 - \mathbf{X}_2), \tag{2.6}$$

and the $L_{\mu\nu}$ are called the phenomenological coefficients. According to the theory, they will satisfy the reciprocal relation[6]

$$L_{01} = L_{10}. \tag{2.7}$$

As they stand, Eqs. (2.5) and (2.6) are not in a very convenient form for statistical discussion. One reason is that the variables $\mathbf{X}_1$ and $\mathbf{X}_2$ involve the temperature gradient implicitly, and it is preferable to work with equations in which the gradients of temperature and concentration appear as separate variables. Let us therefore regard the molecular concentrations n_1, n_2 and the temperature as the variables determining the chemical potentials, and write

$$\mathbf{X}_1 = \mathbf{Y}_1 + \frac{\mu_1}{T}\nabla T - \frac{\partial \mu_1}{\partial T}\nabla T - \frac{\partial \mu_1}{\partial n_1}\nabla n_1 - \frac{\partial \mu_1}{\partial n_2}\nabla n_2, \tag{2.8}$$

$$\mathbf{X}_2 = \mathbf{Y}_2 + \frac{\mu_2}{T}\nabla T - \frac{\partial \mu_2}{\partial T}\nabla T - \frac{\partial \mu_2}{\partial n_1}\nabla n_1 - \frac{\partial \mu_2}{\partial n_2}\nabla n_2. \tag{2.9}$$

Using the thermodynamic relations

$$\mu_1 - T\left(\frac{\partial \mu_1}{\partial T}\right)_{n_1, n_2} = \bar{E}_1, \qquad \mu_2 - T\left(\frac{\partial \mu_2}{\partial T}\right)_{n_1, n_2} = \bar{E}_2, \tag{2.10}$$

and introducing new forces

$$\mathbf{Z}_1 = \mathbf{Y}_1 - \frac{\partial \mu_1}{\partial n_1}\nabla n_1 - \frac{\partial \mu_1}{\partial n_2}\nabla n_2, \qquad \mathbf{Z}_2 = \mathbf{Y}_2 - \frac{\partial \mu_2}{\partial n_1}\nabla n_1 - \frac{\partial \mu_2}{\partial n_2}\nabla n_2, \tag{2.11}$$

we may then rewrite Eqs. (2.5) and (2.6) in the form

$$\mathbf{J}_0 = \left\{\frac{L_{01}}{T}(\bar{E}_1 - \bar{E}_2) - \frac{L_{00}}{T}\right\}\nabla T + L_{01}(\mathbf{Z}_1 - \mathbf{Z}_2), \tag{2.12}$$

$$\mathbf{J}_1 = \left\{\frac{L_{11}}{T}(\bar{E}_1 - \bar{E}_2) - \frac{L_{10}}{T}\right\}\nabla T + L_{11}(\mathbf{Z}_1 - \mathbf{Z}_2). \tag{2.13}$$

$\bar{E}_1$ and $\bar{E}_2$ are, of course, partial energies per unit mass, not per molecule.

As they stand these equations determine the heat and matter fluxes as functions of the temperature gradient and the differential force

$$\Delta\mathbf{Z} = \mathbf{Z}_1 - \mathbf{Z}_2. \tag{2.14}$$

They are, however, still not entirely convenient in form, because we shall find it easier to express the distribution function for a nonequilibrium situation in terms of the mean velocities of the two components than the forces acting upon them. We prefer, therefore, to regard the temperature gradient and the relative mass flux as the determining variables and to write

$$\mathbf{J}_0 = \frac{1}{T}\left\{\frac{L_{01}L_{10}}{L_{11}} - L_{00}\right\}\nabla T + \frac{L_{01}}{L_{11}}\mathbf{J}_1, \tag{2.15}$$

$$\Delta\mathbf{Z} = \frac{1}{T}\left\{\frac{L_{10}}{L_{11}} - (\bar{E}_1 - \bar{E}_2)\right\}\nabla T + \frac{1}{L_{11}}\mathbf{J}_1, \tag{2.16}$$

in which $\Delta\mathbf{Z}$ and $\mathbf{J}_0$ appear as linear functions of $\mathbf{J}_1$ and ∇T.

Having obtained the phenomenological equations in this new form, our program is now to calculate the heat flux and the differential force for steady states defined by predetermined values of $\mathbf{J}_1$ and ∇T. Since the effects of concentration gradients have been absorbed into the differential force, it is sufficient to consider steady states in which the concentration gradients vanish, and this is a great convenience in the statistical calculations. Furthermore, it is unnecessary to consider situations involving both a temperature gradient and a relative matter flux; according to (2.15) and (2.16) their effects are additive, so consideration may be restricted to one at a time. We therefore consider two types of nonequilibrium situation: in one there is a relative flux of the two components but no temperature or concentration gradients, and in the other there is a temperature gradient but no matter fluxes or concentration gradients. The statistical problem is then to calculate the heat flux in both situations and the forces per unit mass required to maintain the matter fluxes, in the former case at their initial values, and in the latter case at zero.

III. THE STATISTICAL EQUATIONS FOR HEAT AND MATTER TRANSPORT

The heat flux $\mathbf{J}_0$ and the matter fluxes $\mathbf{J}_1$, $\mathbf{J}_2$ may be conveniently expressed in terms of one-particle and two-particle distribution functions for the two types of molecule. The one-particle function $f_A(\mathbf{r}, \mathbf{v})$ is defined by the condition that $f_A(\mathbf{r}, \mathbf{v})d\mathbf{r}\,d\mathbf{v}$ is the chance of there being a molecule of type A $(= 1$ or $2)$ in the volume element $d\mathbf{r}$ at $\mathbf{r}$ with a velocity in the three-dimensional element $d\mathbf{v}$ at $\mathbf{v}$. The pair function $f_{AB}(\mathbf{r}_a, \mathbf{v}_a; \mathbf{r}_b, \mathbf{v}_b)$ likewise represents the chance of simultaneously finding an A molecule at $\mathbf{r}_a$ with velocity $\mathbf{v}_a$ and a B molecule at $\mathbf{r}_b$ with velocity $\mathbf{v}_b$. In terms of these distribution functions $(A, B = 1, 2)$ we may now write exact expressions for $\mathbf{J}_0$ and the $\mathbf{J}_A$.

The heat flux $\mathbf{J}_0$ is the sum of a convective and a collisional part. The former is, at the point $\mathbf{r}$

$$\mathbf{J}_0(\text{conv}) = \sum_A \int f_A(\mathbf{r}, \mathbf{v})\,(\tfrac{1}{2}m_A \mathbf{v}^2)\,\mathbf{v}\,d\mathbf{v}, \tag{3.1}$$

and represents the energy carried by the two types of molecule in their motion past the point $\mathbf{r}$. The collisional part of $\mathbf{J}_0$ may most easily be obtained by noting all the binary collisions that occur in a small volume ΔV in a short time Δt, estimating for each collision the amount of kinetic energy transferred, multiplying by the vector distance of transfer and summing the product over all the collisions; the result when divided by $\Delta V \Delta t$ gives the collisional heat flux at a point in ΔV.

Now a sphere of type A at $\mathbf{r}_a$, $\mathbf{v}_a$, will collide with one of type B at $\mathbf{r}_b$, $\mathbf{v}_b$ only if the spheres are already close together and if their velocity of approach is sufficient compared with their separation. We therefore define a function Δ_{ab} to be unity if this condition is satisfied and zero otherwise. Hence if ε_{AB} is the amount of energy transferred to A from B, the distance of transfer being $\mathbf{r}_a - \mathbf{r}_b$, the collisional energy flux is

$$\mathbf{J}_0(\text{coll}) = (\Delta V \Delta t)^{-1}\,\tfrac{1}{2}\sum_A\sum_B \int\cdots\int f_{AB}\,\Delta_{ab}\,\varepsilon_{AB}\,.\,(\mathbf{r}_a - \mathbf{r}_b)\,d\mathbf{r}_a\,d\mathbf{r}_b\,d\mathbf{v}_a\,d\mathbf{v}_b. \tag{3.2}$$

The factor $\frac{1}{2}$ is inserted to avoid counting every collision twice.

The mass fluxes of the two components are the amounts of momentum per unit volume associated with the two types of particle, namely

$$\mathbf{J}_A = \int f_A(\mathbf{r}, \mathbf{v})\,m_A\,\mathbf{v}\,d\mathbf{v}. \tag{3.3}$$

In the absence of externally applied forces these will in general change with time, also by two independent mechanisms. The first is the actual motion of molecules from one region to another, the consequent rates of change being

$$\dot{\mathbf{J}}_A(\text{conv}) = \Delta t^{-1}\int\{f_A(\mathbf{r}-\mathbf{v}\Delta t,\,\mathbf{v})-f_A(\mathbf{r},\,\mathbf{v})\}\,m_A\,\mathbf{v}\,d\mathbf{v}. \tag{3.4}$$

The other process is the collision of particles of a given type, A, with other particles, B, which impart momentum to them. If $\boldsymbol{\eta}_{AB}$ is the amount of momentum acquired by an A molecule at $\mathbf{r}_a$, $\mathbf{v}_a$ in collision with a B molecule at $\mathbf{r}_b$, $\mathbf{v}_b$, the collisional part of $\dot{\mathbf{J}}_A$ may be written

$$\dot{\mathbf{J}}_A(\text{coll}) = \Delta t^{-1}\sum_B\int\cdots\int f_{AB}\,\Delta_{ab}\,\boldsymbol{\eta}_{AB}\,d\mathbf{r}_b\,d\mathbf{v}_a\,d\mathbf{v}_b\,, \tag{3.5}$$

where Δ_{ab} has the same meaning as before. The rate of change of $\mathbf{J}_A$, in the absence of external forces, is therefore the sum of (3.4) and (3.5).

Now $\dot{\mathbf{J}}_A$ may be written

$$\dot{\mathbf{J}}_A = n_A\,m_A\,\dot{\bar{\mathbf{v}}}_A\,, \tag{3.6}$$

where n_A is the number density of A and $\bar{\mathbf{v}}_A$ its mean velocity. To prevent a net acceleration of the particles we must therefore apply to each a steady external force $\mathbf{Z}_A'$ given by

$$\mathbf{Z}_A' = -m_A\,\dot{\bar{\mathbf{v}}}_A\,. \tag{3.7}$$

The external force *per unit mass* required to maintain $\mathbf{J}_A$ at its initial value is therefore given by

$$\mathbf{Z}_A = -(n_A m_A)^{-1}\{\dot{\mathbf{J}}_A(\text{conv})+\dot{\mathbf{J}}_A(\text{coll})\}\,, \tag{3.8}$$

where $\dot{\mathbf{J}}_A(\text{conv})$ and $\dot{\mathbf{J}}_A(\text{coll})$ are defined as above.

In order to evaluate ε_{AB}, $\boldsymbol{\eta}_{AB}$, Δ_{ab} we must consider a typical collision in detail. Since Δt is infinitesimal, $|\mathbf{r}_a-\mathbf{r}_b|$ must differ insignificantly from $2a$, and we may write

$$\mathbf{r}_a-\mathbf{r}_b \simeq 2a\mathbf{l}, \tag{3.9}$$

where $\mathbf{l}$ is a unit vector (see Fig. 1). Further, let u_a and u_b be the components of $\mathbf{v}_a$ and $\mathbf{v}_b$ along $\mathbf{l}$. Then on collision an amount of energy

$$\varepsilon_{AB} = 2\mu_{AB}'(m_A u_a+m_B u_b)(u_b-u_a),\quad \mu_{AB}' = \frac{m_A m_B}{(m_A+m_B)^2} \tag{3.10}$$

will be transferred from B to A through a distance $\mathbf{r}_a - \mathbf{r}_b$, and an amount of momentum

$$\eta_{AB} = 2\mu_{AB}(u_b - u_a)\,\mathbf{l}, \qquad \mu_{AB} = \frac{m_A m_B}{m_A + m_B}. \tag{3.11}$$

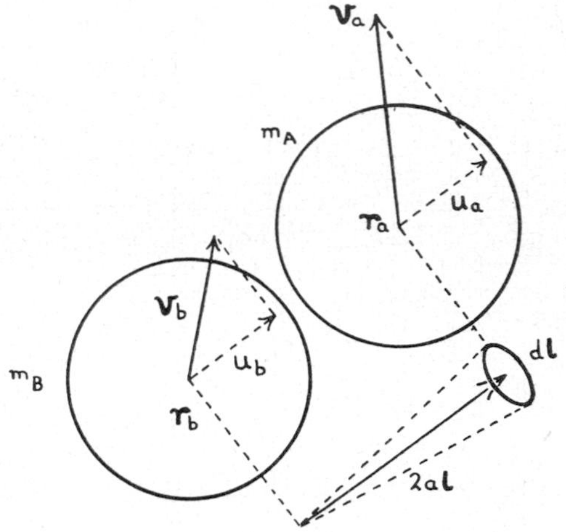

Figure 1

Furthermore, collision will only occur if $u_b > u_a$ and if

$$2a < |\mathbf{r}_b - \mathbf{r}_a| < 2a + (u_b - u_a)\,\Delta t. \tag{3.12}$$

Hence for a given value of $\mathbf{r}_a$ the volume element available to $\mathbf{r}_b$ if Δ_{ab} is not to vanish is

$$4a^2(u_b - u_a)\,\Delta t d\mathbf{l}, \tag{3.13}$$

where $d\mathbf{l}$ is the element of solid angle at $\mathbf{l}$.

Substituting for Δ_{ab}, ε_{AB} and $\mathbf{r}_a - \mathbf{r}_b$ in (3.2) and limiting ΔV to a small volume at $\mathbf{r}$, we obtain

$$\begin{aligned}\mathbf{J}_0 = {} & \sum_A \int f_A(\mathbf{r}, \mathbf{v})\, \tfrac{1}{2} m_A \mathbf{v}^2 \,.\, \mathbf{v}\, d\mathbf{v} \\ & + 8a^3 \sum_A \sum_B \mu'_{AB} \int \cdots \int f_{AB}(\mathbf{r} + a\mathbf{l}, \mathbf{v}_a; \mathbf{r} - a\mathbf{l}, \mathbf{v}_b) \\ & \qquad .\, (m_A u_a + m_B u_b)(u_b - u_a)^2 \mathbf{l}\, d\mathbf{l}\, d\mathbf{v}_a\, d\mathbf{v}_b;\end{aligned} \tag{3.14}$$

and substituting for η_{AB} and Δ_{ab} in (3.5), and putting $\mathbf{r}_a = \mathbf{r}$, we obtain similarly

$$\dot{\mathbf{J}}_A = \lim_{\Delta t \to 0} \Delta t^{-1} \int \{f_A(\mathbf{r}-\mathbf{v}\Delta t, \mathbf{v}) - f_A(\mathbf{r}, \mathbf{v})\} m_A \mathbf{v}\, d\mathbf{v}$$
$$+ 8a^2 \sum_B \mu_{AB} \underset{(u_a < u_b)}{\int \cdots \int} f_{AB}(\mathbf{r}, \mathbf{v}_a; \mathbf{r}-2a\mathbf{l}, \mathbf{v}_b)(u_b - u_a)^2 \mathbf{l}\, d\mathbf{l}\, d\mathbf{v}_a\, d\mathbf{v}_b. \tag{3.15}$$

These expressions are exact.

IV. THE STATISTICAL APPROXIMATIONS

In order to proceed further it is necessary to make some assumptions about the distributions f_A and f_{AB}. We shall assume

(i) That the pair function f_{AB} takes the form

$$f_{AB}(\mathbf{r}_a, \mathbf{v}_a; \mathbf{r}_b, \mathbf{v}_b) = n^0_{AB}(\mathbf{r}_a, \mathbf{r}_b) f'_A(\mathbf{r}_a, \mathbf{v}_a) f'_B(\mathbf{r}_b, \mathbf{v}_b), \tag{4.1}$$

where $n^0_{AB}(\mathbf{r}_a, \mathbf{r}_b)\, d\mathbf{r}_a\, d\mathbf{r}_b$ is the chance of finding simultaneously an A molecule in $d\mathbf{r}_a$ at $\mathbf{r}_a$ and a B molecule in $d\mathbf{r}_b$ at $\mathbf{r}_b$ for the mixture *in equilibrium* at the specified concentrations. It follows that

$$f_A(\mathbf{r}_a, \mathbf{v}_a) = n_B^{-1} \iint_1 f_{AB}(\mathbf{r}_a, \mathbf{v}_a; \mathbf{r}_b, \mathbf{v}_b)\, d\mathbf{r}_b\, d\mathbf{v}_b$$
$$= n_B^{-1} \int_1 n^0_{AB}(\mathbf{r}_a, \mathbf{r}_b)\, d\mathbf{r}_b \,.\, f'_A(\mathbf{r}_a, \mathbf{v}_a) = n_A f'_A(\mathbf{r}_a, \mathbf{v}_a), \tag{4.2}$$

where n_A is the number density of A and $\int_1$ denotes integration over unit volume.

(ii) That the velocity distribution function $f'_A(\mathbf{r}, \mathbf{v})$ is Maxwellian, namely

$$f'_A(\mathbf{r}, \mathbf{v}) = (m_A/2\pi kT)^{3/2} \exp\{-m_A(\mathbf{v}-\bar{\mathbf{v}}_A)^2/2kT\}, \tag{4.3}$$

where $\bar{\mathbf{v}}_A$ is the mean velocity of the A molecules and T is the local temperature *at the point* $\mathbf{r}$.

Two hypotheses are involved in assumption (i). One is that the velocities of neighboring molecules are statistically independent; this assumption is equivalent to Boltzmann's hypothesis of molecular chaos. The other hypothesis, that n_{AB} has its equilibrium value, may be seen to be false from the fact that the spatial pair function is known to be distorted under gradients, and this distortion is the source of collisional transport in assemblies of "soft" molecules. However, as we shall see, collisional transport can occur in the hard sphere assembly even without such a distortion, and the hypothesis in question leads to explicit results for the transport coefficients, so we shall make no further apology for adopting it.

Assumption (ii) is also inexact. However, the attempt to improve upon it made by Enskog in his theory (Chapman and Cowling[2]) of the hard sphere fluid leads to an unavoidably complicated series of approximations whose physical significance is difficult to appreciate. We therefore prefer to work out the consequences of this assumption, on the grounds that its physical transparency compensates largely for its quantitative inadequacy.

V. THE CASE OF A TEMPERATURE GRADIENT

In this section we consider a steady state in which there is a temperature gradient but no net flux or concentration gradient of either component. The convective contributions to $\mathbf{J}_0$ and the $\dot{\mathbf{J}}_A$ are relatively easy to work out. We merely need expressions for the one-particle distribution functions, and according to our assumptions these are

$$f_A(\mathbf{r}', \mathbf{v}) = n_A(m_A/2\pi kT')^{3/2} \exp(-m_A \mathbf{v}^2/2kT'), \tag{5.1}$$

where

$$T' = T + (\mathbf{r}' - \mathbf{r}) \cdot \nabla T, \tag{5.2}$$

T being the local temperature at the point $\mathbf{r}$, and ∇T the temperature gradient. We know in advance that $\mathbf{J}_0$ and the $\dot{\mathbf{J}}_A$ must be in the direction of the temperature gradient, for reasons of symmetry; it is therefore only necessary to take into account the velocity component of a particle in this direction. Furthermore the convective contribution to the heat flux vanishes, owing to the spherical symmetry of f_A in velocity space. This is not true, however, of $\dot{\mathbf{J}}_A(\text{conv})$, since particles of a given type entering a given region from a neighboring hotter region will on the average be moving faster. This is verified by substitution from (5.1) and (3.4), when one obtains, to order ∇T

$$\dot{\mathbf{J}}_A(\text{conv}) = -n_A k \nabla T. \tag{5.3}$$

The collisional contributions to $\mathbf{J}_0$ and the $\dot{\mathbf{J}}_A$ are more complicated. First, one needs an expression for the spatial pair function n^0_{AB}. It is easily shown that the equilibrium value of $n_{AB}(\mathbf{r}_a, \mathbf{r}_b)$ depends only on the number densities n_A, n_B and the distance $|\mathbf{r}_a - \mathbf{r}_b|$. Furthermore, it is known that for spheres nearly in contact*

$$n^0_{AB} = 3n_A n_B \chi / 16\pi n a^3, \tag{5.4}$$

where

$$\chi = P/nkT - 1. \tag{5.5}$$

Since $P \propto T$ for given n, and since by hypothesis there are no concentration gradients, n^0_{AB} may be treated as a constant in the integrations. The collisional integrals thus become:

$$\mathbf{J}_0(\text{coll}) = 8a^3 \sum_A \sum_B \mu'_{AB} n^0_{AB} \int \cdots \int_{(u_a < u_b)} f'_A(\mathbf{r}+a\mathbf{l}, \mathbf{v}_a) f'_B(\mathbf{r}-a\mathbf{l}, \mathbf{v}_b) \cdot (m_A u_a + m_B u_b)(u_b - u_a)^2 \mathbf{l}\, d\mathbf{l}\, d\mathbf{v}_a\, d\mathbf{v}_b, \tag{5.6}$$

$$\dot{\mathbf{J}}_A(\text{coll}) = 8a^2 \sum_B \mu_{AB} n^0_{AB} \int \cdots \int_{(u_a < u_b)} f'_A(\mathbf{r}, \mathbf{v}_a) f'_B(\mathbf{r}-2a\mathbf{l}, \mathbf{v}_b)(u_b - u_a)^2 \mathbf{l}\, d\mathbf{l}\, d\mathbf{v}_a\, d\mathbf{v}_b. \tag{5.7}$$

The evaluation of these integrals is straightforward but lengthy, so it will only be outlined here. One requires their values at the point $\mathbf{r}$, and therefore begins by substituting for the velocity distribution functions from (5.1) and (5.2). It is possible to integrate immediately over the components of $\mathbf{v}_a$ and $\mathbf{v}_b$ perpendicular to the vector $\mathbf{l}$, and this leaves integrations to be carried out over u_a, u_b and the unit vector $\mathbf{l}$. At this stage one expands the integrand in powers of ∇T, retaining only terms of the first order. This is justified by the fact that the theory only applies when the gradients are small. The integration over the space of u_a and u_b is most easily carried out by taking $u_b - u_a$ as one variable, since the integral is restricted to the range $u_a < u_b$. The final step is to integrate over the direction of $\mathbf{l}$. This process is facilitated by the fact that only the components of $\mathbf{J}_0$ and $\dot{\mathbf{J}}_A$ in the direction of ∇T need be considered. The final results are:

* Longuet-Higgins and Pople[5] have shown that in a one-component hard sphere fluid the number of pairs of spheres per unit volume within a small distance δ of contact is $3n\chi\delta/2a$. The probability that a given sphere has a neighbor within this distance is therefore $3\chi\delta/a$. The volume element available to the second if the first is fixed is $16\pi a^2 \delta$. In the mixture the chance of a B molecule being within δ of a given particle is $3\chi\delta n_B/an$ and the chance that an A molecule is at a given point is n_A. Hence $n^0_{AB} = 3\chi n_A n_B/16\pi n a^3$.

$$\mathbf{J}_0(\text{coll}) = -\frac{4a\chi k\nabla T}{n}\sum_A\sum_B \frac{n_A n_B}{m_A+m_B}\left(\frac{2\mu_{AB}kT}{\pi}\right)^{1/2}, \tag{5.8}$$

$$\dot{\mathbf{J}}_A(\text{coll}) = -\frac{2\chi k\nabla T}{n}\sum_B \frac{n_A n_B m_A}{m_A+m_B}. \tag{5.9}$$

The right-hand side of (5.8) represents also the total heat flux, as the convective contribution vanishes. To obtain the requisite force per unit mass on species A it is necessary to add (5.3) to (5.9) and divide by $-n_A m_A$. The result for component 1 is

$$\mathbf{Z}_1 = k\nabla T\left\{\frac{1}{m_1}+\frac{\chi}{n}\left(\frac{n_1}{m_1}+\frac{2n_2}{m_1+m_2}\right)\right\}. \tag{5.10}$$

VI. THE CASE OF A RELATIVE MATTER FLUX

The second of the two steady states to be considered is one in which the two components are flowing through one another, with mean velocities $\bar{\mathbf{v}}_1$ and $\bar{\mathbf{v}}_2$ in the barycentric system. The condition for no total mass flux is therefore

$$\mathbf{J}_1+\mathbf{J}_2 = n_1 m_1 \bar{\mathbf{v}}_1 + n_2 m_2 \bar{\mathbf{v}}_2 = 0. \tag{6.1}$$

As in the case of a temperature gradient, the convective contributions to $\mathbf{J}_0$ and $\dot{\mathbf{J}}_A$ are relatively easily dealt with. The convective heat flux is, as before,

$$\mathbf{J}_0(\text{conv}) = \sum_A \int f_A(\mathbf{r},\mathbf{v})\tfrac{1}{2}m_A \mathrm{v}^2 . \mathbf{v}\, d\mathbf{v}, \tag{6.2}$$

but now the one-particle distribution functions are taken to be

$$f_A(\mathbf{r},\mathbf{v}) = n_A(m_A/2\pi kT)^{3/2}\exp\{-m_A(\mathbf{v}-\bar{\mathbf{v}}_A)^2/2kT\}. \tag{6.3}$$

If (6.3) is substituted into (6.2), and the integral is evaluated to the first order in $\bar{\mathbf{v}}_A$, the result is

$$\mathbf{J}_0(\text{conv}) = \tfrac{5}{2}kT(n_1\bar{\mathbf{v}}_1+n_2\bar{\mathbf{v}}_2). \tag{6.4}$$

The convective contribution to $\dot{\mathbf{J}}_A$, on the other hand, vanishes. This is because $f_A(\mathbf{r},\mathbf{v})$ is independent of $\mathbf{r}$, so that the particles of a given type entering a given region have, on the average, the same momentum as those leaving the region.

The collisional contributions to $\mathbf{J}_0$ and $\dot{\mathbf{J}}_A$ may be calculated in a manner analogous to that described in the previous section. They are given by Eqs. (5.6) and (5.7), with n^0_{AB} determined by (5.4) and (5.5). The only difference to be noted is that the velocity distribution functions $f'_A(\mathbf{r}, \mathbf{v})$ are those appropriate to the mean velocities $\overline{\mathbf{v}}_A$, namely

$$f'_A(\mathbf{r}, \mathbf{v}) = (m_A/2\pi kT)^{3/2} \exp\{-m_A(\mathbf{v}-\overline{\mathbf{v}}_A)^2/2kT\}. \qquad (6.5)$$

They are, of course, independent of position.

Again the integrations are straightforward, and are carried out according to the program described in Section V. In the evaluation of $\mathbf{J}_0(\text{coll})$ it is found necessary to consider separately the terms with $A = B$ and those with $A \neq B$. Those with $A = B$ give

$$\frac{kT\chi}{n}(n_1^2\overline{\mathbf{v}}_1+n_2^2\overline{\mathbf{v}}_2) \qquad (6.6)$$

and those with $A \neq B$ give

$$\frac{2kT\chi}{n} \cdot \frac{n_1n_2(n_2-n_1)\mu_{12}}{n_1m_1+n_2m_2} \cdot (\overline{\mathbf{v}}_1-\overline{\mathbf{v}}_2). \qquad (6.7)$$

Adding (6.4), (6.6), and (6.7) and substituting for $\overline{\mathbf{v}}_1$ and $\overline{\mathbf{v}}_2$ in terms of $\mathbf{J}_1$ we obtain

$$\mathbf{J}_0 = kT\left\{\frac{5}{2}+\frac{\chi(n_1m_2+n_2m_1)}{n(m_1+m_2)}\right\}\left\{\frac{1}{m_1}-\frac{1}{m_2}\right\}\mathbf{J}_1. \qquad (6.8)$$

There remains the collisional contribution to $\dot{\mathbf{J}}_A$. The term with $B = A$ in (5.7) represents a physically impossible effect, namely a net acceleration of the A molecules as a result of their mutual collisions. It vanishes. The term with $A = 1$, $B = 2$ gives

$$\dot{\mathbf{J}}_1 = -\frac{2\chi n_1n_2}{an}\left(\frac{2\mu_{12}kT}{\pi}\right)^{1/2}(\overline{\mathbf{v}}_1-\overline{\mathbf{v}}_2). \qquad (6.9)$$

Substitution for $\overline{\mathbf{v}}_1$, $\overline{\mathbf{v}}_2$ in terms of $\mathbf{J}_1$, and division by $-n_1m_1$, gives the requisite external force per unit mass as

$$\mathbf{Z}_1 = \frac{2\chi n_2}{anm_1}\left(\frac{2\mu_{12}kT}{\pi}\right)^{1/2}\left(\frac{1}{n_1m_1}+\frac{1}{n_2m_2}\right)\mathbf{J}_1. \qquad (6.10)$$

VII. THE VALUES OF THE PHENOMENOLOGICAL COEFFICIENTS

Equations (5.8), (5.10), (6.8), and (6.10) not only confirm that the heat flux and the forces per unit mass are linear in the temperature gradient and the relative flux, when these are small; they also serve to provide explicit values for the phenomenological coefficients $L_{\mu\nu}$ occurring in Eqs. (2.15) and (2.16). Let us take these in turn.

The coefficient L_{11}, according to (2.16), is the ratio of $\mathbf{J}_1$ to the differential force per unit mass $\mathbf{Z}_1-\mathbf{Z}_2$. By (6.10)

$$\mathbf{Z}_2 = -\frac{2\chi n_1}{anm_2}\left(\frac{2\mu_{12}kT}{\pi}\right)^{1/2}\left(\frac{1}{n_1m_1}+\frac{1}{n_2m_2}\right)\mathbf{J}_1, \tag{7.1}$$

and so

$$L_{11} = \frac{an}{2\chi}\left(\frac{\pi}{2\mu_{12}kT}\right)^{1/2}\frac{n_1n_2m_1^2m_2^2}{(n_1m_1+n_2m_2)^2}. \tag{7.2}$$

From this expression for L_{11} it is possible to calculate the mutual diffusion coefficient D_{12} of the two components. When mutual diffusion is studied experimentally, the stationary frame is not the barycentric frame but one in which the sum of the *particle* fluxes $\mathbf{j}_1$, $\mathbf{j}_2$ is zero. D_{12} is then given by the relation

$$\mathbf{j}_1 = -D_{12}\nabla n_1. \tag{7.3}$$

Now it is easily shown from (2.6)* that if the temperature and total concentration n_1+n_2 are uniform, and there are no external forces, then

$$\mathbf{J}_1 = -kTL_{11}\left(\frac{1}{n_1m_1}+\frac{1}{n_2m_2}\right)\nabla n_1. \tag{7.4}$$

But $\mathbf{j}_1$ is related to $\mathbf{J}_1$ by the equation

$$\mathbf{j}_1 = \mathbf{J}_1\left(\frac{n_1m_1+n_2m_2}{nm_1m_2}\right).$$

Hence

$$D_{12} = \frac{a}{2\chi}\left(\frac{\pi kT}{2\mu_{12}}\right)^{1/2}. \tag{7.5}$$

The coefficient of thermal conductivity, by Eq. (2.15) is equal to

$$\frac{1}{T}\left(L_{00}-\frac{L_{01}L_{10}}{L_{11}}\right). \tag{7.6}$$

* If $\nabla T = 0$, $\mathbf{Y}_1 = \mathbf{Y}_2 = 0$, then

$$\mathbf{J}_1 = L_{11}(\mathbf{X}_1-\mathbf{X}_2) = -L_{11}\nabla(\mu_1-\mu_2).$$

But since this is an ideal fluid mixture, the chemical potentials per unit mass are

$$\mu_i = \mu_i^0+(kT/m_i)\ln n_i.$$

Hence Eq. (7.4) follows.

The statistical calculation expounded in Section V, leading to (5.8), gave the value of this expression as

$$\frac{4ak\chi}{n}\sum_A\sum_B\frac{n_A n_B}{m_A+m_B}\left(\frac{2\mu_{AB}kT}{\pi}\right)^{1/2}. \tag{7.7}$$

It may be noted that for $n_A = n$, $n_B = 0$, this reduces to the expression obtained by Longuet-Higgins and Pople[5] for the one-component hard sphere fluid, as would be expected. More surprising, perhaps, is that (7.5) gives the same value for the self-diffusion coefficient of the one-component fluid as was obtained by those authors from a quite different assumption, namely that the velocity autocorrelation function of an individual sphere is an exponentially decaying function of the time. The latter assumption is probably inadequate at very high densities, when the molecules acquire an oscillatory motion, so that (7.5) would also be expected to fail in this region.

The coefficients L_{10} and L_{01} are associated with the Soret and Dufour effects, respectively. A measure of the Soret effect is provided by the thermal diffusion ratio, defined[4] as

$$k_1^T = -\frac{\nabla(n_1/n)}{\nabla T/T} \tag{7.8}$$

for a steady state in which there is a temperature gradient but no pressure gradient, matter fluxes, or external forces. In such a situation, by (2.6),

$$L_{10}\nabla T+L_{11}T^2\{\nabla(\mu_1/T)-\nabla(\mu_2/T)\} = 0.$$

Introducing the partial specific enthalpies $\bar{H}_1$, $\bar{H}_2$, and using the ideality of the mixture, we obtain

$$\{L_{10}-L_{11}(\bar{H}_1-\bar{H}_2)\}\frac{\nabla T}{T}+L_{11}nkT\left(\frac{1}{n_1m_1}+\frac{1}{n_2m_2}\right)\nabla\left(\frac{n_1}{n}\right) = 0$$

in which

$$\bar{H}_A = \bar{E}_A+P/nm_A = \bar{E}_A+\frac{kT}{m_A}(\chi+1). \tag{7.9}$$

Therefore

$$\left[\left\{\frac{L_{10}}{L_{11}}-(\bar{E}_1-\bar{E}_2)\right\}-kT(\chi+1)\left(\frac{1}{m_1}-\frac{1}{m_2}\right)\right]\frac{\nabla T}{T}+nkT\left(\frac{1}{n_1m_1}+\frac{1}{n_2m_2}\right)\nabla\left(\frac{n_1}{n}\right)=0 \tag{7.10}$$

Now by (2.16) $L_{10}/L_{11}-(\bar{E}_1-\bar{E}_2)$ is the coefficient of $\nabla T/T$ in $\Delta\mathbf{Z}$; and according to (5.10), and a similar equation for $\mathbf{Z}_2$, this is

$$kT\left(\frac{1}{m_1}-\frac{1}{m_2}\right)\left\{1+\chi\cdot\frac{n_1m_2+n_2m_1}{n(m_1+m_2)}\right\}. \tag{7.11}$$

Combining (7.8), (7.10), and (7.11) we find

$$k_1^T=\chi\cdot\frac{n_1n_2(m_1-m_2)}{n^2(m_1+m_2)}. \tag{7.12}$$

There remains the coefficient L_{01}. According to Onsager's theorem this coefficient should be equal to L_{10}, but there is no guarantee that this reciprocal relation will be satisfied by the values of L_{01} and L_{10} given by an approximate theory such as this. To test the relation we refer to Eqs. (2.16) and (7.11), according to which

$$\frac{L_{10}}{L_{11}}-(\bar{E}_1-\bar{E}_2)=kT\left(\frac{1}{m_1}-\frac{1}{m_2}\right)\left\{1+\frac{\chi(n_1m_2+n_2m_1)}{n(m_1+m_2)}\right\}. \tag{7.13}$$

For a hard sphere fluid the energy is entirely kinetic, and so

$$\bar{E}_1=3kT/2m_1,\qquad \bar{E}_2=3kT/2m_2. \tag{7.14}$$

But according to (2.15) and (6.8)

$$\frac{L_{01}}{L_{11}}=kT\left(\frac{1}{m_1}-\frac{1}{m_2}\right)\left\{\frac{5}{2}+\frac{\chi(n_1m_2+n_2m_1)}{n(m_1+m_2)}\right\}. \tag{7.15}$$

Combining (7.13), (7.14), and (7.15) we deduce the equality

$$L_{01}=L_{10}, \tag{7.16}$$

so that our calculated values of L_{01} and L_{10} do indeed satisfy the Onsager relations.

VIII. ONSAGER'S RELATIONS

It remains to discuss the question why the coefficients L_{10} and L_{01} calculated from our approximate distribution functions should be equal, thus satisfying Onsager's relations. To do this it is necessary to examine in detail the statistical premises on which these relations are based, and to see how far the approximate theory we have developed is consistent with these premises.

In describing a system which is not in equilibrium it is necessary to assign nonzero expectation values α_μ to certain dynamic variables a_μ

whose average values in equilibrium are zero. The distribution function f^N of the coordinates and momenta of all the particles must then satisfy the restrictions

$$\int f^N d\tau = 1, \qquad \int f^N H d\tau = E, \quad \int f^N a_\mu d\tau = \alpha_\mu , \tag{8.1}$$

where H is the Hamiltonian and E the total energy. By analogy with the procedure for determining equilibrium distribution functions one might then assert that the unnormalized *a priori* probability associated with the distribution f^N is

$$\exp (S/k),$$

where

$$S = -k \int f^N \ln f^N d\tau. \tag{8.2}$$

The most probable distribution for given values of E and the α_μ would then be obtained by maximizing S subject to the above restrictions.

Leaving aside for the moment the question whether this distribution function properly describes a system in decay toward equilibrium, let us trace the mathematical consequences of these assumptions. The conditional maximization of S is most easily performed by Lagrange's method of undetermined multipliers, which leads to the form

$$f^N = C \exp (-\beta H - \sum_\mu \gamma_\mu a_\mu), \tag{8.3}$$

where the values of β and of the γ_μ are to be determined from the expectation values of the Hamiltonian H and the variables a_μ. Similarly, the state of equilibrium to which decay occurs may be described by another distribution function f_0^N, obtained by maximizing the integral

$$S_0 = -k \int f_0^N \ln f_0^N d\tau \tag{8.4}$$

subject only to the restrictions

$$\int f_0^N d\tau = 1, \qquad \int f_0^N H d\tau = E, \tag{8.5}$$

where the energy E has the same value as before. This gives

$$f_0^N = C_0 \exp (-\beta_0 H), \tag{8.6}$$

where β_0 in general differs from β. It may then be proved (see Appendix) that for small values of the α_μ

$$S - S_0 = \tfrac{1}{2} k \sum_\mu \alpha_\mu \gamma_\mu \tag{8.7}$$

and that the γ_μ are related to the α_μ by the equation

$$\alpha_\mu = -\sum_\nu \int f_0^N a_\mu a_\nu d\tau \, . \, \gamma_\nu \equiv -\sum_\nu \langle a_\mu a_\nu \rangle_0 \gamma_\nu . \tag{8.8}$$

Defining a matrix $S_{\mu\nu}$ as the inverse matrix to $\langle a_\mu a_\nu \rangle_0$ one may then write

$$\gamma_\mu = -\sum_\nu S_{\mu\nu} \alpha_\nu , \tag{8.9}$$

so that

$$S - S_0 = -\tfrac{1}{2} k \sum_\mu \sum_\nu \alpha_\mu S_{\mu\nu} \alpha_\nu . \tag{8.10}$$

The normalized probability that the a_μ lie in the ranges $d\alpha_\mu$ at α_μ is therefore

$$W(\alpha_1, \alpha_2, \ldots) \prod_\mu d\alpha_\mu = \frac{\exp\left(-\tfrac{1}{2} \sum_\mu \sum_\nu \alpha_\mu S_{\mu\nu} \alpha_\nu\right) \prod_\mu d\alpha_\mu}{\int \cdots \int \exp\left(-\tfrac{1}{2} \sum_\mu \sum_\nu \alpha_\mu S_{\mu\nu} \alpha_\nu\right) \prod_\mu d\alpha_\mu} . \tag{8.11}$$

Let us now turn to the other postulate on which the reciprocal relations are based, namely that in disequilibrium the rates of change of the α_μ are linear in the γ_μ. That is:

$$\dot{\alpha}_\mu = \sum_\nu \lambda_{\mu\nu} \gamma_\nu . \tag{8.12}$$

Multiplication by γ_μ and summation over μ gives, using (8.9),

$$\sum_\mu \sum_\nu \gamma_\mu \lambda_{\mu\nu} \gamma_\nu = \sum_\mu \dot{\alpha}_\mu \gamma_\mu = -\sum_\mu \sum_\nu \dot{\alpha}_\mu S_{\mu\nu} \alpha_\nu = k^{-1} \dot{S} , \tag{8.13}$$

the last step being inferred from (8.10). Now by Liouville's theorem S, if it is regarded as an integral of the initial distribution, cannot change with time, so it would appear that all the $\lambda_{\mu\nu}$ must vanish. To avoid this dilemma we must redetermine a new distribution function and a new S at every instant from the observed values of the α_μ. This makes it clear that the distribution function f^N can itself contain no "memory" of the previous values of the α_μ, and must therefore represent an ensemble for which S is momentarily at a minimum, rather than an ensemble which is in a steady state of decay. There remains, however, the difficulty that if S is at a minimum at $t = 0$, and if it is a continuous function of time, then $\dot{S}$ will still vanish at $t = 0$, even though it may settle down to a finite value later. This difficulty was resolved by Casimir,[1] who pointed out that in general the $\dot{\alpha}_\mu$ in the linear relations (8.12) should be replaced by expressions of the form

$$\theta^{-1}\{\alpha_\mu(\theta)-\alpha_\mu(0)\},$$

where θ is a time short compared to the macroscopic relaxation time but long enough for a state of steady decay to have been established. The equation for $\dot{S}$ is then replaced by

$$\theta^{-1}\{S(\theta)-S(0)\} = k\sum_\mu\sum_\nu \gamma_\mu\lambda_{\mu\nu}\gamma_\nu \tag{8.14}$$

the left-hand side of which is finite and effectively independent of θ. With this modification of the linear assumption, and by appealing to the principle of microscopic reversibility, it is then possible to prove quite simply[1] that

$$\lambda_{\mu\nu} = \lambda_{\nu\mu} \tag{8.15}$$

if a_μ and a_ν are both even or both odd functions of the molecular velocities, and that

$$\lambda_{\mu\nu} = -\lambda_{\nu\mu} \tag{8.16}$$

if one is an even and the other an odd function.

It might appear from this discussion that the premises on which the Onsager relations are based are scarcely applicable to the present approximate theory of transport in the hard sphere fluid. A fluid of hard spheres is, however, exceptional in that, although S is an even function of the time, its derivative is discontinuous at zero time, and has equal and opposite values just before and just after this moment. Furthermore, if we use the symbol $\dot{\alpha}_\mu$ to denote the "future" derivative

$$\lim_{t\to+0} t^{-1}\{\alpha_\mu(t)-\alpha_\mu(0)\},$$

the linear relations between the $\dot{\alpha}_\mu$ and the γ_μ are indeed found to be satisfied at zero time, for the ensemble described by the distribution function f^N. To prove these assertions we shall show (a) that the distribution functions implicit in our calculations are of the type (8.3), namely

$$f^N = C\exp\left(-\beta H - \sum_\mu \gamma_\mu a_\mu\right),$$

where the a_μ are variables describing a temperature gradient or a relative matter flux, and (b) that the linear relations established in these calculations are indeed relations between the expectation values $\dot{\alpha}_\mu$

and the conjugate variables γ_μ. The following demonstration does not, of course, establish any connection between our calculated transport coefficients and those appropriate to a state of steady decay; but it does show that the distribution functions on which our results are based satisfy at least one set of premises from which the Onsager relations have been shown to follow.

IX. APPLICATION TO THE HARD SPHERE MIXTURE

The first necessity in applying these general considerations to the binary fluid mixture of hard spheres is to find explicit functions $\mathbf{a}_\mu$ of the coordinates and momenta related to the temperature gradient and the mean relative velocity in disequilibrium states.

In equilibrium the energy of the fluid, which is entirely kinetic, is distributed uniformly over all the spheres, regardless of mass. The presence of a temperature gradient therefore implies a finite displacement of the centre of kinetic energy from the center of position $\mathbf{R}$ (not the center of mass) of all the particles, and a measure of this displacement is

$$\mathbf{a}_0 = \sum_i^1 (\mathbf{r}_i - \mathbf{R})\, \tfrac{1}{2} m_1 \mathbf{v}_i^2 + \sum_j^2 (\mathbf{r}_j - \mathbf{R})\, \tfrac{1}{2} m_2 \mathbf{v}_j^2 , \tag{9.1}$$

where the first sum is over the particles of mass m_1, the second over those of mass m_2, and the center of position is defined by

$$(N_1 + N_2)\mathbf{R} = \sum_i^1 \mathbf{r}_i + \sum_j^2 \mathbf{r}_j. \tag{9.2}$$

For the other function of the coordinates and momenta we choose simply the relative velocity of the two components, namely

$$\mathbf{a}_1 = N_1^{-1} \sum_i^1 \mathbf{v}_i - N_2^{-1} \sum_j^2 \mathbf{v}_j. \tag{9.3}$$

It will be noted that $\mathbf{a}_1$ is an odd function of the velocities, in contrast to $\mathbf{a}_0$ which is an even function. It is customary in thermodynamic discussions of irreversible processes to regard odd functions as fluxes and the conjugate even functions as forces, but there is no logical necessity to do this, and it is more convenient not to in this case.

Next we inquire what are the macroscopic quantities represented by the expectation values $\boldsymbol{\alpha}_0$, $\boldsymbol{\alpha}_1$, and their time derivatives $\dot{\boldsymbol{\alpha}}_0$, $\dot{\boldsymbol{\alpha}}_1$. The function $\mathbf{a}_0$ may be written in the equivalent form

$$\mathbf{a}_0 = \sum_i^1 \mathbf{r}_i(\tfrac{1}{2}m_1\mathbf{v}_i^2-\varepsilon) + \sum_j^2 \mathbf{r}_j(\tfrac{1}{2}m_2\mathbf{v}_j^2-\varepsilon), \tag{9.4}$$

where ε is the mean energy per particle. If $\mathbf{R}_1$ and $\mathbf{R}_2$ are the centers of position of components 1 and 2, and if $\mathbf{R}_0$ is the center of energy of the fluid, this may be written

$$\mathbf{a}_0 = \varepsilon(N\mathbf{R}_0-N_1\mathbf{R}_1-N_2\mathbf{R}_2). \tag{9.5}$$

Now the mean energy flux, for instance, is the energy density multiplied by the mean velocity of the center of energy, and a corresponding statement may be made about the matter fluxes. Hence averaging over the volume V and differentiating with respect to time we obtain

$$\dot{\boldsymbol{\alpha}}_0 = V\left\{\mathbf{J}_0-\varepsilon\left(\frac{\mathbf{J}_1}{m_1}+\frac{\mathbf{J}_2}{m_2}\right)\right\}, \tag{9.6}$$

where $\mathbf{J}_0$, $\mathbf{J}_1$, and $\mathbf{J}_2$ are the energy flux and the mass fluxes of the two components previously discussed.

The expectation value of $\mathbf{a}_1$ may be expressed in terms of the macroscopic fluxes of the two components:

$$\boldsymbol{\alpha}_1 = V\left(\frac{\mathbf{J}_1}{N_1m_1}-\frac{\mathbf{J}_2}{N_2m_2}\right). \tag{9.7}$$

It follows that the "flux" represented by the time derivative of $\boldsymbol{\alpha}_1$ involves the mean relative acceleration of the two species, and is given by

$$\dot{\boldsymbol{\alpha}}_1 = \frac{\dot{\mathbf{J}}_1}{n_1m_1}-\frac{\dot{\mathbf{J}}_2}{n_2m_2} = -\mathbf{Z}_1+\mathbf{Z}_2 = -\Delta\mathbf{Z}. \tag{9.8}$$

Having obtained macroscopic interpretations of the "fluxes" $\dot{\boldsymbol{\alpha}}_0$ and $\dot{\boldsymbol{\alpha}}_1$, one must now look for the conjugate "forces" $\boldsymbol{\gamma}_0$ and $\boldsymbol{\gamma}_1$. These are most easily obtained by writing down the nonequilibrium distribution function and transforming it to an expression which can be given a direct statistical interpretation. Referring to the earlier discussion, we set

$$f^N = C\exp(-\beta H-\boldsymbol{\gamma}_0\cdot\mathbf{a}_0-\boldsymbol{\gamma}_1\cdot\mathbf{a}_1) \tag{9.9}$$

where the potential energy term in H is understood to be zero or infinite according as the configuration is geometrically allowed or not. More explicitly

$$f^N = CD(\mathbf{r}_1, \ldots, \mathbf{r}_N) \exp\Big[-\sum_i^1 \{\beta+\boldsymbol{\gamma}_0\cdot(\mathbf{r}_i-\mathbf{R})\}\tfrac{1}{2}m_1\mathbf{v}_i^2 - \sum_j^2 \{\beta+\boldsymbol{\gamma}_0\cdot(\mathbf{r}_j-\mathbf{R})\}\tfrac{1}{2}m_2\mathbf{v}_j^2 - \boldsymbol{\gamma}_1\cdot\Big(N_1^{-1}\sum_i^1 \mathbf{v}_i - N_2^{-1}\sum_j^2 \mathbf{v}_j\Big)\Big], \tag{9.10}$$

where $D(\mathbf{r}_1, \ldots, \mathbf{r}_N)$ is unity for allowed configurations and zero otherwise. Introducing velocities $\bar{\mathbf{v}}_1$, $\bar{\mathbf{v}}_2$ defined* as

$$\bar{\mathbf{v}}_1 = -\frac{\boldsymbol{\gamma}_1}{N_1 m_1 \beta}, \qquad \bar{\mathbf{v}}_2 = \frac{\boldsymbol{\gamma}_1}{N_2 m_2 \beta}, \tag{9.11}$$

we may write this as

$$f^N = CD \exp\Big[-\sum_i^1 \{\beta+\boldsymbol{\gamma}_0\cdot(\mathbf{r}_i-\mathbf{R})\}\tfrac{1}{2}m_1\mathbf{v}_i^2 + \beta\sum_i^1 m_1\mathbf{v}_i\cdot\bar{\mathbf{v}}_1 - \sum_j^2 \{\beta+\boldsymbol{\gamma}_0\cdot(\mathbf{r}_j-\mathbf{R})\}\tfrac{1}{2}m_2\mathbf{v}_j^2 + \beta\sum_j^2 m_2\mathbf{v}_j\cdot\bar{\mathbf{v}}_2\Big], \tag{9.12}$$

which to the first order in the $\boldsymbol{\gamma}_i$ is equal to

$$f^N = CD \exp\Big[-\sum_i^1 \{\beta+\boldsymbol{\gamma}_0\cdot(\mathbf{r}_i-\mathbf{R})\}\tfrac{1}{2}m_1(\mathbf{v}_i-\bar{\mathbf{v}}_1)^2 - \sum_j^2 \{\beta+\boldsymbol{\gamma}_0\cdot(\mathbf{r}_j-\mathbf{R})\}\tfrac{1}{2}m_2(\mathbf{v}_j-\bar{\mathbf{v}}_2)^2\Big]. \tag{9.13}$$

This distribution function is open to immediate statistical interpretation. It represents a situation in which the velocity distribution function of a particular molecule depends only on its species and position (the center of position $\mathbf{R}$ moves insignificantly when a single molecule is moved). The velocities of the two components are seen to be distributed in a Maxwellian fashion about mean values $\bar{\mathbf{v}}_1$ and $\bar{\mathbf{v}}_2$, and the temperature T at the point $\mathbf{r}$ is given by the relation

$$1/kT = \beta+\boldsymbol{\gamma}_0\cdot(\mathbf{r}-\mathbf{R}). \tag{9.14}$$

It follows that

$$\boldsymbol{\gamma}_0 = \nabla(1/kT) = -(1/kT^2)\nabla T. \tag{9.15}$$

Furthermore, having established that $\bar{\mathbf{v}}_1$ and $\bar{\mathbf{v}}_2$ are the mean velocities of the two components, we may relate them to the mass fluxes by the

* These will be seen below to be identical with the velocities $\bar{\mathbf{v}}_1$, $\bar{\mathbf{v}}_2$ defined earlier.

equations

$$\mathbf{J}_1 V = N_1 m_1 \bar{\mathbf{v}}_1, \qquad \mathbf{J}_2 V = N_2 m_2 \bar{\mathbf{v}}_2. \tag{9.16}$$

Finally, in view of the definitions of $\bar{\mathbf{v}}_1$ and $\bar{\mathbf{v}}_2$ the conjugate "force" $\boldsymbol{\gamma}_1$ becomes simply

$$\boldsymbol{\gamma}_1 = -\beta \mathbf{J}_1 V = \beta \mathbf{J}_2 V = -\mathbf{J}_1 V/kT. \tag{9.17}$$

The distribution function (9.13) leads at once to the one- and two-particle distribution functions postulated in Section IV. Its relevant features are the statistical independence of the particle velocities, each of which is distributed in a Maxwellian manner, and the fact that, when it is integrated over all the velocities the temperature, the temperature gradient, and the mean velocities disappear, leaving a configurational factor which depends only on the molecular concentrations. The latter factor is therefore the configurational distribution for equilibrium at the specified concentrations, and when integrated over the positions of $N-1$ or $N-2$ particles gives the equilibrium one- or two-particle functions n_A or n^0_{AB}.

It remains to establish the exact connection between the $L_{\mu\nu}$ and the $\lambda_{\mu\nu}$ defined by the equations

$$\begin{aligned} \dot{\boldsymbol{\alpha}}_0 &= \lambda_{00}\boldsymbol{\gamma}_0 + \lambda_{01}\boldsymbol{\gamma}_1, \\ \dot{\boldsymbol{\alpha}}_1 &= \lambda_{10}\boldsymbol{\gamma}_0 + \lambda_{11}\boldsymbol{\gamma}_1. \end{aligned} \tag{9.18}$$

Substitution for $\dot{\boldsymbol{\alpha}}_0$, $\dot{\boldsymbol{\alpha}}_1$, $\boldsymbol{\gamma}_0$, and $\boldsymbol{\gamma}_1$ from (9.6), (9.8), (9.15), and (9.17) gives, after slight rearrangement,

$$\begin{aligned} \mathbf{J}_0 &= -\frac{\lambda_{00}}{kT^2 V}\nabla T - \left\{\frac{\lambda_{01}}{kT} - \varepsilon\left(\frac{1}{m_1} - \frac{1}{m_2}\right)\right\}\mathbf{J}_1, \\ \Delta\mathbf{Z} &= \frac{\lambda_{10}}{kT^2}\nabla T + \frac{\lambda_{11} V}{kT}\mathbf{J}_1. \end{aligned} \tag{9.19}$$

Comparing the off-diagonal coefficients with those appearing in Eqs. (2.15) and (2.16) we see that

$$\begin{aligned} \frac{L_{01}}{L_{11}} &= -\left\{\frac{\lambda_{01}}{kT} - \varepsilon\left(\frac{1}{m_1} - \frac{1}{m_2}\right)\right\}, \\ \frac{L_{10}}{L_{11}} - (\bar{E}_1 - \bar{E}_2) &= \frac{\lambda_{10}}{kT}. \end{aligned} \tag{9.20}$$

But the arguments presented in Section VIII imply that, since $\mathbf{a}_0$ and

$\mathbf{a}_1$ are of opposite parity in the velocities,

$$\lambda_{01} = -\lambda_{10}. \tag{9.21}$$

Using the relations $\bar{E}_1 = \varepsilon/m_1$, $\bar{E}_2 = \varepsilon/m_2$ we deduce that

$$L_{10} = L_{01}. \tag{9.22}$$

One may summarize this discussion as follows. Although the nonequilibrium distribution function used in calculating the $L_{\mu\nu}$ is not the correct one for an assembly in a steady state of decay, it is in fact the distribution function which is implicit in the thermodynamic description of nonequilibrium states, as shown by the analysis of Sections VIII and IX. Strictly speaking, the distribution function (9.13) represents the extreme point of a fluctuation, at which the entropy is at a momentary minimum. Such a distribution function, if applied to an assembly of soft molecules, would lead to a vanishing entropy production in the first instant; it is a peculiar feature of the hard sphere potential that $\dot{S}$ has equal and opposite finite values on either side of the origin of time. That the instantaneous fluxes are finite and also linear in the conjugate forces means that the Onsager relations will be satisfied by the instantaneous values of the $L_{\mu\nu}$ though these will undoubtedly change somewhat as the system settles down to a steady state of decay.

APPENDIX

To prove Eq. (8.8) we introduce an equilibrium distribution which is isothermal with f^N, namely

$$f_1^N = C_1 \exp(-\beta H), \qquad \int f_1^N \, d\tau = 1.$$

Hence, if $\langle A \rangle_1$ denotes $\int f_1^N A \, d\tau$, we have

$$\alpha_\mu = \int f^N a_\mu \, d\tau = \frac{\int \exp\left(-\beta H - \sum_\nu \gamma_\nu \alpha_\nu\right) . \, a_\mu \, d\tau}{\int \exp\left(-\beta H - \sum_\nu \gamma_\nu \alpha_\nu\right) d\tau}$$

$$= \frac{\langle a_\mu \rangle_1 - \sum_\nu \gamma_\nu \langle a_\nu a_\mu \rangle_1 + O(\gamma_\nu^2)}{1 - O(\gamma_\nu)}.$$

But $\langle a_\mu \rangle_1 = 0$ by hypothesis; hence to the first order in the γ_ν

$$\alpha_\mu = -\sum_\nu \gamma_\nu \langle a_\nu a_\mu \rangle_1 = -\sum_\nu \gamma_\nu \langle a_\nu a_\mu \rangle_0.$$

To prove (8.7) we introduce free energies F, F_1, defined by

$$\beta F = \int f^N(\ln f^N + \beta H)\, d\tau = \int f^N(\ln C - \sum_\mu \gamma_\mu a_\mu)\, d\tau$$
$$= \ln C - \sum_\mu \gamma_\mu \alpha_\mu ,$$
$$\beta F_1 = \int f_1^N(\ln f_1^N + \beta H)\, d\tau = \ln C_1.$$

$$\therefore\ \beta(F-F_1) = -\sum_\mu \gamma_\mu \alpha_\mu - \ln \left\{ \frac{\int \exp(-\beta H - \sum_\mu \gamma_\mu \alpha_\mu)\, d\tau}{\int \exp(-\beta H)\, d\tau} \right\}$$
$$= -\sum_\mu \gamma_\mu \alpha_\mu - \ln \{1 - \sum_\mu \gamma_\mu \langle a_\mu \rangle_1 + \tfrac{1}{2} \sum_\mu \sum_\nu \gamma_\mu \gamma_\nu \langle a_\mu a_\nu \rangle_1 - \cdots \}.$$

But

$$\langle a_\mu \rangle_1 = 0, \qquad \sum_\nu \gamma_\nu \langle a_\mu a_\nu \rangle_1 = -\alpha_\mu ;$$
$$\therefore\ \beta(F-F_1) = -\tfrac{1}{2} \sum_\mu \gamma_\mu \alpha_\mu.$$

But

$$\beta(F-F_1) = \beta(E-E_1) - k^{-1}(S-S_1),$$

where

$$E_1 = \int f_1^N H\, d\tau, \qquad S_1 = -k \int f_1^N \ln f_1^N\, d\tau;$$

and, since f_1^N and f_0^N represent equilibrium ensembles differing only slightly in temperature,

$$S_1 - S_0 = T^{-1}(E_1 - E) = k\beta(E_1 - E).$$

Hence

$$\beta(F-F_1) = k^{-1}(S_0 - S),$$

so that

$$S - S_0 = \tfrac{1}{2} k \sum_\mu \gamma_\mu \alpha_\mu.$$

References

(1) H. B. G. Casimir, *Revs. Mod. Phys.*, **17**, 343 (1945).
(2) S. Chapman and T. G. Cowling, *The Mathematical Theory of Non-uniform Gases*, Cambridge Univ. Press, London, 1939.
(3) S. R. de Groot, *Thermodynamics of Irreversible Processes*, North-Holland, Amsterdam, 1951; Interscience, New York.
(4) J. O. Hirschfelder, C. F. Curtiss, and R. B. Bird, *Molecular Theory of Gases and Liquids*, Wiley, New York, 1954.
(5) H. C. Longuet-Higgins and J. A. Pople, *J. Chem. Phys.*, **25**, 884 (1956).
(6) L. Onsager, *Phys. Rev.*, **38**, 2265 (1931).

MOLECULAR DYNAMICS BY ELECTRONIC COMPUTERS

B. J. ALDER and T. WAINWRIGHT, *Radiation Laboratory, University of California, Livermore, California*

Abstract

The feasibility of the use of fast electronic computers to study the effect of multiple correlation in molecular dynamics is demonstrated. It is shown that the simultaneous equations of motion of several hundred classical particles can be solved exactly, although the present preliminary study is restricted to about 100 particles which interact either as rigid elastic spheres or with square-well potentials.

Starting with several types of initial conditions the time to approach equilibrium is determined and shown to be very rapid, that is, about 3 or 4 mean collision times for hard spheres. In some sample cases the way the Boltzmann H-function reaches its equilibrium value is determined. For hard spheres this approach is monotonic even at high densities. The system is allowed to proceed once equilibrium has been reached in order to evaluate for some representative cases the self-diffusion coefficient, the collision rate, the velocity autocorrelation function, and the thermodynamic functions. These preliminary calculations indicate remarkable agreement with the Enskog theory of transport properties for hard spheres up to quite high densities. The equation of state for hard spheres seems to disagree at intermediate densities slightly with the results of the Monte Carlo calculations. Final comparison with existing theories and experiment is delayed until further quantities have been evaluated. What is hoped to be learned from these calculations with the aid of present and prospective machines is discussed.

Since one of the present principal initial conditions is one where all molecules have the same velocity but in random direction, the Boltzmann equation for that situation in the case of hard spheres is solved also. A comparison is made between the velocity distribution function obtained from the Boltzmann equation and the one from 100 spheres in order to determine at what density the approximations inherent in the Boltzmann equation become poor.

I. INTRODUCTION

Some problems in classical statistical mechanics are ideally suited to machine calculations. One is faced in both equilibrium and nonequilibrium statistical mechanics with complexities of a mathematical nature in situations in which no conceptual difficulties exist. Thus, the elementary processes which occur, for instance the binary interactions of classical molecules, can be described by well-known laws. It is not surprising, therefore, that when a system is in such a state that it can be adequately represented as consisting of a succession of separate simple events, analytical description is possible. If, however, successive events are correlated as, for example, in multiple interactions in dense systems, analytical techniques available at present are unable to cope with the situation. Analytical techniques have great difficulty describing the simultaneous interactions of three particles, let alone the interactions of many molecules.

The recent development of large electronic computing machines makes possible the description of the interactions of many particles by the direct numerical solution of the simultaneous equations of motion. The systems which can be treated are, however, quite small compared with a macroscopic sample. With present-day machines it is possible to treat systems of several hundred molecules and it might be possible with presently planned machines to go up to 10,000 molecules, but this is still small enough so that the nature of the boundary of the sample has to be critically considered and fairly large inherent fluctuations have to be contended with. The small sample also makes it difficult to deal with long-range forces. These numerical calculations, furthermore, have the disadvantage of giving only particular solutions to specific problems, just as any experiment would do. The calculation is, in fact, an experiment which is performed on a working model rather than on a real physical system. It might be possible, when a number of "experiments" have been performed, to deduce analytical generalizations which are now hard to see because of the mathematical complexities involved. In any case, it should be possible to evaluate the validity of various existing analytical approximations. It is interesting to note that some of the "analytical" theories require numerical work of the order of complexity of the present calculation.

The analytical theories to which these numerical solutions can be compared can be classified into two categories in line with what has been said before: those theories which break the correlations between individual molecules and the rest of the system and those which break correlations between pairs of molecules and the rest of the system. An exception to this is the virial expansion of the equation of state where it has been possible to evaluate the interactions of quadruplets of molecules for the simplest type of interaction potential,[1] and more complex interactions yet for certain unrealistic potentials which are chosen for mathematical simplicity. Theories to which reference will be made which fall into the first mentioned category are the simple free-volume theory[2] and the Boltzmann[3] and Enskog[4] theories of transport properties. In the formulation of the free-volume theory the configurational correlations are broken in that each molecule is assumed to move in interaction with its neighbors held at rest in their average positions. Extensions[5] to allow two molecules to move simultaneously are being worked out but no results are presently available. In both the Boltzmann and the Enskog theories the velocity correlations are broken by making the so-called molecular chaos approximation. Kirkwood's theory[6] of transport processes also falls into this category since it resorts to the Langevin equation. An equivalent description of these theories would be in terms of Markoff chains whose behavior can be well characterized and checked. In the second category falls the superposition theory [7–10] of equilibrium statistical mechanics in which all configurational correlations are expressed in terms of pair correlations. Its application to transport properties[11] has led, so far, to no tractable results.

Machine calculations of equilibrium properties have recently been carried out by the so-called Monte Carlo method.[12–14] This method allows the molecules to move one at a time in a random way, but only those moves are allowed which result in small energy deviations from the minimum energy of the system. These moves cause the system to pass through a succession of the more probable states which, taken together, form a canonical ensemble. Equilibrium properties are then calculated by performing averages over the ensemble. Possible errors in this method might be due to slow convergence of the systems to the true equilibrium state; this can be overcome by making a large number of moves.

II. DESCRIPTION OF THE CALCULATION

In order to follow the dynamics of the motion of a system of many particles with any sort of interaction potential, the force on each particle could be calculated by considering the influence of each of its neighbors. The trajectories could thus be calculated by assuming that the total force on a particle is constant during a short time step and by recalculating the force after each time step. The calculation could also be carried out for nonspherical molecules and for molecules with internal degrees of freedom, provided classical description is adequate and the two-body problem can be solved.

Since it was desirable in the present work to test existing theories without making any approximations in the calculations, a simple potential was chosen which also has the virtue of having been extensively investigated from the analytic point of view. This is the rigid-elastic sphere model. The particles in such a system do not experience any force except upon colliding with other particles. The machine is made to calculate exactly, to the number of significant figures carried, the shortest time at which any two particles collide. It does this by evaluating for each pair in the system the time required for the projected particle paths to approach to within one diameter. All particles are advanced at constant velocity for this shortest time and the velocities of the two particles in contact are then changed according to the solution of the two-body problem. The process can then be repeated. Another potential to which such a method is applicable is the square-well potential. The modifications necessary are that two "collision" diameters are involved and that the scheme for changing velocities must include elastic and inelastic "collisions" with the attractive potential as well as elastic collisions of cores. Once the square-well potential case has been solved it is possible to extend the results to more realistic potentials by perturbation techniques and thus comparisons with experiments might be made possible.

The machine calculations can be speeded up considerably by some elementary considerations. The evaluation of the collision time for each of the pairs of particles is the most time-consuming step since for a system of N particles, $N(N-1)/2$ second-order algebraic equations have to be solved. It is possible to eliminate many of these pairs by a simple test which shows their centers are receding. Another simple test (evaluation of the discriminant of the quadratic equation) indicates that, though some of the pairs are approaching, the centers of the two particles will never be as close as a diameter. Some of the remaining second-order equations can be avoided by not considering pairs which are so far apart that their collision time can be expected to be long. A great saving in calculating time can be achieved by holding not only the shortest collision time but also many of the other times arranged in order of increasing magnitude. When the system has been allowed to proceed to the first collision, the time required for the first collision is subtracted from all the other times being held. Then the shortest remaining time on the list is the additional time required for the second collision unless one of the first two particles is immediately involved in a second collision. This possibility is checked by reexamining all the possible collisions these two particles, with their new velocities, can make. For this purpose $2N-3$ pairs must be examined instead of $N(N-1)/2$. All the times which had been previously determined for these two particles are erased, since they had been based on the erroneous assumption that the two were not going to collide and the new times are ordered into the set. This process is continued until the largest time originally saved has elapsed; then a new set of times is calculated for the next cycle.

The problem was first set up for a "Univac" calculator. In this machine the small capacity of the high-speed memory limited the system which could be efficiently handled to about 100 rigid spheres. With this number of particles, roughly 100 collisions, that is about two mean collision times, could be calculated in one hour. A faster machine with a larger memory, the IBM-704, has more recently been employed to handle larger systems of both rigid spheres and particles with the square-well potential. This machine calculates about 2000 collisions per hour for a 100 particle system and is also able to handle larger systems, but the calculating time rather than the size of the memory is the limiting factor, as illustrated in the following example. A 1000 particle system would run somewhat faster than 100 collisions per hour, that is one mean collision time requires about 5 hours. Hence, it is most economical to work with a small sample and remove the effect of inherent fluctuations by averages over many collisions, provided the boundary effects are not serious.

The same periodic boundary conditions have been used in the present work as were previously used in the Monte Carlo work.[12] The system is contained in a cubic box which is surrounded on all sides by other identical boxes, so that when a particle leaves the central box another particle (its "ghost") enters from the opposite side. If the mean free path of a particle is small compared with the size of the box, the ghost will encounter a random sample in the central box. At low densities, when the mean free path becomes comparable to the size of the box, the ghost can, before experiencing a collision, get into the region which the original particle left, resulting in unrealistic correlations. Although no significant trouble has been encountered in this region of density, the effect has not been thoroughly studied. It can only be said at the moment that the hope is that the periodic boundary conditions ameliorate the inaccuracies due to the small size of the sample. Quite pragmatic tests can be made to study the seriousness of the effect by comparing large with small samples. Up to now one study has been made with a 100 and a 256 particle sample at fairly high density with no serious difference detected. It is planned to introduce various types of walls around the central box not only to study the effects of changing the nature of the boundary, but also so that types of problems other than those already studied can be handled, for example problems involving external forces.

As the calculation of the motion of the many-particle system proceeds, the history of each particle is recorded on magnetic tape. A separate process later analyzes this very detailed data for various distribution functions and other numbers which may be desired. These analyzing calculations naturally divide into two parts: those which are concerned with the approach of the system to equilibrium, and those which are concerned with the system at equilibrium. In order to average out fluctuations in the approach to equilibrium, the same problem must be restarted several times with slightly different initial conditions. Averages for equilibrium properties can be attained by running the problem for a long time. The amount of averaging which must be done depends upon the fluctuations that are encountered. Rigid sphere problems do not have to run as long as problems involving attractive potentials because in the former there are no potential energy fluctuations, also equilibrium is reached more quickly. The present results are preliminary because it has been found that for some properties a fairly large number of determinations must be averaged, and the number of determinations available is at present too small.

The analysis carried out until equilibrium is reached depends on the type of problem studied, that is on the initial distribution used. In all cases the Boltzmann H-function is examined. In order to do this the distribution in kinetic energy of the particles, $f(v^2)$, is required and this is of interest in itself. For example, in a problem in which all particles have the same initial kinetic energy it is desirable to ascertain how much time is necessary to produce particles of many times the initial kinetic energy, since these might, in a real situation, be able to react chemically when they collide. Another example would be in the study of temperature equilibrium. If in the initial conditions some molecules in a small region of the box had a very much higher kinetic energy than the rest of the molecules, it would be possible to watch the decay of this hot spot. In this latter case the analysis allows one also to determine how this hot spot spreads out spacially by evaluating $f(r, v^2)$, that is the cubic box is divided into smaller cubes and the kinetic energy distribution is calculated in each. The number of intervals into which the kinetic energy and the cube are divided depends entirely on how small an interval we can use without getting large fluctuations. For each function that is discussed in the analysis, these intervals were set from a knowledge of how many quantities were to be distributed among the intervals.

In the initial phases of a problem $f(v_x)$, $f(v_y)$, and $f(v_z)$, that is the distribution in the components of the velocity, can also be calculated. This could be of interest when, for example, a boundary temperature or velocity component is impressed on the sample. In a calculation where all molecules are bunched up in a small region of the box, the function $f(r)$, the spatial singlet distribution function, is of interest in determining how quickly the subsequent "explosion" fills the container. All these functions, and several others, can be evaluated whenever the problem warrants it and can be cut out of the analysis if they are of no interest.

There are several quantities which it has been found useful to evaluate during the generation of the velocities and positions since they then immediately allow one to determine whether equilibrium has been reached. It is evident that different functions give different criteria as to when equilibrium has been reached. For example, the *H*-function is fairly insensitive to whether a Maxwell-Boltzmann velocity distribution has been reached, since it involves an integral condition. Furthermore, frequently equilibrium with respect to the velocity distribution is reached very fast compared to that in configuration space. The internal energy and particularly the pressure of the system are, however, quite sensitive to small deviations from equilibrium in both the configurational and velocity distributions and they together have been used as criteria for the establishment of equilibrium. They both also have the virtue of being very easy to evaluate when the problem is generated.

The pressure is evaluated directly from the virial theorem, and the internal energy can be evaluated for molecules with square wells by enumerating the number of overlaps. The collision rate, which for rigid spheres at least, is directly related to the pressure, is also calculated simultaneously with the paths of all the particles, and can also be used to help decide when equilibrium is reached. Once equilibrium has been reached several other parts of the analysis are cut in. These include the pair distribution function, $f(r_{12})$, useful for comparison with x-ray scattering data on fluid systems and for calculating the thermodynamic functions. The pair distribution function and the triplet distribution function, $f(r_{12}, r_{13}, r_{23})$, which is evaluated also, can be used to assess errors in theories which neglect higher than pair correlations. For the square-well potential case, the distribution in cluster sizes can be evaluated so that it may be possible to observe the change in this distribution during condensation. Furthermore, the self-diffusion coefficient is evaluated in two ways. In the first place the velocity autocorrelation function is calculated. Its functional behavior yields information on the type of frictional relaxation which occurs in the system. The second way is to evaluate the diffusion coefficient by noting the distance particles move in known time intervals. The distribution in these distances is of interest because it can be compared with random walk calculations. Another calculation allows the determination of the mean free path and the distribution of collision distances about this mean. In addition the analysis includes an evaluation of the distribution of energy of the colliding particles, that is both the total relative kinetic energy of collision and the kinetic energy along lines of centers. These functions might be useful in reaction kinetics.

If all these functions are calculated, it takes about twice as long to analyze as to run the original problem. The heavy time consumers are the pair and particularly the triplet distribution functions; however, these do not need to be evaluated in every instance, since in this calculation, as opposed to the Monte Carlo calculation, alternate ways are available to calculate thermodynamic functions. The pair distribution function is, however, essential for the perturbation treatment mentioned earlier.

Solution of the Boltzmann Equation

For the purpose of comparison with the above calculations, the Boltzmann equation for a gas of rigid spheres has been solved numerically in the case of an initial velocity distribution which is highly peaked. This is analogous to an initial condition previously used where all the spheres were uniformly distributed in space and all had the same absolute velocity but in random directions. The distribution function, $f(\gamma)$, is then the solution of the following integral differential equation:

$$\dot{f} = \frac{\partial f(\gamma)}{\partial \tau} = \frac{1}{2\sqrt{2}} \int_0^\infty d\alpha \int_{-1}^{1} dy \left[f(\gamma+\alpha+2y\sqrt{\gamma\alpha}) \int_{\gamma y^2}^{\infty} f(x)\, dx - f(\gamma) \int_{\gamma y^2+\alpha+2y\sqrt{\gamma\alpha}}^{\infty} f(x)\, dx \right], \tag{1}$$

where $\gamma = mv^2/2kT$, τ is the time measured in units of mean collision times, $\tau = t4(N-1)d^2(\pi kT/m)^{1/2}$, N is the number of spheres per unit volume, m is the mass of each sphere, d is the diameter of the spheres, and T is the equilibrium temperature. The distribution function is so normalized that the number of spheres per unit volume in the energy range $d\gamma$ is given by

$$dN = N(2/\pi^{1/2})\, \gamma^{1/2} f(\gamma)\, d\gamma. \tag{2}$$

The value of $\dot{f}$ at $\tau = 0$ can be calculated analytically if the initial distribution is a delta function in γ; however, for a complete solution the equation must be solved numerically. Such a solution to Eq. (1) was obtained in a straightforward manner with the use of an IBM-650 calculating machine. After some manipulations the right-hand side can be reduced (Eq. 3) to a combination of single integrals involving f and one double integral, which turns out to be the most time-consuming step in the calculation.

$$\begin{aligned} \dot{f} = \frac{\partial f(\gamma)}{\partial \tau} &= \sqrt{\frac{\pi}{\gamma}}\, [2G(\gamma, 0) - f(\gamma)(1/2+\gamma)] \\ &+ G(\gamma, 0) \left[2G(\gamma, 0) - \frac{2}{\sqrt{\gamma}} G(\gamma, 1/2) \right] \\ &- f(\gamma)\, 2 \left[\frac{\gamma}{3} G(\gamma, 0) - \sqrt{\gamma}\, G(\gamma, 1/2) + G(\gamma, 1) - \frac{1}{3\sqrt{\gamma}} G(\gamma, 3/2) \right] \\ &+ 4 \int_{\gamma/2}^{\infty} dp \int_{\gamma-p}^{p} du \sqrt{\frac{p+u}{\gamma} - 1}\, f(p) f(u), \end{aligned} \tag{3}$$

where $G(\gamma, n) = \int_{\gamma}^{\infty} x^n f(x)\, dx.$

Starting with $f(\gamma, 0)$ a first approximation to $f(\gamma, \Delta\tau)$ was calculated by $\bar{f}(\gamma, \Delta\tau) = f(\gamma, 0) + \Delta\tau \dot{f}(\gamma, 0)$. Then an approximation to $\dot{f}(\gamma, \Delta\tau)$ was calculated from Eq. (3) using the approximate $f(\gamma, \Delta\tau)$. The final $f(\gamma, \Delta\tau)$ was then evaluated by: $f(\gamma, \Delta\tau) = f(\gamma, 0) + (\Delta\tau/2)(\dot{f}(\gamma, 0) + \dot{\bar{f}}(\gamma, \Delta\tau))$ and the process repeated to calculate $f(\gamma, 2\Delta\tau)$ and so on.

A 40 by 40 network was used for the double integral and 40 points also for the single integrals. Ten time steps were taken, which was sufficient for present comparison purposes, since in this time the equilibrium distribution was achieved for energies up to a few times the mean energy. In the hundred sphere system the statistics on particles of five or more times the mean energy becomes very poor. The advantage of the numerical solution of the Boltzmann equation, if carried further however, is that it allows a determination of the time necessary to establish equilibrium for particles of very much higher energy than the mean energy of the system. It would also be possible with the present scheme to study the approach to equilibrium for other initial conditions such as one with a two-peaked velocity distribution function.

III. RESULTS

The results will be presented mainly in graphic form to show the qualitative behavior of the various functions. The few quantitative results, for reasons cited previously, should be considered to be provisional.

Figure 1 is presented to show the fluctuations from the Maxwell-Boltzmann velocity distribution for a system of 100 rigid spheres. The solid line represents the Maxwell-Boltzmann distribution and the dots are obtained by averaging the distributions determined each tenth collision for 600 collisions after the system has reached equilibrium. The density corresponds to $v/v_0 = 14.14$, where v_0 is the close-packed volume of hard spheres. As can be seen, the fluctuations are still quite large and would be still larger in the higher energy ranges. The graph extends only to twice the mean velocity squared, although for 100 particles a few molecules have 4 to 5 times the mean kinetic energy, but due to the small number in that velocity region the statistics are quite poor.

For molecules with square-well potentials the final equilibrium temperature depends, of course, on the final potential energy of the system. That is starting with a given total energy, the kinetic and potential energies will be readjusted until equilibrium is reached. The determination of the final temperature is, however, subject to somewhat

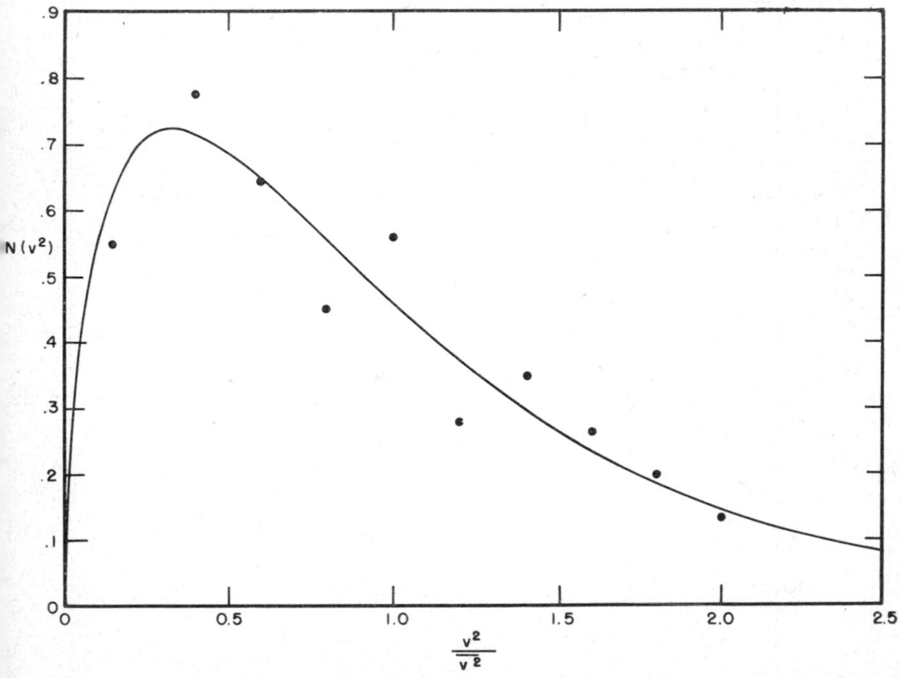

Fig. 1. The velocity distribution function, $N(v^2)$, as a function of velocity squared divided by the average velocity squared, v^2/v^2. The dots refer to a system of 100 hard sphere particles at $v/v_0 = 14.14$, and the solid curve represents the Maxwell-Boltzmann distribution.

greater uncertainty than in the rigid sphere case because additional fluctuations in the potential energy are introduced. Figure 2 shows how the potential energy which is directly proportional to the number of overlaps varies with time or the number of collisions. After almost 2000 collisions the system seems to have reached equilibrium and fluctuations of the order of 10 overlaps are present thereafter. By the number of overlaps is meant the number of pairs of particles whose separations are less than the outside diameter of the square well. In

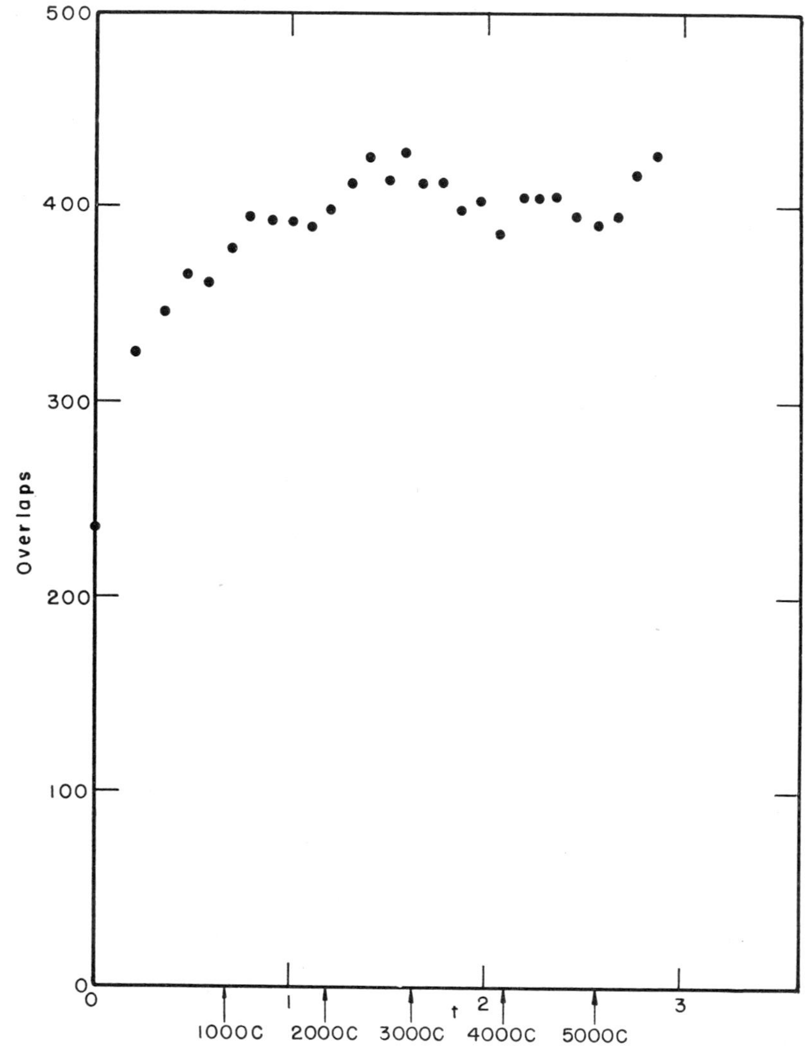

Fig. 2. Variation of the number of overlaps with time, t, or collision number, C, for a system of 100 particles at $v/v_0 = 5$ and $T^* = 1.66$.

the number of "collisions" all the processes that can occur for molecules with square-well potentials are counted; thus a "collision" can be, besides the normal meaning of the hard-core collision, a capture, a dissociation, or a "bounce." A capture occurs when the centers of two particles approach each other to within a distance equal to the outer

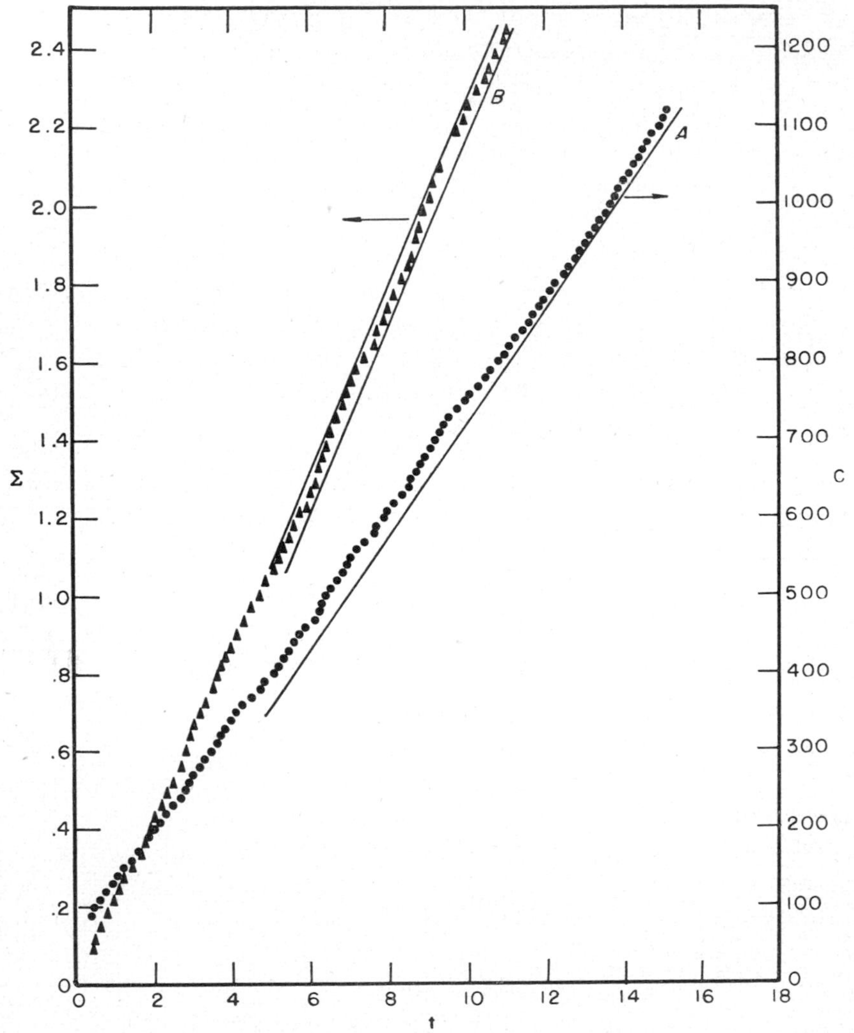

Fig. 3. A plot of the virial, Σ, and collision number, C, as a function of time for a system of 100 hard sphere particles at $v/v_0 = 14.14$. The two parallel solid lines in B refer to the theoretical slope from the virial expansion, and the solid line in A refers to the theoretical collision rate from the Enskog theory.

diameter of the square well. In dissociation the particle centers recede to a separation equal to this diameter and fly apart. If, however, the relative velocity of the particles is not great enough to cause dissociation, the particles bounce and are temporarily bound together. Thus, the number of overlaps can be changed through the mechanisms of dissociation and capture. The final temperature calculated from the number of overlaps for the problem represented by Figure 2 is $T^* = kT/V_0 = 1.66$, where V_0 is the depth of the potential well. v/v_0 is 5 and the diameter of the potential well is 1.8 times that of the hard-core diameter. The only other well diameter studied so far is 1.5 times the hard-core diameter.

Having calculated the internal energy of the system by the above method, the pressure is needed to complete the thermodynamic description of the system. Figure 3 demonstrates how the pressure is determined from the rate of change of Σ with time, where Σ is related to the virial of the internal forces of the system

$$\Sigma = \Sigma_i (\mathbf{r_{a_i}} - \mathbf{r_{b_i}}) \cdot \Delta \mathbf{v_{a_i}}\,, \tag{4}$$

where $\mathbf{r_{a_i}}$ and $\mathbf{r_{b_i}}$ are the positions of particles a_i and b_i which are involved in collision i. $\Delta \mathbf{v_{a_i}}$ is the change of velocity of particle a_i which is equal and opposite to the change in velocity of particle b_i. The virial theorem then relates Σ to the pressure by

$$\frac{pv}{RT} - 1 = -\frac{1}{N\overline{v^2}} \frac{d\Sigma}{dt}. \tag{5}$$

Figure 3 refers to a system of 100 hard spheres at a density of $v/v_0 = 14.14$. The solid lines in curve B are two parallel lines at the theoretical slope as calculated from the virial coefficients. It can be seen that the pressure is quite well defined and the agreement with theory is very good. Curve A of that graph shows the number of collisions in the system as a function of time and allows the evaluation of the collision rate, (Γ). The solid line there refers to the result obtained from the transport theory of Enskog for a dense hard sphere system. That theory takes into account the finite size of the spheres through Y, a factor which is a function of the density and is related to the equation of state[4] by

$$Y = \frac{(pv/RT - 1)}{2/3\pi N\sigma^3}. \tag{6}$$

Thus,

$$\Gamma = (2) N(N-1)\sigma^2 \sqrt{\frac{\pi}{3}} \sqrt{\overline{v^2}}\, Y, \tag{7}$$

where σ is the diameter of hard sphere molecules.

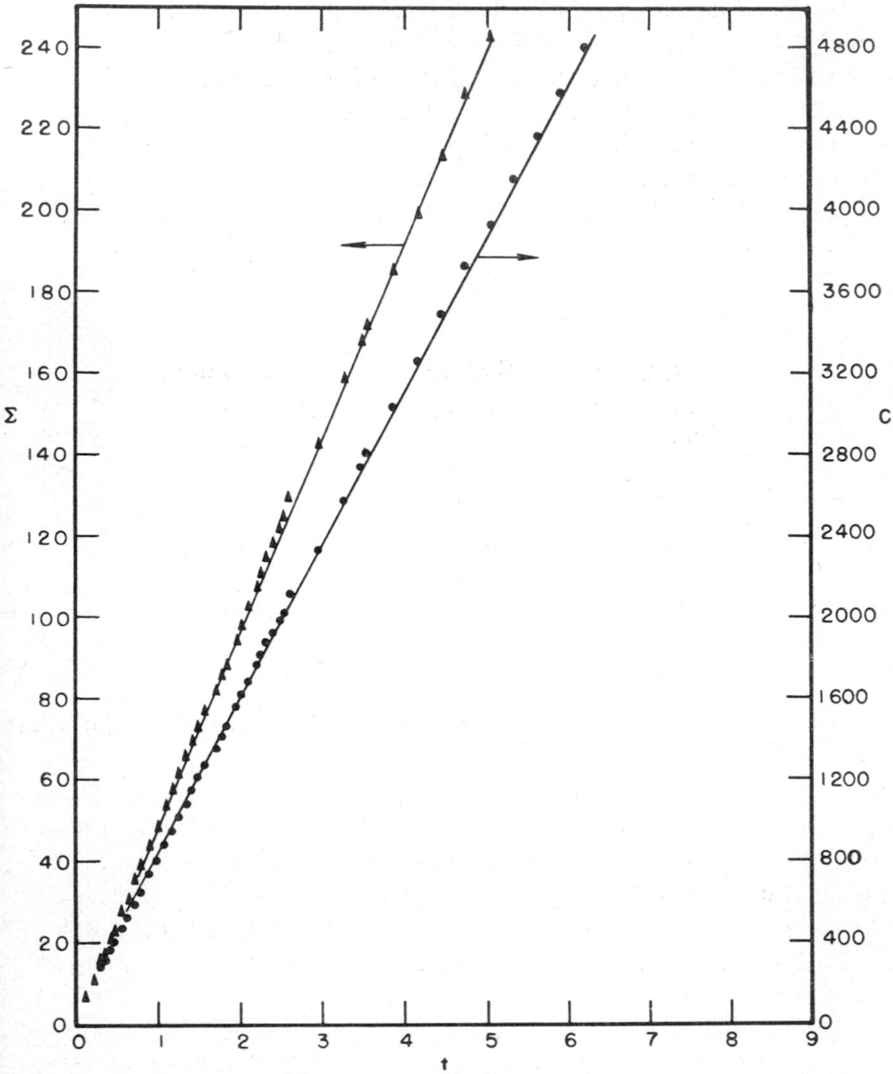

Fig. 4. A plot of the virial (triangles), Σ, and the collision number (circles), C, as a function of time for a system of 100 hard sphere particles at $v/v_0 = 2.00$. The solid line for the collision rate is calculated from Enskog's theory.

The solid line A is shown slightly below the machine-calculated points in order to make visual representation easier, but the agreement is very good when Y is calculated from the virial theorem.

Figure 4 also shows the evaluation of the pressure and the collision rate for 100 hard core particles but at a much higher density, one corresponding to $v/v_0 = 2.00$. At this density the four-term virial theorem no longer converges. However, once the pressure is evaluated from the slope of the straight line in Figure 4, the factor Y can be calculated and hence also the collision rate according to the Enskog theory. The right-hand solid line on the graph is the collision rate so calculated; the

TABLE I

Comparison of Collision Rates

v/v_0	Enskog[4]	Present*
445	6.44	6.42
86	19.6	19.6
14.141	73.3	71.6
2.000	765	765 (a)
1.767	3390	3450 (b)
1.500	1330	1370 (a)
1.345	1640	1680
1.250	2030	2050 (a)
1.031	13700	14300 (a)

* 100 particles were used except when marked (a) when 108 and (b) when 256 particles were used.

comparison with the numerical results is remarkable. In the same manner, Table I presents a comparison of the Enskog theory with the calculated collision rates for a wide range of densities of hard spheres. In some cases 108 or 256 particles have been employed instead of 100. In all instances the collision rate and the pressure are consistent to the accuracy of the determination and, hence, it must be concluded from this and evidence to be presented later that the Enskog theory of transport properties for hard spheres is quantitatively correct within the present accuracy in spite of the apparently severe approximations under which the theory is usually derived.

The equation of state can also be compared with various theories as is done in Table II and Figure 5 for the hard sphere system. At low densities all theories agree except the simple free-volume theory, which is known to become more valid for dense systems. As Table II shows, the agreement of the present calculation with the virial expansion, for example, is as satisfactory as can be expected. Only one very high density point has so far been calculated, namely at $v/v_0 = 1.0306$. The Monte Carlo result at this density seems to be distinctly lower than the present calculation, but the agreement between the free-volume

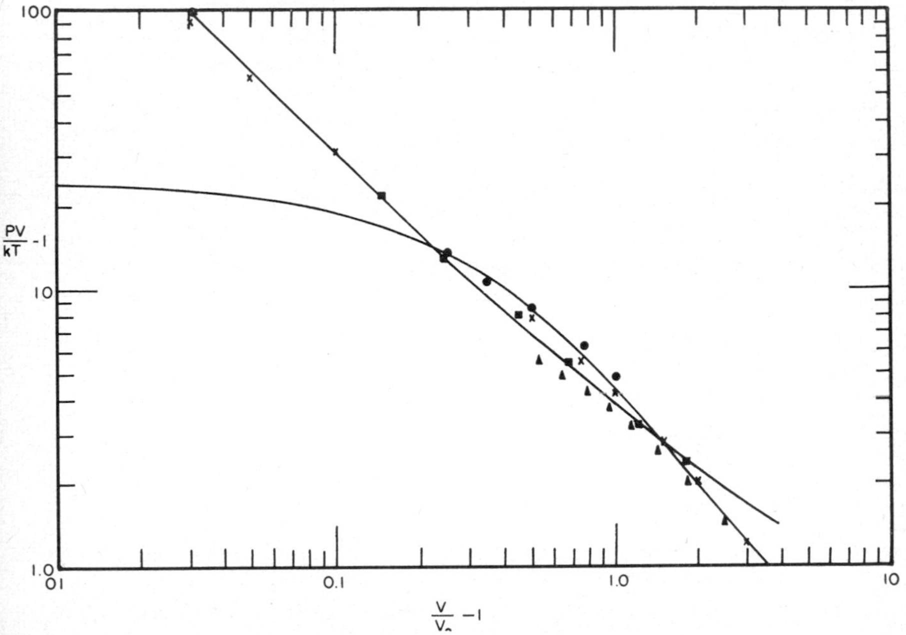

Fig. 5. The hard sphere equation of state: $pv/RT—1$ versus $v/v_0—1$; triangles represent the Kirkwood and Born-Green theories, squares the unsmoothed free-volume theory, crosses the Monte Carlo calculations, curved line the 4-term virial expansion, almost straight line the simple free-volume theory, and circles the present work.

theory and the present calculation is within the uncertainties of determining the pressure. It is somewhat surprising that the very simple model employed in the free-volume theory is as accurate at high densities as this indicates. The simple free-volume theory is, however, definitely too low at intermediate densities. The so called unsmoothed free-volume theory offers little improvement, but present indications are that the modified free-volume theory which allows more correlation between particles yields still higher pressures in this region of the equation of state.

The most unexpected result, however, is the disagreement with the Monte Carlo calculations. Our preliminary results differ by as much as 20 % from the Monte Carlo calculations in the high and intermediate density regions. The reason for this has not yet been traced down. It is apparent, however, that when the spheres are close-packed very many collisions are necessary to remove slight deviations of packing from the true equilibrium arrangement. The two entries in the $v/v_0 = 1.345$ row in Table II refer to systems of 100 and 108 particles.

TABLE II

Comparisons of Equations of State of Hard Spheres

v/v_0	$pv/RT-1$	$pv/RT-1$
445	0.0067 (a)	0.0067 (c)
14.141	0.23 (a)	0.24 (c)
2.000	4.8 (b)	4.3 (d)
1.767	6.7 (a)	6.3 (e)
1.500	8.6 (b)	7.9 (d)
1.345	13.3 (a)	10.8 (b)
1.250	13.6 (b)	13.8 (d)
1.031	99.4 (b)	99.0 (f)

(a) by using 100 particles
(b) by using 108 particles
(c) by virial expansion
(d) by Monte Carlo Method
(e) by using 256 particles
(f) by free volume theory

The 108 particles were initially in a face-centered cubic lattice, while the 100 particles were in an imperfect body-centered cubic arrangement to start out with. The difference in the pressure is due to the fact that the 100 particle system can never get into the more favorable arrangement; the reason that the pressure is high can be ascribed to the system's acting as if it were confined to a smaller volume since the original inefficient packing still persists. The effect of the finite number of particles has been investigated at $v/v_0 = 1.767$, where 100 particles, again in a disorderly initial arrangement, are compared with 256 particles in a perfect lattice. The disagreement may be attributed to the slow attainment of equilibrium in the 256 particle system. However, the difference in pressure between these two cases is smaller than the disagreement with the Monte Carlo result, which is about 10 %

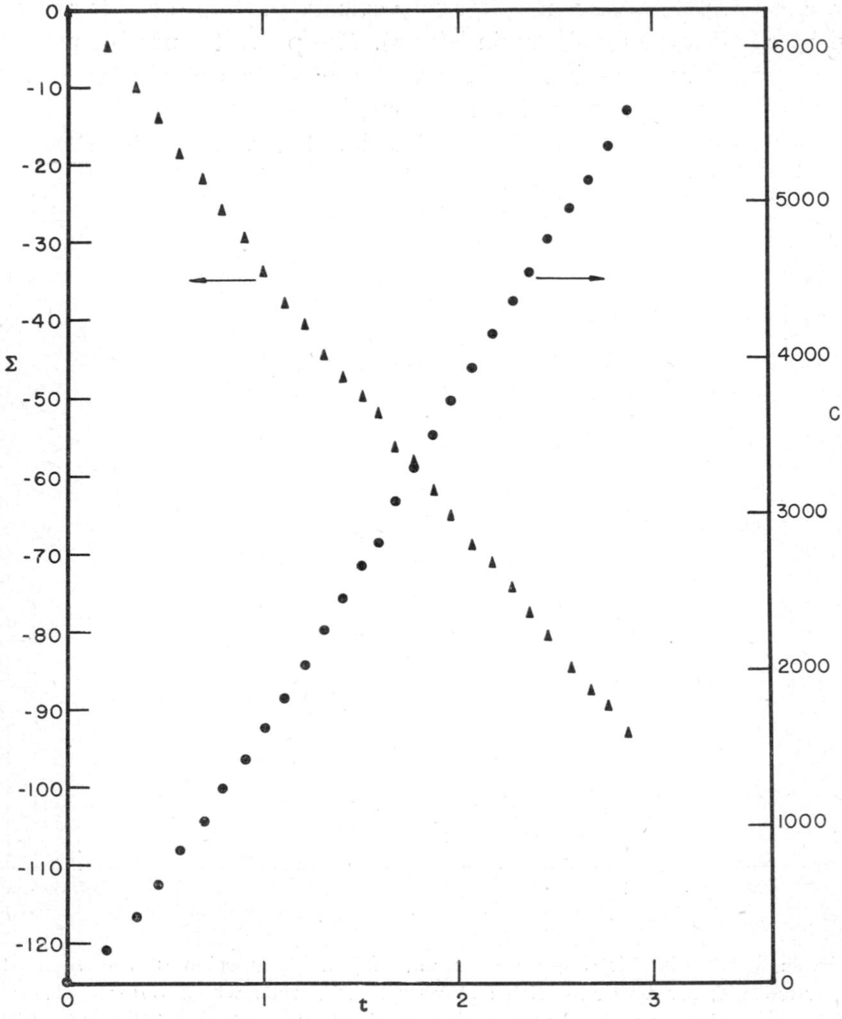

Fig. 6. A plot of the virial, Σ, and collision rate, C, as a function of time for 100 particles with square-well potentials at $v/v_0 = 5$ and $T^* = 1.66$.

lower than the smaller of the other two pressures. It is obvious that further work is necessary to reconcile these differences, but present indications are that it may not be necessarily true that any virial coefficients for a hard sphere system are negative. The contrary inference was drawn from the Monte Carlo results, since some of the pressures were below the values which would be calculated from the four known virial coefficients (solid line in Fig. 4). The present tentative results also seem to show a kink in the equation of state around $v/v_0 = 1.5$, implying a transition for hard spheres.

At intermediate density the Kirkwood and Born and Green theories

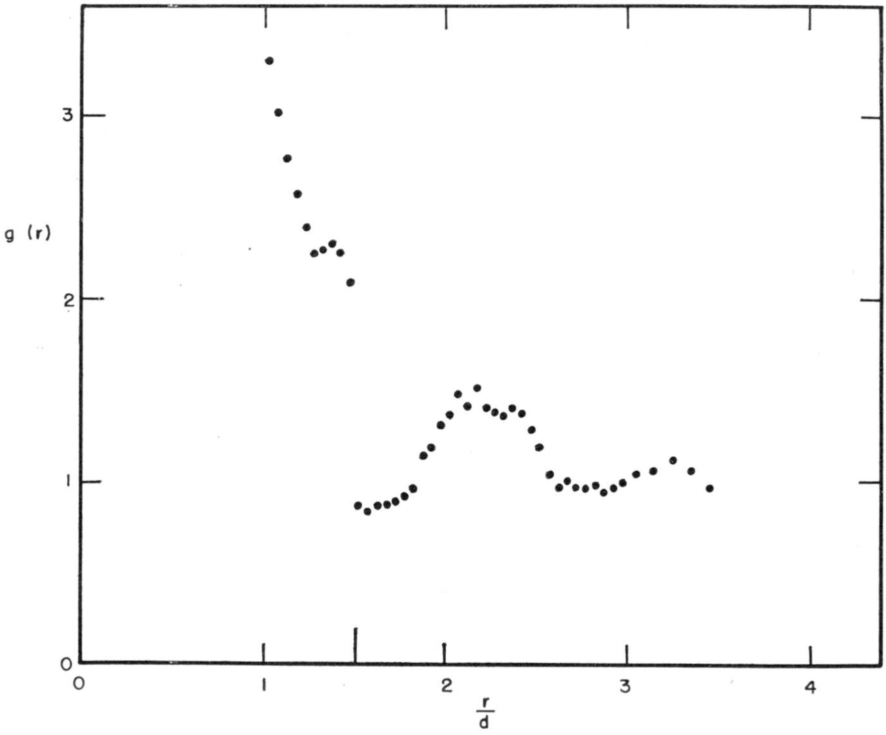

Fig. 7. The radial distribution function, $g(r)$, as a function of the reduced distance, r/d, for particles with square-well potentials whose outer diameter is 1.5 times the hard-core diameter, d, at $v/v_0 = 5$ and $T^* = 0.9$.

give a pressure which is considerably too low, as can be seen in Figure 4. In that method and in the Monte Carlo method the pressure is calculated with the aid of the radial distribution function. Since this function can also be calculated by the present method, one pressure determination was made in this alternative way for a hard sphere system at a density of $v/v_0 = 2$. Instead of $pv/RT-1 = 4.77$ as by the previous method (Eq. 5), a value of 4.98 was obtained from the radial distribution function. This is a quite satisfactory agreement.

For molecules with square-well potentials, the pressure, volume, and temperature diagram has only been covered in a limited region. Therefore only a few random examples can be given at present. To give an idea of how well the pressure can be determined, Figure 6 is presented. It is to be noted that the slope of Σ with time is negative in this graph indicating the presence of an attractive potential. The conditions for this graph are $v/v_0 = 5$, $T^* = 1.66$. The pressure could, of course, again be calculated by the radial distribution function. Figure 7 gives such a distribution function, $g(r)$, as a function of separation of the members of the pair for $v/v_0 = 5$ and $T^* = 0.9$. Although this is very rough, the function shows the typical peaks corresponding to nearest, next nearest and further neighbors. The maximum of $g(r)$ is at the point of contact as it is also for hard spheres at this density.

The discontinuity at $r/d = 1.5$ corresponds to the point where the potential well ends. At $T^* = 2.57$ and $v/v_0 = 5.00$, a comparison of the pressures calculated from the radial distribution function obtained by the superposition theory and the pressure arrived at by the machine calculation has been made. The agreement is very favorable, namely $pv/RT-1$ is -0.33 from the machine calculation, and -0.34 by the superposition approximation.

An evaluation of the self-diffusion coefficient can be carried out from Figure 8. In this graph the velocity autocorrelation function, $\varrho(s)$, is plotted against time, s, and the number of collisions. $\varrho(s)$ is evaluated from the expression:

$$\varrho(s) = \frac{\sum_{i=1}^{N} \mathbf{u_i}(t+s) \cdot \mathbf{u_i}(t)}{\sum_{i=1}^{N} u_i^2(t)} \tag{8}$$

and is related to the diffusion coefficient, D, by:

$$D = \frac{kT}{m} \int_0^\infty \varrho(s)\, ds. \tag{9}$$

Figure 8 shows an unaveraged autocorrelation function for 100 hard spheres at $v/v_0 = 14.14$. To obtain an average $\varrho(s)$ several of these functions are calculated, starting from different base times, (t), and

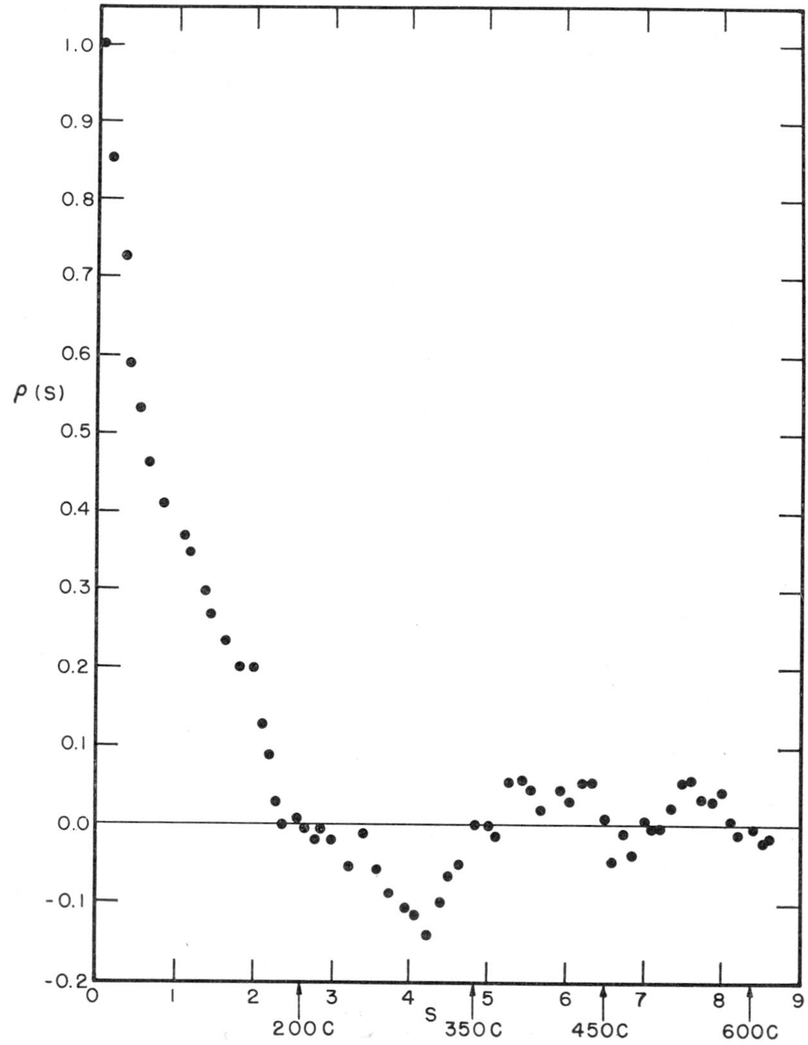

Fig. 8. Variation of the unaveraged velocity autocorrelation function, $\varrho(s)$, with time, s, or with the collision number, C, for 100 hard sphere particles at $v/v_0 = 14.14$.

averaged at equal numbers of collisions. The base time is always chosen to be after equilibrium has been established. Even though individual $\varrho(s)$ functions have wiggles (see Fig. 8), when averages are taken they can be wiped out. This is because of phase differences between these wiggles. Figure 9 shows how an averaged autocorrelation function looks at a higher density, $v/v_0 = 2$, for hard spheres. The structure in the function is almost entirely lost and the calculated points agree remarkably well with an exponential decay (solid line).

$$\varrho(s) = e^{-\beta s}, \tag{10}$$

where β is an effective friction constant, that is

$$D = kT/m\beta. \tag{11}$$

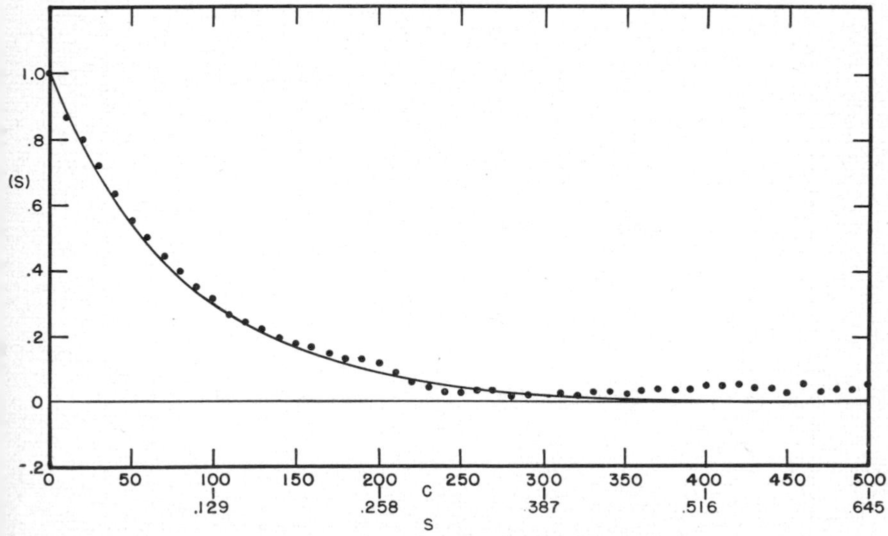

Fig. 9. Comparison of the velocity autocorrelation function, $\varrho(s)$, with an exponential decay (solid line) at $v/v_0 = 2$ for hard spheres. The abscissa is given in terms of collision number, C, and time, s.

The implication of this exponential decay is that the relaxation can be described by a Markoff process even at this quite high density. One might have thought that velocity correlations between successive collisions of two particles would become important at high densities where the molecules are fairly well localized in space, since two partners collide again after only a few collisions with other molecules. This correlation would cause the wiggles in the autocorrelation function, as can be qualitatively seen from the following argument: when a particle is trapped by its neighbors it is forced by them upon collision to reflect its velocity into a narrow range of angles. A frequent reversal of the

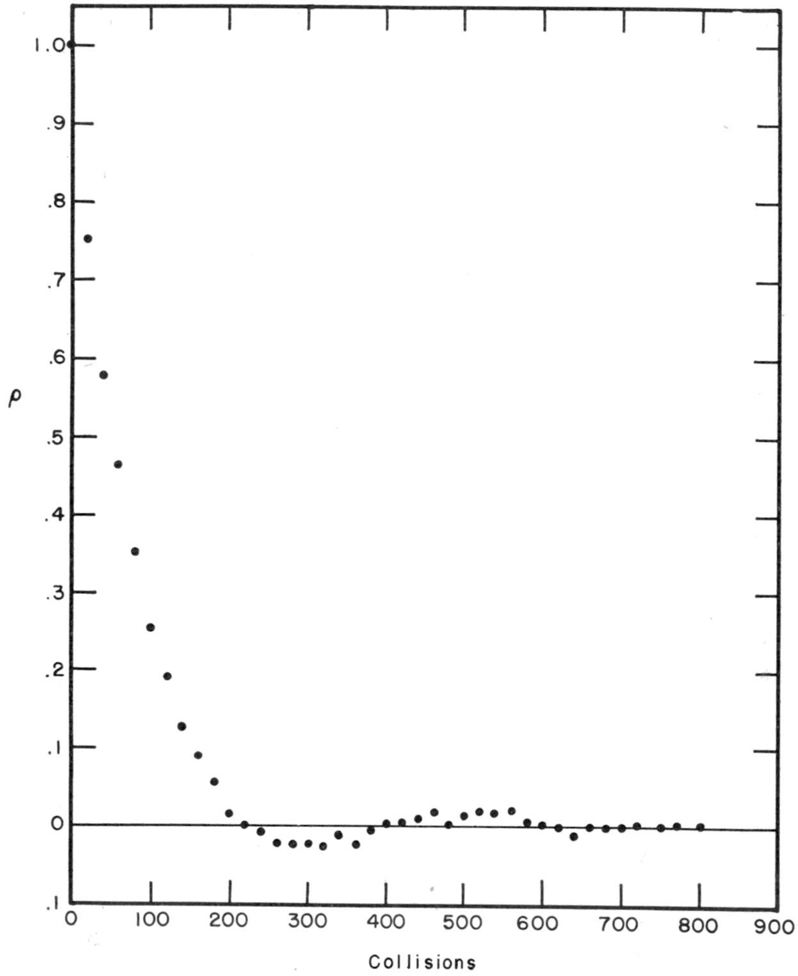

Fig. 10. The velocity autocorrelation function, ϱ, versus collision number for hard spheres at $v/v_0 = 1.767$.

velocity upon collision would result in a negative correlation. At still higher densities than for the case represented in Figure 9, the wiggles in the autocorrelation function seem to remain even in the averaged $\varrho(s)$. Figure 10 represents the average of 15 autocorrelation functions at $v/v_0 = 1.767$. Nevertheless, an exponential decay still is a good approximation for the evaluation of the diffusion coefficient from Eq. (11), as can be seen from Table III. In that table various ways of calculating the diffusion coefficient are compared at several densities. Besides the way already given (Eqs. 9 and 11) it is possible to evaluate the mean-square distance, $\langle r^2 \rangle$, traversed by the particles in a given time, that is

$$D = \langle r^2 \rangle / 6t. \tag{12}$$

It is seen from Table III that these ways of calculating the diffusion coefficient agree within the present uncertainties and they also agree very well with the diffusion constant evaluated from the Enskog theory.[4] In that theory the diffusion coefficient obtained from the Boltzmann equation has again to be corrected by the factor Y. The success of the Enskog theory could have been predicted when the validity of the Markoff process was established from the exponential decay of the autocorrelation function, since this gives some credence to the molecular chaos approximation. How much the Enskog theory improves agreement over the Boltzmann equation is shown in the last column of Table III. It is seen that the Boltzmann equation becomes more valid at low densities.

TABLE III

Comparisons of Diffusion Coefficients

v/v_0	Eq. (11)	Eq. (9)	Eq. (12)	Enskog	Boltzmann
14.141	0.029	—	0.032	0.034	0.039
2.000	0.0037	0.0036	—	0.0033	0.011
1.767	0.0024	0.0026	0.0021	0.0026	0.0098

Figure 11 illustrates the distribution in the squared distances from which the mean used in Eq. (12) is calculated for $v/v_0 = 1.767$. The distribution is given in terms of arbitrary units, where the mean is at 10. This distribution is useful for comparison with various three-dimensional random walk problems.

Two quite crude autocorrelation functions for square-well molecules are shown in Figure 12 and compared with an exponential decay (solid line). The density is very low ($v/v_0 = 158$) and the dots correspond to a T^* of 0.62 and the triangles to a T^* of 0.45. The points follow the exponential decay quite well, as might be surmised at such a low density. It might be remarked that the molecular chaos approximation can be expected to fail at lower density for molecules with attractive potentials

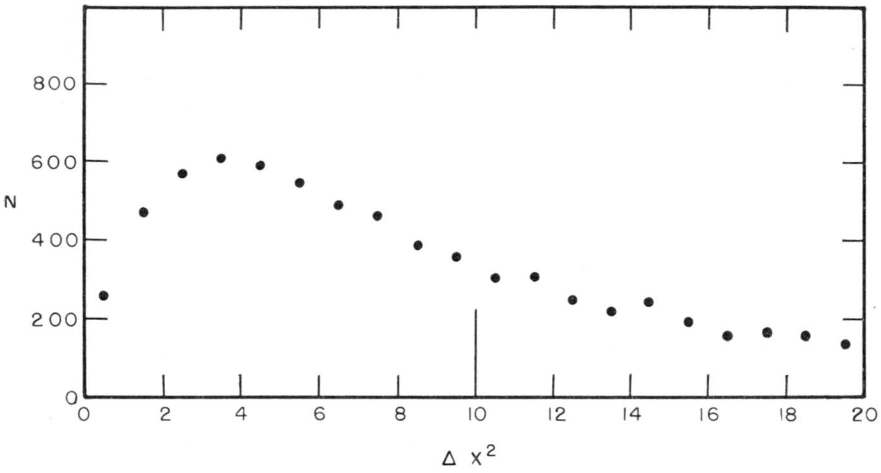

Fig. 11. The distribution, N, in distance squared, Δx^2, in arbitrary units. The mean-square distance is 10 for hard sphere particles at $v/v_0 = 1.767$.

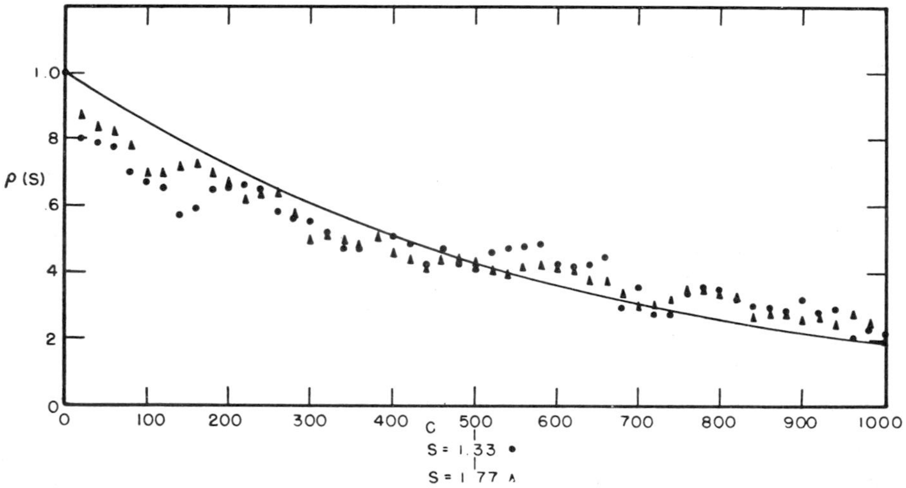

Fig. 12. The velocity autocorrelation function, $\varrho(s)$, at the same density, $v/v_0 = 158$, but two different temperatures (circles $T^* = 0.62$; triangles $T^* = 0.45$) for particles with square-well potentials is compared to an exponential decay (solid line).

than for hard spheres, since strong velocity correlations can be introduced when two molecules are temporarily bound together. Figure 12 also illustrates in a rough way that at the same density but different temperature the autocorrelation functions are the same except for the time scalc. That is the same relaxation processes occur in both cases except that at a higher temperature the processes are speeded up.

The main effort as far as the nonequilibrium properties are concerned has been directed toward an evaluation of the Boltzmann H-function. The initial condition most frequently used was one where all molecules had the same velocity but in a random direction. Figure 13 shows how such a velocity distribution decays toward a Maxwell-Boltzmann distribution for 100 hard spheres at $v/v_0 = 14.14$. This is a plot of the number of particles at a given energy (or velocity squared) divided by the equilibrium number at that energy versus the energy divided by the mean energy. Hence, this is so normalized that at equilibrium a horizontal line at 1 describes the system. Initially all particles are at one energy as represented by the square. After 60 collisions the distribution is shown by circles and at 150 collisions by triangles. Soon after 150 collisions equilibrium is established for the kinetic energy as can be seen in spite of the rather large fluctuations present. The H-function, as will be seen, does not fluctuate as much and after about 150 collisions it is also at its equilibrium value. Hence, for hard spheres only about 3 mean collisions per particle are necessary to establish an equilibrium velocity distribution, which is rather strikingly quick. This seems to be true regardless of the density. It must, of course, be remembered that this does not mean that equilibrium has been established in the higher energy region of the Maxwell-Boltzmann distribution, since the 100 particle system never generates particles there. Figure 13 also shows that the number of particles in an energy range near the original energy of the particles ($v^2 = 1$) builds up to a larger value than the equilibrium value before decaying to the Maxwell-Boltzmann number. This is explained by the fact that at first more particles can flow into this energy range than can pass into further energy regions. This point is also well illustrated in the solution of the Boltzmann equation.

Figure 14 is an analogous graph to the previous one, except that it represents the numerical solution of the Boltzmann equation and is carried out to somewhat higher energies. Since it would be numerically

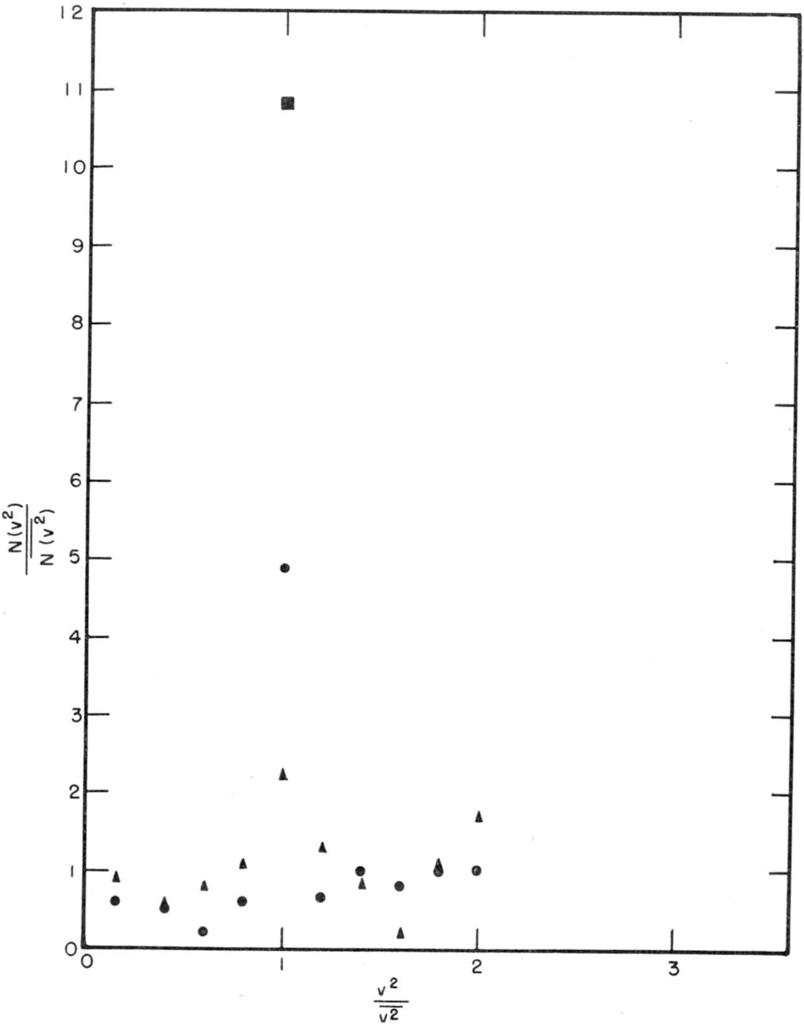

Fig. 13. Decay of the velocity distribution function, $N(v^2)$, with collision number, for a system of 100 hard spheres at 14.14 times the close-packed volume. The square represents the initial distribution, the circles show the distribution in velocity squared, v^2, after 60 collisions, and the triangles after 150 collisions. The number of particles in an interval of velocity squared is divided by the equilibrium number, $\overline{N(v^2)}$, and the velocity squared is normalized by dividing by the mean velocity squared, $\overline{v^2}$.

difficult to start out with a very peaked distribution in velocity, a somewhat broadened distribution was chosen as represented by the top curve in Figure 14. Successive curves downward are, respectively, after

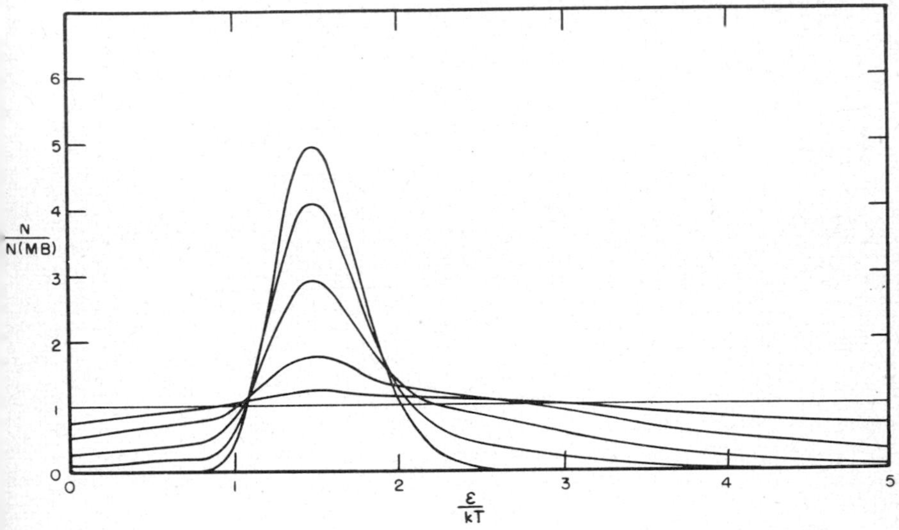

Fig. 14. Solution of the Boltzmann equation for decay of the velocity distribution function. The number of particles at any energy divided by the Maxwell-Boltzmann number, N/N (M.B.), is plotted against the corresponding energy, ε/kT. The most peaked curve represents the initial distribution and in order of height of peak the distribution functions correspond to an ellapse of 0.281, 0.846, 1.974, and 3.666 mean collision times.

0.281, 0.846, 1.974, and 3.666 mean collision times. Hence again in about 4 mean collision times the distribution is very close to the equilibrium one.

Figure 15 makes a direct comparison between the 100 particle system and the solution of the Boltzmann equation for the decay of the energy peak at a density corresponding to $v/v_0 = 32$. The 100 particle system is shown as starting after forty collisions when the peak of the distribution has roughly the same height as the initial peak in the case solved in the Boltzmann equation. The decays agree quite well. If, however, the time scale is changed by the factor Y, as called for by the Enskog theory, agreement is improved (left-hand solid line).

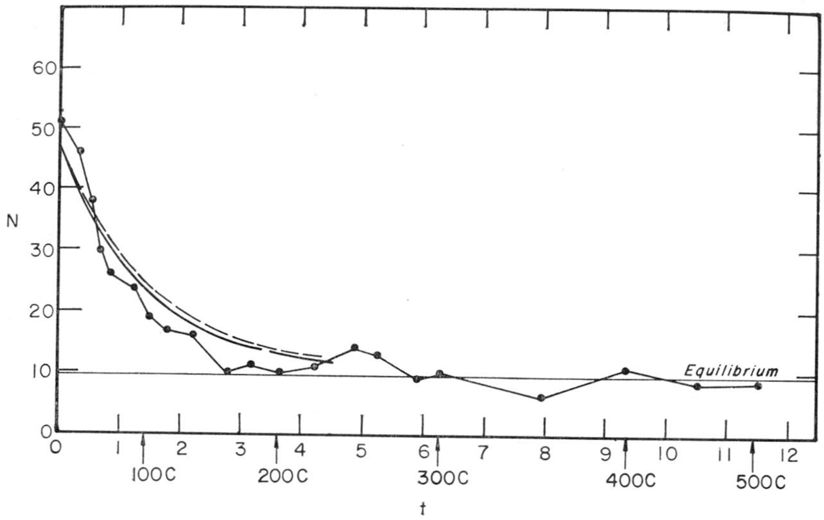

Fig. 15. Comparison of the 100 particle system at $v/v_0 = 32$ with the solution of the Boltzmann equation (dashed line) for the decay of the peak of the velocity distribution function. The left-hand smooth solid line represents the Enskog modification and the horizontal line represents the equilibrium number of particles in the velocity interval chosen.

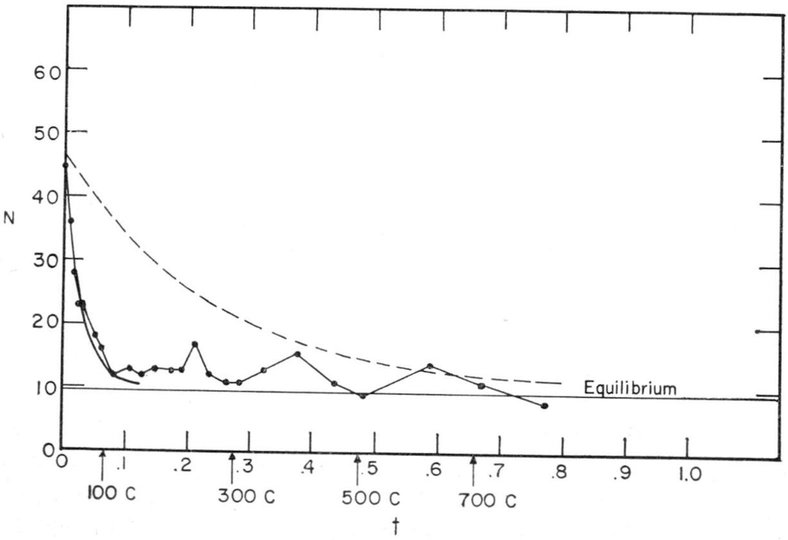

Fig. 16. As in Fig. 15 except $v/v_0 = 1.767$.

Figure 16 shows this up better, since the correction for this higher density situation, ($v/v_0 = 1.767$) is even larger. This again shows the general validity of the Enskog model.

Once the distribution in velocities has been determined it is an easy matter to evaluate the H-function:

$$H = \int f(v) \ln f(v)\, dv = \sum_{i=1}^{N} n_i(v^2) \ln \frac{n_i(v^2)}{4\pi v_i^2 \Delta v_i}, \tag{13}$$

where $n_i(v^2)$ is the number of particles whose velocity squared is in the

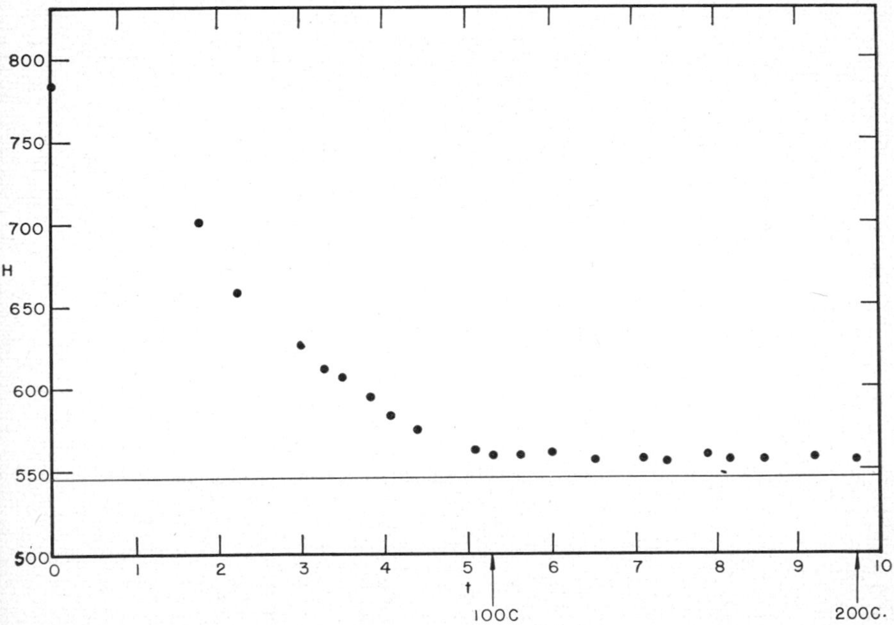

Fig. 17. Behavior of the Boltzmann H-function with time, t, or collision number, C, for 100 hard spheres at $v/v_0 = 14.14$. The horizontal line represents the equilibrium H value.

interval Δv_i. Figure 17 shows the rapid monotonic decrease of this H-function for a system of 100 hard sphere particles at $v/v_0 = 14.14$ from an initial condition where all the velocities squared were the same. The horizontal line in Figure 17 represents the equilibrium value (544.6) in the arbitrary units employed, that is, the H which would be calculated if the Maxwell-Boltzmann velocity distribution were substituted in

Eq. (13). It can be easily demonstrated that the reason the H calculated for the 100 particle system levels out somewhat higher than the equilibrium value is that no high energy particles exist. That is if it is assumed that the equilibrium distribution is a Maxwell-Boltzmann one with the high energy tail cut off at 4 or 5 times the mean energy, the H function should level out in the neighborhood of the value found in Figure 17. Table IV shows at what collision number the H-function reaches its equilibrium value for 100 hard spheres as a function of density. It is seen that the H-function assumes the equilibrium value rapidly and monotonically in about 2 to 4 mean collision times independent of the density of the hard sphere system.

TABLE IV

Collision Number at Which H-Function Reaches Equilibrium Value

v/v_0	Collision Number
86	110
14.14	190
2.72	130
1.77	110
1.35	100

The H-function for the square-well potential case behaves quite differently, as can be seen from Table V. In that table the H-function is compared with the number of overlaps at a density of $v/v_0 = 5$ and $T^* = 0.9$. From the number of overlaps at any given time, it is possible to calculate the kinetic energy and hence a temperature which might be called the instantaneous equilibrium temperature. $\bar{H}$ there refers to the value of the H-function which corresponds to this temperature. The interesting thing that can be observed from Table V is that the velocity distribution, initially peaked at one velocity, again reaches a Maxwell-Boltzmann distribution after about 150 collisions, but that thereafter the mean of this Maxwell-Boltzmann velocity distribution shifts to its final equilibrium value in about 3000 collisions. Again the H-function decreases monotonically, but this cannot be expected to be always true for molecules with attractive potentials. The final equilibrium value is reached only after many more mean collisions per particle than in the hard sphere case; the reason seems to be that the spatial distribution of molecules is slow to come to equilibrium. This has no effect on the temperature for hard sphere molecules but does affect the temperature for molecules with attractive potentials.

TABLE V

The H-Function for Molecules with Square-Well Potentials at $v/v_0 = 5$, $T^* = 0.9$

Collision Number	Overlap Number	H	$\bar{H}$*
0	234	677	381
10	234	560	381
20	234	498	381
50	234	423	381
100	233	402	384
150	231	391	390
200	228	400	400
250	233	385	384
300	240	367	364
350	249	334	342
400	257	324	324
500	261	312	316
600	268	299	303
800	271	293	298
1000	281	287	282
1500	301	242	254
3400	314	227	238
3800	322	225	229
4200	337	204	213
4600	344	200	207
5000	319	222	232

* $\bar{H}$ is the H-function evaluated under the assumption of the existence of an instantaneous temperature.

To show the variety of problems that can be studied by this technique, Figure 18 is presented. This represents a system of 100 hard sphere molecules at $v/v_0 = 2.06$ initially packed tightly in a small region of the cube. The velocity distribution is initially Maxwellian. The system "explodes" till the spheres uniformly fill the cube at a final density of $v/v_0 = 445$. By evaluating Σ as a function of time (Eq. 5) the "dynamic" pressure can be evaluated. Figure 18 shows how the collision rate and Σ change as a function of time from which it would be possible to evaluate the instantaneous pressure of the system. The slopes of the solid lines represent, respectively, the equilibrium value

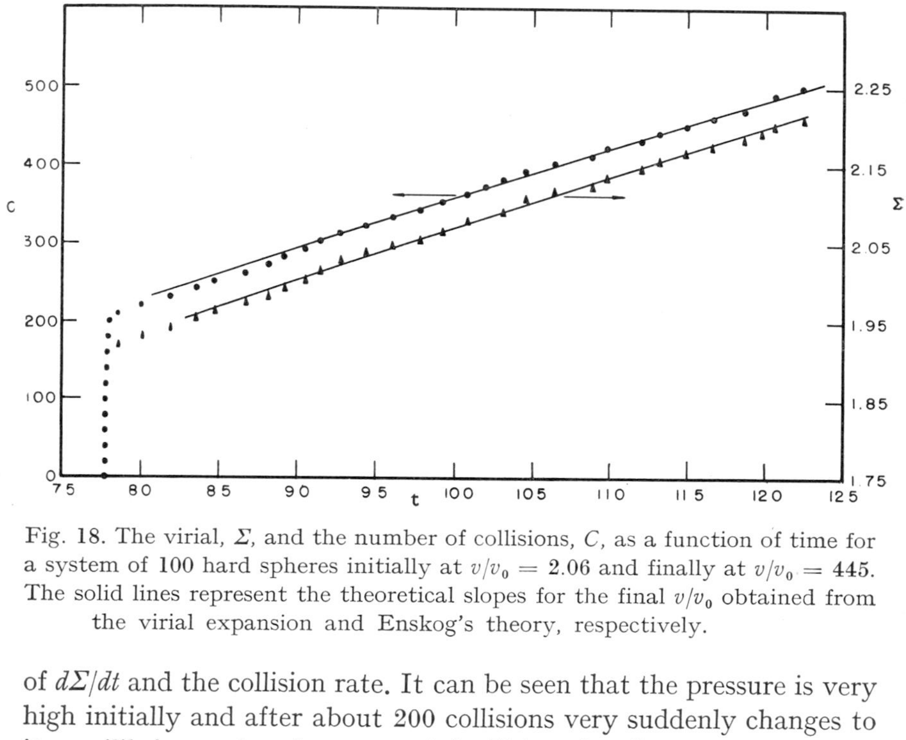

Fig. 18. The virial, Σ, and the number of collisions, C, as a function of time for a system of 100 hard spheres initially at $v/v_0 = 2.06$ and finally at $v/v_0 = 445$. The solid lines represent the theoretical slopes for the final v/v_0 obtained from the virial expansion and Enskog's theory, respectively.

of $d\Sigma/dt$ and the collision rate. It can be seen that the pressure is very high initially and after about 200 collisions very suddenly changes to its equilibrium value. As expected the H-function did not change at all, since the initial Maxwell-Boltzmann distribution was maintained during the explosion; however, it is clear that the entropy is changed. A picture similar to Figure 10 was obtained when the initial velocity distribution was peaked about the root-mean-square value and the system allowed to explode. In this case the H-function reached its equilibrium value after 3 or 4 mean collision times. Finally, a hard sphere system which had reached equilibrium was suddenly changed in density (by changing the sphere diameter). The pressure changed almost instantaneously and the H-function remained unchanged.

We wish to thank the computing group for the tremendous cooperation they have given us and in particular Dr. Sidney Fernbach for generously making machine time available. Only the extremely competent help of Shirley Campbell on the 704, Leota Barr and Douglas Gardner on the Univac, and Ramon Moore and Donald Freeman in the machine solution of the Boltzmann equation made it possible to make any progress at all in this problem.

References

(1) B. R. A. Nijboer and L. Van Hove, *Phys. Rev.*, **85**, 777 (1952).

(2) (a) J. E. Lennard-Jones and A. F. Devonshire, *Proc. Roy. Soc. (London)*, A **163**, 53 (1937).

(b) R.J. Buehler, R. H. Wentorf, J. O. Hirschfelder, and C. F. Curtiss, *J. Chem. Phys.*, **19**, 61 (1951).

(3) (a) S. Chapman and T. G. Cowling, *The Mathematical Theory of Non-uniform Gases*, Cambridge University Press, London, 1939.

(b) J. O. Hirschfelder, C. F. Curtiss, and R. B. Bird, *Molecular Theory of Gases and Liquids*, Wiley, New York, 1954.

(4) D. Enskog, *Kgl. Svenska Vetenskapsakad. Handl.*, **64**, No. 4 (1922), or ref. 3b, Chapter 16.

(5) J. de Boer, *Physica*, **20**, 655 (1954); **21**, 137 (1955).

(6) J. G. Kirkwood, *J. Chem. Phys.*, **14**, 180 (1946).

(7) (a) J. G. Kirkwood, *J. Chem. Phys.*, **3**, 300 (1935).

(b) J. G. Kirkwood, E. K. Maun, and B. J. Alder, *J. Chem. Phys.*, **18**, 1040 (1950).

(c) J. G. Kirkwood, V. A. Lewinson, and B. J. Alder, *J. Chem. Phys.*, **20**, 929 (1952).

(8) M. Born and H. S. Green, *Proc. Roy. Soc. (London)*, A **188**, 10 (1946).

(9) J. Yvon, *Actualitiés Scientifiques et Industrielles*, Hermann, Paris, 1935, p. 203.

(10) J. E. Mayer, *J. Chem. Phys.*, **15**, 187 (1947).

(11) M. Born and H. S. Green, *A General Kinetic Theory of Liquids*, Cambridge Univ. Press, London, 1949.

(12) B. J. Alder, S. P. Frankel, and V. A. Lewinson, *J. Chem. Phys.*, **23**, 417 (1955).

(13) N. Metropolis, A. W. Rosenbluth, M. N. Rosenbluth, A. H. Teller, and E. Teller, *J. Chem. Phys.*, **21**, 1087 (1953).

(14) M. N. Rosenbluth and A. W. Rosenbluth, *J. Chem. Phys.*, **22**, 881 (1954).

ÉQUIVALENCE PHYSIQUE ENTRE LA LOI DE L'ENTROPIE CROISSANTE ET LE PRINCIPE DES ACTIONS RETARDÉES

O. COSTA DE BEAUREGARD, *Institut Henri Poincaré, Paris, France*

Il n'y a peut être pas un seul traité de mécanique statistique qui ne contienne une discussion du paradoxe de Loschmidt; les arguments avancés, tous apparentés entre eux, font intervenir l'inévitable interaction du système considéré avec le reste du cosmos, ou bien avec l'appareillage expérimental; il apparaît en tous cas que la réponse convenable à l'argument de Loschmidt est d'ordre non pas technique, mais épistémologique.

Il en va de même sur le point suivant: on laisse entendre souvent qu'en statistique classique la probabilité s'introduit seulement à la faveur de notre ignorance des paramètres fins, ou de notre incapacité à calculer explicitement avec un nombre immense de variables. Cette affirmation est certainement incomplète, car les distributions statistiques de la thermodynamique sont objectivées comme des fréquences, et leur explication ne peut donc pas reposer uniquement sur un argument subjectif. C'est pourquoi la Cybernétique, précisant cette idée classique sous la forme que l'entropie mesure notre défaut d'information sur un système, ajoute avec L. Brillouin[3] la distinction entre "information liée" aux définitions thermodynamiques et "information libre." Quand le vent disperse un tas de sable, ce ne sera pas de savoir très exactement d'où vient et où va chaque grain qui empêchera le tas d'être dispersé. Nous retrouvons ainsi l'ancienne conclusion de Poincaré:[6] "il faut bien que le hasard soit autre chose que le nom donné à notre ignorance."

Nous voulons aujourd'hui revenir en épistémologue sur ces problèmes, en nous excusant auprès des éminents spécialistes ici rassemblés du fait que nous n'avons jamais apporté aucune contribution technique à la mécanique statistique.

Prenons l'exemple, simple, mais instructif, des petites planètes de Poincaré. Soient a le moyen mouvement et b la longitude initiale d'une petite planète, $f(a, b)$ la densité de distribution attachée à l'intervalle $da\, db$; quelle que soit f supposée simplement continue,

$$C(t) \equiv \iint e^{i(at+b)} f(a, b)\, da\, db \rightarrow 0,$$

quand $t \rightarrow +\infty$; ainsi, sous des conditions très larges, et quelle que soit, par exemple, la loi de l'explosion initiale d'une grosse planète, la distribution actuelle, statistiquement uniforme, des petites planètes, se trouve expliquée. Mais, si $t \rightarrow -\infty$, $C(t) \rightarrow 0$ de la même manière; devrons-nous conclure de là que la grosse planète observée à l'instant *zéro* est née du rassemblement d'un essaim homogène de petites planètes existant dans un lointain passé?

Ce n'est pas exactement là l'argument de Loschmidt, mais c'est un paradoxe philosophiquement équivalent, et qui se retrouve tel quel dans les déductions les plus élaborées du "théorème *H*." Le seul et unique moyen d'éluder ce paradoxe est de *poser en principe* qu'il est permis d'appliquer la mécanique statistique en prédiction, mais qu'il est interdit de l'appliquer "aveuglément"[7] en rétrodiction. L'on ne fait ainsi que retrouver un trait bien connu du calcul élémentaire des probabilités: pour traiter de manière physiquement satisfaisante un problème de probabilité des causes, il faut se donner, en plus de la dynamique interne du problème considéré, un ensemble extrinsèquement choisi de probabilités *a priori*. Autrement dit, dans les problèmes de rétrodiction, il est indispensable de considérer l'interaction du phénomène étudié avec le reste du cosmos.

C'est à la même conclusion qu'aboutissent les discussions du paradoxe de Loschmidt par MM. Borel[2] et Paul Lévy,[5] pour ne citer que des auteurs récents. L'expérience montre qu'une configuration hétérogène n'apparaît jamais dans l'évolution naturelle d'un système isolé, mais toujours comme le résultat de l'interaction momentanée de ce système avec un autre système. De là se déduisent 1° une loi physique et 2° une interprétation épistémologique.

La loi physique est que, statistiquement parlant, l'interaction momentanée de deux systèmes antérieurement et postérieurement séparés, exerce sur chacun d'eux un effet totalement retardé, à l'exclusion de tout effet avancé: quand une météorite traverse l'atmosphère terrestre, elle y perd de l'énergie cinétique et y engendre une onde balistique retardée; elle n'y efface pas une onde balistique avancée dont elle cueillerait l'énergie. L'interprétation épistémologique est qu'aucun système partiel un peu complexe n'est suffisamment isolé pour que son évolution, de droit symétrique entre avenir et passé, ne soit en fait contaminée par celle de la totalité du cosmos.

En effet, la loi des actions retardées, pour deux systèmes dont l'interaction devient tout à coup très forte, se déduit à son tour du principe de l'équipartition de l'énergie cinétique pour l'ensemble des deux systèmes; de chaînon en chaînon, nous sommes ainsi reconduits jusqu'à l'évolution du tout du cosmos.

Mais, puisque la mécanique statistique classique déduit ainsi *physiquement* la loi de l'entropie croissante du principe des actions retardées, ne pourrait-on réciproquement rechercher si d'autres formes de la loi des actions retardées, par exemple celle de la théorie des ondes macroscopiques de l'électromagnétisme ou de la mécanique ondulatoire, ne pourraient pas être déduites du principe de l'entropie croissante? Ceci s'avère effectivement possible à la condition de faire intervenir le dualisme ondes-corpuscules de la mécanique ondulatoire.[4] L'on peut s'en assurer sur des exemples simples, comme celui de la diffraction par un réseau, ou celui de l'émission-absorption de photons par un collectif d'atomes identiques enfermés dans une enceinte rigoureusement adiabatique; ce dernier problème est en somme celui de la tendance vers un équilibre entre deux phases („matière" et „rayonnement"); l'étude correspondante, et également celle du déplacement de l'équilibre par augmentation du volume de l'enceinte, équivalent à une déduction de la loi des ondes électromagnétiques retardées à partir du principe de la tendance vers l'entropie maxima.

Nous considérons donc que le principe des actions retardées est de nature essentiellement statistique, et qu'il n'est pas substantiellement différent du principe de l'entropie croissante; l'un quelconque de ces deux principes peut être déduit de l'autre. Pour le phénomène élémentaire, classique aussi bien que quantique, il n'y a pas de principe des actions retardées.

L'explication de la flèche universelle de l'irréversibilité est donc à chercher non dans l'élémentaire, mais dans le global. Là se présente un redoutable problème épistémologique, car, si l'on considère qu'il est impossible en fait qu'un jeu de cartes trouvé en ordre résulte d'un battage aveugle, ou qu'une grosse planète soit née du rassemblement d'un essaim homogène de petites planètes, comment justifiera-t'on la production d'un „état initial" très hétérogène du tout du cosmos, d'où tous les équilibres métastables que nous voyons exploser tour à tour, et tous les chocs subits de systèmes antérieurement et postérieurement séparés, procèdent sans aucune exception?

Comme le disait déjà Boltzmann,[1] le problème de savoir pourquoi le temps coule dans le sens qui fait apparaître les entropies comme croissantes et les actions comme retardées n'est pas un problème de mécanique objective; c'est un problème d'adaption de la vie et de la conscience au cosmos objectif. La vérité de cette assertion est plus manifeste encore depuis la constitution des théories relativistes, où l'espace-temps est un bloc indivisible. Peut-on rechercher un principe en vertu duquel le temps de la conscience et de la vie doit explorer dans le sens descendant la courbe de la néguentropie universelle?

Il ressort des analyses de M. Léon Brillouin[3] que toute information d'origine expérimentale est acquise au prix d'une dépense plus grande de néguentropie. Le principe dont nous avions besoin peut donc être énoncé comme un principe de recherche de l'information (liée ou libre) d'origine expérimentale, par les organismes vivants.

Reférences

(1) L. Boltzmann, *Vorlesungen über Gas theorie*, Leipzig, 1896, Ch. 7, § 89—90.
(2) E. Borel, Mécanique statistique classique, Paris, 1925, Ch. 3.
(3) L. Brillouin, *Science and Information Theory*, Academic Press, New York, 1956.
(4) O. Costa de Beauregard, *Théorie synthétique de la Relativité restreinte et des Quanta*, Paris, 1957, § VIII. 5 et Ch. XIII.
(5) P. Lévy, *Calcul des Probabilités*, Paris, 1925.
(6) H. Poincaré, *Calcul des Probabilités*, Paris, 1912, Ch. 7, § 93.
(7) S. Watanabé, *Reviews of Modern Physics*, **27**, 26 (1955).

Discussion IV

H. L. Frisch (*to B. Alder*): It appears almost possible now to obtain explicit results by machine computation for certain pressing problems in high-speed aerodynamics and boundary layer behavior. To what extent can one hope to see such calculations realized in the near future?

B. Alder: The problem of deriving hydrodynamics by such calculations very probably awaits the development of still larger computing equipment where a larger number of molecules can be dealt with, although some preliminary investigations are planned to see what can be learned with present facilities.

D. K. C. MacDonald (*to H. C. Longuet-Higgins*): (1) Am I right in concluding that $K \to 0$ for an ideal gas in Professor Longuet-Higgins' analysis? (2) Is not the singularity in the rate of entropy production in this problem of infinitely rapid collisions at $t = 0$ analogous to the situation in Brownian movement if we neglect entirely the inertia of the system? In that case, the autocorrelation function shows a precisely similar cusp at the origin, which is removed as soon as we admit the mass of the particle as nonvanishing.

H. C. Longuet-Higgins (*to D. C. K. MacDonald*): (1) Yes; the pair distribution function postulated would give a zero thermal conductivity at low densities. (2) I would suggest that in the theory of Brownian motion one makes no attempt at evaluating the velocity autocorrelation function for times of the order of the collision time. The whole theory depends on the assumption that the fluctuating force $A(t)$ is randomized in a time of order β^{-1}. I have not seen any discussion of the autocorrelation function at times $t \to +0$.

R. Brout: It is possible to justify the assumed initial distribution of Professor Longuet-Higgins in the case of thermal conductivity of crystals. If the system is characterized by small local inhomogeneities in all quantities but the temperature, the work of Prigogine and collaborators (*Physica,* 1954, 1955) shows that the system in very short time tends to the posed distribution of Longuet-Higgins. One may say that the system is prepared by the free propagation of phonons.

J. L. Lebowitz (*to H. C. Longuet-Higgins*): What expression did you use for the entropy? Was it $\int f_n \ln f_n d\tau$? Why should the entropy be a maximum for a nonequilibrium state?

H. C. Longuet-Higgins (*to J. L. Lebowitz*): The maximization of $-k\int f^{(N)} \ln f^{(N)} d\tau$ subject to specified expectation values of the O_μ, is suggested by the same considerations as those that apply to an equilibrium ensemble. The crucial premise is that the *a priori* probabilities associated with cells of equal volume in phase space are equal.

G. Careri (*to H. C. Longuet-Higgins*): How does your expression of the diffusion coefficient describe the behavior of simple liquids?

H. C. Longuet-Higgins (*to G. Careri*): Insofar as experimental data is available, the present theorem appears to apply reasonably well to monoatomic fluids, provided that P is replaced by $T(\partial P/\partial T)_V$ in χ. Our formulae are not very different from those of Enskog (they are probably rather less accurate) and Enskog's theory has been verified with remarkable accuracy. Our expression for D_{12} is, in fact, identical with that of Enskog.

I. Prigogine (*to H. C. Longuet-Higgins*): I think that in general besides the classical effects considered in the interesting paper by Longuet-Higgins, quantum effects will also play an important role in the liquid state for mixtures of molecules of the same size and same intermolecular forces but different masses. This will perhaps make the verification of his theory rather difficult.

H. C. Longuet-Higgins (*to I. Prigogine*): It would be very interesting to compare the magnitudes of the classical and quantum contributions to thermal diffusion. Here all one can say without such a comparison is that, for a given high density, the quantum effects will become less and less important as the temperature is raised or as the particle masses are increased.

R. Brout (*to J. G. Kirkwood and H. C. Longuet-Higgins*): Is the use of the equilibrium distribution function in connection with the Enskog theory of dense gases justifiable? As $g(r, t)$ is a function which changes with time, this would at first seem doubtful. However, the calculations of Alder seem to confirm the approximation. Also, what can one say about the persistence of the assumed initial velocity distributions in the work of Professor Longuet-Higgins?

H. C. Longuet-Higgins (*to R. Brout*): (1) There is no obvious reason why $g(r, t)$ should not change with time; however, the success of Enskog's theory suggests that the configurational distribution in disequilibrium is exceedingly close to that in equilibrium. It would be very interesting to have some further light on this question from the theoretical angle. (2) There can be no doubt that the initial velocity distributions which we postulated cannot persist; however, the changes which then undergo will probably not affect the order of magnitude of the fluxes considered as functions of time from $t = 0$ and to the time required for steady decay to be established.

R. Brout (*to D. C. K. MacDonald*): One can formulate the problem of thermal conductivity in solids in a rather detailed fashion. Consider that the crystal can be divided into cells each of which contains a statistical number of atoms, over which the temperature and all other measurable quantities are uniform. As stressed by Professor Prigogine, in such a situation it is permissible to use the description of irreversible evolution (dissipation) as given by a phase-independent distribution and add this to the free propagation of phonons due to the harmonic forces. Characteristic of the harmonic equations of motion are certain invariants of the motion. These are the normal mode energies or certain combinations of them. One such combination is the heat flow. Heat flow is an invariant of the harmonic system of motion. This is destroyed by the anharmonic forces. For simplicity consider the one-dimensional case. Let y_{2n} = intermolecular separation distance and y_{2n+1} = velocity of nth atom. Then $I_\nu = \sum_\nu y_n y_{n+\nu}$ are invariants in the harmonic system. I_1 is the heat flow. Near equilibrium for well-prepared crystals one can show that the following equations are (in reduced dimension)

$$dI_\nu/dt = \sum_\mu \lambda_{\nu\mu} I_\mu + \delta_{1\nu} \text{ (grad } T), \; \nu \neq 0, \; \lambda_{\mu\nu} = \lambda_{\nu\mu}. \tag{1}$$

The first of these equations shows how the heat flow changes due to the harmonic propagation of the gradient as well as anharmonic decay. This term only arises from the boundary flows in and out of our cell. In the quasi-stationary state or local equilibrium in a cell, the time-dependence in Eq. (1) is zero. In this case one arrives at the Fourier heat law

$$I_1 = (\Lambda^{-1})_{11} \nabla T \tag{2}$$

where $(\Lambda^{-1})_{11}$ is the element of the inverse of the matrix formed by $\lambda_{\mu\nu}$. These results are easily generalized to three dimensions.

J. G. Kirkwood (*to R. Brout*): Does a one-dimensional crystal have a finite thermal conductivity?

R. Brout: When one takes the one-dimensional lattice with nearest neighbor in harmonic and cubic coupling, development of the cubic term in terms of the zeroth order solution, which are Bessel functions, leads to no change in the heat flow. On the other hand, for three-dimensional discrete structures, where Umklapp processes occur, it is possible to extend the Poincaré theorem and so prove that cubic coupling insures the uniqueness of the energy invariant (that is to say such systems are ergodic). In this context, it turns out that the selection rules in phonon collisions in the one-dimensional case are too demanding and Poincaré's theorem does not go through.

D. C. K. MacDonald (*to I. Prigogine*): When one sets up the thermal conductivity problem as a steady-state situation (i.e., assuming the continued existence of *external* heat reservoirs), it is a bit difficult to see just how the two time scales should be specifically introduced.

I. Prigogine (*to D. C. K. MacDonald*): In problems involving stationary nonequilibrium situations one has often to consider an intermediate time scale. Let us consider, for example, a small system (i.e., a small wire) between two large heat reservoirs at well-defined temperatures. We consider that the whole system (the two reservoirs + the small system) is isolated. After some rather short time the small system will be in a quasi-stationary state. However, the temperatures of the two reservoirs are also slowly changing. For sufficiently long times the whole system will reach thermal equilibrium. We may therefore only hope to have a stationary nonequilibrium situation over times which are neither too short nor too long. This corresponds precisely to the intermediate time scale.

D. ter Haar: In connection with Dr. MacDonald's talk it may be of interest to mention the results of some experiments in progress at the Clarendon Laboratory. Dr. R. W. Hill and Schmidmesser have measured the heat conductivity of solid hydrogen of different ortho-para ratios between 2° and 14° K. They found maxima in the heat conductivity curves at temperatures between 1/20 and 1/10 of the Debye temperature and that the thermal conductivity depends strongly on the amounts of minority isotope present. For isotopically very pure material the thermal conductivity follows closely the Peierls Umklapp law, while in materials with two isotopes of about the same abundance impurity scattering determines the thermal conductivity.

PART V

THE AUTOCORRELATION FUNCTION OF THE INTERMOLECULAR FORCES

R. EISENSCHITZ and R. E. TURNER, *Queen Mary College, University of London, England*

I. RANDOM EVENTS IN LIQUIDS

The irreversible approach of macrophysical systems to thermal equilibrium can, according to our present knowledge, be deduced from the reversible classical or quantum mechanics of molecules if the change in time in a degree of freedom can be broken up into a time series of random events. Collisions between gas molecules are events of this kind; so are all processes which are within the range of validity of quantum mechanical theory of perturbations. The resonance of anharmonically coupled elastic waves in crystals gives rise to similar events.

None of these processes is of any significance in the molecular dynamics of the liquid state. The search for alternative processes was previously the principal subject in the kinetic theory of the liquid state and did not lead to any conclusive results. Kirkwood[2] showed that this problem could be by-passed by assuming that the temporal autocorrelation function of intermolecular forces vanishes after a short but finite time interval. The time integral of the autocorrelation function will then become independent of the upper limit of integration; it plays the part of a friction constant thus insuring the irreversible character of the macroscopic processes involved.

If, in particular, the random relative movement of a pair of molecules (labeled 1 and 2) can be considered to be independent of the movement of their center of gravity the friction constant is equal to

$$\gamma = (2/3mkT) \langle \int_{-\tau}^{0} \mathbf{F}_1'(\mathbf{t}) \cdot \mathbf{F}_{12}'(t+t')\, dt' \rangle, \qquad (1)$$

where τ is a time constant and

$$\mathbf{F}_{12}' = \tfrac{1}{2} \sum_{j=3} (\mathbf{F}_{1j} - \mathbf{F}_{2j})$$

is the indirect force between these two molecules. In the last expression

$\mathbf{F}_{jl}$ is the force between two isolated molecules labeled j and l. The bracket $\langle\,\rangle$ means ensemble average, which in this case is to be taken with respect to the coordinates and momenta of the molecules labeled 3—N.

Starting again with the search for the significant random events in liquids introduction of any artificial break in the temporal correlations must be avoided. Using a reasonably realistic model for the molecular movement the autocorrelation function (1) should be deduced and shown to have a finite time integral. This problem seems to be out of the reach of the traditional methods of analytical mechanics.

Although this paper deals essentially with classical mechanics of molecules it should be pointed out that the same problems arise in the statistical quantum mechanics of irreversible processes (cf. ref. 1).

II. EXPANSION PROCEDURES

A direct and accurate procedure for solving the mechanical equations of motion is expansion in powers of the time of a coordinate or a small number of coordinates. This would be followed by taking the average of the expansion coefficients in an equilibrium ensemble. The resulting power series is supposed to vanish for a fairly wide range of the independent variable; this is obviously possible only if a large number of terms of the series is known. Considering the fact that a molecule is in simultaneous interaction with approximately 10 neighbors it might be expected that a series up to the 30th power is sufficient. Even if this estimate is too high, the procedure appears to be impracticable.

Chances for a solution in terms of Fourier series are better, in spite of the fact that molecular movement in liquids is not multiply periodic. The Fourier series may be approximately represented by an integral; the time integration in (1) can then be extended to infinite limits. In the present paper an attempt is made to apply the theorem of Wiener and Khinchine to the calculation of autocorrelation functions of intermolecular forces. Let $y(t)$ be a function of the time; the "spectral density" is then defined as

$$z(\nu) = \lim_{\Theta\to\infty} (2/\Theta) \left| \int_{-\Theta/2}^{\Theta/2} y(t) \exp(-2\pi i\nu t)\, dt \right|^2 \tag{2}$$

and the following theorems have been proved:

$$\lim_{\Theta\to\infty} (1/\Theta) \int_{-\Theta/2}^{\Theta/2} |y(t)|^2 \, dt = \int_0^\infty z(\nu) \, d\nu, \tag{3}$$

$$\begin{aligned} \Xi(\tau) &= \lim_{\Theta\to\infty} (1/\Theta) \int_{-\Theta/2}^{\Theta/2} y(t+\tau)\, y(t) \, dt \\ &= \int_0^\infty z(\nu) \cos 2\pi\nu\tau \, d\nu. \end{aligned} \tag{4}$$

The expression on the left-hand side is called the autocorrelation function and resembles the integrand in (1). Ignoring at the present stage the difference between a time and an ensemble average the time integral of (3) should be proportional to the friction constant. In calculating the time integral use can be made of a relation which was derived by Suddaby[4]

$$\int_0^\infty \Xi(\tau) \, d\tau = (1/4)\, z(0), \tag{5}$$

showing that the friction constant is determined by the low frequency end of the spectral density.

III. MOVEMENT IN ONE DIMENSION

As a mathematical model consider at first a simple conservative system, i.e., a particle in a one-dimensional field of force. If the particle oscillates about minima of potential energy, its position, velocity, and acceleration are periodic functions of the time and can be represented by a Fourier series, the fundamental period of which depends on the initial conditions. Let the force F be written in the form

$$F = \sum_j [A_j(\omega) \cos j\omega(t-t_0) + B_j(\omega) \sin j\omega(t-t_0).$$

Substituting for the ensemble average of Eq. (1) an average over the initial conditions (conveniently the origin of the time axis and the fundamental period), the time integral of the autocorrelation function becomes

$$\begin{aligned} \alpha &= \int_0^\infty \langle (F(0)\, F(t) \rangle \, dt \\ &= \sum_j \int_{\omega_1}^{\omega_2} g(\omega) \, d\omega \int_0^\infty [a_j \cos j\omega t + b_j \sin j\omega t] \, dt. \end{aligned} \tag{6}$$

In this expression the coefficients a_j depend on the A_j and b_j on the B_j only; $g(\omega)$ is a distribution function for the frequency, which vanishes outside the band $\omega_1 - \omega_2$. It is readily shown that the sin series would make a nonvanishing contribution to α but that, on account of the mechanical equations of motion, the coefficients b_j vanish. The contribution arising from the cos series vanishes unless $\omega_1 = 0$; in this case

$$\alpha = (\pi/2)g(0) \sum_j a_j(0)/j, \tag{7}$$

a result which has a form similar to Eq. (5). It follows that even in a conservative system a dissipative force can arise provided that the initial conditions are indeterminate. The result could, however, not be directly applied to liquids.

IV. MOVEMENT OF A LIQUID MOLECULE RELATIVE TO ITS NEIGHBORS

Consider now a simplified dynamics of a cluster of molecules within a liquid; it is not a conservative system. Let the cluster consist of a "central" molecule which is surrounded by $n-1$ "shell" molecules. The interaction between the central molecule and the shell molecules is derived from the potential of molecular interaction so that it can be expressed as a function of the distance. The shell molecules are, in addition, subject to a fluctuating force which arises from the mutual interaction of the shell molecules and their interaction with molecules outside the cluster. The fluctuating force is not expressed in terms of intermolecular distances but is introduced in the form of an unknown function of the time. It will be attempted to find an approximate expression for the spectral density of this time function.

Because of the assumptions made the equations of motion have the form

$$\tfrac{1}{2}m[d^2(\mathbf{r}_j-\mathbf{r}_1)/dt^2]-\mathbf{F}_{j1} = \mathbf{F}_j^+, \qquad j = 2, 3, \ldots, n, \tag{8}$$

where $\mathbf{F}_j^+$ is the fluctuating force.

It should, on the other hand, be possible to account to the fluctuating force acting on a shell molecule by considering the interaction of the remaining shell molecules with the central molecule. Assuming that these forces accelerate only the relative position and not the centre of gravity of a pair, we have

$$\mathbf{F}_j^+ = \sum_{l \neq j} \mathbf{F}_{l1}. \tag{9}$$

In order to perform all calculations in terms of the spectral density rather than in terms of Fourier transforms it will be assumed that the

$\mathbf{F}_{j1}$ are linear functions of the coordinates of the molecules. This assumption is artificial but simplifies the mathematics appreciably.

Let $\mathbf{r}_j = \mathbf{s}_j + \mathbf{q}_j$ where the first term on the right-hand side denotes the mean positions and where $s_1 = 0$, $s_2 = s_3 = \ldots s_n = s$. Let $q_j/s \ll 1$. The linearised equations of motion have, accordingly, the form

$$\tfrac{1}{2}m[d^2(\mathbf{q}_j - \mathbf{q}_1)/dt^2] + 4\pi^2\nu_0^2 m[\mathbf{s}_j \cdot (\mathbf{q}_j - \mathbf{q}_1)](\mathbf{s}_j/s^2) = \mathbf{F}_j^+, \tag{10}$$

$$\mathbf{F}_j^+ = 4\pi^2 m\nu_0^2 \sum_{l \neq j} [s_l \cdot (\mathbf{q}_l - \mathbf{q}_1)](\mathbf{s}_l/s^2), \tag{11}$$

where ν_0 is the frequency of the oscillations of a pair of isolated molecules about the minimum of intermolecular potential energy.

By Eq. (11) the forces $\mathbf{F}^+$ depend upon the orientation of the vectors $\mathbf{s}_j$, which is conveniently specified in terms of the variables $(\mathbf{s}_j \cdot \mathbf{s}_l/s^2) = \mu_l$. These variables will be eliminated by averaging, whereby it is assumed that the angular distributions of different shell molecules are independent and isotropic. In consequence only the radial components of the force will be taken into account.

By projecting both sides of (11) on the radial direction it follows that

$$\mathbf{F}_j^+ \cdot (\mathbf{s}_j/s) = 4\pi^2 m\nu_0^2 \sum_{l \neq j} [(q_l - q_1) \cdot (\mathbf{s}_l/s)]. \tag{12}$$

In accordance with Eq. (2), the spectral distribution of the two sides of (12) is equated

$$Z(\nu; \ldots \mu_l \ldots) = (4\pi^2 m\nu_0^2)^2 \sum_l [W_l(\nu)\mu_l^2 + \sum_h M_{hl}(\nu)\mu_l\mu_h], \tag{13}$$

where the coefficients W_l and M_{hl} are independent of the μ_l. Averaging with respect to the μ_l results in

$$Z(\nu) = (1/3)(4\pi^2 m\nu_0^2)^2 (n-2) W(\nu), \tag{14}$$

where Z and W are the spectral densities applying after the angular average has been taken. These quantities will be evaluated, whereas the coefficients appearing in Eq. (13) are of minor significance.

The radial component of Eq. (10) is averaged with respect to the μ_l; by taking the spectral distributions of either side it follows that

$$W(\nu) = [(1/4\pi^2 m)^2 (1/(\nu^2 - 2\nu_0^2)^2] Z_s(\nu), \tag{15}$$

where Z_s is the spectral density of the fluctuating force on a shell molecule.

By means of these relations an approximate expression for the spectral distribution of the fluctuating force will be derived.

V. THE FRICTION CONSTANT

The problem of satisfying Eq. (15) and making the mean-square difference of $Z_s - Z$ a minimum

$$\int_0^\infty Z_s(\nu)^2\{[\nu_0^4(n-2)/3(\nu^2-2\nu_0^2)^2]-1\}^2 d\nu = \text{min}, \tag{16}$$

subject to the condition

$$\int_0^\infty Z_s(\nu)\,d\nu = \langle F^{+2}\rangle, \tag{17}$$

has no finite solution. Nevertheless, a relative minimum can be found by substituting in (16) and (17) a test function for $Z(\nu)$ which depends on a number of parameters. In this way an approximation to the spectral density of the fluctuating force is obtained.

In this paper a test function is derived from the spectral density of a harmonic oscillator which, while not damped, is subject to interruptions. The occurrence of the interruptions is a random event and specified by a Poisson distribution. The parameters entering into the test function are related to the frequency of the oscillator, the mean interval between successive interruptions, and the phase shift associated with the interruption. This test function is multiplied by a factor by which the singularities in the integrand of (16) are removed.

The test function has the form

$$Z_s(\nu) = D\left[\frac{1+\beta(\eta-x)}{(\eta-x)^2+\delta^2}+\frac{1+\beta(\eta+x)}{(\eta+x)^2+\delta^2}\right]\left(\frac{x^2-2}{x^2+2}\right), \tag{18}$$

where $x = \nu/\nu_0$ and D, β, δ, and η are parameters. With $n = 9$ the minimum is found to correspond fairly closely to the values

$$\eta = \delta = 1 \qquad \beta = 0 \qquad D = \langle F^{+2}\rangle/(0.914\nu_0\pi).$$

These values of the parameters correspond to a frequency of the oscillator which is equal to $\nu_0\sqrt{2}$, an average time interval of $(1.2\pi\nu_0)^{-1}$ between successive interruptions and a phase shift of $2\pi/3$.

By applying Eq. (5) the friction constant is found to be

$$\gamma = (0.408/2\pi\nu_0)\langle F^{+2}\rangle(1/mkT). \tag{19}$$

By using the spectral density and transforming Eq. (10) the mean-square fluctuating force is obtained as a function of $\langle F_{j1}^2\rangle$ which can be derived from statistical mechanics. In this way it is found that

$$\langle F^{+2} \rangle = 49.9\pi^2 \nu_0^2 mkT,$$

and it follows that

$$\gamma = 9.12\pi\nu_0.$$

Using data for argon, in particular,

$$\nu_0 = 3 \times 10^{10} \text{ sec}^{-1},$$

it follows finally that in liquid argon near the melting point

$$\gamma = 8.56 \times 10^{11} \text{ sec}^{-1}. \tag{20}$$

VI. CONCLUSIONS

As far as the order of magnitude is concerned the result is satisfactory. Kirkwood[2] made an estimate of a friction constant of 43.3×10^{11}; this value is, however, not directly comparable with (20) since it does not refer to the force in relative movement. From a theoretical calculation of the viscosity of liquid argon and comparison with experimental values Orton[3] obtained $\gamma = 2.96 \times 10^{11}$.

The simplified treatment of the dynamics of a cluster is too crude for a scrutiny of the above figures. The present investigation has, however, shown that the method of spectral densities is well applicable to the calculation of the friction constant and will, when further elaborated, yield results of adequate accuracy. In addition it has been shown that the random event in the molecular dynamics of liquids can be associated with the random interruptions of molecular oscillations.

References

(1) R. Eisenschitz, *Phil. Mag.*, **43**, 804 (1952).
(2) J. G. Kirkwood, *J. Chem. Phys.*, **14**, 180 (1946).
(3) B. R. Orton, M. Sc. Thesis, London, 1955.
(4) A. Suddaby, Ph. D. Thesis, London, 1954.

DIFFUSION IN VELOCITY SPACE AND TRANSPORT PHENOMENA

MORIKAZU TODA, *Tokyo University of Education, Japan*

Abstract

This treatment aims at a method for obtaining a rough estimate of the transport coefficients and to clarify the nature of approximations involved in some of the current theories of transport phenomena.

If we assume the well-known formula, due to Langevin, of Brownian motion to be valid for each molecule, we get the equation that gives the rate of change of the distribution function, which is identical with that obtained by Kirkwood in his theory of liquids. In this derivation we are led to the concept of diffusion in velocity or momentum space and its relation to the friction constant.

Langevin's formula implies that the friction constant is independent of both the velocity gradient of mass motion and the temperature gradient. This is a weak point. But to this approximation we obtain the friction constant as a function of molecular force in the case of gases. For degenerate Fermi gas, the circumstance is a little different. In this case, however, we may speak of the diffusion of molecules on the Fermi surface.

I. INTRODUCTION

The purpose of this treatment is to obtain a rough estimate of transport coefficients and clarify the nature of approximations involved in some of the current theories of transport phenomena, as well as to find the relation concerning diffusion in velocity space between the classical Boltzmann case and the case of degenerate Fermi gas.

If we assume the well-known formula of Langevin to be valid down to the Brownian movement of molecules themselves, we can find the equation that governs the rate of change of the distribution function, which is the equation obtained by Kirkwood[1] in his theory of liquid. In this derivation we are led to the concept of diffusion of molecules in velocity space or momentum space and its relation to the friction constant.

In Langevin's formula, the friction constant is independent of both the velocity gradient of mass flow and the temperature gradient. This is certainly a weak point. But to this approximation we can obtain the friction constant as a function of molecular force. A quite natural extension of the theory is obtained by considering the difference of diffusion velocities in each direction, that is to say in the direction of the velocity of the molecule and the direction perpendicular to it. Thus the diffusion coefficient in velocity space is dependent on the direction of diffusion, so that it is a tensor rather than a scalar quantity. With this modification we can see how the diffusion equation in phase space would look in the case of a Fermi system. For degenerate Fermi gas we may speak of diffusion of molecules on the Fermi surface.

II. CLASSICAL STATISTICS

If we assume that the Langevin equation applies to the Brownian motion of each molecule and that the fluctuating force results in the diffusion of molecules in momentum space, we obtain from the Liouville equation the diffusion equation in phase space:

$$\frac{\partial f}{\partial t}+\frac{\mathbf{p}}{m}\cdot\frac{\partial}{\partial \mathbf{r}}f+\frac{\partial}{\partial \mathbf{p}}\cdot(\mathbf{F}f)=\frac{\partial}{\partial \mathbf{p}}\cdot\left\{\zeta\left(\frac{\mathbf{p}}{m}-\mathbf{V}\right)f+\mathbf{D}\cdot\frac{\partial}{\partial \mathbf{p}}f\right\}, \quad (1)$$

where f denotes the single particle distribution function, m the mass of a molecule, $\mathbf{r}$ and $\mathbf{p}$ the position and momentum of a molecule, $\mathbf{F}$ the external force, ζ the friction constant, $\mathbf{V}$ the velocity of mass flow, and $\mathbf{D}$ the diffusion constant in momentum space. In general ζ and $\mathbf{D}$ are functions of the magnitude of the momentum $\mathbf{p}$. Of course they are functions of temperature. And $\mathbf{D}$ will depend on the direction of diffusion and is expressed by a tensor.

At equilibrium f Maxwellian distribution f^0 is assumed, so that the element D_p, connected with the diffusion parallel to momentum $\mathbf{p}$, must satisfy the equation

$$D_p = \zeta kT,$$

whereas the diffusion constant in ordinary space is given by the well-known Einstein relation $D^0 = kT/\zeta$. If we further assume that $\mathbf{D}$ is a scalar quantity equal to D_p, we obtain

$$\zeta kT \sim D \sim \langle \Delta p\rangle^2/\tau,$$

where Δp is the change in momentum during the time interval τ.

A somewhat strange but interesting application of the approximate relation just obtained will be found in the problem of viscosity of liquid.

For a molecular collision in liquid we have $\langle \Delta p \rangle \sim \sqrt{2\pi mkT}$. If ν is the frequency of oscillation of molecules, then $\tau \sim 2/\nu$, so that $\zeta \sim 4\pi m\nu$. If we further make use of Stokes' formula $\zeta = 6\pi a\eta$, where a is the radius of a molecule, one finds for the coefficient of viscosity the relation $\eta \sim (2/3)m\nu/a$, which is nearly identical to the formula due to Andrade.[2]

Application to Gas. For a molecular collision $\langle \Delta p \rangle \sim \sqrt{2\pi mkT}$, and the time interval between successive collisions is $\tau \sim l/v \sim (1/\pi n\sigma^2) \times \sqrt{m/kT}$ where l is the mean free path, v the average speed of molecules, n the number of molecules per unit volume, and σ the diameter of a molecule. The friction constant is thus given by $\zeta = \alpha n a^2 \sqrt{2\pi mkT}$, where α is a constant of the order of unity. Actually, following the method of Lord Rayleigh, M. S. Green[3] had shown that $\alpha = 3/8$ for a heavy particle moving through gas.

To solve Eq. (1) with $D = \zeta kT$, for the gaseous state, we transform, as usual, its left-hand side for the transport phenomena. Thus we have

$$f^0\left\{\frac{1}{kT}\left(p_i u_k - \frac{2}{3}\varepsilon\delta_{ik}\right)\frac{\partial V_k}{\partial x_i} + u_i\left(\frac{\varepsilon}{kT} - \frac{5}{2}\right)\frac{\partial \log T}{\partial x_i}\right\} = -\frac{\partial}{\partial \mathbf{p}}\cdot D\left\{\frac{\mathbf{p}}{mkT} + \frac{\partial}{\partial \mathbf{p}}\right\} f^0\varphi,$$

where we have put $f = f^0(1+\varphi)$, and $u_k = p_k/m$ with $\varepsilon = p^2/2m$. The right-hand side of the above equation can be written in alternative forms, either

$$-\frac{\partial}{\partial \mathbf{p}}\cdot Df^0\frac{\partial}{\partial \mathbf{p}}\varphi \quad \text{or} \quad \frac{\mathbf{p}}{mkT}\cdot f^0 D\frac{\partial}{\partial \mathbf{p}}\varphi - f^0\frac{\partial}{\partial \mathbf{p}}\cdot D\frac{\partial}{\partial \mathbf{p}}\varphi,$$

which are to be compared with the case of degenerate Fermi gas (Section III). We expand the left-hand side of the above equation as

$$f^0 \sum_{nlm} \alpha_{nlm} p^n P_l^m(\cos\theta) \begin{matrix}\sin\\ \cos\end{matrix}\, m\phi$$

and at the same time expand φ as

$$\varphi = \sum_{nlm} \beta_{nlm} p^n P_l^m(\cos\theta) \begin{matrix}\sin\\ \cos\end{matrix}\, m\phi$$

and thus obtain the relation between the coefficients of expansion α and β. For the case of laminar flow in the x-direction with the velocity gradient $G = \partial V_x/\partial z$ along the z-axis, the only coefficient different from zero is $\alpha_{221} = G/mkT$, and then we have $\beta_{221} = -G/2mkTD$. The stress tensor turns out to be

$$T_{zx} = \int f^0 \varphi p_z u_x d^3p = \beta_{221} nm(kT)^2,$$

so that the coefficient of viscosity is given by $\eta = nmkT/2D$.

In the same way for the temperature gradient along the x-axis, $\alpha_{111} = -(5/2)\partial T/\partial x/mT$ and $\alpha_{311} = \partial T/\partial x/2m^2kT^2$. Then $\beta_{111} = (5/2)\partial T/\partial x/DmT$ and $\beta_{311} = -\partial T/\partial x/6Dm^2kT^2$. The heat flow is

$$q_x = kT \int f^0 \varphi \left(\frac{\varepsilon}{kT} - \frac{5}{2}\right) u_x d^3p = -\frac{5nkT(mkT)^2}{m} \beta_{311}.$$

Thus the thermal conductivity $\varkappa$ is given by $\varkappa = (5/6)nk^2T/\zeta$. These values are approximately valid if we insert the above relation between ζ and the temperature.

The value of ζ can be estimated from the relation $\zeta = kT/D^0$, in terms of the coefficient of self-diffusion D^0. One has thus

$$\zeta = \frac{8}{3}\sqrt{\pi}\int_0^\infty g_1^4 e^{-g_1^2} dg_1 \int_0^\pi (1 - \cos^2\theta)\, mgI(g, \theta) \sin\theta \, d\theta,$$

where $g_1 = (m/4kT)^{1/2} g$, g being relative velocity and $I(g, \theta)$ the cross-section. The last equation gives for a hard sphere a slightly different value from that of Green. The difference may be due to the fact that in our case the reduced mass replaces the mass of heavy particle in Green's treatment.

III. FERMI GAS

In the case of Fermi gas the distribution function assumes a Fermi distribution f^0 at equilibrium, so that diffusion parallel to momentum is connected with the friction constant by the relation

$$(1-f^0)D_p = \zeta kT.$$

However, for strongly degenerate Fermi gas, diffusion in momentum space takes place mainly along the Fermi surface. We shall denote the diffusion constant along the Fermi surface by D_S. We may put $D_p \simeq 0$ for degenerate Fermi gas. Then the fundamental equation simplifies itself into

$$\frac{\partial f}{\partial t} + \frac{\mathbf{p}}{m} \cdot \frac{\partial}{\partial \mathbf{r}} f + \frac{\partial}{\partial \mathbf{p}} (\mathbf{F}f) = D_S f^0(1-f^0) \nabla_S^2 \chi, \qquad (2)$$

where we have put

$$f = f^0 + f^0(1-f^0)\chi.$$

The left-hand side of the above equation is for laminar flow,

$$f^0(1-f^0)\frac{m}{kT}\left(\mathbf{uu}-\frac{u^2}{3}\mathbf{1}\right):\frac{\partial \mathbf{V}}{\partial \mathbf{X}},$$

where **u** is the relative velocity of molecule with respect to the mass flow **V**. Or, if the flow has gradient along the z-axis, this term is $f^0(1-f^0)(mu^2/kT)(\partial V_x/\partial z)Y_{21}$, where $Y_{21} = \sin\theta\cos\theta\cos\phi$ with the z-axis as polar axis and angle ϕ being measured from the x-axis. Then we obtain

$$\chi = \frac{P^2}{6D_S}\frac{mv^2}{kT}G,$$

where $P = mv$ is the magnitude of momentum on the Fermi surface and G stands for the velocity gradient of mass flow. After calculating the stress tensor $P_{xz} = m\int fu_x u_z d^3u$, we obtain the coefficient of viscosity

$$\eta = nm^3v^4/60D_S.$$

From the Uhling-Uhlenbeck equation we can verify Eq. (2) for Fermi gas. The right-hand side of this equation is to be replaced by the collision term

$$\left(\frac{\partial f}{\partial t}\right)_c = \int\frac{d\mathbf{p}_1}{h^3}\int gI(g,\theta)\,d\Omega\{f'f_1'(1-f)(1-f_1)-ff_1(1-f')(1-f_1')\},$$

where, as usual, f and f' denote distribution functions before and after collision, suffix 1 stands for the colliding molecule, I is the differential cross-section, g is the relative velocity of collision, Ω is the solid angle of scattering, and $d\mathbf{p}_1$ is the elementary volume in momentum space. With $f = f^0+f^0(1-f^0)\chi$ we have

$$(\partial f/\partial t)_c = \Lambda(\chi_1'-\chi_1+\chi'-\chi),$$

where Λ is an operator defined by

$$\Lambda = \int\frac{d\mathbf{p}_1}{h^3}\int gId\Omega f^0f_1^0(1-f^{0\prime})(1-f_1^{0\prime}).$$

As the collision process takes place only in the vicinity of the Fermi surface and along it, the end points of the momentum vector $\mathbf{p}$, $\mathbf{p}'$, $\mathbf{p}_1$, and $\mathbf{p}_1'$ lie on a circle. The scattering angle θ is the angle between the end points of $\mathbf{p}$ and $\mathbf{p}'$ as observed from the center of this circle. Then

$$\Lambda(\chi'-\chi) = f^0 \int \frac{dS_1}{h^3} \int gI(g, \theta) \sin\theta \, d\theta \int \frac{d\varepsilon_i kT}{\partial E/\partial p} \int \frac{dxkT\partial^2 E/\partial p^2}{(\partial E/\partial p)g/2} \cdot f_1^0(\varepsilon_1)\left(1-f^{0\prime}(\varepsilon-x)\right)\left(1-f_1^0(\varepsilon+x)\right)(\chi'-\chi)$$

with $\varepsilon = (E-E_0)/kT$, $E = P^2/2m$, $E_0 = P^2/2m$; dS stands for the elementary area on the Fermi surface. On the other hand, $\Lambda(\chi_1'-\chi_1)$ is approximately zero. This can be shown by assuming that the scattering angle is so small that $\chi_1'-\chi_1$ can be replaced by $(\partial\chi_1/\partial s)g\sin(\theta/2)$, where s is taken as a circle on the Fermi surface with its center at $\mathbf{p}$. If we integrate first along s keeping θ and g constant, χ_1 returns to its original value and the integral vanishes. Therefore if the scattering angle is small or if the scattering of small angle predominates

$$-\frac{\partial f^0}{\partial \varepsilon}\left(\frac{\partial \chi}{\partial t}\right)_c = \Lambda(\chi'-\chi),$$

where

$$\Lambda(\chi'-\chi) = f^0(\varepsilon) \int \frac{dS_1}{h^3} \int gI(g, \theta) \sin\theta \, d\theta \, \frac{(\partial^2 E/\partial p^2)(kT)^2}{(\partial E/\partial p)^2 g/2} \cdot \int \frac{d\varepsilon_1}{e^{\varepsilon_1}+1} \int \frac{dx}{1-e^{-\varepsilon-\varepsilon_1}} \left\{ \frac{1}{e^{x-\varepsilon}+1} - \frac{1}{e^{x-\varepsilon_1}+1} \right\} (\chi'-\chi).$$

We expand $\chi'-\chi$ in the form

$$\chi'-\chi = \Delta\mathbf{p} \cdot (\nabla\chi) - \tfrac{1}{2}\Delta\mathbf{p}\Delta\mathbf{p} : (\nabla\nabla\chi),$$

where $\Delta\mathbf{p} = \mathbf{p}'-\mathbf{p}$ and ∇ is the gradient operator on the Fermi surface. $(\nabla\chi)$ as well as $(\nabla\nabla\chi)$ stand for the values at $\mathbf{p}$. It can be seen that χ is a complicated function of ε. Integrating with respect to ε we obtain an equation for the averaged value of χ. That is

$$\left(\frac{\partial \chi}{\partial t}\right)_c = D_S \nabla_S^2 \chi,$$

where ∇_S^2 is the Laplacian operator on the Fermi surface ($\nabla_S^2 = \nabla \cdot \nabla$) and with the help of

$$\iint d\varepsilon d\varepsilon_1(\varepsilon+\varepsilon_1)/(e^{\varepsilon}+1)(e^{\varepsilon_1}+1)(1-e^{-(\varepsilon+\varepsilon_1)}) = \tfrac{2}{3}\pi^2$$

we have the diffusion coefficient

$$D_S = \frac{(kT)^2}{h^3}\frac{\pi^3}{12}\frac{m^5}{P^2}\int\int g^3 I(g, \theta) \sin\theta \sin^2\theta \, d\theta \, dg.$$

To see the magnitude of this quantity we may use the hard sphere model, which gives

$$D_S \sim \frac{(kT)^2}{h^3} mP^2\sigma, \qquad \eta \sim \frac{n}{60}\left(\frac{P}{m}\right)^2 \frac{h^3}{(kT)^2\sigma}.$$

The same kind of treatment was carried out for the diffusion of electrons in metals which results in electrical as well as heat resistance.[4]

References

(1) J. G. Kirkwood, *J. Chem. Phys.*, **14**, 180 (1946).
(2) E. N. da C. Andrade, *Phil. Mag.*, **17**, 497 (1934).
(3) M. S. Green, *J. Chem. Phys.*, **20**, 1281 (1952).
(4) M. Toda, *J. Phys. Soc. Japan*, **8**, 339 (1953); **9**, 440 (1954).

RANDOM MOTION OF A HEAVY PARTICLE SUBSTITUTED IN A ONE-DIMENSIONAL CRYSTAL LATTICE

ROBERT J. RUBIN,* *Department of Chemistry and Chemical Engineering, University of Illinois, Urbana, Illinois*

I. INTRODUCTION

In the usual treatment of Brownian motion of a particle, the Brownian particle is assumed to move independently of its surroundings except for (1) a viscous dissipative resistance to its motion which is exerted by the surroundings, and (2) a succession of random forces or impacts which the surroundings exert on the Brownian particle. The equation of motion of the heavy particle is thus assumed to be the Langevin equation

$$dv/d\tau = -\beta v + A(\tau)$$

where v is the velocity of the Brownian particle. The parameter β is the phenomenological "friction" constant which measures the dissipative influence of the surrounding medium on the motion of the heavy particle. The fluctuating force is represented by the function $A(t)$. Starting with the Langevin equation, one can calculate the statistical properties of the motion of the Brownian particle. These statistical properties, such as the velocity correlation function, depend quantitatively on the value of β and the statistical properties of $A(t)$.

In contrast to the usual treatment of Brownian motion, in this paper we shall analyze the solution of the general equations of motion for a particular mechanical system. This mechanical system consists of a single heavy Brownian particle which is coupled to its environment by conservative forces. Starting with the solution of the equations of motion, it is possible to determine the velocity correlation function of the Brownian particle. By comparing the velocity correlation with the one obtained from the Langevin equation, a value of the phenomenological friction constant is obtained.

* Present address: National Bureau of Standards, Washington 25, D. C.

II. THE MECHANICAL SYSTEM

The mechanical system with which we are concerned is a modification of the infinite one-dimensional crystal lattice of identical particles of mass m with harmonic forces between nearest neighbors. The modification is introduced by replacing one of the particles by a particle of arbitrary mass M. We shall later consider the case in which $M > 2m$ for purposes of application. Conceptually, the heavy mass in this mechanical system can be thought of as undergoing a random or Brownian-type motion.

The reason for considering this special system is that the equations of motion for the entire system can be solved explicitly. Thus the motion of the heavy particle can be expressed simply in terms of the initial condition of the entire system. We shall first obtain the solution of the equations of motion of the system in Section III. In Section IV, we shall investigate the statistical properties of the velocity of the "Brownian" particle when the initial velocities and displacements from equilibrium of the light atoms in the crystal are assumed to be independent identically distributed random variables with zero mean value.

III. SOLUTION OF THE DYNAMIC EQUATIONS

The equations of motion of a linear one-dimensional array of particles of mass m with nearest neighbor interactions and with a particle of mass M substituted in the array can be written as

$$\begin{cases} \ddot{x}_r = x_{r+1} - 2x_r + x_{r-1} \\ (Q+1)\ddot{x}_0 = x_1 - 2x_0 + x_{-1} \end{cases}, \quad r = \pm 1, \pm 2, \ldots \qquad (1)$$

where the particle of mass M has been located at the position labeled $r = 0$. A derivative with respect to the time τ is indicated by a dot as $\dot{x}$. The time τ is measured in dimensionless units $\tau = 2\sqrt{k/m}\,t$, where k is the harmonic force constant, and the quantity Q is equal to $(M/m) - 1$. The solution of the equations of motion can be obtained for an arbitrary value of M by generalizing the method used by Schrödinger.[1] If we introduce the variables y_m defined by the relations $y_{2n} = \dot{x}_n$ and $y_{2n+1} = x_n - x_{n+1}$, the equations of motion can be rewritten as

$$\begin{cases} \dot{y}_m = -\tfrac{1}{2}(y_{m+1} - y_{m-1}) \\ (Q+1)\dot{y}_0 = -\tfrac{1}{2}(y_1 - y_{-1}) \end{cases}, \quad m = \pm 1, \pm 2, \ldots \qquad (2)$$

where we have also made use of the derived relation $\dot{y}_{2n+1} = \dot{x}_n - \dot{x}_{n+1}$. If the mth equation in (2) is multiplied by z^m and the resulting set of equations is summed, the following differential equation is obtained for the generating function, $G(z, \tau) = \sum_{-\infty}^{\infty} y_m(\tau) z^m$,

$$Q\dot{y}_0 + \dot{G}(z, \tau) = \frac{1}{2}\left(z - \frac{1}{z}\right) G(z, \tau). \tag{3}$$

The formal solution of this differential equation for $G(z, \tau)$ is

$$G(z, \tau) = -Q\int_0^\tau e^{\frac{1}{2}(\tau-\sigma)\left(z-\frac{1}{z}\right)} \frac{dy_0}{d\sigma} d\sigma + C e^{+\frac{\tau}{2}\left(z-\frac{1}{z}\right)}. \tag{4}$$

In view of the fact that the coefficient of z^m in the power series expansion of $G(z, \tau)$ is $y_m(\tau)$, it is obvious that the expression for $G(z, \tau)$ in Eq. (4) is an integral relation for the various $y_m(\tau)$'s, and the integration constant C is determined by the assumed initial conditions. If it is assumed that

$$y_m(0) = \begin{cases} 1 & \text{if } m = s \\ 0 & \text{if } m \neq s \end{cases}$$

then C has the value z^s.

The coefficient of z^n in Eq. (4) is

$$y_n(\tau) = -Q\int_0^\tau J_n(\tau-\sigma) \frac{dy_0}{d\sigma} d\sigma + J_{n-s}(\tau), \tag{5}$$

and the coefficient of z^0 is

$$y_0(\tau) = -Q\int_0^\tau J_0(\tau-\sigma) \frac{dy_0}{d\sigma} d\sigma + J_{-s}(\tau). \tag{6}$$

Eq. (6), which is an integral equation for $y_0(\tau)$, has the form of a convolution. Thus, if we consider the Laplace transform of Eq. (6), we obtain

$$\eta_0(p) = \frac{\varepsilon_s}{[Qp+\sqrt{1+p^2})][p+\sqrt{1+p^2}]^{|s|}} \tag{7}$$

where $\eta_0(p) = \int_0^\infty e^{-p\tau} y_0(\tau) d\tau$ and $\varepsilon_s = 1$ if $s < 0$ and $\varepsilon_s = (-1)^s$ if $s > 0$. A general solution of the equations of motion (2) may be constructed with the aid of Eq. (7). If the initial values of y_i are denoted by $y_i(0) = a_i$ for $i \neq 0$ and $y_0(0) = 0$, the Laplace transform of the velocity of the particle of mass M is

$$\eta_0(p) = \sum_{n=1}^{\infty} \frac{\varepsilon_n a_n + \varepsilon_{-n} a_{-n}}{[Qp+\sqrt{1+p^2}]\,[p+\sqrt{1+p^2}]^n}. \tag{8}$$

In the discussion in the following section, the a_n's will be assumed to be independent identically distributed random variables with zero mean value.

IV. THE VELOCITY CORRELATION FUNCTION

It is convenient to define the velocity correlation function $g(\tau)$ as

$$g(\tau) = \lim_{\Lambda\to\infty} \frac{1}{\Lambda} \int_0^{\Lambda} y_0^{(\Lambda)}(t)\, y_0^{(\Lambda)}(t+\tau)\, dt \tag{9}$$

where

$$y_0^{(\Lambda)}(\tau) = \mathscr{L}^{-1}\{\eta_0^{(\Lambda)}(p)\},$$

$\mathscr{L}^{-1}\{\}$ denotes the inverse Laplace transform and

$$\eta_0^{(\Lambda)}(p) = \sum_{n=1}^{\Lambda} \frac{\alpha_n}{[Qp+\sqrt{1+p^2}]\,[p+\sqrt{1+p^2}]^n}, \tag{10}$$

where $\alpha_n = \varepsilon_n a_n + \varepsilon_{-n} a_{-n}$. The spectrum $G(\nu)$ is related to the correlation function through the expression

$$g(\tau) = \int_0^{\infty} G(\nu) \cos 2\pi\nu\tau\, d\nu. \tag{11}$$

Since $y_0(\tau)$ has a zero mean value,* the spectrum can also be written as

$$G(\nu) = \lim_{\Lambda\to\infty} \frac{2}{\Lambda} |A(\nu)|^2 \tag{12}$$

where

$$A(\nu) = \int_0^{\infty} y_0^{(\Lambda)}(\tau)\, e^{-2\pi i\nu\tau}\, d\tau. \tag{13}$$

The quantity $A(\nu)$, which is the Fourier transform of $y_0^{(\Lambda)}(\tau)$, is related to the Laplace transform $\eta_0^{(\Lambda)}(p)$ simply as

$$A(\nu) = \eta_0^{(\Lambda)}(2\pi i\nu). \tag{14}$$

* It is also assumed that $y_0(\tau)$ has no periodic components. This assumption will be seen to be valid for $M > 2m$.

It follows therefore that the spectrum can be expressed in terms of the initial velocities α_n as

$$G(\nu) = \lim_{\Lambda\to\infty} \frac{2}{\Lambda} \frac{1}{(Q^2-1)4\pi^2\nu^2+1} \cdot \left\{ \sum_{n=1}^{\Lambda} \alpha_n^2 + 2 \sum_{n>m} \alpha_n \alpha_m (-1)^{n-m} \cos[(2n-2m)\cos^{-1} 2\pi\nu] \right\}. \tag{15}$$

Since the a_n's are assumed to be independent identically distributed random variables, the sums which appear in Eq. (15) have the following limiting values

$$\lim_{\Lambda\to\infty} \left\{ \frac{1}{\Lambda} \sum_{n=1}^{\Lambda} \alpha_n^2 \right\} = 2\overline{a^2} \tag{16}$$

and

$$\lim_{\Lambda\to\infty} \left\{ \frac{1}{\Lambda} \sum_{\substack{n-m=\text{const}\\ n>m}} \alpha_n \alpha_m \right\} = 0 \tag{17}$$

where $\overline{a^2}$ is the mean-square value of a_i. If we use the relations (16) and (17), the expression for the spectrum $G(\nu)$ can be written in the simple form

$$G(\nu) = \frac{4\overline{a^2}}{(Q^2-1)4\pi^2\nu^2+1}. \tag{18}$$

The cosine transform of $G(\nu)$ which is equal to the correlation function is only defined if $(Q^2-1)>0$. This condition is equivalent to $M/m>2$. Physically, when $M/m < 2$, the velocity $y_0(\tau)$ has a periodic component. The condition that $M/m > 2$ is analogous to the condition for overdamping in the case of a damped harmonic oscillator. If $M/m> 2$, the correlation function is

$$\begin{aligned} g(\tau) &= \langle y(t)\, y(t+\tau)\rangle \\ &= \frac{\overline{a^2}}{(Q^2-1)^{1/2}} e^{-\tau/(Q^2-1)^{1/2}} \\ &\cong \overline{a^2} \frac{m}{M} e^{-\frac{m}{M}\tau}, \qquad \text{if } M \gg m. \end{aligned} \tag{19}$$

The functional form for the velocity correlation function in Eq. (19) is identical with that obtained from the Langevin equation for a free particle when the random force term is assumed to be completely uncorrelated.

V. DISCUSSION

There are some obvious questions which arise with regard to the general solution of the equations of motion (2). First, what statistical statements can be made concerning the motion of the heavy particle and how do these statements depend quantitatively on the initial conditions and Q? Second, does the velocity $y_0(\tau)$, in some sense, satisfy a Langevin equation? If it does, how are the initial conditions related to the function $A(t)$, and what is the value of the friction constant β?

We have dealt with the first question in Section IV, where we obtained the velocity correlation function for a heavy particle substituted in an otherwise uniform one-dimensional crystal lattice. The correlation function, which is obtained for this system when the initial velocities and displacements are independent identically distributed random variables, is identical in form with the velocity correlation function obtained from the Langevin equation for a free particle when the random force term is assumed to be completely uncorrelated.

With regard to the second question, the results are as yet incomplete. There is good reason to believe that a time-smoothed $y_0(\tau)$ does satisfy a Langevin equation. Recent work[2] has shown that in the continuous limit of the system considered above, namely an infinite elastic string with a mass $\mathscr{M}$ suspended on it, the velocity of the mass $\mathscr{M}$ does indeed satisfy a Langevin equation. The equation of motion of the limiting system is the ordinary wave equation with special boundary conditions at the suspended particle. The general solution of the wave equation can be obtained for arbitrary initial conditions. It can be shown from this general solution that the velocity of the mass $\mathscr{M}$ is such that it satisfies a Langevin equation. The friction constant has the value $a\varrho/\mathscr{M}$ sec^{-1}, where a is the signal velocity and ϱ is the mass per unit length of the string. If we represent the initial conditions in the system by $A(x)$, then the random force term in the Langevin equation is $A(at)$. It therefore seems that similar results can be obtained for a time-smoothed $y_0(\tau)$, especially since the correlation functions in the case of the discrete particle system and the continuous system are identical.

References

(1) E. Schrödinger, *Ann. Physik*, **44**, 916 (1914).
(2) R. J. Rubin, *Bull. Am. Phys. Soc., Ser.* 2, **1**, No. 4, 221 (1956).

A GENERALIZATION OF A PROBLEM OF RAYLEIGH

G. E. UHLENBECK and C. S. WANG CHANG, *The University of Michigan, Ann Arbor, Michigan*

I. INTRODUCTION

I intended to present to you a summary of the work Dr. Chang and I have been doing on the Boltzmann equation, especially with regard to the problem of the transition of the transport phenomena in gases from the Clausius regime (moderately dense gases, mean free path $\ll$ macroscopic dimensions) to the Knudsen regime, where the mean free path is large compared to macroscopic lengths. However, recently we worked out a generalization of a problem of Rayleigh, on which I prefer to speak since it has perhaps more general interest. Allow me therefore to make only a few methodological remarks about my original topic.

(*a*) The well-known Chapman-Enskog successive approximation method starts from the Clausius regime. In first approximation one obtains for the distribution function $f(\mathbf{r}, \mathbf{v}, t)$ a *local* Maxwell distribution depending still on the density ϱ, average velocity $\mathbf{u}$, and temperature T, which in general will be functions of $\mathbf{r}$ and t. The further approximations may be considered to be a development of f in powers of $\lambda\nabla$, where λ is of the order of the mean free path and where the gradient acts on the macroscopic quantities ϱ, $\mathbf{u}$, T. These successive approximations of $f(\mathbf{r}, \mathbf{v}, t)$ lead to hydrodynamic equations of successive order (Euler, Stokes-Navier, Burnett, etc.), which then can be used to explain the macroscopic phenomena.

(*b*) The development is so *arranged* that at any stage of the approximation the corresponding hydrodynamic equations are of the first order in the time derivatives of ϱ, $\mathbf{u}$, and T. Therefore, the initial values of ϱ, $\mathbf{u}$, and T determine formally the "state" of the gas. This *macroscopic causality theorem* (Hilbert) is of course not a theorem but an "Ansatz." It seems paradoxical because from the Boltzmann equation it clearly follows that one needs initially $f(\mathbf{r}, \mathbf{v}, 0)$ to determine the further state of the gas. One must expect that an arbitrary initial velocity distribution in a very short time (of the order of the time between collisions) degenerates into a "normal" state determined through the local Maxwell distribution by the macroscopic quantities ϱ, $\mathbf{u}$, T, and that the further slow equalization or adjustment of the spatial non-uniformities proceeds according to the hydrodynamic equations and in harmony with the macroscopic causality requirement.

(*c*) The Chapman-Enskog development is a development in inverse powers of the density (since $\lambda \sim 1/\varrho$), and therefore it goes from the Clausius regime toward the Knudsen regime. However, for practical purposes, the development is of not much use beyond the second or Stokes-Navier approximation. The reason is that in the development one does not distinguish between the *magnitude* of the disturbance and the *scale* of the disturbance from equilibrium. In any physical problem these can be well distinguished. For instance, in the propagation of sound they are measured by the intensity and the wave length of the sound, respectively; in the conduction of heat between two parallel plates they are measured by the difference of the temperatures of the plates and by the ratio of the distance between the plates to the mean free path, and so on. If the magnitude of the disturbance is small, it is much better to make a straightforward perturbation expansion of the Boltzmann equation by putting

$$f = f_0(1+h),$$

where f_0 is the *complete* (not the local) equilibrium distribution. The perturbation h then satisfies a linear homogeneous integro-differential equation. By using systematically the method of expanding h in its dependence on $\mathbf{v}$ in the eigenfunctions of the linearized collision operator, we have been able for various special cases to give a detailed discussion of the dependence on the scale or *Knudsen number* K ($\equiv L/\lambda$, where L is a representative length).[1]

(*d*) For small values of K, a power series expansion in K can be obtained for any physical quantity. However, it turns out that it is in general *not* possible to find a series expansion in inverse powers of K, since $K = \infty$ is an essential singularity of the exact solution. The approach to the Clausius regime is therefore more complicated than previously assumed. It is due to the development of successive types of boundary layers.

II. THE RAYLEIGH PROBLEM

Suppose a particle of mass m is bound harmonically to a fixed point with proper frequency ω_0; it is surrounded by a gas of particles of mass M against which it collides according to some force law; the gas is supposed to be in equilibrium at temperature T and the equilibrium is not affected by the motion of the particle m. Finally, an outside alternating force $mE_0 \cos \omega t$ acts, say in the x-direction, on the particle m (not on the molecules of the surrounding gas). The problem is to find the probability $f(\mathbf{r}, \mathbf{v}, t)\, d\mathbf{r}\, d\mathbf{v}$ that the particle m at time t is in the space and velocity range $d\mathbf{r}\, d\mathbf{v}$. Clearly, f will fulfill the so-called linear Boltzmann equation

$$\frac{\partial f}{\partial t} + v_\alpha \frac{\partial f}{\partial x_\alpha} + a_\alpha \frac{\partial f}{\partial v_\alpha} = J(f), \tag{1}$$

where a_i is the acceleration produced by the forces acting on the particle m, so that

$$a_i = -\omega_0^2 x_i + E_0 \cos \omega t\, \delta_{i1}\, .$$

$J(f)$ is the collision term:

$$J(f) = \int d\mathbf{V} \int d\Omega\, g I(g, \theta)[f'F' - fF], \tag{2}$$

where

$$F(V) = N(M/2\pi kT)^{3/2} \exp\left(-MV^2/2kT\right)$$

is the distribution function of the surrounding gas and the primes refer to the velocity variables; the collision $(\mathbf{v}, \mathbf{V}) \to (\mathbf{v}', \mathbf{V}')$ turns the relative velocity $g = |\mathbf{v}-\mathbf{V}|$ over the angle θ and $I(g, \theta)$ is the differential collision cross-section.

The outside force $mE_0 \cos \omega t$ must be considered as the perturbation which prevents the distribution f from going to the equilibrium distribution:

$$f_0 = \left(\frac{m\omega_0}{2\pi kT}\right)^3 e^{-(mv^2+m\omega_0^2 r^2)/2kT}\, . \tag{3}$$

Putting $f = f_0 + f_1$, then in the steady state the perturbation f_1 will be proportional to E_0 and vary in time like the outside force, although, of course, it will not be in phase because of the friction with the surrounding gas.

We will be mainly interested in the average power P absorbed by the particle m as a function of ω_0, ω, the ratio of the masses m/M, and the type of force law between the particle m and the molecules of the surrounding gas. P will be the time average of $m\bar{v}_x E_0 \cos \omega t$, where

$$\bar{v}_x(t) = \iint d\mathbf{r}\, d\mathbf{v}\, v_x f(\mathbf{r}, \mathbf{v}, t).$$

The relation of the problem to the theory of the shape of absorption lines and to the theory of metals will be more or less evident. The problem was in fact suggested in a discussion with Dr. J. M. Luttinger, because of a paradox which he encountered in the theory of metals.[2]

III. APPROXIMATE RESULTS

If the particle m is very heavy compared to a gas molecule ($m/M \gg 1$), and if in addition, we assume that the velocity $\mathbf{v}$ is never very different from the equipartition value, so that v/V is always of order $(M/m)^{1/2}$, then one finds, by an expansion in powers of M/m, that the collision term $J(f)$ can be approximated by the well-known Rayleigh or Brownian motion form

$$J(f) \cong \eta \frac{\partial}{\partial v_\alpha}\left(v_\alpha f + \frac{kT}{m}\frac{\partial f}{\partial v_\alpha}\right), \tag{4}$$

where the friction coefficient can be expressed as a suitable average of the collision cross-section $I(V, \theta)$. Using (4) one easily obtains for the average values $\bar{x}_i$ and $\bar{v}_i$, the equations

$$\begin{aligned} d\bar{x}_i/dt &= \bar{v}_i \\ d\bar{v}_i/dt &= -\omega_0^2 \bar{x}_i + E_0 \cos \omega t\, \delta_{i1} - \eta \bar{v}_i, \end{aligned} \tag{5}$$

which have an obvious physical interpretation. By solving these equations one finds in the steady state for the absorbed power:

$$P = \frac{E_0^2 \eta}{2} \frac{\omega^2}{(\omega^2 - \omega_0^2)^2 + \eta^2 \omega^2}. \tag{6}$$

Clearly, if $m/M \gg 1$, then in each collision the particle m does not change its velocity very much. For "*strong*" collisions it is customary, especially in the theory of metals, to approximate the collision term by assuming

$$J(f) \cong \frac{f_0 - f}{\tau}, \tag{7}$$

where f_0 is the equilibrium distribution (3) and τ is the *relaxation time.*

With (7) one obtains for the average values $\bar{x}_i$ and $\bar{v}_i$ the equations:

$$\frac{d\bar{x}_i}{dt} = \bar{v}_i - \frac{\bar{x}_i}{\tau}$$
$$\frac{d\bar{v}_i}{dt} = -\omega_0^2 \bar{x}_i + E_0 \cos \omega t \, \delta_{i1} - \frac{\bar{v}_i}{\tau}. \tag{8}$$

Note especially the first of these two equations. It says that the average position does *not* change with time according to the average velocity. The origin of this paradoxical result is the fact that with (7)

$$\int d\mathbf{v} J(f) = (1/\tau) \int d\mathbf{v} (f_0 - f),$$

which is not necessarily zero, while from the exact expression (2) follows

$$\int d\mathbf{v} J(f) = 0. \tag{9}$$

This equation is an expression of the fact that in a collision the number of particles does not change. One must say therefore that the strong collision approximation (7) violates this conservation law. A consequence of this is, as Luttinger has pointed out, that it makes a difference whether one calculates the average power absorbed with the help of the average velocity or with the help of $d\bar{x}_i/dt$. Using the average velocity, one obtains from (8), the result first derived by van Vleck and Weisskopf:

$$P = \frac{E_0^2 \tau}{4} \left[\frac{1}{1+(\omega-\omega_0)^2 \tau^2} + \frac{1}{1+(\omega+\omega_0)^2 \tau^2} \right]. \tag{10}$$

While, using $d\bar{x}_i/dt$, one obtains

$$P = \frac{E_0^2 \tau}{4} \frac{\omega}{\omega_0} \left[\frac{1}{1+(\omega-\omega_0)^2 \tau^2} - \frac{1}{1+(\omega+\omega_0)^2 \tau^2} \right], \tag{11}$$

first given by Luttinger.

IV. SOME EXACT RESULTS

Because of the difference between (10) and (11) it is of interest to find some exact solutions. We have succeeded in doing this for the case of the so-called Maxwell molecules, where one assumes that the interaction between particle m and a gas molecule is a repulsion $\varkappa/r^5$. In this case $gI(g, \theta)$ is independent of g. Putting

$$gI(g, \theta) = \left[\frac{2\varkappa(M+m)}{Mm}\right]^{1/2} F(\theta),$$

then $F(\theta)$ is the dimensionless function tabulated by Maxwell.[3] As a result it is possible to find all the eigenfunctions and eigenvalues of the collision operator J. By developing the perturbation f_1 in these eigenfunctions it is possible to discuss in detail the complete initial value problem. However, this is not needed in order to calculate the average power loss. Since the velocity v_i is one of the eigenfunctions of J one easily sees that

$$\int d\mathbf{v}\, v_i\, J(f) = \eta \int d\mathbf{v}\, v_i f, \tag{12}$$

with

$$\eta = 2\pi N \left[\frac{2\varkappa M}{m(M+m)}\right]^{1/2} \int_0^\pi d\theta \sin\theta(1 - \cos\theta) F(\theta). \tag{13}$$

This result can of course also be shown directly. As a consequence one obtains for *all* ratios of the masses m and M the *same* equations (5) as in the Brownian motion limit, and therefore also the same functional dependence of P on ω_0 and ω.

It is therefore clear that the strong collision approximation (7) cannot have a general validity independent of the intermolecular forces. Especially, it cannot be true that in the limit $m/M \ll 1$ (we will call this the *Lorentz limit*), which is opposite to the Brownian motion limit, the collision term can be approximated by (7) for all types of intermolecular force laws.

Of course, it may be that the inverse fifth power law gives too "soft" collisions. We have therefore also investigated the case of elastic spheres, especially in the Lorentz limit.

In this limit, and for $\omega_0 = 0$, one finds by an adaptation of the perturbation method used in the Lorentz theory of electronic conduction in metals:

$$P = \frac{4E_0^2\tau}{3\sqrt{\pi}} \int_0^\infty dc\, c^5 e^{-c^2} \frac{1}{c^2+\omega^2\tau^2}, \tag{14}$$

with

$$\tau = \frac{1}{\pi\sigma^2 N}\left(\frac{m}{2kT}\right)^{1/2},$$

where σ is the average diameter of the spheres with masses m and M.

This result lies between the van Vleck-Weisskopf and the Luttinger results (10) and (11) for $\omega_0 = 0$. Also for $\omega_0 \neq 0$ the power loss can be found in the Lorentz limit, but the computations have not yet been completed. Presumably also in this case $P(\omega, \omega_0)$ will be between the van Vleck-Weisskopf and the Luttinger results.

References

(1) The work was supported by the Office of Naval Research. The results have been published in a number of reports of the Engineering Research Institute at The University of Michigan. For further details we refer especially to the reports:

(*a*) *On the propagation of sound in monoatomic gases* (1952).

(*b*) *The heat transport between two parallel plates as function of the Knudsen number* (1953).

(*c*) *The Couette flow between two parallel plates as function of the Knudsen number* (1954).

(*d*) *On the behavior of a gas near a wall; a problem of Kramers* (1956).

(2) In the following only some of the results will be presented. For the proofs and further details, see our report entitled "The Kinetic Theory of a Gas in Alternating Outside Force Fields," *Eng. Res. Inst. Tech. Rept.*, October, 1956.

(3) Maxwell, *Collected Papers*, Vol. II, p. 42.

Discussion V

J. L. Lebowitz asked the opinion of Professor Uhlenbeck about the work of Gross.

G. Uhlenbeck: I know the work of Gross and agree with his general conclusions. However it does not settle the question as to deciding between the van Vleck-Weisskopf and the Luttinger results.

M. Fierz (*to G. Uhlenbeck*): What do you guess are the consequences of your research in the explanation of Hall effects of Karplus and Luttinger?

G. Uhlenbeck (*to M. Fierz*): I certainly have no definite information about the Hall effect question, since the extension to the quantum theory is required. I understand that Luttinger is working on it. The impression one gets from the simple example discussed is that perhaps the explanation of Karplus-Luttinger can partially be saved.

J. Ross (*to G. Uhlenbeck*): Can you say something about the validity of the use of the time-dependent external forces in the streaming terms of the Boltzmann equation? It appears that analytical derivations of the Boltzmann equation seem to indicate that external time-dependent forces affect the structure of the collision integral.

G. Uhlenbeck (*to J. Ross*): I have not thought about the validity of the use of the external force term in the Boltzmann equation, and have just taken the equation as one finds it in the textbooks. However I think that any interference term between the streaming and collision term will make itself felt only at higher density.

D. C. K. MacDonald (*to G. Uhlenbeck*): Professor Uhlenbeck's analysis of the Smit-Karplus and Luttinger controversy in terms of the collision representation of the Boltzmann equation is most interesting. Experimental work at low temperatures (say 10°K and below) to day shows that in thermoelectricity particularly there are some rather serious discrepancies with the predictions of transport theory. I believe it may well be that the root of this trouble *also* lies in the collision integral in the electron transport Boltzmann equation.

PART VI

ON THE THEORY OF THE TRANSPORT PROPERTIES OF PARA-ORTHO MIXTURES IN THE GAS PHASE

E. G. D. COHEN and M. J. OFFERHAUS, *Instituut voor Theoretische Physica, Universiteit van Amsterdam, The Netherlands*

Abstract

It is shown that at very low temperatures gaseous para-ortho hydrogen mixtures can be treated as a 10-component mixture, which can be reduced to a binary mixture. Generalization to other para-ortho mixtures is straight forward.

In a mixture of gaseous para and ortho hydrogen at temperatures below about 40°K all molecules can be assumed to be in their rotational ground state. This implies that all para hydrogen molecules are in a state with $J = 0$, whereas all ortho hydrogen molecules are in one of 9 degenerate states due to a rotational quantum number $J = 1$ and a total nuclear spin $S = 1$.

If we assume one spherically symmetrical potential field to describe all the interactions present, then each molecule always remains in the same state because transitions are impossible. Thus rather than a binary mixture, para and ortho hydrogen form a 10-component mixture and their transport properties should be treated with the Chapman-Enskog theory of a 10-component gas mixture.

We propose to show that, in the case treated here, the Chapman-Enskog theory for a 10-component mixture reduces to that for a binary para-ortho mixture, where the existence of 9 ortho components is taken into account in the scattering cross-sections only.

In the Chapman-Enskog theory for the 10-component para-ortho hydrogen mixture the central problem is to find a solution to the Boltzmann equations for the velocity distribution functions $f_p(\mathbf{r}, \mathbf{v}_p, t)$ and $f_{oi}(\mathbf{r}, \mathbf{v}_{oi}, t)$ $(i = 1, \cdots, 9)$ for para hydrogen and the 9 different ortho hydrogen components

$$D_k f_k = \sum_l J(f_k, f_l) \qquad (k, l = p, o1, \cdots, o9), \qquad (1)$$

where

$$D_k f_k = \left[\frac{\partial}{\partial t} + \mathbf{v}_k \cdot \frac{\partial}{\partial \mathbf{r}} + \frac{\mathbf{X}}{m} \cdot \frac{\partial}{\partial \mathbf{v}_k}\right] f(\mathbf{v}_k), \tag{1a}$$

$$J(f_k, f_l) = 2\pi \iint [f(\mathbf{v}_k') f(\mathbf{v}_l') - f(\mathbf{v}_k) f(\mathbf{v}_l)] \, \alpha_{kl}(g, \chi) \sin \chi \, d\chi \, d\mathbf{v}_l. \tag{1b}$$

The summation on the right-hand side of (1) extends over all 10 components. $\alpha_{kl}(g, \chi)$ is the quantum mechanical differential cross-section for the scattering of two molecules of component k and l, respectively, with relative velocity g over an angle χ. α_{kl} depends on k and l only through the statistics, the intermolecular potential field and the molecular mass m being the same for all components. Four cross-sections $\alpha_{kl}(g, \chi)$ occur in Eqs. (1):

$$\begin{aligned} \alpha_{pp} &= \alpha_s, & \alpha_{p,oi} &= \alpha, & & \\ \alpha_{oi,oi} &= \alpha_s, & \alpha_{oi,oj} &= \alpha_D, & & (i \neq j). \end{aligned} \tag{2}$$

Here α and α_s are the nonsymmetrized and symmetrized scattering cross-sections for two hydrogen molecules; α_D is the cross-section for scattering for two ortho hydrogen molecules in different states. $\mathbf{v}_k'$ and $\mathbf{v}_l'$ are the velocities of two molecules of component k and l after having collided with initial velocities $\mathbf{v}_k$ and $\mathbf{v}_l$, respectively. They are the same functions of $\mathbf{v}_k$ and $\mathbf{v}_l$ for all k and l. $\mathbf{X}$, the external force acting on a molecule, is assumed to be the same for para and ortho molecules.

Eq. (1) can be solved by setting:

$$f_k = f_k^{(0)} + f_k^{(1)} + \cdots \qquad (k = p, o1, \cdots, o9). \tag{3}$$

We shall restrict ourselves to the first two terms of this series. Introducing (3) into (1) and treating $f_k^{(1)}$ as small compared to $f_k^{(0)}$, leads to the following 10 equations for $f_k^{(0)}$

$$0 = \sum_l J(f_k^{(0)}, f_l^{(0)}) \qquad (k, l = p, oi), \tag{4}$$

which have the solution

$$f_p^{(0)} = n_p (m/2kT)^{3/2} \exp(-mV_p^2/2kT), \tag{5a}$$

$$f_{oi}^{(0)} = (n_o/9)(m/2kT)^{3/2} \exp(-mV_{oi}^2/2kT), \tag{5b}$$

where n_p and n_o are the local number densities of para and ortho hydrogen, each ortho-component having the same concentration. $\mathbf{V} = \mathbf{v} - \mathbf{v}_0$ is the velocity relative to the bulk velocity $\mathbf{v}_0$, k is Boltzmann's constant, and T is the temperature.

$f_k^{(0)}$ now being known, $f_k^{(1)}$ can be determined from the equations:

$$D_k^{(0)} f_k^{(0)} = \sum_l [J(f_k^{(0)}, f_l^{(1)}) + J(f_k^{(1)}, f_l^{(0)})] \tag{6}$$

with

$$D_k^{(0)} = \frac{\partial_0}{\partial t} + \mathbf{v}_k \cdot \frac{\partial}{\partial \mathbf{r}} + \frac{\mathbf{X}}{m} \cdot \frac{\partial}{\partial \mathbf{v}_k}, \tag{6a}$$

where $\partial_0/\partial t$ denotes an approximation to the exact partial time derivative $\partial/\partial t$, which is independent of k.

Eqs. (6) have a solution of the form

$$f_k^{(1)} = f_k^{(0)} \sum_\alpha A_{k\alpha}(\mathbf{V})\, g_\alpha, \tag{7}$$

where g_α stands for the gradients of n_p, $\mathbf{v}_0$, and T and for the external force $\mathbf{X}$. Substitution of the solution $f_k = f_k^{(0)} + f_k^{(1)}$ from (5) and (7) into the equations of transport giving the flow of mass, momentum, and energy in the mixture

$$\mathsf{p} - p\mathsf{U} = \sum_{k=p,\, oi} m \int f_k^{(1)} \mathbf{V}_k \mathbf{V}_k \, d\mathbf{v}_k \tag{8a}$$

$$\mathbf{q} = \sum_{k=p,\, oi} \tfrac{1}{2} m \int f_k^{(1)} V_k^2 \mathbf{V}_k \, d\mathbf{v}_k \tag{8b}$$

$$\overline{\mathbf{V}}_k = (1/n_k) \int f_k^{(1)} \mathbf{V}_k \, d\mathbf{v}_k \tag{8c}$$

gives the transport coefficients as the proportionality factors between the flow quantities on the left-hand sides of (8) and the gradients on the right-hand sides of (8). p is the pressure tensor, U the unit tensor, p the hydrostatic pressure, and $\mathbf{q}$ the heat flux vector.

The set of equations (3), (4), (6), and (8) determines the transport properties of the mixture completely. We may point out that the successive Enskog approximations to the transport properties are obtained by expanding the $A_{k\alpha}(\mathbf{V})$ in an increasing number of Sonine polynomials.

If we now introduce velocity distribution functions for all 9 ortho-components together

$$f_o^{(0)} = 9 f_{oi}^{(1)} \tag{9a}$$

$$f_o^{(1)} = \sum_{i=1}^{9} f_{oi}^{(0)}, \tag{9b}$$

then, by adding, Eqs. (6) can be written:

$$D_k^{(0)} f_k^{(0)} = \sum_{l=p,\, o} [J(f_k^{(0)}, f_l^{(1)}) + J(f_k^{(1)}, f_l^{(0)})], \tag{10}$$

where k and l now only take the two values p and o so that the following cross-sections occur:

$$(k = l = p) : \alpha_{pp} = \alpha_s ; \qquad (k = p; l = o) : \alpha_{po} = \alpha \qquad \text{(11a, b)}$$

$$(k = l = o) : \alpha_{oo} = \tfrac{1}{9}\alpha_s + \tfrac{8}{9}\alpha_D . \qquad \text{(11c)}$$

As $\alpha_D = \frac{1}{2}\alpha_s + \frac{1}{2}\alpha_a$, where α_a is the cross-section for scattering if only antisymmetrical spatial wave functions are used, (11c) can be written in the more familiar form:

$$\alpha_{oo} = \tfrac{5}{9}\alpha_s + \tfrac{4}{9}\alpha_a . \qquad (12)$$

Formula (12) reflects the fact that there is a 5 : 4 probability that, in a collision between two ortho hydrogen molecules, the wave function should be symmetrical or antisymmetrical in the spatial coordinates of the two molecules, respectively.

Eqs. (10) are those for a binary mixture. Similarly Eqs. (3), (4), and (8) can be rewritten as those for a binary mixture. Thus we see that the 10-component mixture is equivalent to a binary mixture, where the 9 ortho-components behave as one single component with a scattering cross-section (12). The reduction was possible because we used the fact that all ortho-hydrogen molecules: (a) had the same mass, (b) had the same intermolecular potential field; (c) had the same concentration; and (d) experienced the same external force.

As we have not used the Sonine expansion for the coefficients $A_{k\alpha}(\mathbf{V})$, the reduction is possible in all Enskog approximations. This implies that the determinants entering into the expressions of the transport coefficients for the 10-component mixture can be reduced to those for a binary mixture.

The results obtained here have been used for the calculation of the transport properties of para-ortho hydrogen mixtures below 40°K.[1] A generalization to other para-ortho mixtures (deuterium, tritium, methane, etc.) is straightforward. A more detailed account will be published soon.[2]

References

(1) E. G. D. Cohen, M. J. Offerhaus, J. M. J. van Leeuwen, B. W. Roos, and J. de Boer, *Physica*, **21**, 737 (1955).

(2) E. G. D. Cohen and M. J. Offerhaus, *Physica* (to be published).

SOLUTION OF THE BOLTZMANN-HILBERT INTEGRAL EQUATION

C. L. PEKERIS, *Department of Applied Mathematics, The Weizmann Institute, Rehovot, Israel*

Abstract

In this investigation we treat the classical transport phenomena problems for a gas model consisting of rigid spheres. For this model Hilbert reduced the Boltzmann integral equation to a much simpler form, which we designate as the Boltzmann-Hilbert integral equation. Our method of solving the Boltzmann-Hilbert integral equation is based first on an explicit evaluation of the coefficient functions in the expansion of the kernel into spherical harmonics. In the application to problems of self-diffusion, heat conduction, and viscosity, this effects a reduction of the original Boltzmann-Hilbert three-dimensional integral equation into a one-dimensional integral equation. The latter is further simplified by reducing it into an ordinary differential equation. In the case of self-diffusion the resulting differential equation for the perturbation in the distribution function is of the second order, in the cases of heat conduction and of viscosity it is of the fourth order. These differential equations have been solved numerically for the respective distribution functions, and from the latter, values were derived for the coefficients of self-diffusion, heat conduction, and viscosity. The results agree well with the values attained from the Chapman-Enskog method.

The purpose of this investigation is to reopen the question of the solution of Boltzmann's integral equation after it had been canonized in the famous treatise of Chapman and Cowling.[1] The Chapman-Enskog method followed there is of course very effective for the evaluation of the classical transport coefficients, but as an essentially variational method it lacks elegance, and is furthermore a poor tool when accurate solutions for the distribution function are sought. The method to be presented here is an extension of the work of Hilbert on the gas model consisting of rigid spheres, for which Boltzmann's integral equation takes on the form

$$\mathfrak{D}f = \frac{\partial f}{\partial t} + \mathbf{c}\cdot\frac{\partial f}{\partial \mathbf{r}} + \mathbf{F}\cdot\frac{\partial f}{\partial \mathbf{c}} = \frac{\sigma^2}{2}\iint (f'f_1' - ff_1)\,|\mathbf{g}\cdot\mathbf{k}|\,d\mathbf{k}\,d\mathbf{c}_1, \qquad (1)$$

σ denoting the diameter of the spheres. Hilbert[2] showed that this integral equation can be simplified to the form

$$\mathfrak{D}f^0 = -\frac{\sigma^2 n^2 m}{2\pi kT}\left\{M(p)\,e^{-2p^2}\varphi(\mathbf{p}) + \frac{1}{\pi}\,e^{-p^2}\int \varphi(\mathbf{p}_1)e^{-p_1^2}\left(R - \frac{2}{R}e^{\omega^2}\right)d\mathbf{p}_1\right\}, \quad (2)$$

where

$$f^0 = n\left(\frac{m}{2\pi kT}\right)^{3/2}\exp\left(\frac{-mC^2}{2kT}\right), \qquad \mathbf{C} = \mathbf{c} - \mathbf{c}_0,$$

$$f = f^0(1+\varphi), \qquad \mathbf{p} = \mathbf{C}\sqrt{\frac{m}{2kT}}, \quad (3)$$

$$M(p) = 1 + \left(2p + \frac{1}{p}\right)P(p), \qquad P(p) = e^{p^2}\int_0^p e^{-x^2}\,dx, \quad (4)$$

$$R = |\mathbf{p} - \mathbf{p}_1|, \qquad \omega = \frac{pp_1 \sin\theta'}{R}, \quad (5)$$

and θ' denotes the angle between $\mathbf{p}$ and $\mathbf{p}_1$. We shall designate Eq. (2) as the Boltzmann-Hilbert integral equation. Hilbert's transformation of (1) into (2) represents a substantial simplification in a problem which is abundantly abstruse, but, except for an investigation of Boguslawski[3] of the longitudinal oscillations of a gas, and for the work of Pidduck[4] on self-diffusion, Hilbert's method was not taken up by subsequent investigators.

We have developed a method by which the Boltzmann-Hilbert integral equation can be solved for the classical problems of self-diffusion, heat conduction, and viscosity. *The method consists in reducing the Boltzmann-Hilbert integral equation into a one-dimensional integral equation, and then transforming the latter into an ordinary differential equation.* Similar results can be traced to the work of Boltzmann.[5] The essential step in our method is the explicit evaluation of the functions $A_n(p, p_1)$ in the expansion of the kernel of the Boltzmann-Hilbert integral equation

$$\left[R - \left(\frac{2}{R}\right)e^{\omega^2}\right] = \sum_{n=0}^{\infty}(n+\tfrac{1}{2})\,A_n(p, p_1)\,P_n(\cos\theta'). \quad (6)$$

Actually one needs only the first three functions for the treatment of self-diffusion, heat conduction, and viscosity, and these are given by

$$pp_1 A_0(p, p_1) = \tfrac{2}{3}p_1^3 + 2p^2 p_1 - 4P(p_1), \qquad p_1 < p, \quad (7)$$

$$p^2p_1^2A_1(p, p_1) = \tfrac{2}{15}p_1^5 - \tfrac{2}{3}p_1^3p^2 - 4g(p_1), \qquad p_1 < p, \tag{8}$$

$$p^3p_1^3A_2(p, p_1) = [\tfrac{2}{35}p_1^7 - \tfrac{2}{15}p_1^5p^2 + 3p^2p_1 - 3p_1^3 + 18p_1 \\ + (-6p_1^4 + 2p^2p_1^2 - 3p^2 + 15p_1^2 - 18)P(p_1)], \quad p_1 < p, \tag{9}$$

where

$$g(p) = [p + (p^2-1)P], \qquad P = e^{p^2}\int_0^p e^{-x^2}\,dx. \tag{10}$$

When $p_1 > p$ we must interchange p with p_1 on the right-hand sides of (7), (8), and (9).

We shall now sketch briefly the application of our method to the problems of self-diffusion, heat conduction, and viscosity. In the case of self-diffusion the function φ of (3), representing the perturbation in the distribution function, is proportional to a function $\delta(p)$ which is governed by the one-dimensional integral equation

$$e^{-p^2}M(p)p^3\delta(p) - p^3 = 4\int_0^p e^{-x^2}g(x)\delta(x)x\,dx + 4g(p)\int_p^\infty e^{-x^2}\delta(x)x\,dx. \tag{11}$$

This integral equation can be reduced to the differential equation

$$\frac{d}{dp}\left[\frac{1}{\dot g}\frac{d}{dp}(p^3M\psi)\right] + 4p\psi(p) = 3\frac{d}{dp}\left(\frac{p^2}{\dot g}\right), \tag{12}$$

where

$$\psi(p) = e^{-p^2}\delta(p). \tag{13}$$

In the case of heat conduction the perturbation function φ is proportional to a function $a(p)$, for which the integral equation is

$$p^5 - (5/2)p^3 - p^3M(p)e^{-p^2}a(p) = \int_0^p e^{-x^2}a(x)x[\tfrac{4}{15}x^5 - 8g(x) - \tfrac{4}{3}p^2x^3]\,dx \\ + \int_p^\infty e^{-x^2}a(x)x[\tfrac{4}{15}p^5 - 8g(p) - \tfrac{4}{3}p^3x^2]\,dx. \tag{14}$$

With

$$S(p) = -\int_p^\infty e^{-x^2}xa(x)\,dx, \tag{15}$$

this leads to the following differential equation for S

$$[p^2 + (2p^3+p)P(p)]S^{\mathrm{IV}} + [7p + 6p^3 + (1 + 20p^2 + 12p^4)P(p)]\dddot S \\ + \left[2 + 42p^2 + 12p^4 + \left(-\frac{2}{p} + 26p + 96p^3 + 24p^5\right)P(p)\right]\ddot S \\ + \left[-\frac{2}{p} + 38p + 72p^3 + 8p^5 + \left(\frac{2}{p^2} - 2 + 140p^2 + 152p^4 + 16p^6\right)P(p)\right]\dot S \\ + [56p^2 + 32p^4 + (32p + 160p^3 + 64p^5)P(p)]S = 30p^2. \tag{16}$$

In the case of viscosity, φ is proportional to a function $b(p)$ which is a solution of the integral equation

$$
\begin{aligned}
& p^5 - p^5 M(p)\, e^{-p^2} b(p) \\
& = \int_0^p e^{-x^2} b(x) [\tfrac{4}{35} x^8 - 6x^4 + 36x^2 + (-12x^5 + 30x^3 - 36x) P(x)]\, dx \\
& + p^2 \int_0^p e^{-x^2} b(x)\, [-\tfrac{4}{15} x^6 + 6x^2 + (4x^3 - 6x) P(x)]\, dx \\
& + [-\tfrac{4}{15} p^5 + 6p + (4p^2 - 6)\, P(p)] \int_p^\infty e^{-x^2} b(x)\, x^3 dx \\
& + [\tfrac{4}{35} p^7 - 6p^3 + 36p + (-12p^4 + 30p^2 - 36) P(p)] \int_p^\infty e^{-x^2} b(x) x dx. \qquad (17)
\end{aligned}
$$

Writing

$$
y(p) \equiv -\tfrac{1}{2} p^2 \int_p^\infty e^{-x^2} b(x)\, x dx + \tfrac{1}{2} \int_p^\infty e^{-x^2} b(x)\, x^3 dx, \qquad (18)
$$

the differential equation for $y(p)$ turns out to be

$$
\begin{aligned}
& [p^2 + (p + 2p^3) P(p)] y^{\mathrm{IV}} + [6p + 4p^3 + (2 + 16p^2 + 8p^4) P(p)] \dddot{y} \\
& + \left[1 + 20p^2 + 4p^4 + \left(-\frac{1}{p} + 10p + 44p^3 + 8p^5\right) P(p)\right] \ddot{y} \\
& + \left[-\frac{1}{p} + 4p + 12p^3 + \left(\frac{1}{p^2} - 10 + 20p^2 + 24p^4\right) P(p)\right] \dot{y} \\
& + [8p^2 + (16p + 32p^3) P(p)]\, y = 15p^2. \qquad (19)
\end{aligned}
$$

We have solved numerically the differential equations (12), (16), and (19) and used these solutions of the respective distribution functions to evaluate the coefficients of self-diffusion,[6] heat conduction, and viscosity.[7] The results are in good agreement with the values derived by the Chapman-Enskog method.

References

(1) S. Chapman and T. G. Cowling, *The Mathematical Theory of Non-uniform Gases,* Cambridge Univ. Press, London, 1952.

(2) D. Hilbert, *Grundzüge einer allgemeinen Theorie der linearen Integral-gleichungen,* Chelsea Pub. Co., New York, 1953, p. 267.

(3) S. Boguslawski, *Math. Ann.*, **76**, 431 (1915).

(4) F. B. Pidduck, *Proc. London Math. Soc.*, **15**, 89 (1916).

(5) L. Boltzmann, *Collected Works*, **2**, 545 (1881).

(6) C. L. Pekeris, *Proc. Natl. Acad. Sci. U. S.*, **41**, 661 (1955).

(7) C. L. Pekeris and Z. Alterman, *Proc. Natl. Acad. Sci. U. S.*, **43**, 998 (1957).

ON A MATHEMATICAL TREATMENT OF DIFFUSION IN GAS MIXTURES

G. KLEIN,* *Royal Holloway College, London, England*

Abstract

In the solution of problems concerning multicomponent gases (e.g. where there is a temperature gradient but negligible pressure variation, as in flames) the complexity of diffusion presents considerable difficulty. A method of solution is suggested in which a problem is first solved for certain *ideal,* fictitious binary diffusion coefficients which describe diffusional behavior of the components as far as one would expect on account of the different molecular masses. The complete problem, involving the *given* binary diffusion coefficients, is then attacked by a perturbation method (and/or parameter expansions) based on the ideal problem already solved. The energy flux has a simple form for the "ideal" binary diffusion coefficients, and this further suggests initial simplifications when methods of successive approximations are applied.

Under stationary conditions, negligible pressure variation and thermodiffusion, the diffusion equations for the components in a gas mixture are

$$(\partial/\partial\mathbf{r})x_S = -x_S \sum (1/D_{SS'})\, x_{S'}\, (\mathbf{v}_s - \mathbf{v}_{S'}), \tag{1}$$

where $D_{SS'}$ is a binary diffusion coefficient and x_S, $\mathbf{v}_S$ denote mole fraction and drift velocity, respectively (cf. ref. 1). The latter quantities are subject to normalization and conservation of momentum, viz.,

$$\sum x_S = 1, \tag{2}$$

$$n \sum m_S x_S \mathbf{v}_S = \mathbf{M},\ \text{say.} \tag{3}$$

There will also be the integrated energy transport equation and detailed density continuity equations containing rates of chemical production. In problems where only one-dimensional variations need be considered the equations may be written more concisely in terms of conveniently defined dimensionless quantities, thus

$$\sum x_S = 1, \tag{4}$$

* Present address: The Royal College of Science and Technology, Glasgow, Scotland.

$$\sum (m_S/m)\, y_S = 1, \tag{5}$$

$$(d/dz)x_S = \sum (1/\delta_{SS'})(x_S\, y_{S'} - x_{S'}\, y_S), \tag{6}$$

together with the equations just mentioned.

Now, the simultaneous solution of all these equations presents great difficulty for which the nonlinearity of (6) is largely responsible. That this nonlinearity is, however, not an intrinsic difficulty can be seen by considering the simplest case of only two components of equal molecular masses. Here,

$$x_A + x_B = 1, \tag{7}$$

$$y_A + y_B = 1, \tag{8}$$

and, consequently,

$$(d/dz)x_A = (1/\delta_{AB})(x_A - y_A) \tag{9}$$

Hence one asks under what conditions the nonlinearity would similarly disappear in the general relations (6). The answer is that, if the reduced binary diffusion coefficients were of the ideal form

$$\delta_{SS'} = (m^2/m_S\, m_{S'})\,\delta, \tag{10}$$

in which m is some standard constant mass and δ is a function of position or temperature only, the equations become practically linear, viz.,

$$(d/dz)\, x_S = (1/\delta)(m_S/m)\{x_S - (\bar{m}/m)\, y_S\} \tag{11}$$

or

$$y_S = (m_S/m)\, x_S - (m/\bar{m})\,\delta(m/m_S)(dx_S/dz), \tag{12}$$

where $\bar{m}$ is the mean molecular mass, $\sum m_S x_S$, and $\bar{m}/m$ is generally a slowly varying quantity for which in a method of successive approximations a lower approximation may usually be taken. It should be noted that the form (10) describes the diffusional behavior of any pair of components at least as far as may be expected on account of their unequal molecular masses.

The preceding consideration suggests the following method of solution. The problem should first be solved with ideal, fictitious diffusion coefficients (10)—owing to the diffusion equations now being linear, this will be relatively simple. A perturbation or parameter expansion method may then be applied to the complete problem with the given coefficients by basing it on the ideal problem already solved. Thus, let $\delta^*_{SS'}$ be ideal reduced binary diffusion coefficients, let $\delta_{SS'}$ be the given ones, and put

$$1/\delta_{SS'} = (1/\delta^*_{SS'})(1+\theta\, d_{SS'}), \tag{13}$$

where

$$d_{SS'} = (\delta^*_{SS'}/\delta_{SS'})-1 \tag{14}$$

is a known quantity and θ is a parameter whose value is left open: it is a device which enables us to pass from the set of ideal coefficients to that of the actually given one. All dependent variables are expanded in powers of θ and on equating coefficients of powers of θ a system of successive linear differential equations is obtained. After evaluation of a sufficient number of terms—rapid convergence was apparent in numerical applications—one puts θ equal to unity.

It will be observed that one is free to assign the function δ of (10). Since it is found that, for a certain form of this function, the energy flux vector will vanish, it is convenient to adopt this form. For further details about the method the reader is referred to a paper on flames by the author.[2]

References

(1) J. O. Hirschfelder, C. F. Curtiss, and R. B. Bird, *Molecular Theory of Gases and Liquids,* Wiley, New York, 1954.

(2) G. Klein, "A Contribution to Flame Theory," *Phil. Trans. Roy. Soc.* **A 249,** 389 (1957).

A SOLUTION OF THE BOLTZMANN EQUATION FOR ELECTRICAL DISCHARGES

TARO KIHARA, *University of Tokyo, Department of Physics, Bunkyo-Ku, Tokyo, Japan*

In the usual theory of transport phenomena in gases the Boltzmann equation is linearized under the assumption of infinitesimal forces, for example infinitesimal temperature gradient for the thermal conduction or infinitesimal velocity gradient for the viscosity. This assumption does not apply to the velocity distribution of electrons, concerning which the electric force cannot be considered to be infinitesimal. However, in the limiting case when the number density of electrons is much smaller than that of the gas molecules, the Boltzmann equation for the velocity distribution of electrons becomes linear. The aim of the present talk is to solve the equation thus linearized with use of a particular model of molecules. We treat the case where both the gas and the field are homogeneous but not necessarily stationary.

Dielectric breakdown of gases occurs as a result of ionization by collision of electrons with gas molecules. Electrons with sufficient kinetic energies can ionize neutral molecules, when they collide, and create further electrons. In a strong electric field, therefore, electrons increase in number; and, when the rate of increase is sufficient, a breakdown occurs.

In a uniform static field in the direction of negative z-axis this electron increase can be expressed by a differential equation

$$dn/dz = \alpha n.$$

This equation indicates that the number density n of electrons increases with the rate α as they drift in the direction of positive z-axis. The constant α, the relative increase per unit drift length, is called Townsend's coefficient. Among α, the pressure P and the field E there is a general relationship at room temperature:

$$\alpha/P = f(E/P).$$

A useful approximation to the function f for a one-component gas is the following:

$$\alpha = AP \exp(-BP/E). \tag{1}$$

Here A and B are characteristic constants of the gas. The expression (1), which has been widely used as a standard empirical formula, will be derived from our model.

Now let us consider, in an electromagnetic field, a gas composed of several species of neutral molecules and a kind of charged particle, electrons. Our model consists of three postulates.

Postulate 1 is that the elastic scattering coefficient $I_s(g_s, \theta)$ of electrons colliding with a molecule of sth species be inversely proportional to the relative speed $g_s = |\mathbf{c}-\mathbf{c}_s|$ before and after the collision ($s = 1, 2, \cdots$). Here $\mathbf{c}$ and $\mathbf{c}_s$ indicate the velocity of an electron and the velocity of a gas molecule of sth species, respectively.

Then an integral of $g_s I_s(g_s, \theta)$ over the scattering angle θ,

$$\lambda_s = 2\pi \frac{m_s}{m_s+m} \int_0^\pi (1 - \cos\theta)\, g_s\, I_s(g_s, \theta) \sin\theta \, d\theta$$

defines a molecular constant λ_s. Here m and m_s indicate the mass of an electron and the mass of a gas molecule of sth species, respectively. In terms of this constant the average value $\langle \mathbf{c} \rangle$ of the electron velocity is determined by the differential equation with respect to the time t:

$$\frac{d\langle \mathbf{c} \rangle}{dt} = \frac{e}{m} (\mathbf{E} + \langle \mathbf{c} \rangle \times \mathbf{H}) - \sum_s N_s \lambda_s \langle \mathbf{c} \rangle. \tag{2}$$

in which $\mathbf{E}$ and $\mathbf{H}$ are electric and magnetic fields both in electrostatic units, $e \equiv -|e|$ the electron charge, and N_s the number density of gas molecules of sth species. The first term on the right-hand side indicates the acceleration due to the Lorentz force, the last term the acceleration caused by collisions with gas molecules. The equation shows that the average velocity $\langle \mathbf{c} \rangle$ is, as regards its absolute value, proportional to the electric field (a generalized Ohm's law).

Since the mass of the electron is much smaller than that of molecules, transfer of energy between electron and molecule at the time of an elastic collision is small. At higher energies, however, electrons can excite gas molecules, and be deprived of the excitation energy. Therefore, the effect of exciting collisions on the energy distribution of electrons cannot be neglected even if their frequency is so small that the effect on the average velocity can be neglected.

Les us denote by $q_s(c_0, c)$ the effective cross-section of a molecule of sth species for such a process that the speeds of electrons decrease from c_0 to values below c because of inelastic collisions. Our *Postulate* 2 is

$$q_s(c_0, c) = \varrho_s c^3/c_0^2,$$

ϱ_s being a constant with the dimension of area divided by velocity. According to this postulate the total exciting cross-section $q_s(c_0, c_0) = \varrho_s c_0$ is proportional to the speed of colliding electrons.

It is a characteristic feature of our molecular model that the velocity distribution f of electrons is Maxwellian

$$f = n\left(\frac{m}{2\pi k T_e}\right)^{3/2} \exp\left[-\frac{m}{2kT_e}(\mathbf{c}-\langle\mathbf{c}\rangle)^2\right] \tag{3}$$

around the average velocity determined by Eq. (2). The electron temperature T_e is determined by a differential equation

$$\frac{3}{2}\frac{dkT_e}{dt} + 3k(T_e - T)\sum_s N_s\lambda_s \frac{m}{m_s} + 3\frac{(kT_e)^2}{m}\sum_s N_s\varrho_s = m|\langle\mathbf{c}\rangle|^2 \sum_s N_s\lambda_s \tag{4}$$

The second and the third terms on the left indicate the energy loss due to elastic and exciting collisions respectively; the right-hand side indicates the energy gain due to drift in the field.

Our *Postulate* 3 is that the effective cross-section Q_s of a molecule of sth species for the process of collision ionization is given by

$$Q_s = \begin{cases} \tau_s(c^2-\gamma_s^2)^{3/2}/c^2 & \text{for } c > \gamma_s \\ 0 & \text{for } c < \gamma_s. \end{cases}$$

Here τ_s is a molecular constant of the same dimension as ϱ_s, and $m\gamma_s^2/2$ corresponds to the ionization energy of the sth species.

Since a few electrons with exceptionally large energies usually take the main part of the ionization, we may consider that the velocity distribution of electrons is not disturbed by the ionization process. We assume Maxwellian distribution (3). The relative rate of increase ν in the electron density n is then given by

$$\nu = \frac{1}{n}\frac{dn}{dt} = \sum_s N_s \int_0^\infty Q_s \frac{f}{n} 4\pi c^3\, dc$$
$$= 3\frac{kT_e}{m}\sum_s N_s\tau_s \exp\left[-\frac{m\gamma_s^2}{2kT_e}\right]. \tag{5}$$

In terms of this ionization rate ν, the Townsend coefficient α in a static electric field E is given by

$$\alpha = \nu / |\langle \mathbf{c} \rangle|,$$

the average velocity $\langle \mathbf{c} \rangle$ of electrons being given by Eq. (2):

$$|\langle \mathbf{c} \rangle| = eE/m \sum N_s \lambda_s.$$

The electron temperature is determined by Eq. (4), which reduces to

$$kT_e = m \left(\frac{\sum N_s \lambda_s}{3 \sum N_s \varrho_s} \right)^{1/2} |\langle \mathbf{c} \rangle|$$

when the electron temperature is so high that excitations occur sufficiently. In this case, therefore, the Townsend coefficient becomes

$$\alpha = \left(\frac{3 \sum N_s \lambda_s}{\sum N_s \varrho_s} \right)^{1/2} \sum N_s \tau_s \exp \left[- \frac{1}{E} \frac{m \gamma_s^2}{2e} 3^{1/2} \left(\sum N_s \lambda_s \right)^{1/2} \left(\sum N_s \varrho_s \right)^{1/2} \right].$$

In particular, for a single-component gas, the above expression is just the same as the empirical formula (1) in which

$$AP = N_1 T_1 \left(\frac{3\lambda_1}{\varrho_1} \right)^{1/2}, \qquad BP = \frac{N_1}{e} \frac{m\gamma_1^2}{2} (3\lambda_1 \varrho_1)^{1/2}.$$

Thus the empirical relation (1) has been derived by means of our molecular model containing four constants λ, ϱ, τ, and γ. These constants can be determined from observed cross-sections for ionization and empirical values of A_0 and B_0. Using the model constants thus determined we are able to treat electrical discharges in a nonstatic field, in the presence of a magnetic field, in a mixed gas, and so on.

Reference

(1) T. Kihara, *Revs. Mod. Phys.*, **24**, 45 (1952); **25**, 831 (1953).

Discussion VI

G. Uhlenbeck (*to E. G. D. Cohen*): Have you obtained numerical answers, and how do they compare with experiment?

E. G. D. Cohen (*to G. Uhlenbeck*): Yes, we have made calculations of all the transport properties of hydrogen at low temperatures using the cross-sections just given. They agree well, on the whole, with experiment.

M. Green (*to C. L. Pekeris*): Can the eigenvalue problem for the hard sphere Boltzmann equation be reduced to a differential equation?

C. L. Pekeris (*to M. Green*): Yes, it can. If we express the perturbation in the distribution function as a series in Legendre polynomials in the angle, with coefficients depending on the magnitude of the momentum, then each coefficient obeys a differential equation. This would be worth carrying but with a view to application to the problem of propagation of sound in highly rarified gases. It was a lecture on the latter problem given by Professor Uhlenbeck at the Institute for Advanced Studies in Princeton in December, 1952, which stimulated my investigation. It is however, not possible to reduce the whole sound propagation problem to an ordinary differential equation, but rather to *a system* of ordinary differential equations.

R. Eisenschitz (*to. C. L. Pekeris*): Is the ordinary Boltzmann equation with an arbitrary force field reductible to a differential equation?

C. L. Pekeris (*to R. Eisenschitz*): This is, of course, an important problem which, however, I have not yet investigated.

R. Brout (*to C. L. Pekeris*): How valid is the Boltzmann equation in shock waves? The streaming terms are doubtful.

M. Green (*to R. Brout*): If Dr. Pekeris will permit me, I would like to give a definite affirmative answer to Dr. Brout's question. To be sure, the derivation of the Boltzmann equation requires spatial uniformity but only over regions which contain a large number of molecules. Since at low densities a cube of side one mean free path contains a large number of molecules, I believe that the Boltzmann equation is valid for shock and other phenomena in which large changes occur within one mean free path.

O. Lamm: It is a question of a more general kind: whether the fact that the pure diffusion of multicomponent systems can be exactly described in terms of thermodynamic factors and friction coefficients (or mobilities) could be made fruitful in the further development of the kinetic theory of real gases. As the thermodynamic factors may be calculated from the equation of state, this question mainly concerns the possibility of a direct computation of the molar frictions.

It is pointed out that, when Onsager's [1] generalization of Fick's first law of diffusion is deduced from the concept of forces and frictions, the diffusion coefficients turn out to be *complicated* functions of the concentrations, the thermodynamic factors, and the frictional coefficients as soon as the number of components exceeds 2. From the point of view of the dynamic theory (as distinct from a kinematic description), it seems that the molar forces and frictions may be regarded as more fundamental properties than are the diffusion coefficients. The question arises whether or not they might also be simpler in the kinetic gas theory? However, the diffusion coefficients have advantages over the (conventional) friction coefficients from the experimental point of view, as illustrated by their independence of the labeling concentration in the limit of self-diffusion. For further details compare ref. 2.

C. F. Curtiss: The equations with which Mr. Klein opened his discussion and which describe the diffusion processes in a multicomponent mixture follow from the set of Boltzmann equations of the mixture. The derivation proceeds in a manner quite analogous to that used by Enskog and Chapman and Cowling in the treatment of binary mixtures. The equations of diffusion as used by Mr. Klein involved the binary diffusion coefficients of all possible pairs of gases in the multicomponent mixtures. These coefficients are very nearly independent of the composition. The derivation of the diffusion equations, since it depends upon the Boltzmann equation, is applicable only in the dilute limit. In this treatment it does not appear to be convenient to introduce the concepts of the thermodynamic factor and the frictional coefficient.

References

(1) L. Onsager, *Ann. N. Y. Acad. Sci.*, **46**, 241 (1945).
(2) O. Lamm, *Acta Chem. Scand.*, **8**, 1120 (1954).

PART VII

STATISTICAL THEORY OF ASYMMETRIC FISSION

MARIA GOEPPERT MAYER, *The University of Chicago, Institute for Nuclear Studies, Chicago, Illinois*

It is somewhat difficult for a nuclear physicist to talk about the subject of statistical mechanics of irreversible processes. There is, however, one case with which I am familiar in which an irreversible nuclear process has been treated by the methods of statistical mechanics. The process in question is that of the fission of uranium.

The work about which I wish to speak is that of P. Fong,[1] now at Utica College of Syracuse University, who did most of the work at Chicago for his Ph. D. thesis.

One of the most puzzling features of the fission process is the marked asymmetry of mass division. In fission produced by the capture of slow neutrons in U^{235}, the most probable mass division is that into two fragments of mass about 138 and 98, respectively. This mode of fission is about 600 times as frequent as that of symmetric fission into two fragments of mass 118. Figure 1 is the well-known double humped curve which one obtains when one plots the relative number of fission fragments against their mass.

For fission produced with higher energy particles, the asymmetry becomes less marked.

Previous calculations[2] have been made in order to investigate the question of how the energy at the saddle point, or, in chemical terms, the activation energy, depends on the nuclear shape. It was found that the lowest energy at the saddle point is obtained for a symmetric shape of the nucleus undergoing fission. Thus these calculations would predict symmetric, not asymmetric, fission.

However, fission is a rather slow process. As the nucleus proceeds from the saddle point to the point of actual separation, surface waves will travel many times across the nucleus, and thus the actual mode of separation is determined not at the saddle point, but at a much later stage. This has been strikingly demonstrated by calculations of Hill.[3]

The fission process thus seems to be similar to the dissociation of a complicated molecule in which the activation energy is the same for all dissociation processes. In such a case, the entropy will determine the probability of the various possible processes.

Fong's attack follows these ideas. His main postulate is that the probability of a mode of fission is proportional to the number of quan-

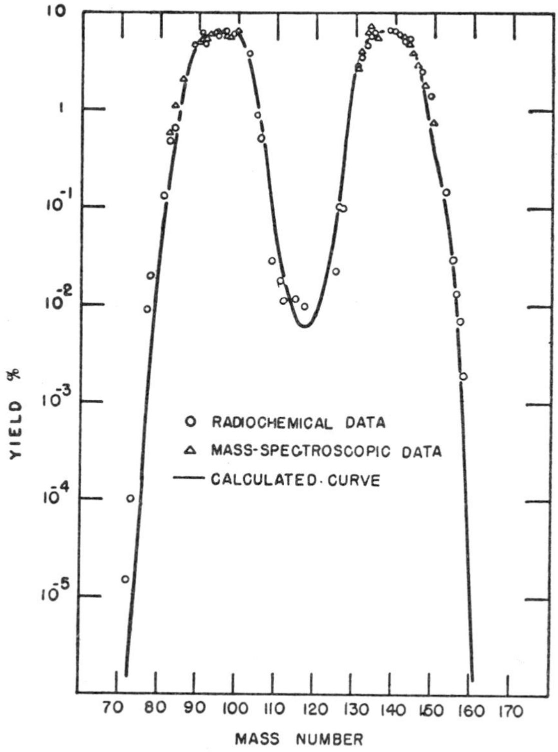

Fig. 1. Calculated mass distribution curve of fission products of U^{235} induced by thermal neutrons as compared with experimental data (P. Fong [1]).

tum states leading to this mode of fission at the critical moment when the decision is irrevocably made.

If one wishes to make any quantitative calculation one has to choose an approximate model of the nuclear shape at the critical moment, or moment of separation. Fong approximates the shape of the nucleus at this moment by two deformed nuclear fragments in contact (Fig. 2). The task is then to determine the number of quantum states for all different mass divisions of the fragments.

The number of quantum states depends sensitively on the amount of internal energy available for the different divisions. This energy can be divided in many ways among the different internal degrees of freedom of the two nuclear fragments, and thus determines the entropy.

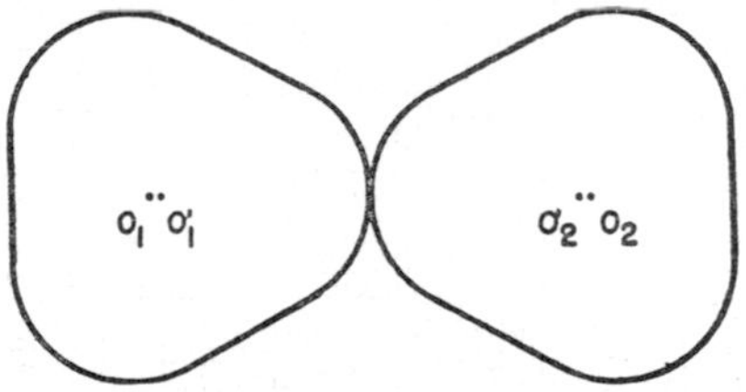

Fig. 2. Most probable deformation shape of symmetric fission of compound nucleus U^{236} just before the fragments separate, calculated on the basis of $P_3(\cos\theta)$ deformation only (P. Fong [1]).

The original nucleus of U^{235}, after capture of a neutron, is the nucleus $A = 236$ in an excited state. Its energy will be designated by m^*_{236}. Consider a division into two fragments A_1 and A_2, with $A_1+A_2 = 236$, and Z_1, Z_2, with $Z_1+Z_2 = 92$. The internal energy of these two deformed fragments in contact, E_i, is the difference between the mass of the excited U^{236} and the mass of the fragments in their ground state, less the Coulomb energy of repulsion (which, after separation, is transformed into kinetic energy), less the energy of deformation:

$$E_i(A_1, A_2) = m^*_{236} - \left[m_{A_1} + m_{A_2} + \frac{Z_1 \cdot Z_2 e^2}{R} + E_{\text{def}}\right]. \qquad (1)$$

The effective distance, R, in the Coulomb repulsion, depends on the deformation, and Eq. (1) will have a maximum for a certain deformation.

With this energy, then, the number of quantum states has to be determined, For nuclei, the relation between excitation energy, E, and the density of quantum states $N(E)$ is usually written in the form

$$N(E) = Ce^{\sqrt{aE}} \qquad (2)$$

Fong has checked this formula carefully against known level densities and finds that C depends only insensitively on the mass. a is proportional to the mass number A, and Fong adopts the value $a = 0.2A$, if the energy is measured in MeV. This form of the level density, incidentally, can be derived by treating the nucleus as a Fermi gas of independent nucleons in a box.

I shall merely sketch the ensuing mathematics. The important point of the level density formula is its strong dependence on the energy. I shall leave out (what Fong does not do) all factors which depend only insensitively on the mass division. The relative probability of a fission mode with given division of mass, charge, and deformation is then

$$P(A_1 A_2, Z_1 Z_2) = \int_0^{E_i} C_1 C_2 e^{\sqrt{a_1(E_i - E)} + \sqrt{a_2 E}} dE, \tag{3}$$

or, by the method of steepest descent

$$P(A_1 A_2, Z_1 Z_2) \, T e^{\sqrt{a_1 + a_2} \sqrt{E_i}} = e^{\sqrt{47.2 \, E_i}}. \tag{4}$$

If we are interested in mass division alone, (4) has to be summed over all charge divisions and all deformations. This is effectively accomplished by replacing E_i in (4) by its maximum value with respect to Z_1 and the deformation. Thus the final formula for the relative probability of a given mass division has, approximately, the simple form

$$P(A_1 A_2) \, T e^{\sqrt{47.2 \, E_i(A_1 A_2)_{\max}}}. \tag{5}$$

This formula shows that the most probable fission mode is that for which the amount of internal energy is largest. It is then necessary to investigate the value of E_i (Eq. 1) carefully.

In Eq. (1), m^*_{236}, the mass of U^{235} plus a neutron, is known. The deformation energy depends on the known surface tension of the nucleus and internal Coulomb repulsion and can thus be calculated. The same holds for the Coulomb repulsion. The main problem that remains is the determination of the masses of the fission fragments $m_{A_1} + m_{A_2}$. To give some orders of magnitude: the total energy released in fission is about 200 MeV. The kinetic energy, which appears in Eq. (1) as Coulomb energy, is about 170 to 175 MeV. The most probable deformation energy is of the order of 13 MeV. The amount of internal energy E_i available for distribution among the internal quantum states is, therefore, only about 7 to 12 MeV. Thus relatively small differences in the sum $m_{A_1} + m_{A_2}$ will have a larger influence on the relative fission probabilities.

The most arduous part of Fong's work was the determination of the masses of the primary fission fragments. I shall not discuss this phase of the work. Fong finds that, indeed, the internal energy has a maximum for fission into fragments of mass 138 and 98, which is about 5 MeV larger than the internal energy for symmetric fission.

Various other investigators have also calculated nuclear masses. Their results are in substantial, although not always detailed agreement with Fong. However, the main feature, that the internal energy is larger for assymetric fission, seems to be consistent with essentially all mass determinations.[4]

Fong calculated the whole fission curve. In Figure 1, the curve is Fong's computation, the points correspond to experimental data. The agreement is surprisingly excellent.

Clearly the method can be extended to fission at higher energies, to the determination of charge division, etc. Fong is continuing these calculations.

References

(1) P. Fong, *Phys. Rev.*, **102**, 434 (1956).

(2) S. Frankel and N. Metropolis, *Phys. Rev.*, **72**, 914 (1947).

(3) D. L. Hill, *Phys. Rev.*, **79**, 197 (1950).

(4) The fact that fission probability is connected with the stability of the resultant fragments has been pointed out by L. Meitner, *Nature*, **165**, 561 (1950); *Arkiv Fysik*, **4**, 383 (1952).

ON THE THEORY OF TRANSPORT PHENOMENA IN SOLIDS

D. TER HAAR, *The Clarendon Laboratory, Oxford, England*

Theoretical solid state physics has recently enjoyed a great deal of popularity. This is partly due to the increased industrial interest in the properties of metals and semiconductors, and partly probably due to the diminishing attractions of the often frustrating modern field theory. One of the objects of the theory of solids is to explain transport properties of metals and semiconductors, and it has become increasingly clear that the Lorentz-Sommerfeld theory is only a first — albeit in many cases a very satisfactory — approximation. For the purpose of the present discussion I shall describe the basic assumptions of this theory to be: (*1*) that the electrons are responsible for the transport of energy and charge, (*2*) that these electrons can be treated as a system of independent particles, apart from (*3*) a certain interaction between them and the lattice which can be described in terms of a mean free path or a relaxation time.

The idea that the carriers can be treated as noninteracting has recently come under fire, especially through the work of a number of Russian theorists (Vlasov, Landau, Bogolyubov, Vonssovski, and many others) and that of Bohm and Pines. I want to discuss a few aspects of these many-body theories with respect to the theory of transport phenomena. These considerations will probably not be of great importance for the theory of metals — at any rate in the present state of approximate answers — but they seem to me to be of relevance to the theory of transport properties of gas discharges (of interest these days as a possible source of thermonuclear energy), ferromagnetics, and dielectrics. First of all, however, I want to set the stage by pointing out a few aspects of solid state physics which clearly demanded a many-body approach, and by recapitulating briefly some other ways of extending and amending the elementary theory. Ferromagnetism and superconductivity show clearly the characteristics of cooperative phenomena (critical temperature, peaks in the specific heat) and thus provide us with a very important indication of the possible importance of many-body theories. In fact, it is rather a mystery why a theory such as the one proposed in 1950 by Fröhlich is at all able to predict superconductivity, since it is based on a one-electron picture. It seems that recently Migdal has definitely proved that Fröhlich's theory will not lead to superconductivity as was suspected for some time. However, we are still confronted here as in many other cases with the question as to why a one-electron theory can give an approximation at all to the behavior of a system of interacting particles. Similar questions are: Why is the elementary electron theory of metals so successful? Why is the shell model of the nucleus able to explain nuclear properties? This question has recently been discussed by Bontsch-Bruewitsch in a survey of many-body theories and to a first approximation the answer is that such many-body theories will often lead to the occurrence of "quasi-particles" which under certain circumstances may behave as the original constituent particles, but without interaction. Many forms of "quasi-particles" are familiar objects in solid state physics; I can mention holes in semiconductor theory, spinwaves in ferro- and antiferromagnetism, and phonons in lattices.

Let us now briefly consider the present status of independent particle transport theory. The elementary theory has been extended both by invoking several kinds of carriers, and by considering several scattering mechanisms. In semiconductor theory, for instance, one considers electron and hole conduction, as well as lattice (phonon) conduction; electrons and holes may be scattered by the lattice or by impurities, while the phonons may be scattered by the electrons, by impurities, by boundaries, or by other phonons. To fix the ideas let us consider how one calculates the thermal conductivity of a metal in the one-band approximation. The boundary conditions are the existence of a temperature gradient (dT/dx) in the x-direction, say, and the vanishing of the electrical current j. The thermal conductivity, $\varkappa$, is defined as the negative coefficient of the temperature gradient in the expression for the thermal current, w. This expression for the thermal current can be obtained, once we know the distribution functions $N(\mathbf{q})$ and $f(\mathbf{v})$ of the phonons and the electrons, and these in turn are solutions of the transport equations. We have thus the following set of equations:

$$-\varkappa\, dT/dx = w = \int c\varepsilon_q N(\mathbf{q})\, d\mathbf{q} + \int \tfrac{1}{2}mv^2 v_x f(\mathbf{v})\, d\mathbf{v}, \tag{1}$$

$$j = 0 = e\int v_x f(\mathbf{v})\, d\mathbf{v}, \tag{2}$$

$$\partial N/\partial t + \text{drift terms} = (\partial N/\partial t)_{\text{coll}}, \tag{3}$$

$$\partial f/\partial t + \text{drift terms} = (\partial f/\partial t)_{\text{coll}}. \tag{4}$$

Here, c is the velocity of sound, ε_q the energy of a phonon of wave vector $\mathbf{q}$, v_x the x-component of the electron velocity $\mathbf{v}$, e the electron charge, and m the (effective) electron mass.

Let us first of all consider the drift terms (the $\partial N/\partial t$ and $\partial f/\partial t$ terms can both be put equal to zero in a steady state). In Eq. (3) there is only one term, $c \operatorname{grad}_x N$, but in Eq. (4) there are two terms, $v_x \operatorname{grad}_x f - (e/m)E\, \partial f/\partial v_x$, where E is the electrical field which will be set up so that the condition of vanishing electrical current can be satisfied. The fact that the m occurring in our equations is an effective mass and not the mass of a free electron shows that one is really introducing a "quasi-particle," since the effective — or renormalized — mass comes about through the interaction of the carriers with the potential field of the lattice in which they are moving.

The right-hand sides of Eqs. (3) and (4) are simple, if one assumes the existence of a mean free path or of a relaxation time τ to enter into the theory as a phenomenological coefficient. In that case the right-hand sides are $(N-N_0)/\tau_q$ and $(f-f_0)/\tau_v$, where N_0 and f_0 are the equilibrium distributions. Here another problem arises, namely the question of the statistics of the particles. In the present case, one uses a Bose-Einstein distribution for the phonons and a Fermi-Dirac distribution for the electrons. If one does not assume the existence of a relaxation time one must consider the scattering processes in detail and matrix elements must be calculated (this must also be done if one wants to calculate the relaxation times). Once again the final expressions for the right-hand sides depend on the statistics of the particles involved.

Let us now consider how far the same procedure can be followed in a theory taking collective behavior into account. First of all we must consider the basic procedure of many-body theories, and we shall use as an example the Bohm-Pines plasma theory of metals, although either Tomonaga's or Brenig's method to introduce collective coordinates is probably more satisfactory. One first of all writes down the Hamiltonian of the system in the original coordinates — say $3N$ Cartesian coordinates and their conjugate momenta. Then one guesses the appropriate collective coordinates — in many cases (see Tomonaga) the Fourier components of the density down to a limiting wave length (collective coordinates q_k with $q_k = \Sigma_i \exp i(\mathbf{k} \cdot \mathbf{x}_i)$, where the summation is over all particles in the system and where $|\mathbf{k}| < k_c$). The system now contains more coordinates than degrees of freedom. This is taken care of by introducing subsidiary conditions which restrict the wave functions in such a way that the expectation values of the collective coordinates are equal to the expectation values of the appropriate functions of the original electron coordinates. Terms are added to the Hamiltonian containing the collective coordinates but possessing zero expectation values because of the subsidiary conditions.

Because of technical difficulties the existence of the subsidiary conditions is not taken into account in the further development of the theory. It is hoped that this will not seriously influence the final results. This is probably justifiable in the case of metals in thermodynamic equilibrium, since in that case the collective modes which possess a relatively high frequency will hardly be excited, which means that one can linearize the theory. This linearization is equivalent to the "random phase approximation" used by Pines, and one can give arguments to make it plausible that a neglect of the subsidiary conditions and the use of the random phase approximation are either both justified or both highly suspect.

As I mentioned a moment ago, the use of subsidiary conditions does not seem to be the best way to take care of the collective degrees of freedom. A more suitable method might be the one developed by Tomonaga, where one explicitly eliminates the extra degrees of freedom — otherwise his method is equivalent to the one of Bohm and Pines. Another possibility is to use Brenig's method, that is, incorporating the subsidiary conditions into the wave functions by using suitably generalized delta functions. In all events one is led to a splitting of the Hamiltonian into a part depending on the collective coordinates only and one depending on the particle (or quasi-particle) coordinates only. It is clearly imperative for the success of a theory of this kind that the interaction terms between collective and individual modes are sufficiently small to be negligible. A sufficient condition for this might be the existence of an energy gap between the lowest excited collective state and the lowest excited individual state.

The next step is the evaluation of the particle (or quasi-particle) energy levels and to find the statistics obeyed by them. In the case of metals the collective quanta are bosons and the quasi-particles fermions that behave as nearly free fermions, which accounts for the success of the free-electron theory. The quasi-particles are electrons surrounded by charge clouds which produce a screened Coulomb field.

The eigenvalues of the Hamiltonian of the system, neglecting interaction terms, are obtained by writing the wave function as a product of two factors, the first one referring to the collective modes, the second one being a Slater determinant of free-particle wave functions. Pines obtained in that way the one-particle energy levels $E(k)$ as a function of the wave number k. If one now assumes that the only change to be made in the evaluation of the transport coefficients is to substitute the new expression $E(k)$ for the one following from the ordinary band theory, one can derive in the usual manner the energy density function and the Fermi level and then derive expressions for the transport coefficients by using the usual formulae. This has been done by Blatt, who has shown that the relative difference between the transport coefficients calculated in this way and those calculated from the free electron theory should be small—provided the matrix elements which enter into the expression for the mean free path are not changed. As was emphasized by Blatt, it is unlikely that it will be possible in the near future to decide on the basis of experimental data whether or not Blatt's expressions give a better fit than the other ones, as there are too many unknown factors entering into the theory (for instance matrix elements are never actually calculated). It is difficult to make any quantitative predictions as to the influence of either the change in $E(k)$ or the change in using the quasi-particle wave functions instead of the particle wave functions in the matrix elements, but there might well be large changes in the cases of metals such as W or Ni where the energy level density function is changing rapidly so that a change in $E(k)$ may well change the Fermi level and thus dE/dk and d^2E/dk^2 at the Fermi level.

There are, however, other changes to be made in the calculation of the transport coefficients as outlined above. We see immediately that apart from the changes in the actual values of the various quantities entering into the theory there are two major additional points to be considered. First of all there enters another possible carrier of energy, and second there are additional scattering mechanisms to be taken into account. The additional carriers are the collective quanta which will behave in most respects as the phonons and which therefore may also contribute to the heat current. This will especiallly play a role in metals such as Bi where the lattice heat current is more important than the electron heat current. Second, the electrons and the phonons (as well as the collective quanta themselves) can now be scattered by the collective quanta; this may well be of importance even at high temperatures, since there electron-phonon scattering is the more important of the scattering mechanisms. If I may hazard a guess, I should say that in metals all these effects may well be small as long as we are dealing with alkali metals, but that they may become increasingly important for metals such as W and Bi. In gas discharges, however, the heat transport by collective modes may well increase the thermal conduction by several factors.

Discussion VII

J. Yvon: Avant d'ouvrir la discussion sur la communication de Madame Goeppert Mayer, je voudrais me permettre quelques remarques. Premièrement, Dr. Alder, dans sa communication, nous a prouvé qu'on pouvait faire de la mécanique statistique avec une centaine de particules. Il n'est sans doute pas souhaitable que la mécanique statistique pratique un impérialisme peu recommandable et s'incorpore abusivement la bonne moitié de la physique nucléaire qui s'intéresse aux noyaux lourds. Mais des problèmes communs paraissent en physique nucléaire et en mécanique statistique. La communication de Madame Goeppert Mayer en est un exemple. Lorsque Weisskopf introduit dans le noyau un potentiel complexe, il cherche à interpréter des phénomènes d'amortissement qui nous préoccupent également. En opposition avec le caractère clairement statistique de certains problèmes nucléaires, c'est le moment de rappeler que Madame Goeppert Mayer a expliqué certaines propriétés des noyaux et en particulier les nombres magiques, en attribuant aux nucléons des états individuels convenablement choisis. L'intervention d'états aussi simples dans les systèmes complexes est une antinomie impressionante et à laquelle il faut consacrer des méditations.

L. Van Hove (*to M. Goeppert Mayer*): What is the separation in energy between the saddle point and the point of separation of the fragments?

M. Goeppert Mayer (*to L. Van Hove*): The saddle point energy is about 5 MeV above the ground state of U^{236}. Thus the energy of the separated fragments in contact is about 6 to 10 MeV below the saddle.

P. G. de Gennes (*to M. Goeppert Mayer*): I would like to understand the argument for not taking into account the surface oscillations when computing the density of final levels, because they would be rather densely distributed in these heavy nuclei.

M. Goeppert Mayer (*to P. G. de Gennes*): The level formula should include *all* internal degrees of freedom, and therefore also those of surface vibrations.

M. Green (*to D. ter Haar*): Did I understand you to say that the plasmons play the role both of scattering centers as well as carriers?

D. ter Haar (*to M. Green*): Yes. This will probably be especially of importance in the case of gas discharges.

POSSIBILITÉ D'UNE THÉORIE MOLÉCULAIRE DE LA TURBULENCE ET LIMITES DE VALIDITÉ DE L'ÉQUATION DE NAVIER-STOKES

DANIEL MASSIGNON,* *Chargé de Recherches au Centre National de la Recherche Scientifique*

On développe habituellement la théorie statistique de la turbulence en admettant que le fluide turbulent est incompressible et que la vitesse locale *fluctuante* $\mathbf{u}(\mathbf{R}, t)$ est solution de la même équation de mouvement hydrodynamique que la vitesse locale *non fluctuante* d'un fluide non turbulent, l'équation de Navier-Stokes, qui est, en l'absence d'un champ de forces extérieures:

$$\varrho \frac{\partial \mathbf{u}}{\partial t} + \varrho \mathbf{u} \cdot \nabla \mathbf{u} + \nabla P - \mu \nabla^2 \mathbf{u} = 0. \tag{1}$$

Le champ aléatoire des vitesses turbulentes est alors défini dans l'espace et dans le temps au moyen de (1) par les valeurs non aléatoires de la pression P et de la viscosité μ et par des conditions aux limites convenablement choisies. En particulier, les coefficients de Fourier de cette vitesse fluctuante définissent le "spectre" de la turbulence et son tenseur de covariance est le tenseur de von Kármán, qui vérifie au cours du temps l'"équation de propagation" de la turbulence.

Dans ce type de théorie statistique, le caractère aléatoire ou fluctuant de la vitesse hydrodynamique est *posé a priori*: on ne le rattache pas d'une façon précise à une connaissance imparfaite des positions $\mathbf{q}_k$ et des impulsions $\mathbf{p}_k$ des corpuscules du fluide à un instant donné, telle que peut la décrire *en mécanique statistique* une solution de l'équation de Liouville:

$$\frac{\partial f_N}{\partial t} + [f_N, H] = 0 \tag{2}$$

du système des corpuscules du fluide.

Il serait pourtant intéressant de développer une théorie de la turbulence par les méthodes de la mécanique statistique des phénomènes de transport: bien que les fluctuations de la vitesse locale soient à

* Actuellement au Commissariat à l'Energie Atomique, Saclay (France).

l'échelle macroscopique, elles peuvent éventuellement être expliquées par une forme particulière de la densité de probabilité $f_N(\mathbf{q}, \mathbf{p}, t)$ dans l'espace des phases Γ. Cette densité doit donner, en principe, la loi des fluctuations de toutes les propriétés de transport d'un fluide, de sa vitesse locale, par exemple.

La Mécanique statistique permettra de préciser les *limites de la validité de l'équation de Navier-Stokes* pour un fluide en régime turbulent. C'est aussi le cadre naturel de l'étude des propriétés des *melanges de fluides* en régime turbulent et dans la région de transition entre les régimes turbulent et laminaire.

Or, une théorie statistique moléculaire de la turbulence rencontre un obstacle dès le départ: comment définir une vitesse locale fluctuante $\mathbf{u}(\mathbf{R}, t)$ en mécanique statistique? En théorie cinétique des gaz, la vitesse $\mathbf{u}$ en un point $\mathbf{R}$ est la valeur moyenne de la vitesse $\mathbf{p}/m$ d'une molécule quand on sait que cette molécule se trouve en ce point $\mathbf{R}$: la seule quantité fluctuante est la vitesse $\mathbf{p}/m$, qui n'est pas fonction de $\mathbf{R}$, ce que devrait être une vitesse hydrodynamique fluctuante. Mais la vitesse en un point $\mathbf{R}$ peut aussi être définie par le rapport

$$\mathbf{u}(R, t) = \frac{\overline{\mathbf{J}}(\mathbf{R}, t)}{\overline{\varrho}(\mathbf{R}, t)} \tag{3}$$

des valeurs moyennes dans l'espace des phases Γ

$$\bar{A} = \int_{\Gamma} d\Gamma\, A(\mathbf{q}, \mathbf{p}, \mathbf{R}) f_N(\mathbf{q}, \mathbf{p}, t) \tag{4}$$

du courant $\mathbf{J}$ et de la densité ϱ de masse:[1,2]

$$\mathbf{J} = \sum_{k=1}^{N} \mathbf{p}_k \delta(\mathbf{q}_k - \mathbf{R}), \qquad \varrho = \sum_{k=1}^{N} m_k \delta(\mathbf{q}_k - \mathbf{R}). \tag{5}$$

Pour un fluide dont les fluctuations en densité sont négligeables à l'échelle macroscopique, les fluctuations de la vitesse locale $\mathbf{u}(\mathbf{R}, t)$ sont proportionnelles à celles du courant de masse $\mathbf{J}$: C'est, en particulier, le cas d'un fluide incompressible. Mais dans le cas général, on ne peut définir les fluctuations de la vitesse locale, tandis que celles du courant de masse sont bien définies, en principe du moins.

Nous rencontrons ici une nouvelle difficulté: les δ de Dirac ne sont pas des fonctions au sens usuel et, par suite, le courant de masse n'a pas de valeur numérique définie. Cette difficulté peut être écartée en prenant une moyenne dans l'espace à trois dimensions du fluide, en effectuant un "coarse-graining in space." Prenons, par exemple, une moyenne du courant de masse **J** de (5) dans une petite sphère v de centre **R**: cette moyenne équivaut à remplacer les δ de Dirac de **J** par une fonction au sens usuel:[3]

$$\theta(\mathbf{q}-\mathbf{R}) = \int_v d\mathbf{s}\,\delta(\mathbf{q}-\mathbf{R}-\mathbf{s}). \tag{6}$$

Dans (6), le point $\mathbf{R}+\mathbf{s}$ est un point intérieur variable dans la petite sphère qui entoure le point **R**.

Cette moyenne dans l'espace du fluide peut être effectuée d'une façon plus générale, en insérant un poids $\theta(\mathbf{s})$, normé à l'unité, dans l'intégrale (6) et en étendant les limites d'intégration à tout l'espace du fluide: le poids $\theta(\mathbf{s})$ peut, par exemple, avoir une forme Gaussienne.

Le courant de masse *semi-fin*, ainsi défini avec une fonction θ de (6), a une valeur numérique en chaque point **R**, à la différence du courant de masse *fin* (5). De plus, on voit aisément que sa valeur moyenne sur l'espace des phases obéit à la même équation de transport que la moyenne dans l'espace des phases du courant fin (5), En effet, la mécanique statistique des phénomènes de transport[1,2] ne dépend pas, malgré les apparences, des propriétés caractéristiques des δ de Dirac, mais seulement de ce que leur argument est de la forme $(\mathbf{q}-\mathbf{R})$. L'équation de transport de l'impulsion du courant de masse semi-fin est encore

$$\frac{\partial \bar{\mathbf{J}}}{\partial t} + \nabla \cdot \bar{\mathbf{\Pi}} = 0, \tag{7}$$

où $\bar{\mathbf{\Pi}}$ est le courant d'impulsion, valeur moyenne d'une grandeur mécanique analogue à (6) (cf. réf. 2, 3):

$$\mathbf{\Pi} = \sum_{k=1}^{N} \left\{ \frac{1}{m_k} (\mathbf{p}_k \mathbf{p}_k) - \sum_{l \neq k}^{N} \frac{(\mathbf{r}_{kl}\mathbf{r}_{kl})}{|\mathbf{r}_{kl}|} u'_{kl}\, \alpha(\mathbf{r}_{kl} \cdot \nabla) \right\} \delta(\mathbf{q}_k - \mathbf{R}). \tag{8}$$

Dans (8), m_k est la masse de la molécule (k) du fluide, u_{kl} l'énergie potentielle d'interaction des molécules (k) et (l), supposée fonction de leur seule distance r_{kl} et $\alpha(x) = (e^x - 1)/x$. L'équation (7) est *équivalente à l'équation de Navier-Stokes pour une vitesse locale non fluctuante*, par example dans le cas d'un régime non turbulent. On le montre en remplaçant la valeur moyenne dans l'espace des phases de **J** par (3) et en introduisant la viscosité μ et la pression d'équilibre $\bar{P}$ par:

$$\bar{\mathbf{\Pi}} = \left[\bar{P} - \mu \left(\nabla \frac{\bar{\mathbf{J}}}{\bar{\varrho}} \right) \right] + \frac{1}{\bar{\varrho}} (\bar{\mathbf{J}}\bar{\mathbf{J}}). \tag{9}$$

(7) se réduit alors à (1) si le fluide est incompressible.

Or, on peut montrer[3] que les valeurs numériques exactes des courants de masse **J** et d'impulsion **Π** vérifient une équation de même forme que (7), conséquence comme (7) des équations canoniques de Hamilton,

$$\frac{\partial \mathbf{J}}{\partial t} + \nabla \cdot \mathbf{\Pi} = 0. \tag{10}$$

Mais cette équation *n'est pas en général equivalente à l'équation de Navier-Stokes* (1) *écrite pour une vitesse locale fluctuante.*

En effet, si l'on veut transformer l'équation (10) entre les courants de masse et d'impulsion fluctuants en une équation de Navier-Stokes, on peut admettre encore que le courant d'impulsion fluctuant est la somme du tenseur des pressions hydrodynamiques et d'un terme "non-linéaire" fluctuants:

$$\mathbf{\Pi} = \left[P - \mu\left(\nabla\frac{\mathbf{J}}{\varrho}\right)\right] + \frac{1}{\varrho}(\mathbf{JJ}). \tag{11}$$

Pour un fluide incompressible, l'équation (10), modifiée par (11), se réduit à l'équation de Navier-Stokes (1) pour une vitesse fluctuante $\mathbf{u} = \mathbf{J}/\varrho$, si la pression hydrodynamique est la somme d'une pression d'équilibre non fluctuante P et d'un terme visqueux fluctuant $-\mu\nabla\mathbf{u}$. Mais, dans le cas général, le fluide peut être compressible et si les fluctuations de la densité de masse sont d'un ordre de grandeur macroscopique, la notion de champ de vitesse doit être remplacée en hydrodynamique statistique par celle de champ de courant de masse. L'équation obtenue en combinant (10) et (11) est une équation en **J** qui n'est plus équivalente à l'équation de Navier-Stokes (1) pour une vitesse fluctuante **u**. Il est, d'ailleurs, possible que les fluctuations de la pression scalaire P, qui est en mécanique statistique la valeur moyenne dans l'espace des phases d'une grandeur mécanique fluctuante (cf. ref. 3), ne soient pas toujours négligeables à l'échelle macroscopique dans certains problèmes de turbulence.

Enfin, le *tenseur de corrélation spatiale du courant de masse* a des propriétés analogues en mécanique statistique à celles du tenseur de corrélation spatiale de von Kármán: son transformé de Fourier est aussi relié à la distribution spectrale de l'énergie sur les modes d'une décomposition harmonique de la vitesse locale, par exemple. Mais, en mécanique statistique, ce tenseur de corrélation est défini par une moyenne (4) sur l'espace des phases du fluide et cette définition conduit à des propriétés nouvelles. Ainsi, un développement du type Chapman-Enskog[4] ou du type Born-Green[5] pour les fonctions de distribution relatives à une ou deux molécules du fluide montre que ce tenseur de corrélation est de la forme

$$\overline{\mathbf{J}(\mathbf{R})\,\mathbf{J}(\mathbf{R}+\mathbf{r})} \\ = \bar{\varrho}(\mathbf{R})\,[3\varkappa T(\mathbf{R})+m\mathbf{u}^2(\mathbf{R})]\,\delta(\mathbf{r})-2m\mu_K(\nabla\mathbf{u})_{\text{sym.}}\delta(\mathbf{r})+\ldots \tag{12}$$

où $T(\mathbf{R})$ est la température de Maxwell et μ_K la partie "cinétique" de la viscosité μ. Dans (12), δ doit être remplacé par θ et $\mathbf{R}$ par $\mathbf{R}+(\mathbf{r}/2)$ quand on effectue sur le courant de masse $\mathbf{J}$ la moyenne (6) dans l'espace du fluide. Cette moyenne dans l'espace du fluide a, d'ailleurs, un vaste domaine d'applications: elle permet de calculer en mécanique statistique les dispersions et les corrélations de toutes les propriétés de transport fluctuantes d'un fluide[6] et de les relier aux propriétés thermodynamiques locales de ce fluide dans la méthode de l'ensemble grand-canonique de Gibbs.[7] On peut ainsi prévoir des anomalies pour la turbulence d'un fluide au voisinage de son point critique et pour celle d'un mélange de fluides au voisinage de son point critique de démixtion. On peut aussi construire un courant de masse fluctuant dans l'espace et dans le temps dans un formalisme du type Koopman.[3]

References

(1) D. Massignon, *Compt. rend.*, **228**, 1280, 1331 (1949).

(2) J. H. Irving et J. G. Kirkwood, *J. Chem. Phys.*, **18**, 817 (1950).

(3) D. Massignon, *Mécanique statistique des fluides. Fluctuations et propriétés locales*, Dunod, Paris, 1957.

(4) S. Chapman et T. G. Cowling, *The Mathematical Theory of Non-uniform Gases*, Cambridge Univ. Press, London, 1939.

(5) M. Born et H. S. Green, *Proc. Roy. Soc. London*, **A190**, 455 (1947).

(6) D. Massignon, *Compt. rend.*, **241**, 1259 (1955).

(7) D. Massignon, *Compt. rend.*, **241**, 1381 (1955).

COMPARISON BETWEEN MOLECULAR AND TURBULENT DIFFUSION PROCESSES

F. N. FRENKIEL, *Applied Physics Laboratory, The Johns Hopkins University, Silver Spring, Maryland*

It was initially my intention to present here some recent results on turbulent diffusion and to discuss their relation to molecular diffusion studies. I have, however, realized during the first days of this colloquium that it may be of some interest to this audience if I should attempt to describe what is being called turbulence by fluid dynamicists and to define at least some of the statistical characteristics used in the statistical theory of turbulence. With Professor Prigogine's agreement, I shall, therefore, emphasize the meaning of the definitions used in this theory.

One of the basic books in fluid dynamics is Sir Horace Lamb's *Hydrodynamics*, which in its last paper cover edition is now being sold in the United States not only in technical bookstores, but also in some drugstores. I have often wished that the publishers of this outstanding book would now include one additional page preceding Lamb's treatise with a statement saying something to the effect that "all fluid flows are turbulent under usual conditions, this book is concerned with the exceptional cases when the fluid flow is laminar." It is too often ignored that turbulence is a normally encountered phenomenon of fluid flow and that there is no need of being apologetic about it and implying that some very unusual imperfections of the physical surroundings are responsible for turbulent fluctuations. It would be more proper to consider laminar flow as an exception even if most of the theoretical knowledge in fluid dynamics refers to this exceptional case and although we are far from having many results for the more usual turbulent flow. I should like, therefore, to start by saying that in what follows I shall be concerned with the usual behavior of fluids which is accompanied by turbulent fluctuations not only in fluid flows, but often, as well, in a fluid which seems to be at rest. The characteristic feature of turbulence is that the turbulent fluctuations are, or at least appear to be, random. This implies immediately a certain similarity with molecular agitation and, indeed, in many studies a similar approach to the one used in kinetic theory of gases has been tried. It is, therefore, essential to emphasize that there are basic differences between the viewpoint of a fluid dynamicist and the viewpoint of a molecular physicist.

To the fluid dynamicist, a fluid is a continuum. The fluid dynamicist deals with such quantities as fluid velocities and attributes a value for this velocity at each point of the fluid. All the derivatives of this velocity are continuous in space and in time. By defining instantaneous fluid velocities at a point, molecular velocities must be eliminated by some averaging procedure. This means that we are separating what we shall call molecular agitation and fluid motion. It is in that arbitrary separation that most of the difficulties will reside in building a theory of turbulent motion which would satisfy both the fluid dynamicist and the molecular physicist. It seems rather logical to try to study turbulence in accordance with a view of statistical mechanics and to consider the fluid to be composed of molecules. If this approach is not widely used, it is because the probability theory and the general knowledge of turbulent behavior are not sufficiently advanced to apply such methods with satisfactory results. Of course, I hope that the participants in this colloquium will be able to advance statistical mechanics in this direction.

We assume that in a turbulent fluid the instantaneous velocities vary in time and in space in a random manner. The turbulent velocity field $\mathbf{V}(x, y, z, t)$ can then be represented as a vector field in space-time. This vector field will be assumed as being a sample selected from a set of vector fields which are functions of a parameter ω chosen at random in a measure space $\Omega = 1$. The physical turbulent velocity field $\mathbf{V}(x, y, z, t)$ is, therefore, represented by a mathematical vector field $\mathbf{V}(x, y, z, t, \omega_0)$ where ω_0 is a particular value of the parameter ω. Let us consider a scalar function $\Psi(x, y, z, t, \omega)$ of $\mathbf{V}$ (such as for instance $u, v, w, uv, \cdots, u^2v, uvw, \cdots$). An ensemble average (or mathematical expectation) of Ψ is defined by

$$\overline{\Psi}(x, y, z, t) = \int_\Omega \Psi(x, y, z, t, \omega)d\omega. \tag{1}$$

Other types of averages representing physically measurable quantities are obtained by averaging over time or space. The time average is defined as

$$\overline{\Psi}^{t}(x, y, z, \omega) = \lim_{T\to\infty} \frac{1}{2T}\int_{t-T}^{t+T} \Psi(x, y, z, t, \omega)dt \tag{2}$$

and a three-dimensional space average is given by

$$\overline{\Psi}^{s}(t, \omega) = \lim_{X, Y, Z\to\infty} \frac{1}{8XYZ}\int_{x-X}^{x+X}\int_{y-Y}^{y+Y}\int_{z-Z}^{z+Z} \Psi(x, y, z, t, \omega)\, dx\, dy\, dz. \tag{3}$$

Similarly one-dimensional averages can be considered along any direction (such as $\overline{\Psi}^{x}(y, z, t, \omega)$ along the x-axis). A space-time average can be defined as

$$\overline{\Psi}^{s,t}(\omega) = \lim_{X, Y, Z, T\to\infty} \frac{1}{16XYZT}\iiiint \Psi(x, y, z, t, \omega)\, dx\, dy\, dz\, dt. \tag{4}$$

The definition of the above averages implies that the limits can be assumed to exist. The relation between these various averages is not very well known and deserves further study. In a theoretical study, it is most convenient to use the ensemble average, and in most studies of the statistical theory of turbulence this average is used implicitly, although quite often it is stated otherwise. These studies usually assume one or more of the following equalities

$$\overline{\Psi}^{t}(x, y, z, \omega) = \overline{\Psi}^{s}(t, \omega) = \overline{\Psi}^{s,t}(\omega) = \overline{\Psi}(x, y, z, t), \tag{5}$$

which are not necessarily equivalent and may indeed be more restrictive than an assumption that the turbulence is a process statistically homogeneous in space and stationary in time.

Let us consider a homogeneous field of turbulence produced by some physical conditions at a given instant t_0 with the space-average velocity components $\bar{u}^s = \bar{v}^s = \bar{w}^s = 0$ and the turbulent energy $\varepsilon^2 = \overline{u^2}^s + \overline{v^2}^s + \overline{w^2}^s \neq 0$. If no other source of energy is available ε^2 decays by the action of the viscous forces. Otherwise saying the turbulent energy is transformed into molecular agitation. The equations of fluid dynamics have been shown to govern the laws of turbulent decay according to an equation of the form $\overline{u^2}^s = f(t-t_0)$. The function f depends on the nature of the turbulent field at the instant t_0. In this description we have not mentioned ensemble averaging, limiting ourselves to space averages. We are, however, assuming that the turbulent field at time t_0 is only a sample from a very large number of velocity patterns which can be produced by the same physical conditions and that for any such sample the statistical characteristics of turbulence are the same.

I shall devote some time to discuss certain types of correlation coefficients used to describe the characteristics of a turbulent field since in some papers presented during this colloquium reference was made to similar coefficients. Let us come back to the scalar functon Ψ and its averages. Whenever we define an average we are concerned with (1) the nature of the averaging process, and (2) the nature of the averaged function. We may consider, for instance, ensemble averages for the case when $\overline{\mathbf{V}} = 0$. A covariance tensor $\overline{\mathbf{VV}}$ with its nine scalar components $\overline{u^2}, \overline{v^2}, \overline{w^2}, \overline{uv}, \overline{uw}, \overline{vw}, \overline{vu}, \overline{wu}, \overline{wv}$ can then be defined. Dividing these components by the products of appropriate standard deviations, we find the corresponding correlation tensor with the components: $1, 1, 1, \overline{uv}/\sqrt{\overline{u^2}}\sqrt{\overline{v^2}}, \overline{uw}/\sqrt{\overline{u^2}}\sqrt{\overline{w^2}}$, etc. This correlation tensor refers to a velocity vector at a single point in space-time. Correlation tensors referring to two or more points in the space-time domain can also be defined. Particularly important in turbulence studies are correlation tensors between velocities at two points.

To simplify the notations when comparing various correlations, I shall refer only to the x-components of the velocities at two points of the space-time domain. In the most general case, we consider the correlation between $u_1(x_1, y_1, z_1, t_1, \omega)$ and $u_2(x_2, y_2, z_2, t_2, \omega)$ in the sample vector field ω. We may, in particular, be concerned with the simultaneous velocities at two points in the space or with succeeding velocities at a single point. Whether the turbulence is homogeneous and stationary or not we can take an ensemble average $\overline{u_1 u_2}$ and define a correlation coefficient $R_{1,2} = \overline{u_1 u_2}/\sqrt{\overline{u_1^2}}\sqrt{\overline{u_2^2}} = f(x_1, y_1, z_1, t_1, x_2, y_2, z_2, t_2)$. In a field of homogeneous turbulence $R_{1,2} = f(x_2-x_1, y_2-y_1, z_2-z_1, t_1, t_2)$ and if the turbulence is also stationary $R_{1,2} = f(x_2-x_1, y_2-y_1, z_2-z_1, t_2-t_1)$. In the first case, we can define space averages and assume $\overline{u_1 u_2}^s = \overline{u_1 u_2}$ and, in the second case, we can also define time- and space-time averages and assume $\overline{u_1 u_2}^s = \overline{u_1 u_2}^t = \overline{u_1 u_2}^{s,t} = \overline{u_1 u_2}$ (relation which corresponds to Eq. (5)).

The velocity averages and correlations to which we referred until now were concerned with instantaneous velocities at geometric points of the fluid. They are Eulerian in character. The instantaneous fluid velocity itself can be defined as a function of molecular velocities using a similar Eulerian viewpoint. In diffusion studies, whether molecular or turbulent, we shall, however, be concerned with the Lagrangian viewpoint. There is no difficulty in such an approach as far as molecular motions are concerned. We can, indeed, follow a molecule along its trajectory and describe the variations of its velocity as a function of time. The situation is different if we consider turbulent diffusion in a continuous fluid where the molecular motions have been eliminated and their velocities replaced by a velocity vector field. Instead of a molecule we must follow some fluid element. We can describe such a fluid element at a given time t as a group of molecules contained in a volume large compared with the molecular dimensions, but small compared to the extent of the fluid field. At time t, we may then assign to the fluid element an instantaneous fluid velocity equal to the space average (other averages can be used for this definition) of its molecular velocities. The study of turbulent diffusion is most often based on following the trajectories of such fluid elements. There is an obvious difficulty in this approach, since the fluid element is not a discrete particle like a molecule. While the group of molecules moves, with the instantaneous fluid velocity, its molecules disperse by molecular agitation. During the turbulent motion through the fluid field, molecules leave and enter the fluid element. After a sufficiently long time, the fluid element exchanges practically all its molecules with the surrounding fluid. One may make some analogies between the molecular free path and the interval of time required for this exchange. However, a molecular free path is unequivocally limited by two collisions, while fluid elements penetrate and mix with one another, and the mixing time is not clearly defined by the character of the turbulent field.

Consider, for a moment, a nonturbulent gas at rest in which we observe the dispersion of discrete particles. In the case of self-diffusion or the diffusion of one gas in another, we shall observe molecular diffusion. When the diffusing particles are colloids of sizes larger than the gas molecules, but not large enough to average out the effects of molecular agitation, then we observe Brownian motion. A particle of the size of our fluid element will average out the effects of molecular agitation and will not move at all in the nonturbulent gas at rest (neglecting the effects of gravitation).

A molecular theory of turbulent diffusion seems to be needed even more than the molecular approach to the Eulerian aspect of turbulence theory. In such a molecular theory it will be difficult to separate the effects of molecular agitation from the effects of turbulence. The question that should be raised is whether such a separation can be made without neglecting some major aspects of turbulent diffusion processes. I am not prepared to discuss this question today. In the description of the Lagrangian quantities, I shall, however, refer to the motion of fluid elements as described here in rather general terms.

Let us consider a fluid element A which at time t is located at a point $P(x, y, z)$ of the turbulent field. The instantaneous fluid velocity (we continue to refer to x-components only) attributed to this element is $u_A(t) = u_P(x, y, z, t)$. After an interval of time h the fluid element A has moved under the effect of turbulent fluctuations to another point of the field and, in general, $u_A(t+h) \neq u_P(x, y, z, t+h)$. We can again define a set of vector fields in a measure space $\Omega = 1$ and consider the turbulent field as represented by a sample ω_0 selected at random from this set. The velocity $u_A(t)$ in the physical field of turbulence is then represented by $u_A(t, \omega_0)$. An ensemble average $\bar{u}_A(t)$ can be easily defined. A time average $\bar{u}^t_A$ can be obtained by following the trajectory of the fluid element (or of its center of gravity). Space averages can be defined in a field of homogeneous turbulence by taking averages over simultaneous velocities of an increasing number of fluid elements.

A theoretical correlation coefficient can be defined as

$$R_A(t, h) = \frac{\overline{u_A(t, \omega)u_A(t+h, \omega)}}{\sqrt{\overline{u^2_A(t, \omega)}}\sqrt{\overline{u^2_A(t+h, \omega)}}}, \tag{6}$$

where ensemble averages are taken. In a field of homogeneous and stationary turbulence we may also consider a similar correlation coefficient by taking time averages along the trajectory of the same fluid element

$$R_A(h, \omega_0) = \frac{\overline{u_A(t, \omega_0)u_A(t+h, \omega_0)}^t}{\overline{u^2_A(\omega_0)}^t}. \tag{7}$$

In the latter case we refer to a single sample of a vector field ω_0 representing our physical turbulence field. One can also consider space averages in a field of homogeneous turbulence by averaging over simultaneous velocities of N fluid elements

$$R(t, h, \omega_0) = \frac{\overline{u_N(t, \omega_0)\, u_N(t+h, \omega_0)}^s}{\overline{u^2_N(t, \omega_0)}^s} \tag{8}$$

and a space-time correlation can be defined in a field of homogeneous and isotropic turbulence as

$$R(h, \omega_0) = \frac{\overline{u_N(t, \omega_0)\, u_N(t+h, \omega_0)}^{s,\,t}}{\overline{u_N^2(t, \omega_0)}^{s,\,t}}. \tag{9}$$

The two last correlation coefficients, (8) and (9), are of a mixed Lagrangian-Eulerian type, since, although the averaging procedure is applied to all fluid elements without regard to their individual identity, the product $u_N(t, \omega)u_N(t+h, \omega)$ under the averaging sign refers to the same fluid element.

The assumption of equality between averages, similar to (5), leads to assuming

$$R_A(h, \omega) = R(t, h, \omega) = R(h, \omega) = R_A(t, h). \tag{10}$$

It should be noted that, on this same basis, one cannot assume an equality between Lagrangian and Eulerian correlations. In particular, $\overline{u_A(t, \omega)u_A(t+h, \omega)}$ cannot be considered *a priori* equal to $\overline{u(x, y, z, t, \omega)u(x, y, z, t+h, \omega)}$. The relation between Eulerian and Lagrangian correlations (including Lagrangian-Eulerian type similar to (8) and (9)) is, in fact, a very fundamental problem for further research.

The correlation coefficients described by (6) to (9) are obtained following the velocities of the same fluid element. In the theory of turbulent diffusion, we shall also be concerned with Lagrangian correlations between two (or more) fluid elements in the space-time domain. In the most general case of the velocities of two fluid elements A and B, we shall be concerned with $u_A(x_1, y_1, z_1, t_1, \omega)$ and $u_B(x_2, y_2, z_2, t_2, \omega)$ in a sample vector field ω. A Lagrangian correlation coefficient $R_{A,B} = u_A u_B/\sqrt{\overline{u_A^2}}\sqrt{\overline{u_B^2}}$ can be defined whether the turbulence is or is not homogeneous and stationary. In general, $R_{A,B} = \psi(x_1, y_1, z_1, x_2, y_2, z_2, t_1, t_2)$. In homogeneous turbulence $R_{A,B} = \psi(x_2-x_1, y_2-y_1, z_2-z_1, t_1, t_2)$ and in homogeneous and stationary turbulence $R_{A,B} = \psi(x_2-x_1, y_2-y_1, z_2-z_1, h)$, where $h = t_2-t_1$. The Lagrangian correlation coefficient $R_{A,B}$ is, in general not equal to the Eulerian correlation coefficient $R_{1,2}$ mentioned before.

The statistical characteristics of turbulence can be described using a Fourier analysis of the vector velocity field. The field of velocity is considered as a superposition of periodical fluctuations of amplitudes varying as function of frequencies or wave numbers. Spectra of turbulence will describe the turbulent energy distribution according to frequency and wave number. The relation between the spectral tensors and correlation tensors have been studied by several authors. We shall here only indicate one example of the relations between the components of these tensors, referring to a correlation coefficient $R(h) = \overline{u_1 u_2}/\overline{u^2}$:

$$F(n) = 4\int_0^\infty \cos(2\pi nh)\, R(h)\, dh \quad \text{and} \quad R(h) = \int_0^\infty \cos(2\pi nh)\, F(n)\, dn,$$

where $F(n)$ is a one-dimensional spectrum and $\overline{u^2}F(n)$ is the distribution of the x-component of turbulent energy as a function of frequency.

During the present colloquium the question of representing correlation curves by an empirical function was mentioned. I shall, therefore, refer to some such representations used in turbulence studies. Four conditions necessary, but not sufficient, can be put down for the correlation functions:

$$-1 \leqq R(h) \leqq +1 \qquad \int_0^\infty R(h)\, dh > 0$$

$$\lim_{h\to 0} R(h) = 1 \qquad \lim_{h\to\infty} R(h) = 0.$$

Functions of the type $\exp(-k|h|)\Phi(h)$ and $\exp(-kh^2)\Phi(h)$ can, for instance, be used to represent correlation coefficients. In turbulence studies the additional condition, $d^2R(0)/dh^2 < 0$, may also be required. The first type of these functions does not fulfill this condition, but it can, nevertheless, be used to represent correlation coefficients as long as some precautions are taken.

Let us consider again a fluid element A now placed at time 0 at the origin of the coordinate axes in a field of homogeneous and stationary turbulence in which the mean velocity is zero. After an interval of time θ the fluid element will be located at a point (X, Y, Z) whose coordinates are

$$X(\theta) = \int_0^\theta u_A(\alpha)d\alpha; \quad Y(\theta) = \int_0^\theta v_A(\alpha)d\alpha; \quad Z(\theta) = \int_0^\theta w_A(\alpha)d\alpha.$$

Not much can be said about the individual values of X, Y, Z as functions of the dispersion time θ. However, one can say much more about the averages of X, Y, Z or of their functions (such as for instance X^2, Y^2, Z^2, XY, etc). We can again consider various average processes but for the present purpose we shall refer to ensemble averages and consider only the x-components. Since the fluid is at rest, $\bar{u} = 0$ and $\bar{X} = 0$. However, the variance $\overline{X^2}$ is a function of the dispersion time θ and depends on the nature of the turbulent field. Following the basic studies of G. I. Taylor, one can express $\overline{X^2}$ in either of the two forms

$$\overline{X^2}(\theta) = \overline{u^2} \int_0^\theta \int_0^\theta R_A(\alpha_2 - \alpha_1)\, d\alpha_1\, d\alpha_2 = 2\overline{u^2} \int_0^\theta (\theta - \alpha)\, R_A(\alpha) d\alpha \tag{11}$$

where $R_A(h)$ is the Lagrangian correlation coefficient. There are two asymptotic cases when $\overline{X^2}(\theta)$ does not depend on the shape of the correlation coefficient. The first is when the dispersion time θ is very large as compared to the Lagrangian scale of turbulence $L_A = \int_0^\infty R_A(\alpha) d\alpha$ and in which case

$$\overline{X^2}(\theta) \approx 2\overline{u^2}\, L_A \theta \qquad (\theta \gg L_A) \tag{12}$$

and the second when θ is very small as compared to the Lagrangian scale of turbulence, and

$$\overline{X^2}(\theta) \approx \overline{u^2}\, \theta^2 \qquad (\theta \ll L_A). \tag{13}$$

In the first case the variance $\overline{X^2}$ is proportional to the dispersion time θ; in the second it is proportional to its square.

When the dispersion time θ cannot be considered large enough to apply Eq. (12) or small enough to use Eq. (13), then the variance $\overline{X^2}(\theta)$ depends on the shape of the Lagrangian correlation coefficient. It should, however, be noted that there are still two other relations which can be used to represent $\overline{X^2}(\theta)$ without having to use explicitly the correlation coefficient itself. These relations are

$$\overline{X^2}(\theta) \approx 2\overline{u^2}\,(L_A \theta - \mathscr{L}) \qquad (\theta \gg L_A) \tag{14}$$

where $\mathscr{L} = \int_0^\infty \alpha R_A(\alpha)\, d\alpha$, and

$$\overline{X^2}(\theta) \approx \left[1 - \frac{1}{6}\frac{\theta^2}{\lambda^2}\right] \overline{u^2}\, \theta^2 \qquad (\theta \ll L_A) \tag{15}$$

where $1/\lambda^2 = -\frac{1}{2} d^2 R_A(0)/dh^2$ (λ is called the Lagrangian microscale of turbulence).

The case of a free particle moving under the influence of molecular agitation was first solved by Einstein in his studies of Brownian motion. The variance for the molecular diffusion is then

$$\overline{X^2}_{\text{mol}} = 2D\theta \tag{16}$$

where D is a diffusion coefficient. The similarity between this equation and Eq. (12) is evident. Equation (12) is valid only when the dispersion time θ is very large compared to the Lagrangian scale of turbulence. In Einstein's study of Brownian motion a similar relation between θ and the mean free path is implied. An equation similar to Eq. (16) can also be obtained from the molecular diffusion law stated by Fick in the form of a partial differential equation. In fact the Fickian law is sometimes applied in turbulence studies using a so-called coefficient of eddy diffusion K instead of the coefficient of molecular diffusion. Such an application is justified when $\theta \gg L_A$ and in which case we can rewrite Eq. (12) as

$$\overline{X^2}_{\text{turb}} = 2K\theta \qquad (\theta \gg L_A) \tag{17}$$

with $K = \overline{u^2}\, L_A$. When θ is not large compared to the Lagrangian scale of turbulance the use of the Fickian law will not be appropriate (unless we describe K as being variable).

Let us now consider a free particle moving under the simultaneous influence of molecular agitation and turbulent fluctuations. If we assume that there is no correlation between the molecular agitation and the turbulent fluctuations then one finds that the total variance for the particle is

$$\overline{X^2}_{\text{tot}}(\theta) = \overline{X^2}_{\text{turb}}(\theta) + \overline{X^2}_{\text{mol}}(\theta). \tag{18}$$

It is usual to expect that in a turbulent field the effects of turbulence will be much larger than the effects of molecular agitation. This is not always correct. Let us, for instance, consider the case when the dispersion time θ is very small compared to the Lagrangian scale of turbulence but still large compared to the mean free path of the molecules. In such a case Eq. (13) gives $\overline{X^2}_{\text{turb}} \approx \overline{u^2}\theta^2$ while Eq. (16) leads to $\overline{X^2}_{\text{mol}} \approx 2D\theta$ and therefore

$$\overline{X^2}_{\text{mol}}(\theta) > \overline{X^2}_{\text{turb}}(\theta) \text{ when } \theta < 2D/\overline{u^2}. \tag{19}$$

In the above relation we are assuming that there is no correlation between the molecular agitation and turbulence, although they are related since the turbulent energy is being destroyed by the viscosity of the fluid and transfers into molecular agitation. How it transfers and how to separate the two classes of fluctuations may become a basis of a more correct application of statistical mechanics to the future theories of turbulence.

The present paper was prepared for publication during the author's part-time association with David Taylor Model Basin. A part of the work was supported by the Bureau of Ordnance, Department of the Navy, under Contract NOrd 7386.

Discussion VIII

R. Eisenschitz (*to D. Massignon*): Does Reynold's law of similarity remain valid in your approach?

D. Massignon (*to R. Eisenschitz*): This law of similarity remains valid when the fluid is incompressible: then the Navier-Stokes equation may be derived from the principles of statistical mechanics for a fluctuating velocity. But if the fluctuations of mass density are on a macroscopic scale, there may be anomalies.

C. M. Tchen (*to L. Onsager*): The existing theories on the spectrum of isotropic turbulence are based either on dimensional reasonings (Kolmogoroff and Weiszäcker) or on the hypothesis of turbulent dissipation (Heisenberg). Your theory is based on the nature cascade of the transfer term. I wonder whether you have any hint of analytical basis (extremum methods of the transfer term) of the cascade phenomenon, and how it leads to the spectral law $a^2 \sim k^{-11/3}$ other than dimensional reasonings.

L. Onsager (*to C. M. Tchen*): Not much. The cascade hypothesis is supported by a comparison of the orders of magnitude of the various terms in the equation of motion. Once the cascade is accepted, the similarity theory and the associated spectral law seem very plausible.

M. Green (*to L. Onsager*): I would like to ask Dr. Onsager's opinion about where molecular statistical mechanics might impinge on the theory of turbulence. Is there perhaps a need for a statistical mechanical explanation of the nonviscous dissipation?

L. Onsager (*to M. Green*): No. In reality, the dissipation is always viscous and in the idealized case of a nonviscous liquid the molecular structure is not needed nor even recognized. The cascade mechanism assumed in the similarity theory needs no auxiliary mechanism if the theory is valid at all. Molecular fluctuations might perhaps provide a mechanism for *initiation* of instability where none other is available.

I. Prigogine: I think that a really satisfactory theory of turbulence has to have its roots in the Liouville equation. Let us consider the case of a dilute gas. So far as I understand from Batchelor's well-known book, the basic problem is to understand the decay of long-range correlations. Now in Liouville's equation the terms corresponding to streaming without interaction between molecules will propagate correlations while collisions cut them. Therefore, Liouville's equation may give us really some information about the evolution of the basic correlations.

H. L. Frisch: It would appear that turbulent diffusion can be described by a Fickian diffusion equation with a time-dependent diffusion coefficient for all time only when the Lagrangian correlation coefficient is sufficiently "peaked," since only then the Einstein-Smoluchowski integral equation can be replaced by the Fickian differential equation. The Lagrangian correlation coefficient is presumably determined by the dynamics of the turbulent fluid motion (i.e., is connected to the Navier-Stokes equations). Can it be shown from the details of the dynamics of the turbulent fluid motion that the Lagrangian correlation coefficient must indeed be "peaked"? In this connection the fact that the asymptotic limit for long times and the short time limit of the mean-square displacement is independent of the exact shape of the Lagrangian correlation coefficient is very noteworthy and indicative of the importance of recognizing the existence of a double time scale already emphasized in other connections during this congress.

F. N. Frenkiel: In the case of Brownian motion the correlation coefficient has the form $\exp(-k|h|)$ and is peaked. This is not the case for the turbulent fluctuations for which the second derivative of the Lagrangian correlation coefficient $d^2R(h)/d^2h$ is negative at $h = 0$. In fact this condition is not in general verified for such functions as $\exp(-k|h|)\,\Phi(h)$ and one has to take some precautions when using them to represent a correlation coefficient.

G. Uhlenbeck (*to F. N. Frenkiel*): There exists a derivation of the Stokes-Navier equations from the Boltzmann equation, assuming that the relative gradients over the mean free path are small. Have you any doubts about the validity of this derivation?

F. N. Frenkiel (*to G. Uhlenbeck*): Several mathematicians have some doubts about the validity of the Navier-Stokes equations as applied to a turbulent field. Their objections are based on the fact that the turbulent components are treated as regular functions with derivatives and that such an assumption is not compatible with the random behavior of a turbulent field. In fact, this difficulty can be solved by using "statistical derivatives." I have, however, no doubts about the validity of the derivation of the Navier-Stokes equations, and I have no objection to their present use in the theory of turbulence.

G. Klein (*to F. N. Frenkiel*): What is the relevance of the Ornstein formula

$$\bar{x}^2 = 2\,\frac{nT}{\gamma}\,t + \frac{m\bar{n}^2}{\gamma}\,(e^{-2\gamma t}-1)$$

to turbulence theory?

F. N. Frenkiel (*to G. Klein*): There is a direct similarity between the Ornstein formula and the turbulence theory. Indeed if the Langrangian correlation coefficient would be of the form $R_A = \exp\ (-|h|/L_A)$ then $\overline{X^2} = 2\overline{u^2}L_A\theta + 2\overline{u^2}L_A^2[\exp\ (|\theta|/L_A)-1]$.

R. Brout (*to F. N. Frenkiel*): What is the meaning of turbulent energy? Where does turbulent energy end and thermal energy begin? One says this turbulent energy is dissipated. Can this be made precise?

F. N. Frenkiel (*to R. Brout*): This question involves a very fundamental problem in the theory of turbulence. The separation between what is called turbulent energy and the thermal energy is made in a somewhat arbitrary way. Present theories of turbulence are based on a continuum approach to the fluid. One refers to "instantaneous velocities at a point" of the fluid. The turbulent energy refers to the velocities of the fluid while the thermal energy refers to the velocities of molecules. How small should an interval of time be to be "instantaneous" and an element of volume to become a "point" is a matter of physical assumptions. It sometimes depends on the instruments which are used by the experimental scientists and which often determine the scale at which the turbulence is observed. Turbulent energy is said to be dissipated by viscosity and transformed into thermal energy.

R. Brout: I may comment briefly about the recent theory of turbulence due to Chandrasekhar. One may try to justify the Chandrasekhar assumption in a naive fashion by expanding the Fourier components $a_k(t)$ in a power series in time by formally solving the equations of motion. One then examines the fourth moment $a_{k_1}a_{k_2}a_{k_3}a_{k_4}$ and finds that this fourth moment is nonvanishing for all k's different. This is in disagreement with what Chandrasekhar assumes. This does not necessarily invalidate the theory. It may happen that these annoying terms combine to give a vanishing contribution after long times.

G. Uhlenbeck (*to R. Brout*): I am not in a position to speak with any authority on the Chandrasekhar theory. However, I would like to point out that the superposition approximation refers to correlations in two different space *and* time points, and may not be valid if the two times coincide.

H. N. V. Temperley: I agree entirely with the point made by Dr. Frenkiel that my treatment of the steady state implicitly involves some assumption about the "time of a measurement." For my treatment to hold, local pressures must stay reasonably constant during the time the assembly takes to work through a large number of the accessible states. This seems reasonable, for example, for a gas being forced steadily through a nozzle. A simple example of a "steady" assembly to which my treatment would *not* be valid would be a cavitating liquid.

J. G. Kirkwood (*to G. Uhlenbeck*): Dr. Kirkwood asked Dr. Uhlenbeck's opinion about the validity of the Stokes-Navier equations.

G. Uhlenbeck (*to J. G. Kirkwood*): I agree that there is *no* derivation of the Stokes-Navier equations from the molecular point of view if the system is dense (like liquids). However, I think that there is little doubt at present that turbulence may be based on the Stokes-Navier equations. It may be of course *convenient* to start from the Boltzmann equation instead.

G. Careri (*to F. N. Frenkiel*): In some experiments in liquid metals we have found that the turbulence diffusion might well be lower than the molecular diffusion, in agreement with the conclusion of Dr. Frenkiel.

PART IX

THE APPROACH TO EQUILIBRIUM IN QUANTUM STATISTICS — A PERTURBATION TREATMENT TO GENERAL ORDER

LÉON VAN HOVE, *Instituut voor Theoretische Fysica der Rijksuniversiteit, Utrecht, The Netherlands*

1. Of all the well-known examples of perturbations occurring in quantum mechanical many-particle systems and giving rise to an irreversible behavior toward thermodynamic equilibrium (such as the interaction between phonons in crystals, the interaction between electrons and phonons in crystalline conductors, the intermolecular forces in imperfect gases), some common characteristic properties can be isolated which are to be held responsible for the irreversible effects. They are here adopted as a basis for a general perturbation theory of the approach to thermodynamic equilibrium for quantum systems.

Most of these characteristic properties also hold for the perturbations occurring in another class of quantum systems with many degrees of freedom, the familiar interactions between quantized fields. We have analyzed these properties in some detail in Sections 1, 2, and 3 of a paper dealing with perturbations of the field-theoretical type,* neglecting the complications connected with polarization and other discrete quantum numbers (see Section 1 of a second paper[2] on the same subject). These properties will be used hereunder.

The formal distinction between the perturbations of field-theoretical type and those occurring in the many-particle system of statistical mechanics is quite simple. With the notation introduced in I it amounts to the existence or absence of poles in the quantity $D_l(\alpha)$ considered, for each unperturbed stationary state $|\alpha\rangle$, as a function of the complex variable l. Our first aim in the present lecture is to indicate by a simple argument how this formal distinction is related to the main physical difference between the two types of perturbation, to wit the presence or absence of a dissipative character in the perturbed motion of the system. We shall afterward indicate how the perturbations

* See ref. **1.** This paper will be quoted as "I" and its equations as e.g. (I. 1.1).

typical of statistical mechanics, i.e., the perturbations for which the functions $D_l(\alpha)$ have no poles, can be shown to produce a time evolution leading toward thermodynamic equilibrium, thereby extending to general order in the perturbation the well-known linear differential equation describing slow irreversible motions.[3]

2. Consider at time 0 a state φ_0 coinciding with an unperturbed stationary state $|\alpha_0\rangle$. Consider its time variation under the perturbation V

$$\varphi_t = \exp\left[-it(H+\lambda V)\right]\varphi_0. \tag{2.1}$$

The probability of finding the state φ_t in the initial state φ_0 is expressed by

$$p_t = |\langle\varphi_0|\varphi_t\rangle|^2. \tag{2.2}$$

We shall establish that

$$\begin{cases} \lim_{t\to\infty} p_t \neq 0 & \text{when } D_l(\alpha_0) \text{ has one or more poles,} \quad (2.3) \\ \lim_{t\to\infty} p_t = 0 & \text{when } D_l(\alpha_0) \text{ has no pole.} \quad (2.4) \end{cases}$$

The result (2.3) means that, when $D_l(\alpha_0)$ has a pole, the state φ_t retains the initial state φ_0 as a nonvanishing component, even after very long times. This is expected[1] for perturbations of the field-theoretical type, causing self-energy and cloud effects (at least in the absence of divergences, a prerequisite for straight application of the formalism). According to (2.4), on the contrary, if $D_l(\alpha_0)$ has no pole, the initial state φ_0 is no longer represented in φ_t after long times, as is natural to expect in the case of a dissipative system where the characteristics of the initial state are eventually lost into complicated motion of all the many degrees of freedom.

The proof of (2.3) and (2.4) runs as follows. Since we work as in I in the limit of an infinite system, the spectrum of unperturbed states $|\alpha\rangle$ forms a continuum. In order to insure proper normalization we have therefore to adopt for φ_0 a wave packet of narrow extension in α-space around the unperturbed stationary state

$$\varphi_0 = (\Delta\alpha)^{-1/2}\int_{\Delta\alpha}|\alpha\rangle\, d\alpha, \tag{2.5}$$

where $\Delta\alpha$ indicates the small volume of α-space over which the packet extends. The point α_0 is supposed to lie in $\Delta\alpha$. We have to work in the limit of small $\Delta\alpha$ (otherwise the spreading of the wave packet due to the unperturbed motion would always cause p_t to vanish for large t, so that our considerations would become irrelevant). We have with (I.5.4)

$$\langle\varphi_0|\varphi_t\rangle = (i/2\pi)\int dl \exp(-ilt)\,\langle\varphi_0|R_l|\varphi_0\rangle, \tag{2.6}$$

the integration being extended counterclockwise along a contour encircling a sufficiently large portion of the real axis. Taking into account the δ-singularity in the matrix element of the resolvent $R_l = (H+\lambda V-l)^{-1}$,

$$\langle\alpha'|R_l|\alpha\rangle = \delta(\alpha'-\alpha)D_l(\alpha) + \text{regular part},$$

one easily concludes that in the limit of small $\Delta\alpha$

$$\langle\varphi_0|R_l|\varphi_0\rangle = D_l(\alpha_0).$$

Consequently

$$\langle\varphi_0|\varphi_t\rangle = \sum_{E_n} \exp(-iE_nt)[\partial D_l^{-1}(\alpha_0)/\partial l]^{-1}_{l=E_n}$$
$$+ (i/2\pi)\int_{-\infty}^{\infty} dE\cdot\exp(-iEt)\,[D_{E-i0}(\alpha_0)-D_{E+i0}(\alpha_0)].$$

The E_n's are the poles of $D_l(\alpha_0)$. As shown in I, they are necessarily real. The integral extends over the intervals of the real axis where $D_l(\alpha_0)$ has a finite discontinuity for l crossing the axis. We now note that this integral tends to zero for $t\to\infty$. The results (2.3) and (2.4) are thereby established.

3. In order to study the way in which the statistical properties of the system vary with time under the influence of the perturbation, we investigate the t-dependence of the probabilities $P(t|\alpha_1, \alpha_0)$ for transitions in the time interval t between groups of unperturbed stationary states composed each of many states $|\alpha\rangle$, but having each a very narrow extension in α-space. The accurate definition of $P(t|\alpha_1, \alpha_0)$ in the formalism of continuous spectra here used can be given as follows. Take the initial state (2.5) considered above. Take also an operator A diagonal in the unperturbed representation,

$$A|\alpha\rangle = A(\alpha)|\alpha\rangle. \tag{3.1}$$

Consider the average value $\langle\varphi_t|A|\varphi_t\rangle$, φ_t being again given by (2.1).

In the limit of small $\Delta\alpha$ one has the relation

$$\langle\varphi_t|A|\varphi_t\rangle = \int A(\alpha)\, d\alpha P(t|\alpha, \alpha_0). \tag{3.2}$$

Explicit calculation of $\langle\varphi_t|A|\varphi_t\rangle$, along the lines already used in Section 2, shows that (3.2) is the eigenvalue for $|\alpha_0\rangle$ of the operator (diagonal in the $|\alpha\rangle$-representation)

$$\{\exp[i(H+\lambda V)t] \cdot A \cdot \exp[-(iH+\lambda V)t]\}_d$$

where the symbol $\{\cdots\}_d$ for the diagonal part of an operator has the same meaning as in I. The relation (3.2) may therefore be chosen as the defining equation for the transition probabilities $P(t|\alpha, \alpha_0)$. These probabilities also occur in the average value $\langle\varphi_t|A|\varphi_t\rangle$ when the initial state is of the more general form

$$\varphi_0 = \int |\alpha\rangle d\alpha c(\alpha),$$

under the assumption that the phases of the amplitudes $c(\alpha)$ are incoherently distributed. One then finds

$$\langle\varphi_t|A|\varphi_t\rangle = \int A(\alpha)\, d\alpha P(t|\alpha, \alpha_0)\, d\alpha_0 |c(\alpha_0)|^2.$$

We now proceed to study $P(t|\alpha, \alpha_0)$ for $t > 0$. Consider the eigenvalue for $|\alpha_0\rangle$ of the diagonal* operator $\{R_l A R_{l'}\}_d$, where A is diagonal as in (3.1). This eigenvalue depends linearly on the $A(\alpha)$'s and can therefore be written

$$\int A(\alpha)\, d\alpha X_{ll'}(\alpha, \alpha_0),$$

where $X_{ll'}(\alpha, \alpha_0)$ is independent of A. From the definition of the transition probabilities one then obtains

$$P(t|\alpha, \alpha_0) = -(2\pi)^{-2} \int dl \int dl' \cdot \exp[i(l-l')t] \cdot X_{ll'}(\alpha, \alpha_0),$$

the integration paths being the same as in (2.6). A simple transformation gives

$$P(t|\alpha, \alpha_0) = \int_{-\infty}^{\infty} dE \cdot P_E(t|\alpha, \alpha_0) \tag{3.3}$$

with for positive t

$$P_E(t|\alpha, \alpha_0) = (2\pi)^{-2} \int_{-\infty}^{\infty} dE' \cdot \exp(iE't) \cdot X_{E+\frac{1}{2}E'-i0,\, E-\frac{1}{2}E'+i0}(\alpha, \alpha_0). \tag{3.4}$$

* By diagonal we will always understand diagonal in the $|\alpha\rangle$-representation.

It will appear that the quantity $P_E(t|\alpha, \alpha_0)$, in contrast to the transition probability $P(t|\alpha, \alpha_0)$ itself, satisfies a simple integro-differential equation in time. To derive it we need the following definition. Consider, for arbitrary diagonal A, the eigenvalue for $|\alpha_0\rangle$ of the diagonal operator

$$\{(V-\lambda VD_lV+\lambda^2VD_lVD_lV-\cdots)A(V-\lambda VD_{l'}V+\lambda^2VD_{l'}VD_{l'}V-\cdots)\}_{id},$$

where the symbol $\{\cdots\}_{id}$ for irreducible diagonal part is taken over from I. This eigenvalue is a linear functional of the eigenvalues $A(\alpha)$ of A and can consequently be written

$$\int A(\alpha)d\alpha W_{ll'}(\alpha, \alpha_0),$$

where $W_{ll'}(\alpha, \alpha_0)$ is independent of A. A simple reduction of diagonal parts of operators, of the type repeatedly used in I, gives an explicit expression of $X_{ll'}(\alpha, \alpha_0)$ in terms of the newly defined $W_{ll'}(\alpha, \alpha_0)$. It is

$$\left.\begin{aligned} X_{ll'}(\alpha, \alpha_0)=&D_l(\alpha)D_{l'}(\alpha)\delta(\alpha-\alpha_0)+\lambda^2D_l(\alpha)D_{l'}(\alpha)W_{ll'}(\alpha, \alpha_0)D_l(\alpha_0)D_{l'}(\alpha_0)\\ &+\lambda^4D_l(\alpha)D_{l'}(\alpha)\int W_{ll'}(\alpha,\alpha')D_l(\alpha')D_{l'}(\alpha')d\alpha'W_{ll'}(\alpha',\alpha_0)D_l(\alpha_0)D_{l'}(\alpha_0)+\cdots. \end{aligned}\right\} \quad (3.5)$$

On the other hand, the basic identity of I, Eq. (I.3.13), taken for two values l and l' of the complex argument and subtracted, gives

$$G_l-G_{l'}=\{(V-\lambda VD_lV+\cdots)(D_l-D_{l'})(V-\lambda VD_{l'}V+\cdots)\}_{id},$$

i.e., an identity for the function $W_{ll'}(\alpha, \alpha_0)$:

$$\int[D_l(\alpha)-D_{l'}(\alpha)]\,d\alpha W_{ll'}(\alpha, \alpha_0) = G_l(\alpha_0)-G_{l'}(\alpha_0). \quad (3.6)$$

Using the relation (I.3.12) between the diagonal operators G_l and D_l it is then a simple matter to derive from (3.6) the following identity for $X_{ll'}(\alpha, \alpha_0)$:

$$\left.\begin{aligned} i(l-l')X_{ll'}(\alpha, \alpha_0) =& i[D_l(\alpha)-D_{l'}(\alpha)]\cdot\delta(\alpha-\alpha_0)\\ &+\lambda^2\int\tilde{W}_{ll'}(\alpha, \alpha')d\alpha'X_{ll'}(\alpha', \alpha_0)-\lambda^2\int d\alpha'\tilde{W}_{ll'}(\alpha', \alpha)\cdot X_{ll'}(\alpha, \alpha_0), \end{aligned}\right\} \quad (3.7)$$

where we have put

$$\tilde{W}_{ll'}(\alpha, \alpha_0) = i[D_l(\alpha)-D_{l'}(\alpha)]\,W_{ll'}(\alpha, \alpha_0). \quad (3.8)$$

In view of (3.4) it is directly clear that (3.7) implies an integro-differential equation in time for the quantity $P_E(t|\alpha, \alpha_0)$. After some algebra the equation is found to be $(t > 0)$

$$\left.\begin{aligned} dP_E(t|\alpha, \alpha_0)/dt &= \pi^{-2}\delta(\alpha-\alpha_0)\cdot \mathscr{I}m\, e^{2iEt}\int_{-\infty}^{\infty} dE'\cdot e^{-2iE't}D_{E'+i0}(\alpha) \\ &\quad + 2\pi\lambda^2\int_0^t dt'\int w_E(t-t'|\alpha, \alpha')\,d\alpha' P_E(t'|\alpha', \alpha_0) \\ &\quad - 2\pi\lambda^2\int_0^t dt'\int d\alpha'\, w_E(t-t'|\alpha', \alpha)P_E(t'|\alpha, \alpha_0) \end{aligned}\right\} \tag{3.9}$$

with the definition (for $t > 0$)

$$w_E(t|\alpha, \alpha_0) = (2\pi)^{-2}\int_{-\infty}^{\infty} dE' \exp(iE't)\,\tilde{W}_{E+\frac{1}{2}E'-i0,\, E-\frac{1}{2}E'+i0}(\alpha, \alpha_0). \tag{3.10}$$

(3.3) and (3.9) are our *fundamental equations for the approach to thermodynamic equilibrium,* valid to general order in the perturbation. In order to insure unicity of the solution they have to be supplemented by the initial condition

$$P_E(0|\alpha, \alpha_0) = 0, \tag{3.11}$$

easily derived from (3.4) by noting that $X_{E+l,\, E-l}(\alpha, \alpha_0)$ tends to zero as l^{-2} for $|l| \to \infty$.

A short and incomplete analysis of the fundamental equations will be given in the following sections. First, however, a remark must be made concerning the initial condition (3.11). The initial value of $P(t|\alpha, \alpha_0)$ is obviously, from the definition,

$$P(0|\alpha, \alpha_0) = \delta(\alpha-\alpha_0),$$

which seems to be in conflict with (3.11) in view of (3.3). This difficulty is only apparent and is due to the fact that the convergence of the integral over E in (3.3) becomes increasingly bad when $t \to 0$. The situation is cleared up by studying the small t behavior of $P_E(t|\alpha, \alpha_0)$, which is determined to the second order in t by the inhomogeneous term on the right-hand side of (3.9).

4. We consider in the present section the implications of (3.9) in the case of very small perturbations (limiting case $\lambda \to 0$). For finite t the value of $P_E(t|\alpha, \alpha_0)$ can then be obtained by explicit integration of (3.9), neglecting the two last terms, which are of order λ^2, and replacing $D_{E'+i0}(\alpha)$ by its unperturbed value $[\varepsilon(\alpha)-E'-i0]^{-1}$. The result is

$$P_E(t|\alpha, \alpha_0) \simeq \pi^{-1}\cdot[\varepsilon(\alpha)-E]^{-1}\cdot \sin(2[\varepsilon(\alpha)-E]t)\cdot\delta(\alpha-\alpha_0).$$

For t finite but large compared to characteristic times of the unperturbed motion this reduces to the constant value

$$P_E(t|\alpha, \alpha_0) \simeq \delta[\varepsilon(\alpha)-E] \cdot \delta(\alpha-\alpha_0). \tag{4.1}$$

Coming to the region of very large times, of order λ^{-2}, we may use Eq. (3.9) without the inhomogeneous term (which is then zero) and adopt (4.1) as the initial condition. We may further neglect the t'-dependence of $P_E(t'|\alpha, \alpha_0)$ in the time integrals because the time variation of $w_E(t|\alpha, \alpha_0)$ takes place over periods characteristic of the unperturbed motion. This gives the purely differential equation

$$\left.\begin{aligned} dP_E(t|\alpha, \alpha_0)/dt &= 2\pi\lambda^2 \int w_E(\alpha, \alpha')\, d\alpha' P_E(t|\alpha', \alpha_0) \\ &\quad - 2\pi\lambda^2 \int d\alpha' w_E(\alpha', \alpha) \cdot P_E(t|\alpha, \alpha_0) \end{aligned}\right\} \tag{4.2}$$

with (see (3.10))

$$w_E(\alpha, \alpha_0) = \int_0^\infty dt\, w_E(t|\alpha, \alpha_0) = (2\pi)^{-1} \tilde{W}_{E-i0,\, E+i0}(\alpha, \alpha_0). \tag{4.3}$$

For the latter expression we can restrict ourselves to the limiting value for $\lambda \to 0$, which is found to be

$$w_E(\alpha, \alpha_0) \simeq \delta[\varepsilon(\alpha)-E]\, w^0(\alpha, \alpha_0), \tag{4.4}$$

where $w^{(0)}(\alpha, \alpha_0)$ is the quantity defined by the condition that for any diagonal operator A the eigenvalue of $\{VAV\}_d$ for the state $|\alpha_0\rangle$ is

$$\int A(\alpha)\, d\alpha w^{(0)}(\alpha, \alpha_0).$$

In view of (4.1) and (4.4) the solution of (4.2) must have the form

$$P_E(t|\alpha, \alpha_0) = \delta[\varepsilon(\alpha)-E]\, P(t|\alpha, \alpha_0). \tag{4.5}$$

Eliminating E from (4.2) through this substitution one finds that the transition probability $P(t|\alpha, \alpha_0)$ verifies

$$\left.\begin{aligned} dP(t|\alpha, \alpha_0)/dt &= 2\pi\lambda^2 \int \delta[\varepsilon(\alpha)-\varepsilon(\alpha')]\, w^{(0)}(\alpha, \alpha')\, d\alpha' P(t|\alpha', \alpha_0) \\ &\quad - 2\pi\lambda^2 \int d\alpha' \cdot \delta[\varepsilon(\alpha')-\varepsilon(\alpha)]\, w^{(0)}(\alpha', \alpha) \cdot P(t|\alpha, \alpha_0), \end{aligned}\right\} \tag{4.6}$$

which is the familiar equation for the approach to equilibrium in quantum statistics under the influence of a small perturbation.[3]

The important difference between the approximate equations (4.2) and (4.6) and the exact equation (3.9) is of course that the latter expresses dP_E/dt in terms of integrals over the values of P_E at previous times, whereas the approximate equations only involve the values of P_E or P at one single time. In other words, the approximate equations describe a Markoff process, while the exact one, involving an integration over the past history of the system, is non-Markoffian. The origin of this situation is clearly revealed by the analysis of the present section. The integration over the past history extends over time intervals characteristic of the unperturbed system, and, in the case of small perturbations, the change of P_E is very slow and is negligibly small over such intervals.

There is still another difference between the exact and the approximate equations. The latter are completely homogeneous in the time (i.e., invariant for translations in time), whereas the time $t = 0$ plays a special role in the first. This can best be understood when the transition probabilities are used to describe the time evolution of the system for an initial state $\varphi_0 = \int |\alpha\rangle d\alpha c(\alpha)$ with incoherently distributed phases. This incoherence of phases in the $|\alpha\rangle$-representation is destroyed under the action of the perturbation, and it is only for very small perturbations, where long times are involved before the perturbation has any appreciable effect, that enough incoherence is maintained at all times to make the stochastic process homogeneous in the time. A more detailed analysis of this situation was published earlier.[4]

5. We return to the exact equation (3.9) and investigate in the present section its asymptotic solution for large times. We are not yet able to give a complete treatment of this important question[5] and we take as our starting point the assumption that $P_E(t|\alpha, \alpha_0)$ becomes time-independent for large t. Let us call $P_E^{\mathrm{as}}(\alpha, \alpha_0)$ this constant value ("as" stands for asymptotic). It satisfies the equation obtained by leaving out in (3.9) the left-hand side and the first term of the right-hand side. Using (4.3) we find this equation to be

$$\int \tilde{W}_{E-i0,\, E+i0}(\alpha, \alpha')d\alpha' P_E^{\mathrm{as}}(\alpha', \alpha) = \left[\int d\alpha' \tilde{W}_{E-i0,\, E+i0}(\alpha', \alpha)\right] \cdot P_E^{\mathrm{as}}(\alpha, \alpha_0). \quad (5.1)$$

It is an eigenvalue equation which can be shown to determine $P_E^{\mathrm{as}}(\alpha, \alpha_0)$ uniquely (except for a normalization factor).[5]

We further assume (as is always done implicitly in the usual discussion of the asymptotic solution for the approximate equation (4.6)) that, whenever the dissipation of a state $|\alpha_0\rangle$ under the effect of the perturbation involves a state $|\alpha\rangle$, the former state is involved in a symmetrical way in the dissipation of the latter. In more accurate mathematical terms (see the definition of the family of states x_α in Section 4 of I) what we mean by our assumption is that $|\alpha_0\rangle$ is included in x_α whenever $|\alpha\rangle$ is included in x_{α_0}, the transition schemes involved in ascertaining these inclusions (see (I.4.3) and the text thereafter) being inverse of each other. It can be shown that this condition can be satisfied only when the functions $D_l(\alpha)$ have no poles, i.e., for the dissipative systems considered in this lecture. In view of the hermiticity of V this condition implies the symmetry relation

$$W_{ll'}(\alpha, \alpha_0) = W_{l'l}(\alpha_0, \alpha), \tag{5.2}$$

which is nothing but the extension to general order of the well-known symmetry property

$$w^{(0)}(\alpha, \alpha_0) = w^{(0)}(\alpha_0, \alpha)$$

commonly used (but usually very incompletely justified by invoking only the hermiticity of V) in connection with the approximate equation (4.6). Using (5.2) in conjunction with the identity (3.6), one easily verifies that the eigenvalue problem (5.1) has the solution

$$P_E^{\text{as}}(\alpha, \alpha_0) = f_E(\alpha_0)\, i[D_{E-i0}(\alpha) - D_{E+i0}(\alpha)], \tag{5.3}$$

which verifies $P_E^{\text{as}} \geqq 0$ if the normalization constant $f_E(\alpha_0)$ is positive. This constant is easily calculated from the normalization condition

$$\int d\alpha\, P_E^{\text{as}}(\alpha, \alpha_0) = (2\pi i)^{-1}[D_{E+i0}(\alpha_0) - D_{E-i0}(\alpha_0)] \tag{5.4}$$

itself a consequence of (3.4) and of the identity

$$\int d\alpha X_{ll'}(\alpha, \alpha_0) = (l-l')^{-1} \cdot [D_l(\alpha_0) - D_{l'}(\alpha_0)] \tag{5.5}$$

(the latter relation readily obtains from (3.5) and (3.6)). Applying (5.4), one finds for $f_E(\alpha_0)$ a value which, substituted in (5.3), gives

$$P_E^{\text{as}}(\alpha, \alpha_0) = \left[\int \Delta_E(\alpha')d\alpha'\right]^{-1} \cdot \Delta_E(\alpha) \cdot \Delta_E(\alpha_0), \tag{5.6}$$

where we have used the abbreviation

$$\Delta_E(\alpha) = (2\pi i)^{-1}[D_{E+i0}(\alpha) - D_{E-i0}(\alpha)].$$

The asymptotic transition probabilities are of course, according to (3.3),

$$P^{\text{as}}(\alpha, \alpha_0) = \int_{-\infty}^{\infty} dE\, P_E^{\text{as}}(\alpha, \alpha_0). \tag{5.7}$$

Eqs. (5.6) and (5.7) constitute an important result. We affirm that it corresponds to *asymptotic establishment of microcanonical equilibrium.*

To verify this point, we note first that the microcanonical average of a diagonal operator A for the value E of the total energy $H+\lambda V$ is

$$\langle A\rangle_E = \left[\int \Delta_E(\alpha)\,d\alpha\right]^{-1} \cdot \int A(\alpha)\Delta_E(\alpha)\,d\alpha.$$

On the other hand, when the system is in the initial state φ_0 given by (2.5) with small $\Delta\alpha$, the probability of having the value E for the energy $H+\lambda V$ is $\Delta_E(\alpha_0)$. Consequently the average value to be expected for A if the system, initially in the state φ_0, has been brought in the course of time to microcanonical equilibrium is

$$\int_{-\infty}^{\infty} dE \cdot \langle A\rangle_E \cdot \Delta_E(\alpha_0),$$

an expression indeed identical to

$$\int A(\alpha)\,d\alpha\, P^{\text{as}}(\alpha, \alpha_0), \tag{5.8}$$

as seen from (5.6) and (5.7). The same verification can of course be repeated for an initial state φ_0 of the form $\int |\alpha\rangle d\alpha c(\alpha)$ with incoherent phases in the amplitudes $c(\alpha)$. The expression (5.8) is then replaced by

$$\int A(\alpha)\,d\alpha\, P^{\text{as}}(\alpha, \alpha_0)\,d\alpha_0 |c(\alpha_0)|^2.$$

We still want to stress two points. First, as required in a general perturbation treatment, the microcanonical distribution describing the statistical properties of the system after long times is the exact distribution in presence of the perturbation, and not the unperturbed distribution as is conventionally obtained from the approximate equation (4.6). Second, our discussion suggests for the quantity P_E, until now used as a purely formal tool, a simple physical interpretation: it is that portion of the total transition probability P which is contributed by the motion in the energy shell $H+\lambda V = E$. One will notice that this interpretation is corroborated by our result (4.5) relative to small perturbations.

References

(1) L. Van Hove, *Physica*, **21**, 901 (1955).

(2) L. Van Hove, *Physica*, **22**, 343 (1956).

(3) W. Pauli, *Festschrift zum* 60. *Geburtstage A. Sommerfelds*, Hirzel, Leipzig, 1928, p. 30; L. Van Hove, *Physica*, **21**, 517 (1955).

(4) See L. Van Hove, ref. 3.

(5) *Note added in proof:* A complete treatment has been given since and can be found in a more detailed paper dealing with the subject of the present lecture. See L. Van Hove, *Physica*, **23**, 441 (1957).

THE BOLTZMANN EQUATION IN QUANTUM-STATISTICAL MECHANICS

SYU ONO, *College of General Education, University of Tokyo, Tokyo, Japan*

I. INTRODUCTION

There have been three attempts to derive the quantum mechanical Boltzmann equation from the Liouville equation: by Green,[1] by Kirkwood and Ross,[2] and by Mori and Ono.[3] The latter two are based on the time-average procedure over a small interval of time. In our previous article it was, however, shown that, if the perturbation theory is used to calculate time average of the density matrix, one obtains the Uhling-Uhlenbeck equation in the first order corresponding to the Born collision approximation.

In the present article it will be shown that the Uhling-Uhlenbeck equation with the exact collision cross-section can be obtained if one carries out exactly the time-averaging procedure with the use of the mathematical technique mainly developed by Watson and Bruekner[4, 5] in the theory of multiple scattering. The brief description of the scattering matrix which is most essential for our present theory will be given below.

II. SCATTERING MATRIX

Les us consider a system of two colliding molecules. Separating off the over-all translational motion of the system, one may write the Schrödinger equation in the form

$$-\frac{\hbar^2}{2\mu}\nabla^2\psi(\mathbf{r})+u(\mathbf{r})\,\psi(\mathbf{r}) = \varepsilon\psi(\mathbf{r}), \tag{2.1}$$

where $\mathbf{r}$ is the relative coordinate, ∇^2, the Laplacian operator with respect to $\mathbf{r}$, μ the reduced mass, and $u(\mathbf{r})$ the intermolecular potential.

If the incident beam is described by $\psi_0 = e^{i\mathbf{k}_0\cdot\mathbf{r}}$, the complete wave function is given by

$$\psi = e^{i\mathbf{k}_0\cdot\mathbf{r}}+g(\mathbf{r}). \tag{2.2}$$

Here, $g(\mathbf{r})$ represents the outgoing scattered wave, which approaches asymptotically

$$g(\mathbf{r}) \to \sigma(\theta, \varphi)\frac{e^{ikr}}{r}, \tag{2.3}$$

$\sigma(\theta, \varphi)$ being the strength of the scattered wave as a function of the angle of scattering.

It is known that the outgoing scattered wave is given by

$$g(\mathbf{r}) = -\frac{\mu}{2\pi\hbar^2}\int u(\mathbf{r}')\psi(\mathbf{r}')\frac{e^{ik_0|\mathbf{r}-\mathbf{r}'|}}{|\mathbf{r}-\mathbf{r}'|}d\mathbf{r}'. \tag{2.4}$$

From the above equation, we have

$$\sigma(\theta, \varphi) = -\frac{\mu}{2\pi\hbar^2}\int e^{-i\mathbf{k}'\cdot\mathbf{r}'}u(\mathbf{r}')\psi(\mathbf{r}')d\mathbf{r}', \tag{2.5}$$

with $\mathbf{k}' = k\mathbf{n}$, $\mathbf{n}$ being the unit vector in the direction of $\mathbf{r}$.

Here let us introduce the operator

$$\frac{1}{\frac{\hbar^2}{2\mu}(k_0^2+\nabla^2)+i\varepsilon},$$

which acts on the function $e^{i\mathbf{k}\cdot\mathbf{r}}$ in the following way:

$$\frac{1}{\frac{\hbar^2}{2\mu}(k_0^2+\nabla^2)+i\varepsilon}e^{i\mathbf{k}\cdot\mathbf{r}} = \frac{1}{\frac{\hbar^2}{2\mu}(k_0^2-k^2)+i\varepsilon}e^{i\mathbf{k}\cdot\mathbf{r}} \tag{2.6}$$

Throughout this article ε is a small positive parameter which is set equal to zero after the integration is carried out. From (2.6) we can show

$$\lim_{\varepsilon\to+0}\frac{1}{\frac{\hbar^2}{2\mu}(k_0^2+\nabla^2)+i\varepsilon}f(\mathbf{r}) = -\frac{\mu}{2\pi\hbar^2}\int\frac{e^{ik_0|\mathbf{r}-\mathbf{r}'|}}{|\mathbf{r}-\mathbf{r}'|}f(\mathbf{r}')d\mathbf{r}' \tag{2.7}$$

Then the asymptotic form of $\psi(\mathbf{r})$ may be written as

$$\psi(\mathbf{r}) = e^{i\mathbf{k}_0\cdot\mathbf{r}} + \frac{1}{\frac{\hbar^2}{2\mu}(k_0^2+\nabla^2)-u(\mathbf{r})+i\varepsilon}u(\mathbf{r})\psi(\mathbf{r}). \tag{2.8}$$

By an algebraic manipulation, we obtain

$$\psi(\mathbf{r}) = e^{i\mathbf{k}_0 \cdot \mathbf{r}} + \frac{1}{\frac{\hbar^2}{2\mu}(k_0^2+\nabla^2)+i\varepsilon} u(\mathbf{r})\,\psi(\mathbf{r}). \tag{2.9}$$

If ε is negative, the second term of the right-hand side of (2.9) represents an incoming wave. Substitution of (2.9) into (2.5) leads to

$$\sigma(\theta, \varphi) = -\frac{\mu}{2\pi\hbar^2}\int e^{-i\mathbf{k}'\cdot\mathbf{r}'}\,\mathbf{t}\,e^{i\mathbf{k}_0\cdot\mathbf{r}'}\,d\mathbf{r}', \tag{2.10}$$

where $\mathbf{t}$ is the operator defined as

$$\mathbf{t} = u(\mathbf{r})+u(\mathbf{r})\frac{1}{\frac{\hbar^2}{2\mu}(k_0^2+\nabla^2)-u(\mathbf{r})\pm i\varepsilon}u(\mathbf{r}). \tag{2.11}$$

We call $\mathbf{t}$ the scattering matrix. This type of operator was first introduced in the multiple scattering theory.

On the other hand, the Born approximation for $\sigma(\theta, \varphi)$ is

$$\sigma(\theta, \varphi) = -\frac{\mu}{2\pi\hbar^2}\int e^{-i\mathbf{k}'\cdot\mathbf{r}'}\,u(\mathbf{r}')\,e^{i\mathbf{k}_0\cdot\mathbf{r}'}\,d\mathbf{r}'. \tag{2.12}$$

Comparing (2.11) with (2.12), it is seen that the exact cross-section of collision is obtained instead of the Born approximation if $\mathbf{t}$ is used in place of $u(\mathbf{r})$.

III. WAVE MATRIX

In the case of a system consisting of N identical molecules, the Schrödinger equation is written as

$$(\mathbf{K}+U)\Psi = E\Psi, \tag{3.1}$$

where

$$\mathbf{K} = -\sum_{i=1}^{N}\frac{\hbar^2}{2m}\nabla_i^2 \tag{3.2}$$

$$U = \tfrac{1}{2}\sum_{i\neq j} u_{ij}, \tag{3.3}$$

u_{ij} being the intermolecular potential between the ith and jth molecules. Let Φ be the eigenfunction of $\mathbf{K}$ corresponding to the eigenvalue E. In terms of the Møller[6] wave matrix $\Omega^{(\pm)}$, Ψ may be expressed in the form

$$\Psi^{(\pm)} = \Omega^{(\pm)} \Phi. \tag{3.4}$$

$\Omega^{(\pm)}$ satisfies the Lippman-Schwinger equation[7]

$$\Omega^{(\pm)} = 1 + \frac{1}{E \pm i\varepsilon - \mathbf{K}} U \Omega^{(\pm)}, \tag{3.5}$$

to which Chew and Goldberger introduced the solution

$$\Omega^{(\pm)} = 1 + \frac{1}{E \pm i\varepsilon - \mathbf{K} - U} U \tag{3.6}$$

Using the Schrödinger equation

$$\Psi = \frac{1}{E - \mathbf{K}} U \Psi,$$

we obtain from (3.4) and (3.5)

$$\Phi = \frac{i\varepsilon}{(E - \mathbf{K}) \pm i\varepsilon} \Psi^{(\pm)} \tag{3.7}$$

In the same manner, we have from (3.4), (3.6), and $(\mathbf{K} - E)\Phi = 0$,

$$\Psi^{(\pm)} = \frac{i\varepsilon}{(E - \mathbf{K} - U) \pm i\varepsilon} \Phi. \tag{3.8}$$

We can show that $U\Omega^{(\pm)}$ may be developed in the series as follows:[5, 9]

$$U\Omega^{(\pm)} = \tfrac{1}{2} \sum_{i \neq j} \mathbf{t}_{ij} + \tfrac{1}{4} \sum_{i \neq j} \sum_{i' \neq j'} u_{ij} \frac{1}{a} \mathbf{t}_{i' j'} + \cdots, \tag{3.9}$$

where

$$a = E - \mathbf{K} \pm i\varepsilon, \tag{3.10}$$

and

$$\mathbf{t}_{ij} = u_{ij} + u_{ij} \frac{1}{E - \mathbf{K} - u_{ij} \pm i\varepsilon} u_{ij}. \tag{3.11}$$

$\mathbf{t}_{ij}$ is the scattering matrix (2.11) defined in the space of the wave function of N molecules.

Further, $\Omega^{(\pm)}$ is not unitary, but satisfies the relations

$$\Omega^{(\pm)\dagger} \Omega^{(\pm)} = 1 \tag{3.12}$$

and

$$\Omega^{(\pm)}\,\Omega^{(\pm)\dagger} = 1 - \sum_{\alpha} \Psi_{\alpha}\rangle\langle\Psi_{\alpha}, \tag{3.13}$$

where Ψ_α are the wave functions of bound states.

IV. MODIFICATION OF THE LIOUVILLE EQUATION

The Gibbsian ensemble of the quantum mechanical system is described by the density matrix $\boldsymbol{\rho}$, which obeys the quantum mechanical Liouville equation

$$\begin{aligned}\frac{d\boldsymbol{\rho}}{dt} &= \frac{i}{\hbar}[\boldsymbol{\rho}\mathbf{H}-\mathbf{H}\boldsymbol{\rho}] \\ &= \frac{i}{\hbar}[\boldsymbol{\rho}\mathbf{K}-\mathbf{K}\boldsymbol{\rho}]+\frac{i}{\hbar}[\boldsymbol{\rho}U-U\boldsymbol{\rho}].\end{aligned} \tag{4.1}$$

For simplicity no external fields are assumed to be exerting.

The formal solution of (4.1) is given by

$$\begin{aligned}\boldsymbol{\rho}(t+\tau) = e^{-i\mathbf{K}\tau/\hbar}\,\boldsymbol{\rho}(t)e^{i\mathbf{K}\tau/\hbar} + \frac{i}{\hbar}\int_0^\tau d\sigma e^{i\mathbf{K}(\sigma-\tau)/\hbar} \\ \times\{e^{-i\mathbf{H}\sigma/\hbar}\,\boldsymbol{\rho}(t)e^{i\mathbf{H}\sigma/\hbar}\,U - Ue^{-i\mathbf{H}\sigma/\hbar}\,\boldsymbol{\rho}(t)e^{i\mathbf{H}\sigma/\hbar}\}e^{-i\mathbf{K}(\sigma-\tau)/\hbar}.\end{aligned} \tag{4.2}$$

We shall restrict ourselves to the case of no bound states. Then the operator $\Omega^{(-)}$ can be considered as a unitary operator, and we may rewrite (4.1) as

$$\frac{d\boldsymbol{\rho}}{dt} = \frac{i}{\hbar}[\boldsymbol{\rho}\mathbf{K}-\mathbf{K}\boldsymbol{\rho}] + \frac{i}{\hbar}[\boldsymbol{\omega}\mathbf{T}^\dagger - \mathbf{T}\boldsymbol{\omega}^\dagger], \tag{4.3}$$

where

$$\mathbf{T} = U\Omega^{(-)}, \tag{4.4}$$

$$\boldsymbol{\omega} = \boldsymbol{\rho}\Omega^{(-)\dagger}. \tag{4.5}$$

Let $\{\psi_t(\mathbf{r})\}$ be a complete orthonormal set of functions of a single molecule. We introduce the quantized wave functions defined by

$$\boldsymbol{\psi}(\mathbf{r}) = \sum_t a_t \psi_t(\mathbf{r}), \tag{4.6}$$

$$\boldsymbol{\psi}^\dagger(\mathbf{r}) = \sum_t a_t^\dagger \psi_t^*(\mathbf{r}), \tag{4.7}$$

where a_t and a_t^+ are an annihilation operator and a creation operator, respectively.

In this article the calculations will be carried out only for the case of Bose-Einstein statistics, but the calculations can be done in the same manner for the Fermi-Dirac case.

Here we shall use the reduced density matrices of a system of identical particles in **r**-representation:

$$\varrho^{(n)}(\mathbf{r}_1, \mathbf{r}_2, \cdots, \mathbf{r}_n; \mathbf{r}_1', \mathbf{r}_2', \cdots, \mathbf{r}_n') = \text{trace}\,[\boldsymbol{\psi}^\dagger(\mathbf{r}_1')\boldsymbol{\psi}^\dagger(\mathbf{r}_2') \cdots \boldsymbol{\psi}^\dagger(\mathbf{r}_n')\boldsymbol{\psi}(\mathbf{r}_1) \cdots \boldsymbol{\psi}(\mathbf{r}_n)\boldsymbol{\rho}], \tag{4.8}$$

which was given by Husimi and Nishiyama.[10]

Differentiating (4.8) for the singlet reduced density matrix $\varrho^{(1)}$ and using the Liouville equation (4.3), we have

$$\frac{d\varrho^{(1)}(\mathbf{r}, \mathbf{r}')}{dt} = \frac{i}{\hbar}\,\text{trace}\,[\boldsymbol{\psi}^\dagger(\mathbf{r}')\boldsymbol{\psi}(\mathbf{r})\{\boldsymbol{\rho}\mathbf{K} - \mathbf{K}\boldsymbol{\rho}\}] + \frac{i}{\hbar}\,\text{trace}\,[\boldsymbol{\psi}^\dagger(\mathbf{r}')\boldsymbol{\psi}(\mathbf{r})\{\boldsymbol{\omega}^\dagger\mathbf{T}^\dagger - \mathbf{T}\boldsymbol{\omega}\}]. \tag{4.9}$$

Using (3.9) and retaining only the first term, which corresponds to a single binary collision, we obtain

$$\mathbf{T} = \tfrac{1}{2}\sum_{i\neq j}\mathbf{t}_{ij} \tag{4.10}$$

In terms of the quantized wave functions, we may rewrite (4.10) as

$$\mathbf{T} = \tfrac{1}{2}\int \boldsymbol{\psi}^\dagger(\mathbf{r}_1)\,\boldsymbol{\psi}^\dagger(\mathbf{r}_2)\,\mathbf{t}_{12}\,\boldsymbol{\psi}(\mathbf{r}_1)\,\boldsymbol{\psi}(\mathbf{r}_2)\,d\mathbf{r}_1\,d\mathbf{r}_2. \tag{4.11}$$

Inserting the above equation in (4.9) we obtain

$$\begin{aligned}
\frac{d\varrho^{(1)}(\mathbf{r}, \mathbf{r}')}{dt} &= \frac{i}{\hbar}\frac{\hbar^2}{2m}[\nabla_{\mathbf{r}}^2\varrho^{(1)}(\mathbf{r}, \mathbf{r}') - \nabla_{\mathbf{r}'}^2\varrho^{(1)}(\mathbf{r}, \mathbf{r}')] \\
&- \frac{i}{\hbar}\Big[\text{trace}\Big\{\int \boldsymbol{\psi}^\dagger(\mathbf{r}')\boldsymbol{\psi}^\dagger(\mathbf{r}_1)\,\mathbf{t}(\mathbf{r}, \mathbf{r}_1)\,\boldsymbol{\psi}(\mathbf{r})\,\boldsymbol{\psi}(\mathbf{r}_1)\,\boldsymbol{\omega}\,d\mathbf{r}_1\Big\} \\
&- \text{trace}\Big\{\int \boldsymbol{\psi}^\dagger(\mathbf{r}')\,\boldsymbol{\psi}(\mathbf{r}_1)\,\mathbf{t}(\mathbf{r}', \mathbf{r}_1)\,\boldsymbol{\psi}(\mathbf{r})\,\boldsymbol{\psi}(\mathbf{r}_1)\,\boldsymbol{\omega}\,d\mathbf{r}_1\Big\}\Big] \\
&- \frac{i}{2\hbar}\Big[\text{trace}\Big\{\int\int \boldsymbol{\psi}^\dagger(\mathbf{r}')\,\boldsymbol{\psi}^\dagger(\mathbf{r}_1)\,\boldsymbol{\psi}(\mathbf{r}_2)\,\mathbf{t}\,\boldsymbol{\psi}(\mathbf{r})\,\boldsymbol{\psi}(\mathbf{r}_1)\,\boldsymbol{\psi}(\mathbf{r}_2)\,\boldsymbol{\omega}\,d\mathbf{r}_1\,d\mathbf{r}_2\Big\} \\
&- \text{trace}\Big\{\int\int \boldsymbol{\psi}^\dagger(\mathbf{r}')\,\boldsymbol{\psi}^\dagger(\mathbf{r}_1)\,\boldsymbol{\psi}(\mathbf{r}_2)\,\mathbf{t}\,\boldsymbol{\psi}(\mathbf{r})\,\boldsymbol{\psi}(\mathbf{r}_1)\,\boldsymbol{\psi}(\mathbf{r}_2)\,\boldsymbol{\omega}\,d\mathbf{r}_1\,d\mathbf{r}_2\Big\}\Big].
\end{aligned} \tag{4.12}$$

Although the physical significance of the last term is rather vague, it seems to be small correction to the binary collision process.

The phase space distribution functions first introduced by Wigner are defined by

$$f^{(1)}(\mathbf{r}, \mathbf{p}; t) = h^{-3}N^{-1}\int e^{-\mathbf{p}\cdot\mathbf{y}}\,\varrho^{(1)}\,\mathbf{r}-\frac{\mathbf{y}}{2}, \mathbf{r}+\frac{\mathbf{y}}{2}; t)\,d\mathbf{y}, \tag{4.13}$$

and

$$f^{(2)}(\mathbf{r}, \mathbf{p}; t) = h^{-6}N^{-2}\int e^{-(\mathbf{p}_1\cdot\mathbf{y}_1, +\mathbf{p}_2\cdot\mathbf{y}_2)}$$

$$\times\varrho^{(2)}(\mathbf{r}_1-\tfrac{1}{2}\mathbf{y}_1, \mathbf{r}_2-\tfrac{1}{2}\mathbf{y}_2; \mathbf{r}_1+\tfrac{1}{2}\mathbf{y}_1, \mathbf{r}_2+\tfrac{1}{2}\mathbf{y}_2; t)\,d\mathbf{y}_1 d\mathbf{y}_2. \tag{4.14}$$

The equation of motion for $f^{(1)}$ is obtained as a Fourier inversion of (4.12) of which the last term is dropped:

$$\frac{\partial f^{(1)}}{\partial t}+\frac{\mathbf{p}_1}{m}\cdot\nabla_{\mathbf{r}_1}f^{(1)} = N^{-1}(T_1+T_1^*), \tag{4.15}$$

$$T_1 = \frac{im}{2\hbar^2}\left(\frac{1}{h^7}\right)\int d\mathbf{p}_2\,\gamma^{(2)}(p, q; r, s; t)\,\sigma(2, s)$$

$$\times\exp\left[-2(\mathbf{p}_1-\mathbf{p}_p)\cdot\mathbf{r}_1/i\hbar\right]\delta(\mathbf{p}_2-\mathbf{p}_1)$$

$$\times\,\delta(\mathbf{p}_1+\mathbf{p}_2-\tfrac{1}{2}(\mathbf{p}_p+\mathbf{p}_q+\mathbf{p}_r+\mathbf{p}_s)), \tag{4.16}$$

$$\sigma(2, s) = -\frac{m}{4\pi\hbar^2}\int e^{-\frac{i\mathbf{p}_2\cdot\mathbf{r}}{\hbar}}\,\mathbf{t}_{2s}\,e^{\frac{i\mathbf{p}_s\cdot\mathbf{r}}{\hbar}}\,d\mathbf{r}, \tag{4.17}$$

$$\gamma^{(2)}(p, q; r, s) = \text{trace}\,[a_p^*\,a_q^*\,a_r\,a_s\,\boldsymbol{\omega}]. \tag{4.18}$$

V. THE TIME AVERAGE OVER A MICROSCOPIC INTERVAL OF TIME

Kirkwood[11] derived the Boltzmann equation in classical statistical mechanics by means of time averaging the equation of motion for the singlet distribution function obtained from the Liouville equation. In the present article, we shall attempt to derive the Uhling-Uhlenbeck equation with the exact cross-section from (4.16), with the use of the time averaging over a finite interval of time in the same manner as in the Kirkwood theory. This time average will be denoted by a bar. Thus we obtain from (4.16)

$$\frac{\partial \bar{f}^{(1)}}{\partial t}+\frac{\mathbf{p}}{m}\nabla_{\mathbf{r}}\bar{f}^{(1)} = N^{-1}(\bar{T}_1+\bar{T}_1^*), \tag{5.1}$$

where

$$\bar{T}_1 = \frac{i}{2\hbar^2}\left(\frac{1}{h^7}\right)\int d\mathbf{p}_2 \bar{\gamma}^{(2)}(p, q; r, s; t)\,\sigma(2, s)$$
$$\times \exp\left[-2(\mathbf{p}_1-\mathbf{p}_p)\cdot\mathbf{r}_1/i\hbar\right]\delta(\mathbf{p}_2-\mathbf{p}_1)$$
$$\times\, \delta(\mathbf{p}_1+\mathbf{p}_2-\tfrac{1}{2}(\mathbf{p}_p+\mathbf{p}_q+\mathbf{p}_r+\mathbf{p}_s)). \tag{5.2}$$

The symmetrized eigenfunction of the kinetic energy **K** is given by

$$\Phi_\varkappa = \det{}^\dagger\left[e^{\frac{i\mathbf{p}_{t1}\cdot\mathbf{r}_1}{\hbar}}\cdots e^{\frac{i\mathbf{p}_{tN}\cdot\mathbf{r}_N}{\hbar}}\right], \tag{5.3}$$

where $\varkappa$ denotes a set of number n_t, n_t being the number of particles with the momentum $\mathbf{p}_t$.

To express the matrix element, we shall use the symbol

$$\langle\varkappa|\mathbf{A}|\varkappa'\rangle = \int \Phi_K^*(\mathbf{r}_1,\cdots,\mathbf{r}_N)\,\mathbf{A}\Phi_K(\mathbf{r}_1,\cdots,\mathbf{r}_N)\,d\mathbf{r}_1\cdots d\mathbf{r}_N. \tag{5.4}$$

Then from (4.18) we have

$$\bar{\gamma}^{(2)} = \sum_K \{n_s(n-\delta_{sr})(n_q+1-\delta_{sq}-\delta_{rq})$$
$$\times (n_p+1-\delta_{sp}-\delta_{rq}+\delta_{qp})$$
$$\times \langle\varkappa|\overline{\boldsymbol{\omega}^\dagger(t)}|\cdots n_p+1, n_q+1, n_r-1, n_s-1,\cdots\rangle, \tag{5.5}$$

where $\boldsymbol{\omega}^\dagger(t)$ satisfies the relation

$$\langle\varkappa|\overline{\boldsymbol{\omega}}^\dagger(t)|\varkappa'\rangle^* = \langle\varkappa'|\overline{\boldsymbol{\omega}}(t)|\varkappa\rangle = \frac{1}{T}\int_0^T \langle\varkappa'|\boldsymbol{\rho}(t+\tau)\Omega^{(-)}|\varkappa\rangle d\tau. \tag{5.6}$$

The average in (5.6) may be given approximately by

$$\langle\varkappa'|\overline{\boldsymbol{\omega}}(t)|\varkappa\rangle = \varepsilon\int_0^\infty \langle\varkappa'|\boldsymbol{\rho}(t+\tau)\,\Omega^{(-)}|\varkappa\rangle\, e^{-\varepsilon\tau}\,d\tau \tag{5.7}$$

$1/\varepsilon$ being the time of the order of the magnitude of T.

After the rather complicated calculations, we can prove the following relations

$$\langle\varkappa'|\overline{\boldsymbol{\omega}}(t)|\varkappa\rangle = \langle\varkappa'|\boldsymbol{\rho}(t)|\varkappa\rangle + \sum_\lambda\sum_\mu \frac{\langle\varkappa|\Omega^{(-)}|\lambda\rangle\langle\lambda|\Omega^{(-)\dagger}\boldsymbol{\rho}\Omega^{(-)}|\mu\rangle\langle\mu|\Omega^{(-)\dagger}U|\varkappa\rangle}{i(E_\mu-E_\lambda)-\varepsilon}$$
$$-\sum_\lambda\sum_\mu \frac{\langle\varkappa'|U\Omega^{(-)}|\lambda\rangle\langle\lambda|\Omega^{(-)\dagger}\boldsymbol{\rho}\,\Omega^{(-)}|\mu\rangle\langle\mu|\Omega^{(-)\dagger}|\varkappa\rangle}{i(E_\lambda-E_\mu)-\varepsilon} \tag{5.8}$$

Furthermore, according to the relation (3.9), we obtain from (2.10)

$$\langle \varkappa | U\Omega^{(-)} | \cdots, n_p+1, n_q+1, n_r-1, n_s-1, \cdots \rangle$$
$$= \{n_r n_s (n_p+1)(n_q+1)\}^{1/2} \{\langle rs|\mathbf{t}|pq\rangle + \langle rs|\mathbf{t}|qp\rangle\}. \tag{5.9}$$

VI. THE BOLTZMANN-UHLING-UHLENBECK EQUATION

It is seen that the off-diagonal elements of the matrix $\langle \lambda|\Omega^{(-)+}\boldsymbol{\rho}\Omega|\mu\rangle$ vanish for the system in equilibrium. And, if we neglect the quantities of the order of the magnitude of the second virial coefficients, we may ignore the off-diagonal elements of $\langle \lambda|\boldsymbol{\rho}|\mu\rangle$. This corresponds to the approximation

$$\langle \mu|\Omega^{(-)}|\varkappa\rangle = 1+\delta_{\mu\varkappa}. \tag{6.1}$$

Using (5.9) and the postulate of random *a priori phases*, we obtain from (5.2), (5.5), and (5.8)

$$\frac{\partial \bar{f}^{(1)}}{\partial t} + \frac{\mathbf{p}_1}{m} \nabla \bar{f}^1 \tag{6.2}$$
$$= \frac{h^{-9}}{N} \int d\mathbf{p}_2 \int d\omega \{\bar{g}_r \bar{g}_s (\bar{g}_1+1)(\bar{g}_2+1) - \bar{g}_1 \bar{g}_2 (\bar{g}_r+1)(\bar{g}_s+1)\, \alpha(|\mathbf{p}_1-\mathbf{p}_2|, \theta),$$
$$[\mathbf{p}_1+\mathbf{p}_2=\mathbf{p}_r+\mathbf{p}_s]$$

where $\alpha(|\mathbf{p}_1-\mathbf{p}_2|, \theta)$ is the exact scattering intensity, and $\bar{g}_r = \bar{g}(\mathbf{p}_r)$ is the distribution function in the momentum space. Here we assumed that $\langle rs|\mathbf{t}|pq\rangle$ is real as in the case of the Born approximation for the spherical interaction, and used the relation

$$\lim_{\varepsilon\to 0} \frac{\varepsilon}{x^2+\varepsilon^2} = \pi\delta(x). \tag{6.3}$$

If we introduce $n^3\bar{f}^{(1)}$ instead of $\bar{g}$ in the expression (6.2), we obtain the Boltzmann-Uhling-Uhlenbeck equation

$$\frac{\partial \bar{f}^{(1)}}{\partial t} + \frac{\mathbf{p}_1}{m} \cdot \nabla \bar{f}^{(1)} = \frac{h^{-9}}{N} \int d\mathbf{p}_2 \int d\omega$$
$$\times \{\bar{f}_r \bar{f}_s (1+h^3\bar{f}_1)(1+h^3\bar{f}_2) - \bar{f}_1 \bar{f}_2 (1+h^3\bar{f}_r)(1+h^3\bar{f}_s)\} \alpha(|\mathbf{p}_1-\mathbf{p}_2|, \theta). \tag{6.4}$$

It is, however, known that the distribution function becomes independent of the spatial coordinates if we adopt the postulate of random *a priori phases*. The more rigorous method of the derivation of the Uhling-Uhlenbeck equation based upon the cell method is applicable to the present case.

References

(1) H. S. Green, *Proc. Phys. Soc. (London)*, **A64**, 325 (1953).
(2) J. Ross and J. G. Kirkwood, *J. Chem. Phys.*, **22**, 1094 (1954).
(3) H. Mori and S. Ono, *Prog. Theor. Phys. (Japan)*, **8**, 327 (1952).
(4) K. M. Watson, *Phys. Rev.*, **89**, 575 (1953).
(5) K. A. Brueckner and K. M. Watson, *Phys. Rev.*, **92**, 1023 (1953).
(6) C. Møller, *Kgl. Danske Videnskab. Selskab, Mat-fys. Medd.*, **23**, No. 1 (1945).
(7) B. A. Lippman and J. Schwinger, *Phys. Rev.*, **79**, 469 (1950).
(8) G. F. Chew and M. L. Goldberger, *Phys. Rev.*, **87**, 778 (1952).
(9) K. A. Brueckner, C. A. Levinson, and H. M. Mahmoud, *Phys. Rev.*, **95**, 217 (1954).
(10) T. Nishiyama and K. Husimi, *Prog. Theor. Phys. (Japan)*, **5**, 909 (1950).
(11) J. G. Kirkwood, *J. Chem. Phys.*, **15**, 72 (1947).
(12) S. Ono, *Prog. Theor. Phys. (Japan)*, **12**, 113 (1954).

CORRESPONDENCE PRINCIPLE IN QUANTUM STATISTICS

N. G. VAN KAMPEN, *Instituut voor Theoretische Fysica der Rijksuniversiteit, Utrecht, The Netherlands.**

Classically, the evolution of an ensemble may be described by the so-called master equation

$$dP_J/dt = \sum_{J'} (W_{JJ'}P_{J'} - W_{J'J}P_J). \tag{1}$$

Here J denotes the various phase cells, P_J is the fraction of the ensemble in phase cell J, and $W_{JJ'}$ is the transition probability per unit time from J' into J. Microscopic reversibility is expressed by

$$W_{JJ'}G_{J'} = W_{J'J}G_J, \tag{2}$$

where G_J is the phase volume of cell J. Eq. (1) describes the macroscopic behavior of the classical ensemble as a random process of the Markoff type. Of course, this is possible only if the cells are large enough, and if the appropriate randomness assumption is satisfied. From (1) together with (2) the approach to equilibrium and the usual results of statistical mechanics follow easily; the fundamental difficulties are all concentrated in the derivation of (1).

In the usual formulation of *quantum statistics* the same equation (1) has been used, J denoting the separate eigenfunctions of some unperturbed Hamiltonian. The probability P_J of finding the system in the eigenstate J is then identified with the absolute square of the expansion coefficient, or probability amplitude, relative to that eigenstate. The transition probability $W_{JJ'}$ arises from a perturbation term in the Hamiltonian. In order that (1) shall be valid, it is necessary to get rid of the phase relations between the probability amplitudes; this is achieved by introducing an ensemble with randomly varying phases. However, this artifice is unsatisfactory, because it only helps out for one particular time, $t = 0$ say. After a short while phase relations will arise so that (1) is no longer true.

Yet, even in quantum mechanics Eq. (1) may be maintained, provided one uses a different approach, which follows more closely the

* Present address: Physics Department, Columbia University, New York, N.Y.

lines of the classical approach.[1] First, phase cells must be introduced. This is done by decomposing Hilbert space in suitable linear subspaces J, which will now serve as phase cells. The precise choice of these subspaces is determined by the operators that represent the macroscopic observables, in such a way that each phase cell corresponds to definite values of these macroscopic observables. A corresponding orthonormal set of functions is $\xi_{J\iota}$, such that, for fixed J, the $\xi_{J\iota}$ $(\iota = 1, 2, \cdots, G_J)$ span the G_J-dimensional phase cell J. The expansion of the wave function ψ in this set has the form

$$\psi(t) = \sum_{J\iota} b_{J\iota}(t)\, \xi_{J\iota}. \tag{3}$$

The probability of finding the system in phase cell J is defined by

$$P_J(t) = \sum_{\iota=1}^{G_J} |b_{J\iota}(t)|^2.$$

Since the J are not eigenfunctions of the total Hamiltonian, the probability amplitudes $b_{J\iota}$ depend on t in a complicated fashion. But it can be shown that the P_J satisfy again an equation of form (1), provided that the G_J are large and certain assumptions of randomness are satisfied. The symmetry relation (2) also holds true.

Thus we have determined the description in terms of a Markoff random process, in complete analogy with the classical one. However, the starting point is essentially different: we have not used an ensemble of systems, but one single system in a pure (i.e., not "mixed") state ψ. Hence the result: *one pure quantum mechanical state ψ corresponds to a classical ensemble.*

This state of affairs may be analyzed more closely by recalling that the correspondence principle, as originally formulated for atoms, states the following. When in the region of high quantum numbers a *special wave* packet is constructed in such a way that both the q's and p's are sufficiently well defined, then these q's and p's vary according to the classical Hamiltonian equations. Such special wave packets, however, constitute only a small minority among all possible wave functions. Our result above states that, *in general*, a wave function which does not happen to be a special wave packet corresponds to an ensemble of classical phase points (provided, of course, that the system has many degrees of freedom). Thus the concept of a "state of the system" in quantum mechanics is more comprehensive than the classical state of the system as given by a set of $6N$ variables q, p; one should rather put *the totality of all possible state vectors ψ on the same level with the totality of all possible classical ensembles.*

CONCLUSIONS

(*1*) In quantum statistics there is no need to introduce ensembles, as already one single ψ provides probabilities P_J satisfying (1). Nor should one use density matrices, unless one actually deals with a large number of identical replicas of the same system (e.g. in particle beams).

(*2*) Statistical fluctuations arise classically from the distribution of sample systems in the ensemble. In the present quantum mechanical treatment they are identical to the familiar unsharpness of a quantity in a quantum mechanical state of the total system.

(*3*) Eq. (1) breaks down when the numbers G_J of independent states in each phase cell are no longer large, also when in the expansion (3) only few terms are appreciable. In other words, statistical mechanics is only valid in the region of high quantum numbers of the system, i.e., in the region of validity of the correspondence principle.

(*4*) For extremely low energies, only a few quantum states are represented in (3); hence the system does not obey a statistical equation, but must be treated as one gigantic molecule. In particular, the usual derivation of Nernst's law based on the nondegeneracy of the ground state is fallacious.

(*5*) In the current perturbation method the transition probabilities between levels vary at first quadratically with t and become time proportional only after this induction period. This is a consequence of the very special choice for the density matrix, namely diagonal at $t = 0$. In the present treatment no such difficulty arises, because the entire statistical method (and hence the use of transition probabilities) is restricted to the coarse-grained level, and no meaning is attached to transition probabilities between individual levels.

Reference

(1) N. G. van Kampen, *Physica,* **20**, 603 (1954); *Fortschr. Physik,* **4,** 405 (1956).

MISE EN ÉQUILIBRE D'UN PETIT SYSTÈME COUPLÉ À UN THERMOSTAT

J. YVON, *C. E. N. de Saclay, Gif sur Yvette, Seine et Oise, France*

Résumé

Un petit système est couplé à un thermostat. Si on admet en première approximation qu'il n'y a aucune corrélation entre le système et le thermostat, on en déduit, par la méthode de variation, un régime "adapté" de corrélations. Une équation de Boltzmann en résulte et de celle-ci on déduit un théorème *H*.

I. LE PROBLÈME

Un très petit système est couplé à un thermostat. Il s'agit de savoir comment il tend vers l'équilibre. C'est le problème de ce genre le plus simple qu'on puisse imaginer.

Il s'agit d'une étude beaucoup moins fondamentale que celle qui vient d'être présentée par le Professeur Van Hove. Le problème mérite néanmoins d'être examiné par ce que la question est abordée sous un angle différent. Les conclusions se résument ici dans une équation de Boltzmann.

Le système étudié, appelé A, est très petit:

1°. Son couplage avec le thermostat ne perturbe celui-ci en aucune manière.

2° Les différents niveaux d'énergie étant E_a, E_b, ..., on suppose à propos de toutes les différences:

$$E_b - E_a,$$

que:

$$|E_b - E_a| \ll kT,$$

quels que soient a et b.

Des exemples de ce genre se rencontrent dans la théorie de la résonance magnétique.

Le thermostat est désigné par B. Les états sont notés α, β, etc. Ils forment une suite quasi-continue.

II. ÉQUATIONS RIGOUREUSES D'ÉVOLUTION

$$\mu = \mu(A+B)$$

est l'opérateur densité du système global. Les opérateurs densités de A et de B sont respectivement:

$$\mu_A = T_B \mu,$$
$$\mu_B = T_A \mu.$$

L'Hamiltonien du système A est H_A, celui du thermostat est H_B. V représente le couplage. Les équations d'évolution sont, respectivement:

$$i\hbar\frac{\partial}{\partial t}\mu = (H_A+H_B+V)\mu-\mu(H_A+H_B+V), \tag{1}$$

$$i\hbar\frac{\partial}{\partial t}\mu_A = H_A\mu_A-\mu_A H_A+T_B(V\mu-\mu V), \tag{2}$$

$$i\hbar\frac{\partial}{\partial t}\mu_B = H_B\mu_B-\mu_B H_B+T_A(V\mu-\mu V). \tag{3}$$

Dans la présente étude nous supposons que H_A et V sont indépendants du temps.

III. APPROXIMATIONS

Puisque le thermostat est insensible à la perturbation, il faut négliger l'équation (3). Il n'est pas question d'imaginer, en procédant à des hypothèses sur la diagonalité, que μ n'a que des composantes diagonales vis-à-vis de l'hamiltonien global. Il est clair que dans ce cas μ ne varierait pas du tout. Ce n'est pas la situation physique.

On doit faire une hypothèse sur μ. L'idée la plus simple est qu'il n'y a pas de corrélations entre A et B. Nous écrirons:

$$\mu = \mu_A\,\mu_B. \tag{4}$$

Une telle relation n'est possible que si A et B n'échangent pas de particules. Nous nous tiendrons à ce cas.

Supposons provisoirement cette relation satisfaite à tout instant. L'équation (1) n'est pas vérifiée. L'équation (2) se transcrit:

$$i\hbar\frac{\partial}{\partial t}\mu_A = (H_A+T_B V\mu_B)\mu_A-\mu_A(H_A+T_B V\mu_B). \tag{5}$$

C'est l'équation d'évolution d'un système isolé dont l'hamiltonien serait:

$$H_A + T_B V \mu_B .$$

La séparation de l'Hamiltonien entre H_A et V est quelque peu arbitraire. On ne change pas la généralité en posant désormais:

$$T_B V \mu_B = 0.$$

L'équation (5), ainsi remaniée, est celle du système A supposé isolé.

Il faut obtenir une expression de μ meilleure que l'expression (4).

Supposons maintenant que μ soit, à l'instant zéro par exemple, effectivement égal à

$$\mu_A \mu_B .$$

Revenons à l'équation (1) et résolvons la à partir de cette condition initiale en traitant H_A+V comme une perturbation. On peut se permettre de considérer H_A, aussi bien que V, comme une perturbation, par ce que le système A est très petit.

L'intégration, compte tenu du fait que H_B imprime au système une évolution infiniment plus rapide que H_A+V, conduit à la conclusion que μ "s'adapte" presqu'instantanément, dans des délais qui sont très courts devant l'évolution imposée par H_A+V, et prend la forme standard:

$$\mu(t) = \mu_A(t)\mu_B + L\mu_A(t)\mu_B - \mu_A(t)\mu_B L, \tag{6}$$

valable désormais à tout instant.

L'opérateur L est du premier ordre en V. Désignons par $V_{\alpha\beta}$ les éléments de matrice de V par rapport aux seuls états de B. $V_{\alpha\beta}$ est donc un opérateur pour A. L s'écrit:

$$L_{\alpha\beta} = \frac{V_{\alpha\beta}}{(E_\alpha - E_\beta)_{E_\alpha \neq E_\beta}} - \pi i \delta_{E_\alpha, E_\beta} V_{\alpha\beta}. \tag{7}$$

Notre hypothèse fondamentale, de caractère statistique, est que μ est représenté correctement, à l'approximation indiquée, par (6).

IV. ÉQUATION DE BOLTZMANN ET THÉORÈME H

L'équation d'évolution du système A s'obtient maintenant en insérant l'expression de μ que nous avons retenue dans l'équation (2).

Divisons L en deux parties, évidentes sur la formule (7):

$$L = L' - iK. \tag{8}$$

Définissons un nouvel Hamiltonien:

$$H'_A = H_A + T_B V L' \mu_B .$$

L'équation cherchée s'écrit:

$$i\hbar \frac{\partial}{\partial t}\mu_A = H'_A \mu_A - \mu_A H'_A + iT_B(V\mu_A \mu_B K + K\mu_A \mu_B V - VK\mu_A \mu_B - \mu_A \mu_B KV). \qquad (9)$$

C'est l'équation de Boltzmann du problème. Elle comporte un terme de "propagation":

$$H'_A \mu_A - \mu_A H'_A.$$

Quant au deuxième terme du second membre, il provoque l'amortissement.

Calculons en effet la dérivée temporelle de l'entropie changée de signe, soit à un facteur k près,

$$\frac{d}{dt} T_A \mu_A \log \mu_A .$$

Il vient, en utilisant à chaque instant une représentation où l'opérateur μ_A est diagonal:

$$\hbar \frac{d}{dt} T_A \mu_A \log \mu_A = -\pi \sum_{\alpha,\beta}^{ij} \delta_{E_\alpha, E_\beta} \mu_{\alpha\alpha} |K_{\alpha\beta}^{ij}|^2 \log \frac{\mu ii}{\mu jj} (\mu_{ii} - \mu_{jj}), \qquad (10)$$

i, j, etc. désignant les états propres de μ_A.

L'entropie est donc continuellement croissante. Les probabilités $\mu_{ii}, \mu_{jj}, \ldots$ cessent d'évoluer lorsqu'elles sont égales c'est-à-dire lorsque μ_A se confond avec la matrice identique à un facteur de normalisation près. Alors tous les états définis par l'Hamiltonien H'_A sont également probables: c'est l'équilibre thermodynamique.

Ce résultat repose sur l'hypothèse (6). Par contre il n'est fait mention d'aucune hypothèse sur la valeur instantanée ou même initiale des éléments de matrice de μ_A dans une représentation où un hamiltonien, que ce soit H_A ou H'_A, est diagonal.

Des applications seront nécessaires pour décider de l'intérêt de l'équation (9).

Discussion IX

G. Uhlenbeck (*to L. Van Hove*): I would like to ask whether the $P(t/\alpha, \alpha_0)$ is always defined in the same way. Then I would like to know whether the development with strong perturbation still uses the expansion in powers of the time used in the original development and which seems to me "ein Schönheitsfehler." Finally I would like to urge making some examples in order to bring this beautiful, but for my taste too abstract, development more down to earth.

L. Van Hove (*to G. Uhlenbeck*): The $P(t/\alpha_1\alpha_0)$ are defined in the same way in the general order treatment as in the lowest order case. The proof in the case of strong perturbation does not use an expansion in powers of the time. The necessity of treating examples is recognized and something will be done about it. An oversimplified but exactly soluble example has already been considered (in another context, however) in a published paper (*Physica*, **22**, 343 (1956)).

M. S. Watanabe: I should like to call attention to the fact that the paper I am to present tomorrow will also discuss Pauli's equation (the master equation). The conditions mentioned by Van Hove will reappear under different guise. Furthermore several other conditions will be introduced. Van Hove considers the long-time development also in quantum mechanics. In my paper it will be shown that, perhaps except in pathological cases, it is not necessary to use quantum mechanical considerations for a time period longer than a certain order of magnitude. The method I shall use is the one mentioned by Mr. van Kampen as the third alternative formulation.

R. Brout (*to G. Uhlenbeck*): In answer to Professor Uhlenbeck's request for examples we have studied the one photon-one atom radiation problem in the quantum mechanical formalism of Van Hove. This was suggested by Van Hove himself.

One finds all the usual results: the Wigner-Weisskopf spontaneous emission formulae, line shape of spontaneous emission, and resonance fluorescence. This repeats in all essentials the calculation carried out by Dirac, but perhaps is helped in understanding by the general formalism developed by Van Hove.

H. C. Longuet-Higgins (*to L. Van Hove*): I take it that those properties of the perturbation V which were postulated by Professor Van Hove are sufficient to insure passage to equilibrium. Are these properties also necessary?

L. Van Hove (*to H. C. Longuet-Higgins*): This has not been proved, although it is known that perturbations V such that all matrix elements $\langle\alpha|VA_1V\cdots A_nV|\alpha'\rangle$ are regular and (for $(A_1\ldots A_n)$ diagonal in the $|\alpha\rangle$-representation) never can give rise to approach to statistical equilibrium.

I. Prigogine: In the classical mechanical case, it is as least possible to obtain some information about the necessary conditions in order to have no other analytical invariants apart from energy as was shown long ago by Poincaré (*Méthodes Nouvelles,* 1892).

M. Green (*to L. Van Hove*): Do you think that the equation which is correct to arbitrary order will reduce to one of the Champan-Kolmogoroff type for times which lie between the large and the small time scale?

L. Van Hove (*to M. Green*): Of course if the probability varies slowly enough in time the integration over the transition kernels can be carried out and an equation of such a type formally derived. However, higher order in $|V|$ means that the long-time scale becomes shorter and the variation of the probabilities more rapid. I therefore believe that an equation of the Chapman-Kolmogoroff type is probably not valid.

R. Brout: It is possible to study the quantum mechanical master equation of Pauli in the limit $\hbar\to 0$. As one is interested in the classical limit the stationary states of H^0 may be described by specifying the action associated with each degree of freedom (for oscillators or collisionless gases, this is exact). The difference $P_{\alpha'}-P_\alpha$ may now be written $P_{\{J'\}}-P_{\{J\}}$. Now expand V in Fourier transform in angle variables

$$V=\sum_{\{n\}}V_{\{n\}}(\{J\})\,e^{i\Sigma n_k\alpha_k}.$$

The coefficient $V_{\{n\}}$, by the correspondence principle, induces transition from $\{J\}$ to $\{J+n\hbar\}$. Thus a typical term in the Pauli equation is of the type (we simplify the situation slightly, neglecting the dependence of the matrix element on $\hbar$)

$$\frac{1}{\hbar^2}|V_{\{n\}}|^2 \delta\left[\frac{E(J)-E(\{J+n\hbar\})}{\hbar}\right] \varrho(\{J+n\hbar\})-\varrho(\{J\}).$$

One now expands all terms around $\hbar = 0$. A term in $1/\hbar$ vanishes because of symmetry reasons. The term independent of $\hbar$ is the Fokker-Planck equation as derived by Brout and Prigogine (*Physica*, 1956) for weak coupling in phase independent classical ensembles.

M. Fierz (*to N. G. van Kampen*): The analogy between classical and quantum mechanics breaks down as soon as one actually tries to prove equation (1) of your paper. Then the fundamental difference between the classical and the quantum mechanical formulations becomes important, as for instance in the ergodic theorem.

N. G. van Kampen (*to M. Fierz*): I do not think that the actual mechanism which is responsible for the fact that, on a macroscopic scale, the system can be described by a Markoff process, is fundamentally different in classical and quantum mechanics. In fact, the above-mentioned randomness assumptions look very similar in both cases. Also, von Neumann's treatment of the ergodic theorem in quantum statistics closely parallels the classical treatment.

J. G. Kirkwood: In view of the fact that Professor Ono could unfortunately not be here to present his paper on the Boltzmann equation in quantum statistics, I would like to make a few remarks on recent developments of the theory of transport processes in quantum statistical mechanics. In particular I would like to compare our work (J. Ross and J. G. Kirkwood, *J. Chem. Phys.*, **22**, 1094 (1954)) on the quantum mechanical analog of the Boltzmann equation with the very interesting work of Van Hove.

We discuss quantum statistical mechanics in terms of the Wigner function, a phase space distribution function which has some advantageous similarities to the classical quantity $\alpha(p, q)$ and is simply

$$\alpha = \int \cdots \int \alpha(p, q)\, f^{(N)}(p, q; t)\, dp\, dq,$$

where $f^{(N)}$ is the normalized Wigner function. Furthermore one has simply

$$\sigma^{(N)}(p; t) = \int \cdots \int f^{(N)}(p, q; t)\, dq$$

and

$$\varrho^{(N)}(q; t) = \int \cdots \int f^{(N)}(p, q; t)\, dp$$

where $\sigma^{(N}$ and $\varrho^{(N)}$ are the distribution function in momentum space and configuration space, respectively.

The Wigner function obeys the following integro-differential equation

$$\frac{\partial f^{(N)}}{\partial t} + \sum_{j=1}^{N} \frac{p_j}{m_j} \cdot \nabla_{R_j} f^{(N)} + \theta \cdot f^{(N)} = 0$$

which was first obtained by Wigner and in which θ is an integral operator. Liouville's equation is obtained at once if Planck's constant is allowed to approach zero.

Again we introduce phase space transformation functions defined by the integral equation

$$f^{(N)}(p, q; t+s) = \int \cdots \int K^{(N)}(p, q/p', q'; s)\, f^{(N)}(p', q'; t)\, dp'\, dq'$$

and find that $K^{(N)}$ obeys Wigner's equation with δ-function initial conditions. The development towards the Boltzmann equation is very similar to our classical derivation presented earlier in this conference. The essential difference is that we have been able to verify the Uhling-Uhlenbeck equation, i.e., the Boltzmann equation with the classical cross-section replaced by its quantum mechanical counterpart, only in the Born approximation.

The comparison between the work of Van Hove and ours can be made with a diagram analogous to the one drawn by Professor Uhlenbeck for classical statistical mechanics:

Wigner equation	⟶	"Master equation"
↓		⋮ ↓
Hierachy of integro-differential equations	⟶	Quantum mechanical analog of Boltzmann equation

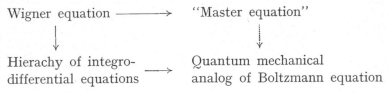

where solid lines indicate derivations which have been accomplished. Van Hove derives the "master equation" in the Born approximation and in the general case for certain forms of the potential energy of interaction, and finds that the application of the assumption of *a priori* random phases at all times is not necessary but suffices at one initial time. In our derivation, which proceeds as indicated in the diagram, the problem of random phases is also avoided, except at some initial time, by considering distribution functions which have spatial dependence only over regions large compared to the range of the intermolecular forces. We feel that the formalism of phase space transformation functions is a very useful one which will lend itself readily to a derivation of the "master equation."

J. Ross: It seems that the development of the quantum mechanical scattering cross-section, as it appears in the Uhling and Uhlenbeck equation, by the usual one-dimensional *W.K.B.* method is not valid. Brooks, Kirkwood, and Ross have derived the quantum mechanical Boltzmann equation in a series in $\hbar$. The work shows that, except for Cartesian coordinate systems, the three-dimensional problem, involving the evaluation of triadics, must be solved.

G. Uhlenbeck (*to J. G. Kirkwood*): 1) In the equation called the Uhling-Uhlenbeck equation, the factors $(1+f)(1+f_1)$ etc. do not appear. Is this just an omission? 2) I would like to urge the sharp distinction between (a) the *general* hydrodynamic equations, which are just an expression of the general conservation theorems, and (b) the *ordinary* hydrodynamic equations, which are the Euler or Stokes-Navier equations, in successive approximations.

R. Eisenschitz (*to J. G. Kirkwood*): If the "hydrodynamic" equations of Irving and Zwanzig are, by consistent use of the Wigner representation, time-smoothed, the result is the quantum analog of the Fokker-Planck equation. It is obtained as an equation in 3 dimensions containing correction terms in ascending powers of Plank's constant. By this procedure the ideal liquid is rendered dissipative.

PART X

BEMERKUNGEN ZU EINIGEN NEUEREN ERGEBNISSEN DER THEORIE STARKER ELEKTROLYTE

HANS FALKENHAGEN, *Institut für Theoretische Physik der Universität Rostock, Germany*

Die klassische Arrhenius'sche Elektrolyttheorie ist durch die Hypothese gekennzeichnet, daß in ihr die Kräfte zwischen den Ionen völlig vernachlässigt werden. Demzufolge ist die unvollständige Dissoziation der Elektrolytmolekeln in Ionen von Wichtigkeit und es sind die Molekeln eines schwachen Elektrolyten beispielsweise einer schwachen organischen Säure oder Base in wässeriger Lösung nur zu einem geringen Prozentsatz in Ionen dissoziiert, sodaß die interionischen Kräfte nur eine untergeordnete Rolle spielen. Starke Elektrolyte, also beispielsweise Kochsalz, in Wasser gelöst, weisen dagegen ein von der Arrhenius'schen Theorie abweichendes Verhalten auf. Um diese Anomalien bei starken Elektrolyten zu verstehen, wurde die moderne, interionische Theorie geschaffen, die zum erstenmal von S. R. Milner klar herausgearbeitet wurde. P. Debye, E. Hückel, L. Onsager und H. Falkenhagen gelang dann die quantitative Theorie der reversiblen thermodynamischen und der irreversiblen Erscheinungen in starken Elektrolyten. Diese Theorie gilt für genügend verdünnte Lösungen quantitativ und führte zu Grenzgesetzen, die den Charakter von Naturgesetzen besitzen. Ja, überdies führte sie sogar zur Voraussage von Effekten, beispielsweise des Debye-Falkenhagen-Effektes, der Zunahme der Hochfrequenzleitfähigkeit mit wachsender Frequenz des elektrischen Wechselfeldes und der allgemeinen Viskositätstheorie von H. Falkenhagen und Mitarbeitern, die quantitativ mit dem experimentellen Befund übereinstimmen. Die Viskosität η z.B. genügt nach der zuletzt genannten Theorie dem Grenzgesets

$$\eta = \eta_0(1+A'\sqrt{c}) \tag{1}$$

Hierin bedeuten η_0 die Viskosität des reinen Lösungsmittels, c die Konzentration des Elektrolyten in Mol pro Liter Lösung und A' einen Koeffizienten, der in komplizierter Weise von den Ionenbeweglichkeiten bei unendlicher Verdünnung, den Wertigkeiten der Ionen, den Zerfallszahlen der Ionen, der absoluten Temperatur, der Dielektrizitätskonstante des reinen Lösungsmittels und η_0 abhängt. Dieses Grenzgesetz wurde von zahlreichen Forschern an vielen Elektrolyten quantitativ bestätigt. Zuletzt hat mein Schüler M. Kaminsky[1] auch die Temperaturabhängigkeit an einer Reihe von Elektrolyten untersucht und konnte auch hier die Theorie verifizieren, wie folgende kleine Tabelle zeigt.

t°C	A' (exp.)	A' (theor.)
	KJ	
20	0,0045	0,0049
30	0,0052	0,0051
40	0,0054	0,0054
	NH_4Cl	
15	0,0049	0,0048
25	0,0052	0,0050
35	0,0052	0,0053
	Na_2SO_4	
15	0,0148	0,0149
30	0,0155	0,0155
40	0,0159	0,0157
	$FeCl_3$	
25	0,0164	0,0167
35	0,0172	0,0170
40	0,0178	0,0174

Die wesentliche Idee der interionischen Theorie beruht auf dem Bild der Ionenverteilung als notwendigen Folge der Existenz der Ionenkräfte. Das bedingt eine Struktur der mittleren Ladungsverteilung in der Lösung, die eine gewisse Ähnlichkeit mit der Ladungsverteilung in einem Steinkristall zeigt und die für die reversiblen und irreversiblen Erscheinungen von wesentlicher Bedeutung ist. Man kennzeichnet das Verhalten der Elektrolyte durch die Ionenwolke, die jedes Ion umgibt und die bestimmte Eigenschaften: Dicke und Relaxationszeit besitzt.

Seit der Aufstellung der grundlegenden Grenzgesetse in der Theorie starker Elektrolyte bemüht sich die Forschung auf diesem Gebiet um eine Ausdehnung auf höhere Konzentrationen. Die ersten Versuche in dieser Richtung führen einen Ionenparameter a ein, der etwa dem mittleren Abstand des Ionenmittelpunktes des positiven und negativen Ions bei der Berührung der Ionenkugeln entspricht; die endliche Größe der Ionen findet so ihre Berücksichtigung. Hierdurch erwies es sich als notwendig, das grundlegende Randwertproblem anders zu formulieren. Es muss die Normalkomponente der relativen Ionenflüsse auf der Oberfläche der Ionen verschwinden. Die neuen Formeln, in denen nur der Parameter a auftritt, sind sehr befriedigend, da sie bei plausiblen Werten für den Parameter a die Messwerte bis zu ziemlich hohen Konzentrationen ausgezeichnet wiederzugeben vermochten. Die Durchführung dieses Gedankens berücksichtigt jedoch das Eigenvolumen der Ionen nur im Randwertproblem, nicht aber in der Statistik selbst. Dutta und Bagchi[2] versuchten als erste auf der Grundlage der Zellenmethode das Eigenvolumen in die Statistik einzubauen. Strukturell ähnliche Formeln erhielten Eigen und Wicke[3] bei der Behandlung desselben Problems durch Gleichgewichtsbetrachtungen. Von meinem Mitarbeiter Kelbg[4] und mir wurde diese Formel auf beliebig viele Teilchensorten verallgemeinert. Die Berücksichtigung der Ionengröße, entsprechend dem oben erwähnten Randwertproblem, führte für die molare Leitfähigkeit zu folgender Endformel:

$$\Lambda = \Lambda_\infty - \frac{e^2\varkappa}{2D_0kT}\Lambda_\infty A(\varkappa a) - \frac{Le^2\varkappa}{27\pi\sqrt{2}\,10^{11}\eta_0} B(\varkappa a), \tag{2}$$

wobei die Koeffizienten sich in nachstehend aufgeführter Form ergaben:

$$A(\varkappa a) = \tfrac{1}{3}(2-\sqrt{2})\frac{1}{(1+\varkappa a)\left(1+\frac{\sqrt{2}}{2}\varkappa a+\frac{1}{6}\varkappa^2 a^2\right)}, \tag{2'}$$

$$B(\varkappa a) = \sqrt{2}/(1+\varkappa a). \tag{2''}$$

Hierin bedeuten:

Λ_∞ = molare Leitfähigkeit bei unendlicher Verdünnung
e = Ladung des positiven Ions
D_0 = Dielektrizitätskonstante des reinen Lösungsmittels
k = Boltsmannkonstante

T = absolute Temperatur
η_0 = Viskosität des reinen Lösungsmittels
L = Loschmidtzahl
$1/\varkappa$ = reziproker Radius der Ionenwolke
a = mittlerer Abstand der Ladungszentren beider Ionen bei Berührung.

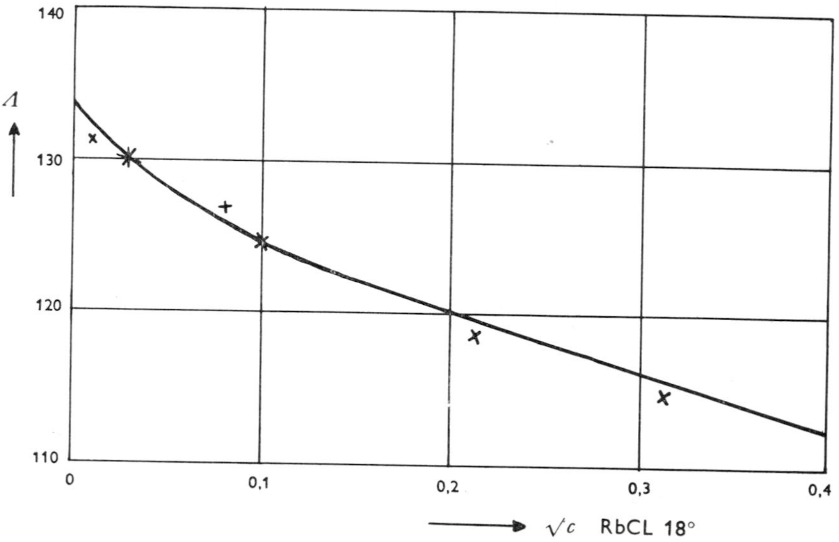

Abb. 1

In Abb. 1 ist als Beispiel die molare Leitfähigkeit für wässerige RbCl bei 18°C wiedergegeben. Man sieht, daß die Übereinstimmung mit der theor. Kurve ausgezeichnet ist. Die Formel (2), die nur für binäre Elektrolyte abgeleitet wurde, wurde in der Dissertation von M. Leist[5] auf beliebige Elektrolyte erweitert. Das Ergebnis der erhaltenen ziemlich umständlichen halbempirischen Formel ist in Abb. 2 wiedergegeben, in der die molare Leitfähigkeit von wässerigem NaCl bei 18°C über der Wurzel aus der molaren Konzentration aufgetragen ist.

Man erkennt, daß die Gleichung bei etwa 0,25 mol/Ltr. Lsg. ein Abbiegen der Kurve von den Meßwerten nach oben verursacht. Die Durchführung der Viskositätskorrektur ergab die ausgezogene Kurve, die sich bis zu hohen Konzentrationen in gutem Einklang mit den Meßwerten befindet.

Das Modell von Eigen-Wicke, wonach sich entgegengesetzt geladene

Ionen durchdringen mögen, wurde von meinem Mitarbeiter Schmutzer[6] kritisiert. Auf der Grundlage des Modells starrer Kugeln gelangt dieser

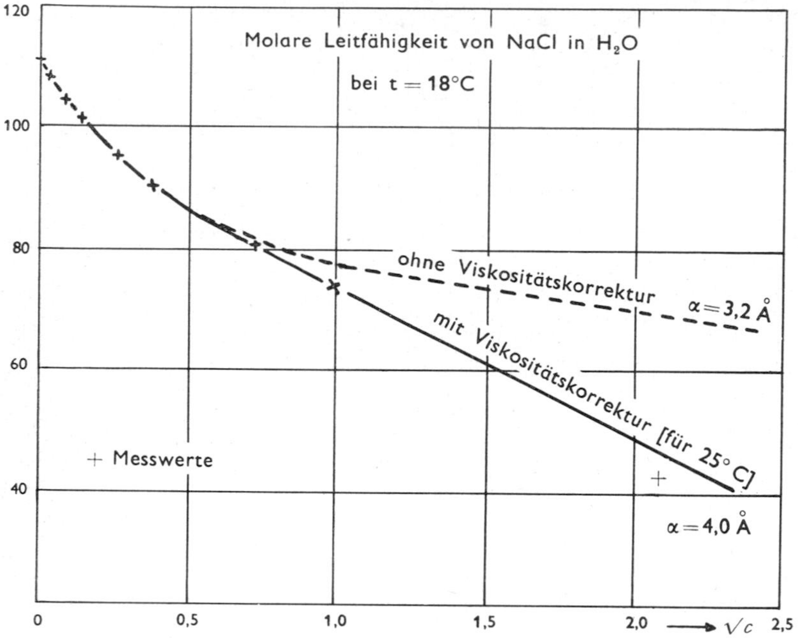

Abb. 2

mit Hilfe der Eigen-Wicke Verteilungsformel zu dem Ergebnis, daß die Debyesche Ionenatmosphäre näherungsweise durch die Eigen-Wicke-Formel nicht verändert wird, so daß die elektrostatischen Glieder von Debye keine Änderung erfahren. Eine Erweiterung gelang nun durch die Anführung von thermodynamische Kovolumengliedern in das chemische Potential. Die daraus resultierenden Formeln führten für eine Reihe von Effekten zu guten Ergebnissen. Das Zusatzglied zu den Aktivitätskoeffizienten hat z.B. die einfache Form:

$$f = 1/(1-vn), \tag{3}$$

wobei v dem Volumen eines Ions entspricht. Eine Anwendung dieser Theorie auf den Aktivitätskoeffizienten von Rohrzucker zeigt Abb. 3. Auch bei den Diffusionskoeffizienten und den Diffusionspotentialen ergibt sich gegenüber der Theorie von Hermans eine Korrektur. Die Formel für den differentiellen Diffusionskoeffizienten Δ lautet:

$$\Delta = \frac{kT\,(\nu_1+\nu_2)}{\varrho_1\nu_1+\varrho_2\nu_2}\left(\frac{1}{1-nv} - \frac{z_1 z_2 e_2}{4D_0 kT}\,\frac{\varkappa}{(1+a\varkappa)^2}\right)\left(1 - \frac{\nu_1 p_1+\nu_2 p_2}{\nu_1\varrho_1+\nu_2\varrho_2}\right), \tag{4}$$

$$p_i = \frac{2}{3\eta}\left(\frac{n_1 e_1}{\omega_1}+\frac{n_2 e_2}{\omega_2}\right)\frac{\varrho_1\varrho_i}{D_0\varkappa T}\,\frac{1}{\varkappa(1+a\varkappa)} - \frac{1}{3\eta}\left(\frac{n_1 e_1^2}{\omega_1}+\frac{n_2 e_2^2}{\omega_2}\right)\frac{e_i^2\varrho_i}{(D_0\varkappa T)^2}\,\phi(\varkappa a),$$

wobei gilt

$$\omega_i = \frac{1}{\varrho_i};\quad \phi(\varkappa a) = \frac{e^{2\varkappa a}}{(1+a\varkappa)^2}\cdot\int_{2\varkappa a}^{\infty}\frac{e^{-t}}{t}\,dt. \tag{4''}$$

Dabei bedeuten die ν_i die Zerfallszahlen, die z_i die Wertigkeiten, ϱ_i die Reibungsgrößen der Ionen und die p_i sind durch den Ausdruck (4′) gegeben, die die Elektrophorese beinhalten. Man erkennt aus dieser Gleichung, daß sie für $v \to 0$ in die bekannte Formel von Hermans übergeht. In die Reibungsgrößen selbst geht die Viskosität ein.

Abb. 4 gibt den Verlauf der etwas umständlichen Formel für die Diffusionskoeffizienten Δ von NaCl bei 25°C wieder.

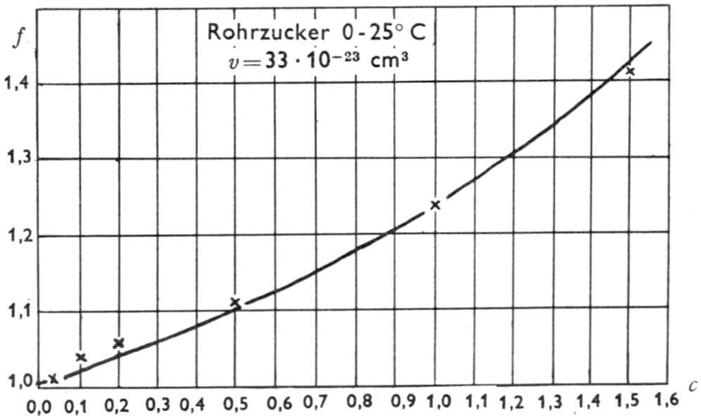

Abb. 3

Man erkennt aus dieser Abbildung, daß die Durchführung der Viskositätskorrektur unerläßlich ist. Dadurch wird dann eine gute Übereinstimmung mit dem Experiment erreicht. Grundsätzlich ist zu dieser Anwendung der Eigen-Wicke-Formel zu bemerken, daß sie aufgrund ihrer Ableitung nur die 2er Stöße berücksichtigt, also bei sehr hohen Konzentrationen nicht mehr zu gebrauchen ist.

Auf der Grundlage des Modells starrer Kugeln wurden auch die Oberflächenspannungen von Elektrolyten untersucht. Es ergab sich eine längere Formel für die Oberflächenspannungszunahme mit der Konzentration, die für verschwindende Konzentrationen in das bekannte Grenzgesetz von Onsager-Samaras übergeht. Die Formel für die

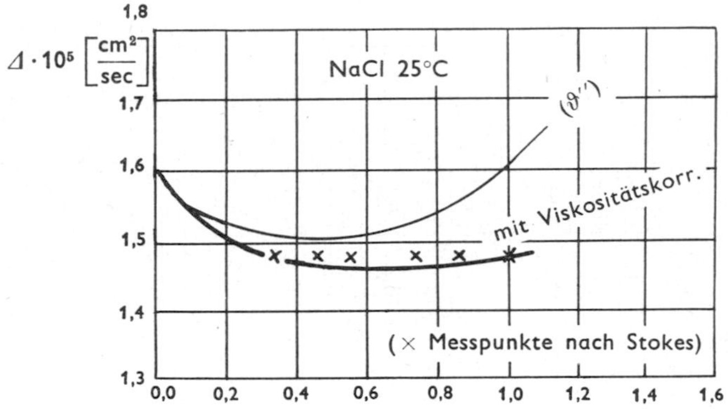

Abb. 4

Oberflächenspannungserhöhung $\Delta\gamma$ gegenüber dem Lösungsmittel hat folgende Gestalt:

$$\Delta\gamma = n\nu kTg\delta + \frac{2kT}{\varkappa^2} n \sum \nu_i I_i. \tag{5}$$

n bedeutet die Anzahl der gelösten Moleküle pro cm^3, ν ist die Anzahl der Ionen pro Molekül, g ist der osmotische Koeffizient. I_i sind Integrale, deren Wert graphisch ermittelt wird. In dieser Gleichung tritt die Konstante δ auf.[7] Die konsequente Durchführung des Modells starrer Kugeln zwingt nämlich zu der Annahme einer ionenfreien Oberflächenschicht der Dicke δ, die in die Endformel eingeht.

Eigentlich müßte man natürlich ein Kraftgesetz für die starken, nicht elektrostatischen Oberflächenabstoßungskräfte einführen. Ein solches Gesetz wäre allerdings beim heutigen Stand der Kenntnisse in dieser Hinsicht ziemlich willkürlich. Deshalb erscheint es sinnvoll, im Abstand δ von der geometrischen Oberfläche das elektrostatische Abstoßungspotential abzuschneiden und eine Potentialbarriere anzusetzen. Wie die rechnerische Durchführung zeigt, ergeben sich für δ sehr einleuchtende Werte, die mit dieser Modellbetrachtung in gutem Einklang stehen, nämlich Werte, die etwas größer als a/ν sind.

In Abb. 5 ist die der Oberflächenspannungsformel entsprechende Kurve eingezeichnet. Man erkennt eine sehr gute Übereinstimmung mit den experimentellen Meßpunkten. γ_0 bedeutet die Oberflächenspannung des reinen Lösungsmittels; γ die der Lösung.

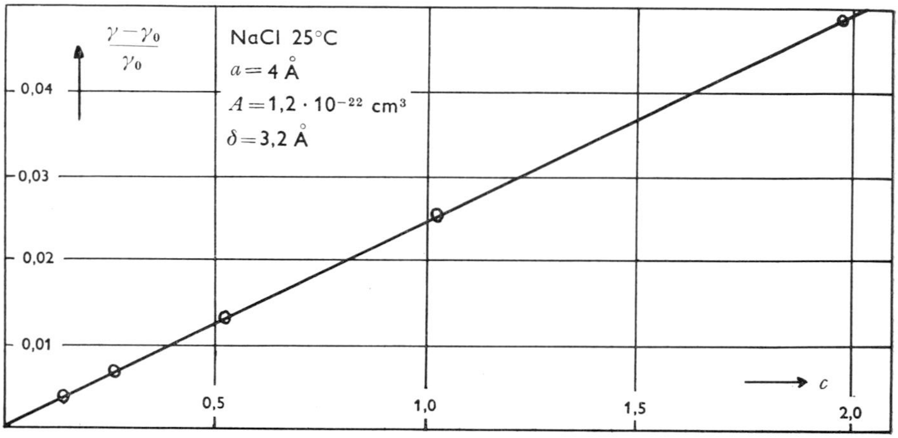

Abb. 5

In einer gegenwärtig unter meiner Betreuung laufenden Dissertation von U. Möller wird nun der Versuch unternommen, auf streng statistischer Grundlage im Sinne von Kirkwood das Elektrolytproblem näher zu beleuchten. Die linearisierten Integralgleichungen von Born-Green, Yvon bzw. Bogoljubow werden auf das Elektrolytproblem angewandt, wobei wieder das Modell starrer, glatter mit Punktladungen im Zentrum versehener Kugeln zugrundegelegt wird. Es können näherungsweise die radialen Verteilungsfunktionen durch Fouriertransformationen berechnet werden. Dabei wird im Gegensatz zu analogen Berechnungen, von S. Ono[8] und I. E. Mayer[9] und E. Haga[10] die zur Berechnung der divergenten Clusterintegrale konvergenzerzeugende Faktoren benutzen, die Methode der komplexen Integration verwandt.

Die radiale Verteilungsfunktion wird durch komplizierte Quadraturen angebbar. Mit wachsendem Abstand r von einem Zentralion nimmt die Ladungsdichte für kleine r zunächst schwächer ab, um dann für größere r stärker als die nach der Debye-Theorie berechneten absufallen. Durch das endliche Volumen der Ionen wird also in der näheren Umgebung des Zentralions eine Auflockerung der Ionenatmosphäre bewirkt. Es schließt sich mit wachsendem r eine Zone an, in der die Ionenwolke etwas komprimiert erscheint.

Daran schließen sich Bereiche an, in denen die Dichte abwechselnd schwächer und stärker als $e^{-\varkappa r}/r$ fällt. Die Amplitude dieser Schwingung nimmt mit wachsendem r stark ab. Die Funktion der Ladungsdichte schmiegt sich für große r ebenfalls der Debyeschen an. Das Potential

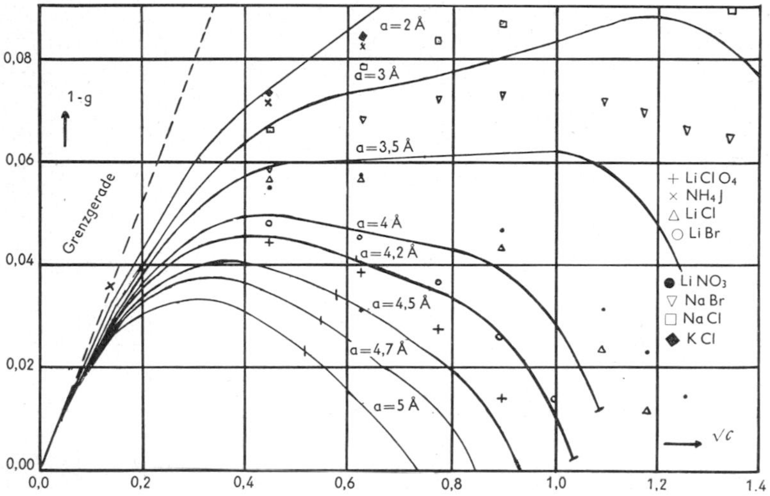

Abb. 6

der starren Kugeln beeinflußt also die Ladungsverteilung etwa bis zu $r = 6a$.

Abb. 6 zeigt die graphische Darstellung der Ergebnisse, für die osmotischen Koeffizienten bei Wahl von verschiedenen Zahlwerten für a.

Literatur

(1) M. Kaminsky, *Z. physik. Chem.*, **5**, 154 (1955).

(2) M. Dutta und S. N. Bagchi, *Ind. J. Phys.*, **24**, 2, 61 (1950); *J. Chem. Soc.*, **27**, 4 (1950); M. Dutta, *Naturwissensch.*, **40**, 51 (1953); *Ann. Physik*, **14**, 188 (1954); S. N. Bagchi, *Z. Elektrochem*, **57**, 138 (1953).

(3) M. Eigen und E. Wicke, *Naturwissensch.*, **38**, 453 (1951); **39**, 345 (1952); *Z. Elektrochem.*, **56**, 551 (1952); *Z. Naturforsch.*, 8*a*, 161 (1953).

(4) H. Falkenhagen und G. Kelbg, *Ann. Physik*, **11**, 60 (1852); **14**, 391 (1954); *Naturwissensch.*, **42** 10 (1955); *Z. physik. Chem.*, **204**, 111 (1955).

(5) M. Leist, *Z. physik. Chem.*, **205**, 16 (1955).

(6) H. Falkenahegen und E. Schmutzer, *Naturwissensch.*, **40**, 319 (1953); E. Schmutzer, *Z. physik. Chem.*, **203**, 292 (1954).

(7) E. Schmutzer, Diss. Rostock, 1955; S.a. *Z. physik. Chem.*, **204**, 131 (1955).

(8) J. O. Hirschfelder, C. F. Curtiss, and R. B. Bird, *Molecular Theory of Gases and Liquids*, W. Tey, New York, 1954.

(9) J. E. Mayer, *J. Chem. Phys.*, **18**, 1426 (1950).

(10) E. Haga, *J. Phys. Soc.* (*Japan*), **8**, 714 (1953).

A KINETIC THEORY OF THE VISCOSITY OF LIQUID HELIUM II

R. M. MAZO and J. DE BOER, *Instituut voor Theoretische Physica, Universiteit van Amsterdam, The Netherlands*

Abstract

This work constitutes an attempt to generalize the theory of the viscosity of liquid helium II, due to Landau and Khalatnikov, in two directions. It allows for an arbitrary excitation spectrum, and tries to provide a more accurate solution of the Boltzmann equation.

We suppose that liquid helium II can be adequately described as a "gas of excitations in a background fluid," and apply the kinetic theory to this gas, using the quantum mechanical Boltzmann equation in a form appropriate to massless excitations. The equation is treated by the well-known Chapman-Enskog methods. If we introduce the distribution function appropriate to excitations in a moving background fluid, the zero-order equations of motion are the familiar Landau two-fluid equations. This is analogous to choosing a locally Maxwellian distribution in the classical case. The next approximation introduces terms corresponding to shear viscosity, bulk viscosity, and thermal conductivity.

We have concentrated on the shear viscosity. Using the variation principle of Enskog we have obtained an expression for the shear viscosity.

The anomalous properties of liquid helium have been discussed in recent years primarily in terms of the two-fluid model, and, in particular, of the interpretation of this model afforded by the energy spectrum first proposed by Landau.[1] There has been a renewed interest in the Landau spectrum, and many authors have tried to derive it from reasonable models.[2–5]

Let us assume that the energy levels of a system are given by a spectrum of the form:

$$\varepsilon = \varepsilon(p),$$

where p is a quantum number with the dimensions of momentum. This spectrum is of a single particle form, and so we can form wave packets with more or less definite energy, ε, and more or less definite momenta, p. We call these packets excitations. When the number of these excitations is small, i.e., when the system is in a low lying state, we may describe the situation statistically by the singlet distribution functions for the excitations. Further, we assume that these functions, f_i, obey a Boltzmann equation:

$$\frac{\partial f_i}{\partial t} + \dot{\mathbf{r}} \cdot \frac{\partial f_i}{\partial F} + \dot{\mathbf{p}}_i \cdot \frac{\partial f_i}{\partial \mathbf{p}} = \sum_j J(f_i, f_j). \tag{1}$$

We have placed subscripts on the distribution functions in case there is a point in dividing the excitations into types. The actual form of the collision term, J, will not be essential for many of our arguments, but we shall assume it to be of the Uhling-Uhlenbeck structure:

$$J(f_i, f_j) = (V/h^3) \iint d\,\mathbf{p}_j\, dW_{ij} \{f_i' f_j' (1+f_i)(1+f_j) - f_i f_j (1+f_i')(1+f_j')\}. \tag{2}$$

dW_{ij} is the transition probability per unit incident beam for scattering from $(\mathbf{p}_i, \mathbf{p}_j)$ to $(\mathbf{p}_i', \mathbf{p}_j')$. The consequences of this assumption will be discussed later. At present we are unable to derive the Boltzmann equation (1) explicitly because we do not really know how the excitations arise from the Hamiltonian for the N-particle system. Its validity, however, is an extremely plausible ansatz.

Landau and Khalatnikov[6] have used the Landau spectrum and an approximate solution to the Boltzmann equation to calculate the viscosity of liquid helium II. Their work has been of great importance for the interpretation of experiments, and indeed gives semiquantitative agreement; yet it is proper to class their theory with the free path theories of molecular transport in gases. The object of the present communication is to show how the ideas of Landau and Khalatnikov can be utilized in a more precise theory.

It is quite important to realize that these excitations are only defined with respect to a "background fluid" in which they move.[7,8] In the laboratory system the energy of an excitation is given by the Doppler formula

$$\varepsilon'(p) = \varepsilon(p) + \mathbf{V}_s \cdot \mathbf{p}, \tag{3}$$

where $\mathbf{V}_s$ is the velocity of the background fluid (superfluid) in the laboratory system. ε' may depend on position, for example, through $\mathbf{V}_s$ and also through the density.

If we multiply Eq. (1) by $\mathbf{p}_i$ and ε_i', respectively, and assume that momentum and energy are conserved on collision, we obtain, after some simplification:

$$\sum_i \left[\frac{\partial}{\partial t}\int f_i \mathbf{p}_i d\mathbf{p}_i + \frac{\partial}{\partial \mathbf{r}} \cdot \int f_i \mathbf{p}_i \frac{\partial \varepsilon_i'}{\partial \mathbf{p}_i} d\mathbf{p}_i + \int f_i \frac{\partial \varepsilon_i'}{\partial \mathbf{r}} d\mathbf{p}_i\right] = 0, \tag{4a}$$

$$\sum_i \left[\frac{\partial}{\partial t}\int f_i \varepsilon_i' d\mathbf{p}_i + \frac{\partial}{\partial \mathbf{r}} \cdot \int f_i \varepsilon_i' \frac{\partial \varepsilon_i'}{\partial \mathbf{p}_i} d\mathbf{p}_i - \int f_i \frac{\partial \varepsilon_i'}{\partial t} d\mathbf{p}_i\right] = 0. \tag{4b}$$

Let us assume that local equilibrium obtains in the system, so that we may set:

$$f_i = f_i^{(0)} = h^{-3}(e^{\beta\varepsilon_i'} - 1)^{-1}. \tag{5}$$

Then we obtain from (4a):*

$$\frac{\partial \mathbf{G}^{(\mathrm{ex})}}{\partial t} = -\frac{\partial}{\partial \mathbf{r}} \cdot \mathsf{P}^{(\mathrm{ex})} + \varrho \frac{\partial}{\partial \mathbf{r}} \cdot \sum_i \int f_i^{(0)} \frac{\partial \varepsilon_i}{\partial \varrho} d\mathbf{p}_i,$$

$$\mathsf{P}^{(\mathrm{ex})} = \sum_i \left[\int f_i^{(0)} \mathbf{p}_i \frac{\partial \varepsilon_i'}{\partial \mathbf{p}_i} d\mathbf{p}_i + \mathsf{1}\, \varrho \int f_i^{(0)} \frac{\partial \varepsilon_i}{\partial \varrho} d\mathbf{p}_i\right] \tag{6}$$

From (5) the chemical potential of the excitation gas is zero, but the quantity $\sum \int f^{(0)} (\partial\varepsilon_i/\partial\varrho)\, d\mathbf{p}_i$ may be identified with the chemical potential of the entire system, which does not vanish. $\mathbf{G}^{(\mathrm{ex})}$ is the current density of the excitations with respect to the bearer fluid. We define a quantity ϱ_n by

$$\mathbf{G}^{(\mathrm{ex})} = \varrho_n \mathbf{V} = \varrho_n(\mathbf{V}_n - \mathbf{V}_s), \tag{7}$$

where $\mathbf{V}_n$ is the mean velocity of the excitations in the laboratory system.

Now the right-hand member of (6) can be written:

$$-\frac{\partial}{\partial \mathbf{r}} P^{(\mathrm{ex})} + \varrho \frac{\partial \mu}{\partial \mathbf{r}} = \frac{\partial F^{(\mathrm{ex})}}{\partial \mathbf{r}} - \mu \frac{\partial \varrho}{\partial \mathbf{r}},$$

$$P^{(\mathrm{ex})} = \tfrac{1}{3} \operatorname{trace} \mathsf{P}^{(\mathrm{ex})}. \tag{8}$$

Using the thermodynamic formula

$$dF^{(\mathrm{ex})} = -S^{(\mathrm{ex})} dT + \mu\, d\varrho, \tag{9}$$

and linearizing, we may finally write Eq. (6) as

$$\varrho_n \frac{\partial \mathbf{V}}{\partial t} = -S^{(\mathrm{ex})} \frac{\partial T}{\partial \mathbf{r}}. \tag{10}$$

Equation (4b) may be treated quite similarly. We find that

* For vector and tensor notation see ref. 10.

$$\frac{\partial S^{(\text{ex})}}{\partial t} = -\frac{\partial}{\partial \mathbf{r}} \cdot (S^{(\text{ex})}\mathbf{V}_n). \tag{11}$$

Eq. (10) and (11) are the well-known Landau two-fluid equations.

If we do not assume $f_i = f_i^{(0)}$ (cf. (5)), but write

$$f_i = f_i^{(0)}(1+\Phi_i),$$

where Φ_i is assumed small, we find, in the standard manner of kinetic theory, and after much algebra, that

$$(1+f_i^{(0)})^{-1}\Phi_i = \frac{1}{kT}\left[A_i \frac{\partial}{\partial \mathbf{r}} \cdot \mathbf{V}_n + B_i \frac{\partial}{\partial \mathbf{r}} \cdot (\mathbf{J}-\varrho\mathbf{V}_n) + \frac{\mathbf{C}_i}{T} \cdot \frac{\partial T}{\partial \mathbf{r}} + \mathsf{D}_i : \overset{\circ}{\overline{\overline{\frac{\partial \mathbf{V}_n}{\partial \mathbf{r}}}}}\right], \tag{12}$$

where A_i, B_i, $\mathbf{C}_i$, and D_i are functions to be determined by solution of the linearized Boltzmann equation.

Putting this result in Eqs. (4) we obtain two equations which involve dissipative effects. The equation of motion is:

$$\begin{aligned} \varrho_n \frac{\partial \mathbf{V}}{\partial t} &= \frac{\partial}{\partial \mathbf{r}} \cdot \left[P\mathsf{1} - 2\eta \overset{\circ}{\overline{\overline{\frac{\partial \mathbf{V}_n}{\partial \mathbf{r}}}}} - \mathsf{1}\left(\varphi_1 \frac{\partial}{\partial \mathbf{r}} \cdot \mathbf{V}_n + \varphi_2 \frac{\partial}{\partial \mathbf{r}} \cdot (\mathbf{J}-\varrho\mathbf{V}_n)\right)\right] \\ &\quad -\varrho \frac{\partial \mu}{\partial \mathbf{r}} + \frac{\partial \varrho}{\partial \mathbf{r}}\left[\varphi_3 \frac{\partial}{\partial \mathbf{r}} \cdot \mathbf{V}_n + \varphi_4 \frac{\partial}{\partial \mathbf{r}} \cdot (\mathbf{J}-\varrho\mathbf{V}_n)\right]. \end{aligned} \tag{13}$$

The last term should be omitted in a consistent linearization procedure, but we have included it to show the occurrence of the coefficients φ_3 and φ_4, which, together with φ_1 and φ_2, are coefficients of bulk viscosity. η is a coefficient of shear viscosity and is given by:

$$2\eta = \sum_i \int f_i^{(0)}(1+f_i^{(0)})\,\mathbf{p}\frac{\partial \varepsilon_i}{\partial \mathbf{p}_i} : \mathsf{D}_i d\mathbf{p}_i. \tag{14}$$

The coefficients φ_1, φ_2, φ_3, φ_4 should not all be independent (cf. ref. 9) but we have not yet investigated them thoroughly. The energy flow equation is:

$$\begin{aligned} &\frac{\partial U^{(\text{ex})}}{\partial t} + \frac{\partial}{\partial \mathbf{r}} \cdot (H^{(\text{ex})}\mathbf{V}_n) - \mu \frac{\partial \varrho}{\partial t} = -\frac{\partial}{\partial \mathbf{r}} \cdot \left(\lambda \frac{\partial T}{\partial \mathbf{r}}\right) \\ &+ \frac{\partial}{\partial \mathbf{r}} \cdot \left(\mathbf{V}_s \cdot \left[-P\mathsf{1} + 2\eta \overset{\circ}{\overline{\overline{\frac{\partial \mathbf{V}_n}{\partial \mathbf{r}}}}} + \mathsf{1}\left(\varphi_1 \frac{\partial}{\partial \mathbf{r}} \cdot \mathbf{V}_n + \varphi_2 \frac{\partial}{\partial \mathbf{r}} \cdot (\mathbf{J}-\varrho\mathbf{V}_n)\right)\right]\right) \\ &+ \frac{\partial \varrho}{\partial t}\left(\varphi_3 \frac{\partial \cdot \mathbf{V}_n}{\partial \mathbf{r}} + \varphi_4 \frac{\partial}{\partial \mathbf{r}} \cdot (\mathbf{J}-\varrho\mathbf{V}_n)\right). \end{aligned} \tag{15}$$

To calculate η we proceed by the standard techniques of the kinetic theory of gases.[10] Our use of the collision integral (2) means that we are neglecting the possibility of creation or annihilation of particles during collision. With this provision, the problem of calculating η is, in principle, reduced to the performance of relatively simple operations on known functions.

Unfortunately the transition probabilities are not known. We have made exploratory calculations to obtain these quantities using the field theory of Kronig and Thellung[2] and Ziman,[4] a crude form of which was used by Landau and Khalatnikov.[6] The calculations indicate that the standard perturbation theory used does not give results reliable enough to justify extensive numerical work. Perhaps application of some of the newer perturbation techniques of quantum field theory may improve the situation.

To summarize, we have shown how the Landau equations and equations of motion involving dissipative effects can arise from the existence of excitations whose distribution functions obey a Boltzmann equation. We have found an explicit expression for the viscosity which can yield numerical results when the interaction between excitations is known.

One of us (R.M.M.) would like to thank the National Science Foundation (United States) for a fellowship under the tenure of which this work was done.

References

(1) L. Landau, *J. Phys. (U. S. S. R.)*, **5**, 71 (1941); **8**, 1 (1944).
(2) R. Kronig and A. Thellung, *Physica*, **18**, 749 (1952).
(3) A. Thellung, *Physica*, **19**, 217 (1953).
(4) J. Ziman, *Proc. Roy. Soc. (London)*, **A219**, 257 (1953).
(5) R. Feynman, in *Progress in Low Temperature Phyics*, Vol. I, North-Holland, Amsterdam, Interscience, New York, 1955, p. 17.
(6) L. Landau and I. Khalatnikov, *J. Exptl. Theor. Phys. (U. S. S. R)*, **19**, 637, 709 (1949).
(7) H. Kramers, *Physica*, **18**, 653 (1952).
(8) R. Kronig, *Physica*, **19**, 535 (1953).
(9) I. Khalatnikov, *J. Exptl. Theor. Phys. (U. S. S. R.)*, **23**, 8 (1952).
(10) S. Chapman and T. G. Cowling, *The Mathematical Theory of Non-uniform Gases*, Cambridge Univ. Press, London, 1952.

TRANSPORT OF MOMENTUM AND ENERGY BY PHONONS IN FLUIDS

R. EISENSCHITZ, *Queen Mary College, University of London, England*

I. GENERAL SURVEY

Liquid helium at the lowest accessible temperatures has been described as a superfluid in which phonons are propagated. This intuitive approach was successful in interpreting experimental facts and has been given some, although not very much, support by the fundamental theories. This support amounts to a transformation of the dynamic variables appropriate to a disordered assembly of interacting molecules. By this transformation the energy operator is given the form of the energy of a wave field which differs significantly from the familiar result of second quantization and corresponds closely to sound waves. It has not yet been possible to define precisely the conditions of validity of this phonon theory; it is restricted to extremely low energy levels.

The flow of momentum and of energy, as observed in fluids during their irreversible approach to thermal equilibrium, can be expressed in terms of the ordinary variables of particle dynamics. These expressions are well founded, being derived from the general principles of quantum mechanics independently of any unresolved difficulties of transport theory. Using these expressions, the flow of momentum and energy will be subjected to the transformation by means of which the energy is represented as the energy of quantized sound waves. In this way the consistency and power of the phonon theory is put to a test.

II. PHONON REPRESENTATION OF THE ENERGY

In summarizing the transformation formulae we follow the presentation of the subject by Zubarev[3] and by Bogolyubov and Zubarev.[1] An infinite set of dynamic variables is defined as

$$\varrho_k = (1/N)^{1/2} \sum_{j=1}^{N} \exp(-i\mathbf{k} \cdot \mathbf{r}_j), \qquad k \neq 0, \tag{1}$$

where N is the number of molecules, $\mathbf{r}_j$ are their position vectors, and

$\mathbf{k}$ is a wave vector. Denoting by $u(r)$ the interaction potential between two molecules let

$$u(r) = (1/V) \sum_{k} U(k) \exp(i\mathbf{k} \cdot \mathbf{r}). \tag{2}$$

The energy operator is originally given in familiar notation by

$$H = \sum_{j} [(p_j^2/2m) + \tfrac{1}{2} \sum_{l} u_{jl}]. \tag{3}$$

By allowing the wave function to depend on the $\varrho_{\mathbf{k}}$ in addition to the coordinates and by putting

$$\mathbf{p}_j = (\hbar/i)[(\partial/\partial \mathbf{r}_j) + (\partial \varrho_{\mathbf{k}}/\partial \mathbf{r}_j)(\partial/\partial \varrho_{\mathbf{k}})], \tag{4}$$

the Schrödinger equation is formulated in terms of "redundant" variables which, however, may be handled as if they were independent variables.

A second transformation is performed by substituting new wave functions (Φ) for the original wave functions (φ)

$$\Phi = \varphi \exp(-\tfrac{1}{4} \sum \varrho_{\mathbf{k}} \varrho_{-\mathbf{k}}). \tag{5}$$

Finally, dimensionless variables (q_k) are substituted for the ϱ_k according to

$$\varrho_{\mathbf{k}} = a_k q_{\mathbf{k}}, \tag{6}$$

where

$$a_k = (\hbar^2 k^2/m)^{1/4}\{[NU(k)/V] + (\hbar^2 k^2/4m)\}^{-1/4}. \tag{7}$$

A quantity having the dimension of an energy is defined as

$$E(k) = (\hbar k/m^{1/2})\{[NU(k)/V] + (h^2 k^2/4m^{1/2})\}^{1/2}, \tag{8}$$

so that

$$a_k^2 = (\hbar k)^2/mE(k). \tag{9}$$

By these transformations the operator (1) assumes the form

$$H = H_0 + \tfrac{1}{2} \sum_{\mathbf{k}} E(k)[-\partial^2/\partial q_{\mathbf{k}} \partial q_{-\mathbf{k}} + q_{\mathbf{k}} q_{-\mathbf{k}}] \tag{10}$$

in the "$q_{\mathbf{k}}$-representation." H_0 is the energy of the ground state of noninteracting particles; the numerous terms that are omitted are negligibly small provided that k is small enough.

The eigenvalues of the operator (10) are obtained by resolving the $q_{\mathbf{k}}$

in their real and imaginary parts. They are equal to $H_0+E(k)[\frac{1}{2}+n(\mathbf{k})]$; $n(k)=0, 1, 2, \cdots$. The eigenfunctions for a single term in the above sum are products of two Hermitean orthogonal functions, one having the real part, the other having the imaginary part of $q_\mathbf{k}$ as its argument. Using these eigenfunctions, expressions for matrix elements are obtained:

$$\langle \partial^2/\partial q_\mathbf{k}\,\partial q_{-\mathbf{k}}\rangle_{n(\mathbf{k})\,n(\mathbf{k})} = \tfrac{1}{2}+n(\mathbf{k}). \tag{11}$$

The corresponding matrix elements for the first or the third derivatives vanish.

The energy as determined by (10) is infinite but can be rendered finite by an obvious subtraction. The above transformations apply to assemblies of bosons or fermions. $E(k)$ and $n(\mathbf{k})$ are interpreted as the energies and the numbers of phonons present.

It will be assumed that in the limit of small values of k the Fourier transform $U(k)$ becomes virtually independent of k, approaching a finite and positive limit $U(0)$. In this case there is no dispersion of sound and the bulk modulus of the fluid has the form

$$K = (N/V)^2\,U(0). \tag{12}$$

III. FLOW OF MOMENTUM AND ENERGY

By using a generalized virial theorem the flow of momentum (P) and of energy ($\mathbf{Q}$) were obtained[2] in the form:

$$\langle \mathsf{P}\rangle = (1/mV)\sum_j \langle (\mathbf{p}_j\,\mathbf{p}_j) - \tfrac{1}{2}m\sum_l (\mathbf{r}_j-\mathbf{r}_l)[\partial u_{jl}/\partial(\mathbf{r}_j-\mathbf{r}_l)]\rangle, \tag{13}$$

$$\langle \mathbf{Q}\rangle = (1/2m^2V)\sum_j \langle \mathbf{p}_j\mathbf{p}_j^2 + \tfrac{1}{2}m\sum_l [u_{jl}-(\mathbf{r}_j-\mathbf{r}_l)(u_{jl}/(\mathbf{r}_j-\mathbf{r}_l)](\mathbf{p}_j+\mathbf{p}_l)\rangle. \tag{14}$$

The average, as indicated by the $\langle\ \rangle$ brackets, is, in the present context, understood to be the expectation in states of well-defined numbers of phonons; it is equal to the diagonal elements of the matrices derived from the operators P or $\mathbf{Q}$ and the eigenfunctions of the operator (10). For the purpose of calculating these matrix elements the operators must be transformed to the $q_\mathbf{k}$ representation.

At first the Fourier transform of the last term in (13) will be obtained. It follows from equation (2) that

$$\mathbf{r}[\partial u(r)/\partial \mathbf{r}] = (1/V) \sum_k \{\partial[U(k)\mathbf{k} \exp(i\mathbf{k}\cdot\mathbf{r})]/\partial\mathbf{k}$$
$$- \exp(i\mathbf{k}\cdot\mathbf{r})\partial[\mathbf{k}U(k)/\partial\mathbf{k}]\}.$$

The first sum is replaced by an integral which vanishes. The required Fourier transform is accordingly

$$-U(k)\mathsf{I}-\mathbf{k}[\partial U(k)/\partial\mathbf{k}],$$

where I is the unit tensor. The first term in this expression does not contribute to the anisotropic part of the tensor and is therefore without any significance in viscous flow. The second term vanishes for small values of k on account of the assumptions made. It follows that in transforming P to the $q_{\mathbf{k}}$ representation the last term in (13) does not make any contribution.

The terms in Eq. (14) which depend on the u_{jl} or their gradients contribute to the operator $\mathbf{Q}$ a number of terms depending on $U(k)$; it is, however, found that these terms do not contribute to the expectation of $\mathbf{Q}$ in states with well-defined numbers of phonons. It is accordingly not necessary to take these terms into consideration.

In transforming the operators P and $\mathbf{Q}$ it is accordingly sufficient to consider the first terms in Eqs. (13) and (14). By performing the transformations determined by Eqs. (4) and (5) we obtain as leading terms:

$$\mathsf{P} = (\hbar^2/2mV) \sum \mathbf{k}\mathbf{k}[-2\partial^2/\partial\varrho_{\mathbf{k}}\partial\varrho_{-\mathbf{k}}+\tfrac{1}{2}\varrho_{\mathbf{k}}\varrho_{-\mathbf{k}}], \qquad (15)$$

$$\mathbf{Q} = (\hbar^3/4m^2V) \sum \mathbf{k}k^2[-2\partial^2/\partial\varrho_{\mathbf{k}}\partial\varrho_{-\mathbf{k}}+\tfrac{1}{2}\varrho_{\mathbf{k}}\varrho_{-\mathbf{k}}]. \qquad (16)$$

If, in accordance with Eqs. (6) to (9) the $q_{\mathbf{k}}$ are substituted for the $\varrho_{\mathbf{k}}$, it is readily seen that the second terms in (15) and (16) are negligibly small as compared with the first terms provided that k is small enough; neglecting the second terms it follows that:

$$\mathsf{P} = -(1/V) \sum (\mathbf{k}\mathbf{k}/k^2)E(k)(\partial^2/\partial q_{\mathbf{k}}\partial q_{-\mathbf{k}}), \qquad (17)$$

$$\mathbf{Q} = -(\hbar/2mV) \sum \mathbf{k}\, E(k)(\partial^2/\partial q_{\mathbf{k}}\partial q_{-\mathbf{k}}). \qquad (18)$$

The matrix elements are evaluated by means of Eq. (11):

$$\langle\mathsf{P}\rangle = (1/V) \sum (\mathbf{k}\mathbf{k}/k^2)E(k)[\tfrac{1}{2}+n(\mathbf{k})], \qquad (19)$$

$$\langle\mathbf{Q}\rangle = (\hbar/2mV) \sum \mathbf{k}\, E(k)[\tfrac{1}{2}+n(\mathbf{k})]. \qquad (20)$$

IV. CONCLUSIONS

The mean values of the flow of momentum and energy are found to be infinite on account of the "zero-point energy" terms in Eqs. (19) and (20). This cannot be remedied by simply subtracting the infinity in Eq. (10). This divergency is, however, not a serious objection to the transformation applied, since the meaning of the result is unambiguous.

Apart from the divergent term Eq. (19) is fully in accordance with the phonon model. The flow of momentum is found to be equal to the density of energy multiplied by an appropriate angular function. With regard to the flow of energy, agreement is not perfect. The terms in Eq. (20) can be written as:

$$(1/V)[E(k)/\hbar k](\hbar^2 k^2/2m)(\mathbf{k}/k).$$

The second factor is, by Eq. (11), equal to the velocity of sound: the third factor should accordingly be equal to the energy of a phonon; it has in actual fact the dimension of an energy but is not capable of any simple interpretation. According to the present calculation the intermolecular forces do not participate in transmitting momentum and energy. An assembly of molecules in the neighborhood of the ground state resembles accordingly a classical gas rather than a classical liquid. This result ties up well with the form of expression (11): the bulk modulus can be proportional to $U(0)$ only if intermolecular repulsion is rendered ineffective. This property of an assembly of molecules could be readily explained for bosons: particles of extremely small velocity can obviously penetrate through the repulsive potential barrier. The fact that the same result when applied to fermions appears to be a paradox shows that the significance of the $q_{\mathbf{k}}$ representation is not yet fully understood.

The range of applicability of the phonon interpretation is increased by the present investigation, but its limits are clearly demonstrated. Further tests of this approach are possible and will be carried out shortly.

References

(1) N. N. Bogolyubov and D. N. Zubarev, *J. Exptl. Theor. Phys. (U. S. S. R.)*, **28**, 129 (1955).

(2) R. Eisenschitz, *Phys. Rev.*, **99**, 1059 (1955).

(3) D. N. Zubarev, *J. Exptl. Theor. Phys. (U. S. S. R)*, **25**, 548 (1953).

Discussion X

I. Prigogine (*to H. Falkenhagen*): Wurde für die Berechnung die Superposition approximation angewandt?

H. Falkenhagen (*to I. Prigogine*): Ja.

F. P. Buff (*to H. Falkenhagen*): Did you calculate the surface tension change by integrating the Gibbs adsorption equation or by directly evaluating the stress tensor integral. When rigorous distribution functions are used, both methods must give the same answer so that the utilization of both approaches also provides a consistency test for approximate theories. We recently carried out such a comparison for the dilute solution case.

H. Falkenhagen (*to F. P. Buff*): Our calculations are based on the Gibbs adsorption equation. The aim of our work was to extend the theory of Onsager-Samaras to higher concentrations.

L. Onsager: We found the Gibbs equation easier to handle and used that (L. Onsager and N. N. T. Samaras, *J. Chem. Phys.*, **1934**).

M. Green (*to R. M. Mazo*): Do the phenomenological equations which you derive agree with those suggested by irreversible thermodynamics?

R. M. Mazo (*to M. Green*): The equations of motion are linear in the appropriate gradients and so are consistent with the thermodynamics of irreversible processes. The linear region may, however, be difficult to find experimentally, as is apparently the case in heat conduction.

D. ter Haar (*to R. Eisenschitz*): How far is the vanishing of the term involving $\partial u/\partial r$ in $\langle P \rangle$ related to the cut-off in wave number and/or to a random phase approximation.

R. Eisenschitz (*to D. ter Haar*): The vanishing Fourier transform of $(\partial u/\partial r)$ is due to the assumption lim $U(R) =$ finite and independent of R. It does not apply to electrons. The formulae do depend only on averaging over a time-independent ensemble. No assumptions of the particular kind of average are involved.

I. Prigogine (*to R. Eisenschitz*): I did not read the paper by Zubarev to which you referred. We have, however, discussed a similar paper by Bogolyubov and we have not been able to understand his intent. The correct way would have been to introduce the corresponding momenta after the definition of the collective coordinates. This problem is studied in two recent very interesting papers by Tomonoga. The result of the Zubarev or the Bogolyubov method is that the Hamiltonian is even not real. What this means I do not know.

R. Eisenschitz (*to I. Prigogine*): The use of "redundant variables" is justified by Zubarev on the following basis: let $y(x)$ be a function of x only, and L a linear operator so that

$$L[y(x)] = 0. \tag{1}$$

Let a well-behaved function of x be defined as

$$u = u(x). \tag{2}$$

Let $p(u, x)$ and $q(x)$ be functions of two and one independent variables, respectively, so that

$$p(u, x) = q(x). \tag{3}$$

If all functions are well behaved there exists a linear operator M operating on u and x such that

$$M[p(u, x)] = L[q(x)]. \tag{4}$$

If a function p satisfies the equation,

$$M[p] = 0, \tag{5}$$

then the function q as defined by (3) solves Eq. (1) and can therefore be written as

$$q(x) = y(x). \tag{6}$$

N. H. V. Temperley: (1) The result of Zubarev would lead to a velocity of sound that, even for very small atoms, would tend to infinity as they became more and more rigid. This seems physically incorrect. I believe that it arises from the fact that Zubarev completely ignores boundary conditions, which means that his wave function consists of a sum of the true wave functions and of others that remain finite even when one or more atoms are outside the vessel. I believe that this results in an incorrect method of averaging over the interaction potential in order to arrive at the phonon spectrum. (2) It seems to be fairly well established that a two-fold spectrum of excitations is what is required to account directly for the properties of He^3 and, by well known steps involving the two-fluid picture, this model also describes many of the properties of He^4. The two types of excitation have been given various names; the *essential* difference is that some of them involve the collective motion of a great many atoms, while others only involve a few atoms effectively. The problem remains of showing that such a spectrum is the correct consequence of the Hamiltonian. Many attempts have been made to do this via the quantum hydrodynamics of Landau, but these suffer from the disadvantage of involving a large number of adjustable constants, also difficulties associated with wave length cut-off. Moreover, it does not even seem to have been derived whether or not quantum hydrodynamics can be correctly deduced from the Hamiltonian. Under these circumstances, I should like to say that I agree entirely with Dr. Eisenschitz that the method of transforming the Hamiltonian (due essentially to Bijl and involving various applications of the Bohm-Pines transformation) is worth following up. For various reasons, I consider that the treatment of Brenig (*Z. Physik*, **144**, 488 (1956)) is better than that of Zubarev.

P. G. de Gennes: I would first like to point out that the zero-point energy of the collective motion is to be interpreted as a part of the correlation energy of the individual particles. So should it not be excluded from the energy transfer by the collective modes? Second, it should be noted, in connection with Professor Prigogine's remark, that Bohm and Pines have given an explicit form for the collective coordinate assuming a rather general form of interaction potential, which is an improvement of the ϱ_k. However, the whole derivation is based on the so-called "random phase approximation," whose validity is doubtful in the case of a classical liquid.

R. Brout: It is possible to study the collective coordinates corresponding to density fluctuations in liquids by studying the collective coordinate $\varrho_k = \sum e^{ik \cdot r_i}$. If one uses the density of the system or correspondingly the fact that it is nearly incompressible, one may derive approximate statistical equations of motion for ϱ_k for large wave lengths, corresponding to sound waves.

PART XI

ON THE STATISTICAL BASIS OF ONSAGER'S RECIPROCAL RELATIONS

S. R. DE GROOT and P. MAZUR, *Institute-Lorentz, University of Leiden, The Netherlands*

Abstract

A survey and discussion is given of various derivations of the Onsager reciprocal relations between irreversible processes.

I. INTRODUCTION

The traditional derivation of the Onsager reciprocal relations between irreversible processes is based on the consideration of fluctuations in an aged (equilibrium) system.[1] It makes use of the principle of microscopic reversibility and of a hypothesis for the average decay of fluctuations. This hypothesis has been discussed in great detail by various authors.[2,3] It can be justified on the basis of a Brownian motion assumption.[4] (For extensive references on this point see E. P. Wigner.[3])

We wish to present here an alternative derivation of the reciprocal relations which does not make use of a regression hypothesis, but is based on a "master equation" inferred from statistical considerations of irreversible processes.[5] This type of derivation is not concerned with fluctuations in an aged system but deals explicitly with nonequilibrium situations. Besides being more straightforward, the "nonequilibrium derivation" gives a clear connection with macroscopic phenomenological theory.

The traditional "equilibrium method" of derivation will be briefly sketched and compared to the nonequilibrium method.

For simplicity's sake it is assumed in the main text that the systems under consideration are described by even or α-type variables, i.e., variables which are even functions of the particle velocities. The generalization to systems with even and odd variables and the influence of a magnetic field are treated in an appendix.

II. NONEQUILIBRIUM METHOD

(*a*) *Starting points*. The state of the system will be described by a set of macroscopic (gross or coarse-grained) variables $A_1, \cdots, A_n$ with equilibrium values $A_1^e, \cdots, A_n^e$. This (gross)state can be represented by a point in the so-called $\boldsymbol{\alpha}$-space of which the coordinates are the deviations of the gross variables from their equilibrium values:

$$\alpha_i = A_i - A_i^e, \qquad (i = 1, \cdots, n). \tag{1}$$

The probability of finding the system in a certain state is obtained by means of a probability distribution function $f(\boldsymbol{\alpha}, t)$, where the vector $\boldsymbol{\alpha}$ has the components (1). The *observed* macroscopic values $\bar{\boldsymbol{\alpha}}$ of the variables $\boldsymbol{\alpha}$ are given by

$$\bar{\boldsymbol{\alpha}} = \int \boldsymbol{\alpha} f(\boldsymbol{\alpha}, t)\, d\boldsymbol{\alpha} \tag{2}$$

where f is normalized to unity. According to the definition (1) the left-hand side of (2) is zero when f is the equilibrium distribution function f^e

$$\int \boldsymbol{\alpha} f^e(\boldsymbol{\alpha})\, d\boldsymbol{\alpha} = 0. \tag{3}$$

The equilibrium distribution function has the well-known Gaussian form

$$f^e(\boldsymbol{\alpha}) = c e^{-\frac{1}{2}\mathsf{g} : \boldsymbol{\alpha\alpha}/k}, \tag{4}$$

where g is a symmetric positive definite tensor, $\boldsymbol{\alpha\alpha}$ a dyadic product, and c a normalizing factor. It follows from (4) that

$$\int \boldsymbol{\alpha\alpha} f^e\, d\boldsymbol{\alpha} = k\mathsf{g}^{-1}, \tag{5}$$

$$\int \boldsymbol{\alpha} \mathbf{X} f^e\, d\boldsymbol{\alpha} = -k\mathsf{U}, \tag{6}$$

where U is the unit tensor and the vector $\mathbf{X}$ is defined as

$$\mathbf{X} = -\mathsf{g} \cdot \boldsymbol{\alpha}. \tag{7}$$

From statistical considerations on irreversible processes it may be argued[5] that the nonequilibrium distribution $f(\boldsymbol{\alpha}, t)$ obeys a so-called "master equation"

$$\partial f(\boldsymbol{\alpha}, t)/\partial t = \int W(\boldsymbol{\alpha}', \boldsymbol{\alpha}) f(\boldsymbol{\alpha}', t)\, d\boldsymbol{\alpha}', \tag{8}$$

where $W(\boldsymbol{\alpha}', \boldsymbol{\alpha})$ is the transition probability from a state $\boldsymbol{\alpha}'$ to a state $\boldsymbol{\alpha}$, obeying the condition

$$\int W(\boldsymbol{\alpha}', \boldsymbol{\alpha})\, d\boldsymbol{\alpha} = 0. \tag{9}$$

Eq. (8) expresses the Markoffian character, which arises from coarse graining and certain assumptions of randomness. Furthermore, it can be shown[3, 5] that the principle of microscopic reversibility or detailed balancing holds in $\boldsymbol{\alpha}$-space

$$W(\boldsymbol{\alpha}', \boldsymbol{\alpha}) f^e(\boldsymbol{\alpha}') = W(\boldsymbol{\alpha}, \boldsymbol{\alpha}') f^e(\boldsymbol{\alpha}). \tag{10}$$

This property follows from the time reversal invariance of the microscopic equations of motion.

The definitions and results given above will be used as starting points for the subsequent derivation of the Onsager reciprocal relations.

(*b*) *The nonequilibrium distribution function.* We shall write the nonequilibrium distribution function in the form

$$f(\boldsymbol{\alpha}, t) = f^e(\boldsymbol{\alpha})\{1+\varphi(\boldsymbol{\alpha}, t)\}, \tag{11}$$

where $f^e \varphi$ represents the deviation from the equilibrium distribution satisfying the condition

$$\int f^e \varphi \, d\boldsymbol{\alpha} = 0, \tag{12}$$

since f (and f^e) are normalized to unity.

There corresponds to every observed value $\bar{\boldsymbol{\alpha}}$ of the vector $\boldsymbol{\alpha}$ a certain distribution function $\varphi(\boldsymbol{\alpha}, t)$. (For vanishing $\bar{\boldsymbol{\alpha}}$ the function φ reduces to zero.) Writing φ as a linear function of the vector $\bar{\boldsymbol{\alpha}}$, we have

$$\varphi = \mathbf{C}(\boldsymbol{\alpha}) \cdot \bar{\boldsymbol{\alpha}}, \tag{13}$$

where the components of the vector $\mathbf{C}$ are functions of $\boldsymbol{\alpha}$. Expanding $\mathbf{C}(\boldsymbol{\alpha})$ in a Taylor series around $\boldsymbol{\alpha} = 0$ and neglecting terms of degree higher than one, we obtain

$$\mathbf{C}(\boldsymbol{\alpha}) = \mathbf{C}^0 + \mathsf{C}^1 \cdot \boldsymbol{\alpha}. \tag{14}$$

The constant quantities $\mathbf{C}^0$ and C^1 may now be determined by inserting (11) with (13) and (14) into (2) and (12). This gives

$$\bar{\boldsymbol{\alpha}} = \int \boldsymbol{\alpha}(1+\mathbf{C}^0 \cdot \bar{\boldsymbol{\alpha}} + \mathsf{C}^1 : \boldsymbol{\alpha}\bar{\boldsymbol{\alpha}}) f^e \, d\boldsymbol{\alpha}, \tag{15}$$

$$0 = \int (\mathbf{C}^0 \cdot \bar{\boldsymbol{\alpha}} + \mathsf{C}^1 : \boldsymbol{\alpha}\bar{\boldsymbol{\alpha}}) f^e \, d\boldsymbol{\alpha}. \tag{16}$$

From (3) and (5) it then follows that the vector $\mathbf{C}^0$ vanishes whereas the tensor C^1 is given by

$$\mathsf{C}^1 = k^{-1} \mathsf{g}. \tag{17}$$

Thus the explicit expression for φ is

$$\varphi = k^{-1}\mathbf{g} : \boldsymbol{\alpha}\bar{\boldsymbol{\alpha}} = -k^{-1}\boldsymbol{\alpha} \cdot \overline{\mathbf{X}} = -k^{-1}\mathbf{X} \cdot \bar{\boldsymbol{\alpha}}, \tag{18}$$

where the definition (7) has been used.

(*c*) *Derivation of the phenomenological equations.* We now proceed to derive the so-called phenomenological equations, i.e., the equations for the change with time of the observed macroscopic quantities. Taking the time derivative of both members of (2) one obtains

$$\dot{\bar{\boldsymbol{\alpha}}} = \int \boldsymbol{\alpha} \dot{f}(\boldsymbol{\alpha}, t)\, d\boldsymbol{\alpha} = \int \boldsymbol{\alpha} f^e(\boldsymbol{\alpha}) \dot{\varphi}(\boldsymbol{\alpha}, t)\, d\boldsymbol{\alpha}, \tag{19}$$

using (11) and the fact that the equilibrium distribution function (4) does not depend explicitly on time. The equation for $\dot{\varphi}$ is obtained from (8)

$$f^e(\boldsymbol{\alpha}) \dot{\varphi}(\boldsymbol{\alpha}, t) = \int W(\boldsymbol{\alpha}', \boldsymbol{\alpha}) f^e(\boldsymbol{\alpha}') \varphi(\boldsymbol{\alpha}', t)\, d\boldsymbol{\alpha}'. \tag{20}$$

Inserting (20) into (19) the following equation for $\dot{\bar{\boldsymbol{\alpha}}}$ is obtained

$$\dot{\bar{\boldsymbol{\alpha}}} = -k^{-1} \int\int \boldsymbol{\alpha}\boldsymbol{\alpha}' W(\boldsymbol{\alpha}', \boldsymbol{\alpha}) f^e(\boldsymbol{\alpha}')\, d\boldsymbol{\alpha}\, d\boldsymbol{\alpha}' \cdot \overline{\mathbf{X}}, \tag{21}$$

where the expression (18) has been used for φ. We shall write (21) in the usual form

$$\dot{\bar{\boldsymbol{\alpha}}} = \mathsf{L} \cdot \overline{\mathbf{X}}, \tag{22}$$

where

$$\mathsf{L} = -k^{-1} \int\int \boldsymbol{\alpha}\boldsymbol{\alpha}' W(\boldsymbol{\alpha}', \boldsymbol{\alpha}) f^e(\boldsymbol{\alpha}')\, d\boldsymbol{\alpha}\, d\boldsymbol{\alpha}' \tag{23}$$

is the matrix of phenomenological coefficients. The linearity of the phenomenological equations is a consequence of the Markoffian character of (8).

(*d*) *Derivation of the Onsager reciprocal relations.* Applying microscopic reversibility (10) in (23) and subsequently interchanging the variables $\boldsymbol{\alpha}$ and $\boldsymbol{\alpha}'$ one obtains the reciprocal relations:

$$\begin{aligned} \mathsf{L} &= -k^{-1} \int\int \boldsymbol{\alpha}\boldsymbol{\alpha}' W(\boldsymbol{\alpha}, \boldsymbol{\alpha}') f^e(\boldsymbol{\alpha})\, d\boldsymbol{\alpha}\, d\boldsymbol{\alpha}' \\ &= -k^{-1} \int\int \boldsymbol{\alpha}'\boldsymbol{\alpha} W(\boldsymbol{\alpha}', \boldsymbol{\alpha}) f^e(\boldsymbol{\alpha}')\, d\boldsymbol{\alpha}\, d\boldsymbol{\alpha}' = \tilde{\mathsf{L}}, \end{aligned} \tag{24}$$

where $\tilde{\mathsf{L}}$ is the transposed matrix of L.

III. EQUILIBRIUM METHOD

In the more usual type of derivation[1, 2] of the Onsager relations an aged system is considered, described by the equilibrium distribution function (4). We briefly reproduce this derivation here.

(*a*) *Fluctuation theory*. The proof also uses the result (6), which follows from the form (4) of the equilibrium distribution function:

$$\int \boldsymbol{\alpha}\mathbf{X}f^e \, d\boldsymbol{\alpha} = -k\mathsf{U}. \tag{25}$$

(*b*) *Microscopic reversibility*. The principle of microscopic reversibility is expressed by the following equality of functions giving the correlation between values of the variables $\boldsymbol{\alpha}$ at two different times (in the equilibrium system)

$$\overline{\boldsymbol{\alpha}(t+\tau)\,\boldsymbol{\alpha}(t)} = \overline{\boldsymbol{\alpha}(t-\tau)\,\boldsymbol{\alpha}(t)} \tag{26}$$

or

$$\overline{\boldsymbol{\alpha}(t+\tau)\,\boldsymbol{\alpha}(t)} = \overline{\boldsymbol{\alpha}(t)\,\boldsymbol{\alpha}(t+\tau)} \tag{27}$$

or

$$\overline{\left\{\frac{\overline{\boldsymbol{\alpha}(t+\tau)-\boldsymbol{\alpha}(t)}}{\tau}\right\}_{\boldsymbol{\alpha}(t)}\boldsymbol{\alpha}(t)} = \overline{\boldsymbol{\alpha}(t)\left\{\frac{\overline{\boldsymbol{\alpha}(t+\tau)-\boldsymbol{\alpha}(t)}}{\tau}\right\}_{\boldsymbol{\alpha}(t)}}\,. \tag{28}$$

The last form (28) is obtained by subtracting the dyadic $\boldsymbol{\alpha}(t)\boldsymbol{\alpha}(t)$ from both sides of (27). Furthermore the averaging process of (27) is performed in (28) in two successive steps, first by taking the average of the difference $\boldsymbol{\alpha}(t+\tau)-\boldsymbol{\alpha}(t)$ for a fixed value of $\boldsymbol{\alpha}(t)$, and subsequently by averaging over the hitherto fixed $\boldsymbol{\alpha}(t)$. In the notation of the previous section this first conditional average is

$$\left\{\frac{\overline{\boldsymbol{\alpha}(t+\tau)-\boldsymbol{\alpha}(t)}}{\tau}\right\}_{\boldsymbol{\alpha}(t)} = \int \boldsymbol{\alpha}' W(\boldsymbol{\alpha}, \boldsymbol{\alpha}')\, d\boldsymbol{\alpha}'. \tag{29}$$

Since the second average is performed with the weight function $f^e(\boldsymbol{\alpha})$, Eq. (28) can be written as

$$\iint \boldsymbol{\alpha}'\boldsymbol{\alpha}\, W(\boldsymbol{\alpha}, \boldsymbol{\alpha}')\, f^e(\boldsymbol{\alpha})\, d\boldsymbol{\alpha}\, d\boldsymbol{\alpha}' = \iint \boldsymbol{\alpha}\boldsymbol{\alpha}'\, W(\boldsymbol{\alpha}, \boldsymbol{\alpha}')\, f^e(\boldsymbol{\alpha})\, d\boldsymbol{\alpha}\, d\boldsymbol{\alpha}' \tag{30}$$

or interchanging variables $\boldsymbol{\alpha}$ and $\boldsymbol{\alpha}'$ on the left-hand side:

$$\iint \boldsymbol{\alpha}\boldsymbol{\alpha}'\, W(\boldsymbol{\alpha}', \boldsymbol{\alpha})\, f^e(\boldsymbol{\alpha}')\, d\boldsymbol{\alpha}\, d\boldsymbol{\alpha}' = \iint \boldsymbol{\alpha}\boldsymbol{\alpha}'\, W(\boldsymbol{\alpha}, \boldsymbol{\alpha}')\, f^e(\boldsymbol{\alpha})\, d\boldsymbol{\alpha}\, d\boldsymbol{\alpha}'. \tag{31}$$

(*c*) *Average regression of fluctuations*. It is now assumed that the macroscopic phenomenological equations hold also for the average regression of a fluctuation in the equilibrium system:

$$\left\{\frac{\overline{\boldsymbol{\alpha}(t+\tau)-\boldsymbol{\alpha}(t)}}{\tau}\right\}_{\boldsymbol{\alpha}(t)} = \mathsf{L}\cdot\mathbf{X} \tag{32}$$

or with the notation (29)

$$\int \boldsymbol{\alpha}' W(\boldsymbol{\alpha}, \boldsymbol{\alpha}')\, d\boldsymbol{\alpha}' = \mathsf{L} \cdot \mathbf{X}. \tag{33}$$

(*d*) *Derivation of the Onsager reciprocal relations,* Inserting (33) into (30) one obtains

$$\int \mathsf{L} \cdot \mathbf{X} \boldsymbol{\alpha} f^e(\boldsymbol{\alpha})\, d\boldsymbol{\alpha} = \int \boldsymbol{\alpha}\, \mathsf{L} \cdot \mathbf{X} f^e(\boldsymbol{\alpha})\, d\boldsymbol{\alpha}. \tag{34}$$

With (25) follows immediately

$$\mathsf{L} = \tilde{\mathsf{L}}, \tag{35}$$

which is again the result (24).

IV. COMPARISON OF THE TWO METHODS

We shall now compare the two types of derivations given in the two preceding sections and discuss the assumptions needed in both cases.

(*a*) *Fluctuation theory.* Both derivations make use of the result (6) or (25) of the traditional fluctuation theory of equilibrium systems.

(*b*) *Microscopic reversibility.* In the first derivation the property of microscopic reversibility which followed from the principles of statistical mechanics and from time reversal invariance was expressed by relation (10). It is easily seen that the form (30) or (31) of this property, used in the second derivation, follows from (10) by multiplying both members with the dyadic $\boldsymbol{\alpha}\boldsymbol{\alpha}'$ and integrating over $\boldsymbol{\alpha}$ and $\boldsymbol{\alpha}'$.

(*c*) *The derivation.* In Section II the phenomenological equation (22) for the observed macroscopic quantities $\bar{\boldsymbol{\alpha}}$ follow in a straightforward way from the master equation (8). The Onsager relations (24) are then immediately obtained from microscopic reversibility (10). On the other hand, in the second derivation phenomenological equations of the form (33) are assumed to hold for the average decay of a fluctuation in the equilibrium system. The Onsager relations follow here also by applying microscopic reversibility.

The hypothesis (33) for the average decay of fluctuations has been the subject of much discussion.[2, 3] It was noted in particular that the validity of the hypothesis (33) for small fluctuations (which form the overwhelming majority of the deviations from equilibrium) is difficult to assess[2] and is perhaps even doubtful.[3]

However, with the special assumption that the processes involved have *Gaussian* Markoff character,[3, 4] (33) will hold. We note that integration of both sides of (33) over space with the weight factor $f(\boldsymbol{\alpha}, t)$, i.e., the *nonequilibrium distribution function*,* yields (interchanging $\boldsymbol{\alpha}$ and $\boldsymbol{\alpha}'$ at the left-hand side)

$$\iint \boldsymbol{\alpha} W(\boldsymbol{\alpha}', \boldsymbol{\alpha}) f(\boldsymbol{\alpha}', t)\, d\boldsymbol{\alpha}\, d\boldsymbol{\alpha}' = \mathsf{L} \cdot \int \mathbf{X} f(\boldsymbol{\alpha}, t)\, d\boldsymbol{\alpha}, \tag{36}$$

which is identical with the phenomenological equation (22) derived according to the first method. It would of course be completely unwarranted to conclude on the basis of (22) or (36) alone that the hypothesis (33) is justified.

Finally we note that the expression (23) for the coefficient matrix L can be derived from hypothesis (33) by integrating with the weight factor $\boldsymbol{\alpha} f^e(\boldsymbol{\alpha})$.

(*d*) *Second law of thermodynamics and H-theorem.* In the nonequilibrium method of Section II the entropy is defined in the usual way as

$$S = -k \int f \ln (f/f^e \Omega)\, d\boldsymbol{\alpha}, \tag{37}$$

where Ω is a constant (determining the value of the entropy at equilibrium). It can easily be shown from the master equation (8) and from microscopic reversibility (10) that, for this quantity, an H-theorem holds,

$$dS/dt \geqq 0. \tag{38}$$

The deviation ΔS of S from its equilibrium value S^e follows from (37) with (11), and is up to second order in φ

$$\Delta S = S - S^e = -\tfrac{1}{2} k \int f^e \varphi^2\, d\boldsymbol{\alpha}, \tag{39}$$

where (12) has been used. With (18) and (6) this becomes

$$\Delta S = -\tfrac{1}{2} \mathsf{g} : \bar{\boldsymbol{\alpha}} \bar{\boldsymbol{\alpha}} = \tfrac{1}{2} \bar{\boldsymbol{\alpha}} \cdot \bar{\mathbf{X}}. \tag{40}$$

The time derivative of ΔS is

$$d\Delta S/dt = \dot{\bar{\boldsymbol{\alpha}}} \cdot \bar{\mathbf{X}}. \tag{41}$$

The quantities $\dot{\bar{\boldsymbol{\alpha}}}$ and $\bar{\mathbf{X}}$ are the conjugated fluxes and forces (affinities) appearing in the phenomenological equations (22) of which the coefficients L obey the Onsager relations (24). The prescription to find conjugated fluxes and forces from the entropy production, which is

* If one integrates (33) with the equilibrium distribution function $f^e(\boldsymbol{\alpha})$ as a weight factor both sides will vanish.

used in thermodynamics of irreversible processes,[6] is hereby substantiated.

Using (22), formula (41) may also be written as

$$d\Delta S/dt = \mathsf{L} : \overline{\mathbf{X}}\,\overline{\mathbf{X}}. \tag{42}$$

According to the H-theorem (38), expression (41) is positive definite. It therefore follows that L is a positive definite matrix. This property of the matrix L follows also directly from its definition (23) together with (9) and (10).

The corresponding considerations in the equilibrium method follow a completely different line of thought. The entropy $\mathscr{S}(\boldsymbol{\alpha})$ of a specified state $\boldsymbol{\alpha}$ is now defined by (cf. (4))

$$\Delta\mathscr{S}(\boldsymbol{\alpha}) = \mathscr{S}(\boldsymbol{\alpha})-\mathscr{S}(0) = k \ln (f^e/c) = -\tfrac{1}{2}\mathsf{g} : \boldsymbol{\alpha\alpha} = \tfrac{1}{2}\boldsymbol{\alpha}\cdot\mathbf{X}. \tag{43}$$

As is well known, the equilibrium value S^e of (37) is practically identical with $\mathscr{S}(0)$, which is the entropy of the most probable state in equilibrium. Furthermore this latter quantity is also almost equal to the average value of $\mathscr{S}(\boldsymbol{\alpha})$ since

$$\overline{\mathscr{S}(\boldsymbol{\alpha})} = \mathscr{S}(0)+\tfrac{1}{2}\int \boldsymbol{\alpha}\cdot\mathbf{X} f^e\, d\boldsymbol{\alpha} = \mathscr{S}(0)-\tfrac{1}{2}kn, \tag{44}$$

where the second term is negligible compared to the first (n is the number of macroscopic variables).

The average value of the rate of change with time of (43) is given by

$$\overline{\frac{\mathscr{S}(t+\tau)-\mathscr{S}(t)}{\tau}} = \tfrac{1}{2}\iint \boldsymbol{\alpha}'\cdot\mathbf{X}'\, W(\boldsymbol{\alpha},\boldsymbol{\alpha}')\, f^e(\boldsymbol{\alpha})\, d\boldsymbol{\alpha}\, d\boldsymbol{\alpha}', \tag{45}$$

It follows from microscopic reversibility (10), using also (9), that this quantity vanishes, so that a proper H-theorem cannot be obtained in this way.

If, however, we define the time derivative of (43) as

$$\frac{d\Delta\mathscr{S}}{dt} = \left\{\frac{\boldsymbol{\alpha}(t+\tau)-\boldsymbol{\alpha}(t)}{\tau}\right\}\cdot\mathbf{X}(t), \tag{46}$$

and then take the conditional average of this quantity, we obtain with the help of the regression hypothesis (33):

$$\left(\overline{\frac{d\Delta\mathscr{S}}{dt}}\right)_{\boldsymbol{\alpha}(t)} = \overline{\left\{\frac{\boldsymbol{\alpha}(t+\tau)-\boldsymbol{\alpha}(t)}{\tau}\right\}}_{\boldsymbol{\alpha}(t)}\cdot\mathbf{X}(t) = \mathsf{L} : \mathbf{XX}. \tag{47}$$

Since the matrix L is positive definite (the same expression (23) for L holding in both derivations; cf. Section IVc), (47) will also be positive definite and can be considered as an H-theorem within the framework of the second derivation. Formula (47) does not have the same direct connection as (41) and (42) with macroscopic theory which is concerned with nonequilibrium average values of quantities $\boldsymbol{\alpha}$.

APPENDIX

Nonequilibrium Method for Systems with α and β-Variables in a Magnetic Field

If both (even) $\boldsymbol{\alpha}$- and (odd) $\boldsymbol{\beta}$-variables are needed for the description of the system, the equilibrium distribution function (cf. Eq. 4) becomes

$$f^e = ce^{-\frac{1}{2}(\mathsf{g}:\boldsymbol{\alpha\alpha}+\mathsf{h}:\boldsymbol{\beta\beta})/k}, \tag{48}$$

where both g and h are positive definite matrices. The following fluctuation formulae are then needed for the derivation

$$\int \boldsymbol{\alpha}\mathbf{X} f^e\, d\boldsymbol{\alpha}\, d\boldsymbol{\beta} = -k\mathsf{U}, \tag{49}$$

$$\int \boldsymbol{\beta}\,\mathbf{Y} f^e\, d\boldsymbol{\alpha}\, d\boldsymbol{\beta} = -k\mathsf{U}, \tag{50}$$

$$\int \boldsymbol{\alpha\beta} f^e\, d\boldsymbol{\alpha}\, d\boldsymbol{\beta} = 0, \tag{51}$$

where

$$\mathbf{Y} = -\mathsf{h}\cdot\boldsymbol{\beta}. \tag{52}$$

The master equation (8) now reads

$$\partial f(\boldsymbol{\alpha}, \boldsymbol{\beta}, t)/\partial t = \int W(\boldsymbol{\alpha}', \boldsymbol{\beta}'; \boldsymbol{\alpha}, \boldsymbol{\beta}; \mathbf{H})\, f(\boldsymbol{\alpha}', \boldsymbol{\beta}', t)\, d\boldsymbol{\alpha}'\, d\boldsymbol{\beta}', \tag{53}$$

and microscopic reversibility is given by the following generalization of (9)

$$W(\boldsymbol{\alpha}', \boldsymbol{\beta}'; \boldsymbol{\alpha}, \boldsymbol{\beta}; \mathbf{H})\, f^e(\boldsymbol{\alpha}', \boldsymbol{\beta}') = W(\boldsymbol{\alpha}, -\boldsymbol{\beta}; \boldsymbol{\alpha}', -\boldsymbol{\beta}'; -\mathbf{H})\, f^e(\boldsymbol{\alpha}, \boldsymbol{\beta}), \tag{54}$$

where $\mathbf{H}$ is the magnetic field strength. Instead of (18) we derive here

$$\varphi = k^{-1}(\mathsf{g} : \boldsymbol{\alpha}\overline{\boldsymbol{\alpha}} + \mathsf{h} : \boldsymbol{\beta}\overline{\boldsymbol{\beta}}) = -k^{-1}(\boldsymbol{\alpha}\cdot\overline{\mathbf{X}} + \boldsymbol{\beta}\cdot\overline{\mathbf{Y}}). \tag{55}$$

For the phenomenological equations one then obtains

$$\dot{\overline{\boldsymbol{\alpha}}} = \mathsf{L}_{\alpha\alpha}\cdot\overline{\mathbf{X}} + \mathsf{L}_{\alpha\beta}\cdot\overline{\mathbf{Y}}, \tag{56}$$

$$\dot{\overline{\boldsymbol{\beta}}} = \mathsf{L}_{\beta\alpha}\cdot\overline{\mathbf{X}} + \mathsf{L}_{\beta\beta}\cdot\overline{\mathbf{Y}}, \tag{57}$$

with

$$\mathsf{L}_{\alpha\alpha}(\mathbf{H}) = -k^{-1}\int\int \boldsymbol{\alpha}\boldsymbol{\alpha}' W(\boldsymbol{\alpha}', \boldsymbol{\beta}'; \boldsymbol{\alpha}, \boldsymbol{\beta}; \mathbf{H}) f^e(\boldsymbol{\alpha}', \boldsymbol{\beta}')\, d\boldsymbol{\alpha}\, d\boldsymbol{\beta}\, d\boldsymbol{\alpha}'\, d\boldsymbol{\beta}', \tag{58}$$

$$\mathsf{L}_{\alpha\beta}(\mathbf{H}) = -k^{-1}\int\int \boldsymbol{\alpha}\boldsymbol{\beta}' W(\boldsymbol{\alpha}', \boldsymbol{\beta}'; \boldsymbol{\alpha}, \boldsymbol{\beta}; \mathbf{H}) f^e(\boldsymbol{\alpha}', \boldsymbol{\beta}')\, d\boldsymbol{\alpha}\, d\boldsymbol{\beta}\, d\boldsymbol{\alpha}'\, d\boldsymbol{\beta}', \tag{59}$$

$$\mathsf{L}_{\beta\alpha}(\mathbf{H}) = -k^{-1}\int\int \boldsymbol{\beta}\boldsymbol{\alpha}' W(\boldsymbol{\alpha}', \boldsymbol{\beta}'; \boldsymbol{\alpha}, \boldsymbol{\beta}; \mathbf{H}) f^e(\boldsymbol{\alpha}', \boldsymbol{\beta}')\, d\boldsymbol{\alpha}\, d\boldsymbol{\beta}\, d\boldsymbol{\alpha}'\, d\boldsymbol{\beta}', \tag{60}$$

$$\mathsf{L}_{\beta\beta}(\mathbf{H}) = -k^{-1}\int\int \boldsymbol{\beta}\boldsymbol{\beta}' W(\boldsymbol{\alpha}', \boldsymbol{\beta}'; \boldsymbol{\alpha}, \boldsymbol{\beta}; \mathbf{H}) f^e(\boldsymbol{\alpha}', \boldsymbol{\beta}')\, d\boldsymbol{\alpha}\, d\boldsymbol{\beta}\, d\boldsymbol{\alpha}'\, d\boldsymbol{\beta}'. \tag{61}$$

From microscopic reversibility (54) the following reciprocal relations can be derived

$$\mathsf{L}_{\alpha\alpha}(\mathbf{H}) = \tilde{\mathsf{L}}_{\alpha\alpha}(-\mathbf{H}), \tag{62}$$

$$\mathsf{L}_{\alpha\beta}(\mathbf{H}) = -\tilde{\mathsf{L}}_{\beta\alpha}(-\mathbf{H}), \tag{63}$$

$$\mathsf{L}_{\beta\beta}(\mathbf{H}) = \tilde{\mathsf{L}}_{\beta\beta}(-\mathbf{H}). \tag{64}$$

References

(1) L. Onsager, *Phys. Rev.*, **37**, 405 (1931); **38**, 2265 (1931).

(2) H. B. G. Casimir, *Rev. Mod. Phys.*, **17**, 343 (1945).

(3) E. P. Wigner, *J. Chem. Phys.*, **22**, 1912 (1954).

(4) L. Onsager and S. Machlup, *Phys. Rev.*, **91**, 1505 (1953); S. Machlup and L. Onsager, *Phys. Rev.*, **91**, 1512 (1953).

(5) N. G. van Kampen, *Physica*, **20**, 603 (1954); *Fortschr. Physik*, **4**, 405 (1956).

(6) I. Prigogine, *Étude thermodynamique des phénomènes irréversibles*, Desoer, Liège, 1947. S. R. de Groot, *Thermodynamics of Irreversible Processes*, North-Holland, Amsterdam, Interscience, New York, 1951.

LE CONCEPT DE TEMPS DANS LE PRINCIPE D'ONSAGER

SATOSI WATANABÉ,* *U. S. Naval Postgraduate School, Monterey, California*

Résumé

On dérivera du point de vue purement quantique le principe d'Onsager de moindre dissipation d'énergie. Voici les principaux concepts critiquement analysés dans la suite: La durée d'une observation macroscopique. L'intervalle entre deux observations macroscopiques consécutives. La dépendance linéaire du temps de la transition. L'intervalle de temps dont il s'agit dans la probabilité de transition d'Onsager. La réalite physique macroscopique, indépendante de l'observateur. L'évanouissement de "mémoire" dans le temps. L'asymétrie entre le passé et l'avenir.

I. INTRODUCTION

Nous nous proposons de donner dans cette communication une dérivation purement quantique du principe d'Onsager de dissipation minimum d'énergie,[1] en analysant avec un soin tout particulier les différents concepts de durées de temps employés dans cette dérivation.

Dans la description *macroscopique* de l'état d'un système physique, on s'imagine le système comme ayant à chaque instant un état macroscopique bien déterminé, bien qu'on ne fasse pas une observation continue. Supposons qu'on ait trouvé à l'instant $t = 0$ un grand nombre N de systèmes dans un état macroscopique μ.† Si l'on fait une seconde observation à l'instant $t = t$, le nombre de systèmes qui se trouvent dans l'état macroscopique ν sera donné, à l'aide de la probabilité macroscopique de transition, par

$$NP(\mu \rightarrow \nu, t). \tag{1.1}$$

Si l'on a, au moins approximativement, pour $0 < t_1 < t$,

$$P(\mu \rightarrow \nu, t) = \sum_{\varkappa} P(\mu \rightarrow \varkappa, t_1)\, P(\varkappa \rightarrow \nu, t-t_1), \tag{1.2}$$

* A présent: IBM Research Laboratory, Poughkeepsie, New York.

† Le système des états μ considéré ici doit être "complet" comme description macroscopique.

on pourra dire (bien qu'on ne fasse pas en réalité une observation à l'instant t_1), que $NP(\mu \to \varkappa, t_1)$ systèmes étaient dans l'état $\varkappa$ à l'instant t_1.[2] La question qui se pose alors est: "Peut-on diviser t indéfiniment en petits intervalles et dire qu'un certain nombre de systèmes ont suivi une voie continue bien déterminée?"

La réponse est certainement négative, déjà pour la simple raison que l'intervalle entre deux observations ne peut être plus petit que la durée d'une seule observation, et que si celle-ci devenait infiniment petite, l'indétermination d'énergie deviendrait infiniment grande. Mais cette limitation n'est pas la seule. Si, par exemple, $P(\mu \to \nu, \tau)-\delta_{\mu\nu}$ pour une très petite durée τ était proportionnel au carré du temps τ, l'équation (1.2) ne se vérifierait pas pour $t = 2\tau$, $t_1 = \tau$. On est ainsi amené à chercher l'ordre de grandeur du petit intervalle τ pour lequel la probabilité $P(\mu \to \nu, \tau)-\delta_{\mu\nu}$ est proportionnelle à τ.

L'existence de l'ordre de grandeur de τ, satisfaisant cette condition de dépendence linéaire est assurée par le fait qu'il y a un très grand nombre d'états quantiques correspondant à un seul état macroscopique, fait dont la portée importante à cet égard ne saura être surestimée. S'il existe un tel ordre de grandeur de τ, on pourra parler du développement presque continuel d'un objet macroscopique, qui est indépendant du sujet observateur. Cette proposition est d'une telle importance pour justifier la méthode générale de la physique macroscopique, qu'on pourrait l'appeler "principe de la réalité physique macroscopique."

La condition de dépendance linéaire, à laquelle on est ainsi amené par la considération abstraite concernant la réalité physique, est d'ailleurs la base même de la loie dite "phénoménologique" en thermodynamique des processus irréversibles. Pour cette raison, l'examen soigneux de l'intervalle τ est indispensable dans cette branche de thermodynaimque.

Par une analyse détaillée, on verra plus tard que cette valeur de τ est conditionnée par de diverses limites, les plus importantes étant

$$\tau > \hbar/\Delta E, \tag{1.3}$$

$$\tau \ll \hbar\varrho, \tag{1.4}$$

où ΔE est l'indétermination macroscopique d'énergie, et ϱ la densité (dans l'échelle d'énergie) d'états quantiques dans un état macroscopique. L'équation (1.4) implique que le système doit contenir un nombre suffisamment grand de degrés de liberté. Les autres conditions sur τ seront discutées en détail dans le texte.

Cet intervalle ne peut, pourtant, être le même que l'intervalle ΔT dont il s'agit dans la probabilité de transition dans la théorie d'Onsager, et de Hashizume[1], car la fluctuation de grandeurs macroscopiques α_k pendant ΔT doit être presque gaussienne, tandis que la fluctuation des α_k pendant τ ne peut l'être en général. On a donc

$$\Delta T \gg \tau. \tag{1.5}$$

D'autre part, ΔT doit être beaucoup plus petit que le temps de relaxation T_R:

$$\Delta T \ll T_R. \tag{1.6}$$

En dehors de ces conditions, comme Siegel l'a montré,[3] si ΔT devient trop petit, la fluctuation pendant ΔT deviendra plus grande que le changement déterminé par l'équation phénoménologique. Il s'ensuit que

$$\Delta T \gg kT_R/\Delta S, \tag{1.7}$$

où ΔS est l'écart de l'entropie (par degré de liberté macroscopique) d'un état considéré de l'entropie de l'équilibre. k est la constante de Boltzmann.

Les fluctuations qui jouent le rôle principal dans la théorie d'Onsager est une manifestation de la mémoire du parcours passé de chaque système, c'est à dire, l'effet du passé inobservé sur le parcours futur. On verra dans la suite une discussion du degré auquel cette mémoire individuelle s'évanouit pendant des durées de temps de l'ordre de τ, de ΔT et de T_R. Cette considération de "mémoire" nous amènera à une autre question souvent posée: "Pourquoi la loi d'Onsager ne s'applique-t-elle pas au passé aussi bien qu'à l'avenir?" Nous donnerons une réponse à cette question à l'aide de la notion de "probabilité rétrodictive" introduite auparavant par l'auteur.[4]

II. LES OPÉRATEURS MACROSCOPIQUES

Nous allons nous servir dans la suite de la méthode d'opérateurs macroscopiques introduite par von Neumann.[5] Pour préciser la signification des symboles, nous donnons une courte esquisse de cette méthode.

Soit H l'Hamiltonien exact du système, et soient E_n et φ_n ($n=1, 2, \ldots$) ses valeurs propres et ses fonctions propres, c. à. d. que

$$H = \sum_n E_n \mathfrak{P}[\varphi_n], \tag{2.1}$$

où $\mathfrak{P}[\varphi_n]$ est l'opérateur de projection sur le vecteur φ_n. L'opérateur de l'énergie macroscopique $\mathfrak{H}$ commute avec H, mais il est hautement dégénéré. Le sous-espace G_a est défini par N_a vecteurs φ_n dont les valeurs propres E_n se trouvent dans un domaine de l'épaisseur ΔE_a autour de la valeur moyenne E_a. Tout vecteur de ce sous-espace G_a aura une même valeur propre E_a de $\mathfrak{H}$.

$$[\mathfrak{H}, H]_- = 0, \tag{2.2}$$

$$\mathfrak{H} = \sum_a E_a \mathfrak{P}[G_a], \quad \mathfrak{P}[G_a] = \sum_{n \in a} \mathfrak{P}[\varphi_n], \quad \text{trace}\, \mathfrak{P}[G_a] = N_a, \tag{2.3}$$

où $\mathfrak{P}[G_a]$ est l'opérateur de projection sur le sous-espace G_a. G_a représente ainsi la couche macroscopique d'énergie de l'épaisseur ΔE_a.

Les autres opérateurs macroscopiques α_k ($k = 1, 2, \ldots$) commutent avec $\mathfrak{H}$, mais ne commutent pas nécessairement avec H.

$$[\alpha_\varkappa, \mathfrak{H}]_- = 0. \tag{2.4}$$

A l'aide de tous les opérateurs macroscopiques α_k disponibles, la couche d'énergie G_a sera subdivisé en cellules macroscopiques C_μ ($\mu=1, 2, \ldots$). Si l'opérateur α_k a la valeur $a_{k\mu}$ dans la cellule C_μ, l'opérateur α_k sera donné par

$$\alpha_k = \sum_\mu a_{k\mu} \mathfrak{P}[C_\mu], \tag{2.5}$$

et on aura aussi

$$\sum_{\mu \in a} \mathfrak{P}[C_\mu] = \mathfrak{P}[G_a], \quad \text{trace}\, \mathfrak{P}[C_\mu] = N_\mu, \quad \sum_{\mu \in a} N_\mu = N_a, \tag{2.6}$$

où N_μ est le nombre de dimensions du sous-espace C_μ. On remarque que

$$(\varphi_n, \alpha_k \varphi_m) = 0, \tag{2.7}$$

si

$$(E_n - E_m) > \Delta E_a. \tag{2.8}$$

Une cellule C_μ sera identifiée par un système de valeurs $a_{k\mu}$ ($k = 1, 2, \ldots$).

On désignera par ψ_i ($i = 1, 2, \ldots$) le système de fonctions propres communes des α_k et de $\mathfrak{H}$:

$$\sum_{i\in\mu} \mathfrak{P}[\psi_i] = \mathfrak{P}[C_\mu]. \tag{2.9}$$

Les fonctions ψ_i ne sont pas uniquement définies par cette définition, car on peut appliquer aux ψ_i une transformation unitaire arbitraire qui transforme chaque cellule C_μ en elle-même.

On emploiera plus tard un opérateur d'énergie auxiliaire K, qui commute avec les opérateurs macroscopiques, mais qui n'est pas dégénéré comme $\mathfrak{H}$. On peut introduire un tel opérateur K, par exemple, par la définition:

$$K = \sum_i E_i \mathfrak{P}[\psi_i], \tag{2.10}$$

avec

$$E_i = (\psi_i, H\psi_i) + \varepsilon_i, \tag{2.11}$$

où une petite quantité ε_i sera ajoutée pour éviter dégénérescence (si deux expressions $(\psi_i, H\psi_i)$ pour différents indices i se coincident par accident), tout en conservant la propriété que la valeur moyenne de K dans la couche G_a soit E_a.

III. LA DURÉE Δt_0 D'UNE SEULE OBSERVATION

L'intervalle τ entre deux observations macroscopiques ne peut être plus petit que la durée Δt_0 d'une seule observation macroscopique. Celle-ci ne peut être plus petite que $\hbar/\Delta E_a$, puisque l'indétermination macroscopique d'énergie est supposée de l'ordre de grandeur de ΔE_a:

$$\tau \geqq \Delta t_0 \geqq \hbar/\Delta E_a. \tag{3.1}$$

On peut probablement estimer ΔE_a comme de l'ordre de $\sqrt{N}\,kT$ où N est le nombre de molécules dans le systèmc. $\hbar/\Delta E_a$ est ainsi beaucoup plus petit que $\hbar/kT$ qui est de l'ordre de 10^{-14} sec. à une temperature ordinaire.

Il faut aussi imposer à la durée Δt_0 d'une seule observation la condition que le changement d'une grandeur macroscopique α_k pendant Δt_0 soit plus petit que la grandeur α_k elle-même. Dans la représentation dans laquelle H est diagonal, c. à d. dans la représentation des φ_n, on a

$$-i\hbar\,\dot{\alpha}_{nm} = (E_n - E_m)\,\alpha_{nm}. \tag{3.2}$$

Si $|E_n - E_m| > \Delta E_a$, on a $\alpha_{nm} = 0$, comme on a vu dans (2.7). Dans ce cas il n'y a pas de problème. Si $|E_n - E_m| < \Delta E_a$, on obtient de (3.2)

$$|\dot{\alpha}_{nm}|\,\Delta t_0 < |\alpha_{nm}|\,\Delta E_a \Delta t_0/\hbar, \tag{3.3}$$

qui doit être plus petit que $|\alpha_{nm}|$. Cela est assuré si

$$\Delta t_0 \leqq \hbar/\Delta E_a. \tag{3.4}$$

En comparant (3.1) avec (3.4), on voit qu'il est suffisant de supposer que Δt_0 soit de l'ordre de $\hbar/\Delta E_a$:

$$\tau \geqq \Delta t_0 \approx \hbar/\Delta E_a \tag{3.5}$$

Dans le cas où $|E_n - E_m|$ est de l'ordre de grandeur de ΔE_a, on obtient de (3.2)

$$|\alpha_{nm}| \approx |\dot{\alpha}_{nm}| \Delta t_0. \tag{3.6}$$

Ceci est permissible, si α_{nm} lui-même est plus petit que la grossièreté de l'observation de la grandeur macroscopique α. Le lecteur trouvera une analyse très intéressante de cette condition dans les travaux de M. van Kampen.[6]

IV. LA CONDITION IMPOSÉE À L'INTERVALLE τ PAR LA DENSITÉ DE NIVEAUX D'ÉNERGIE

Le problème qui a souvent abouti à une certaine confusion se rapporte à la dérivation quantique de la formule qui donne le changement de $\alpha_\varkappa$ comme fonction linéaire du temps. Pour éclaircir ce problème, il faut d'abord examiner soigneusement les conditions sous lesquelles on peut obtenir la probabilité de transition comme fonction linéaire du temps. La probabilité en question est celle de trouver le système physique en cellule C_ν à l'instant $t+\tau$ lorsque le système s'est trouvé en état $\psi_i \in C_\mu$ à l'instant t, τ étant ainsi l'intervalle entre deux observations consécutives. On désignera cette probabilité par $P(i \to \nu, \tau)$. La transition est causée par le fait que la fonction ψ_i n'est pas une fonction propre de l'Hamiltonien exact H. Si l'on emploie la différence entre H et l'énergie macroscopique $\mathfrak{H}$ comme perturbation, on ne pourra pas se servir de la méthode de perturbation à cause de la haute dégénérescense de $\mathfrak{H}$. Pour cette raison on emploiera K défini dans la Section II, au lieu de $\mathfrak{H}$, mais le résultat final ne dépendra que de la densité d'états quantiques du système, qui est plus ou moins indépendante de l'Hamiltonien approximatif, à partir duquel la méthode de perturbation procède.

La probabilité de transition de ψ_i à ψ_j pendant τ est donnée par la formule bien connue:

$$P(i \to j, \tau) = \delta_{ij}[1 - f_i(\tau)] + |T_{ji}|^2_{j \neq i} F(E_j - E_i, \tau), \tag{4.1}$$

où

$$F(E_j-E_i, \tau) = 4 \sin^2[(E_j-E_i)\tau/2\hbar]/(E_j-E_i)^2. \tag{4.2}$$

$f_i(\tau)$ est déterminé par la condition:

$$\sum_j^{\text{tous}} P(i \to j, \tau) = 1. \tag{4.3}$$

Dans la première approximation, on a

$$T_{ji} = (\psi_j, (H-K)\psi_i). \tag{4.4}$$

E_i est la valeur propre de K pour la fonction ψ_i.

Pour obtenir la probabilité $P(i \to \nu, \tau)$, il faut additionner (4.1) pour tous les états $\psi_j \in C_\nu$.

$$P(i \to \nu, \tau) = \sum_{j \in \nu} P(i \to j, \tau). \tag{4.5}$$

Rappelons-nous que la quantité F (4.2), regardée comme fonction de E_j-E_i, n'est sensiblement différente de zéro que dans le domaine de l'ordre de $\hbar/\tau$ autour de l'origine, et que l'intégrale de F sur E_j donne une grandeur proportionnelle à τ. Pour justifier le remplacement de la sommation par l'intégrale, il faut que le domaine $\hbar/\tau$ contienne un grand nombre d'états ψ_j appartenant à C_ν. Soit ϱ_ν la densité d'états dans la cellule C_ν, qui peut être évaluée approximativement par

$$\varrho_\nu = N_\nu/\Delta E_a < N_a/\Delta E_a. \tag{4.6}$$

$(1/\varrho_\nu)$ sera alors l'intervalle moyenne d'énergie entre deux états voisins dans la cellule C_ν. Ce qui a été expliqué plus haut signifie

$$(\hbar/\tau) \gg (1/\varrho_\nu), \quad \text{ou} \quad \tau \ll \varrho_\nu \hbar, \tag{4.7}$$

ou encore

$$\tau \ll \hbar N_\nu/\Delta E_a, \tag{4.8}$$

ce qui ne contredit pas la condition (3.5). Dans ces conditions, on a

$$\sum_j F(E_j-E_i, \tau) = \int F(E_j-E_i, \tau)\, \varrho_\nu\, dE_j = 2\pi\varrho_\nu \tau/\hbar. \tag{4.9}$$

Mais cette expression n'est correcte que si les limites d'intégration peuvent être déplacées à $-\infty$ et $+\infty$. Ceci n'est possible que si $F(E_j-E_i, \tau)$ se détruit quand $|E_j-E_i|$ dépasse ΔE_a. En d'autres termes, $\hbar/\tau$ doit être plus petit que ΔE_a, c. à d. que

$$\tau > \hbar/\Delta E_\alpha, \tag{4.10}$$

qui n'est autre que la condition (3.5).

Si $i \in \mu$, $j \in \nu$ et $\mu \neq \nu$, on obtiendra

$$P(i \to \nu, \tau) = |T_{ji}|^2_{j \in \nu}\, 2\pi \varrho_\nu \tau/\hbar, \tag{4.11}$$

à condition que $|T_{ji}|$ soit sensiblement constante pour différents $\psi_j \in C_\nu$ dans le domaine $\hbar/\tau$. Soit $\Delta\mathfrak{E}_{\nu i}$ le domaine de E_j ($j \in \nu$) dans lequel $|T_{ji}|$ peut être considérée comme constante. On a alors $(\hbar/\tau) < \Delta\mathfrak{E}_{\nu i}$, ou, si $\Delta\mathfrak{E}_{\nu i}$ ne dépend pas trop sensiblement de i,

$$\tau > \hbar/\Delta\mathfrak{E}_\nu. \tag{4.12}$$

Cette condition est compatible avec (4.7), si

$$\Delta\mathfrak{E}_\nu \gg (1/\varrho_\nu) = \Delta E_a/N_\nu\,, \tag{4.13}$$

ce qui est une condition imposée à l'Hamiltonien de perturbation $(H-K)$. On constate aussi que, si

$$\Delta\mathfrak{E}_\nu \geqq \Delta E_a\,, \tag{4.14}$$

la condition (4.12) n'ajoute aucune nouvelle restriction au delà de (3.5). De plus, si (4.14) est le cas, la condition (4.13) sera automatiquement satisfaite. La condition (4.14) semble très raisonable dans la plupart des applications, mais si (4.14) ne se vérifie pas, la limite inférieure de τ sera restrainte par (4.12), plutôt que par (3.5), et la limite supérieure par (4.7) ou (4.8).

Il est vrai que, si l'on fixe ψ_j dans l'expression (4.1), la probabilité deviendra proportionnelle au carré de τ pour de petites valeurs de τ, mais cette propriété ne nous intéresse point, parce que l'observation macroscopique par sa nature nécessite une sommation sur ψ_j dans la cellule C_ν.

V. LA CONDITION IMPOSÉE À τ PAR LA CONVERGENCE DE LA MÉTHODE DE PERTURBATION

Comme il est bien connu, la convergence de la fonction d'état perturbée nécessite la condition:

$$|T_{ji}|_{\max}\, \tau \ll \hbar, \qquad i \neq j. \tag{5.1}$$

La souscription „max" signifie qu'on prend un tel j ($\neq i$) que $|T_{ji}|$ soit le maximum pour un ψ_i donné. Si l'on écrit la partie de l'hamiltonien H qui intéresse le sous-espace G_a dans la forme:

$$H = \sum E_n \mathfrak{P}[\varphi_n] = E_a \mathfrak{P}[G_a] + \sum \Delta E_n \mathfrak{P}[\varphi_n], \tag{5.2}$$

on obtiendra d'après (4.4)

$$T_{ji} = \sum_{n}^{Na} \Delta E_n(\psi_j, \mathfrak{P}[\varphi_n]\psi_i), \qquad i \neq j, \tag{5.3}$$

parce que ψ_i (ou ψ_j) est contenu dans le sous-espace G_a.

Si le système de fonctions φ_n et le système de fonctions ψ_i coincident, T_{ji} se détruira, et la condition (5.1) sera automatiquement satisfaite pour une valeur arbitraire de τ. Mais ce ne sera pas en général le cas. Une évaluation pessimiste de la grandeur de T_{ji} peut s'obtenir par une considération qui se lie intimement à la méthode de moyennes dans l'espace hilbertien introduite par von Neumann.[5] Si le système φ_n et le système ψ_j ne sont assujettis qu'à la condition:

$$\sum_{n}^{Na} \mathfrak{P}[\varphi_n] = \mathfrak{P}[G_a] = \sum_{i}^{Na} \mathfrak{P}[\psi_i], \tag{5.4}$$

la valeur d'expectation de $|(\psi_j, \mathfrak{P}[\varphi_n]\psi_i)|$ sera de l'ordre de $1/N_a$. Si tous les termes ΔE_n sont de l'ordre de ΔE_a, et si $(\psi_j, \mathfrak{P}[\varphi_n]\psi_i)$ est remplacé par sa valeur absolue, T_{ji} dans (5.3) deviendra de l'ordre de ΔE_α, et la relation (5.1) deviendra $\tau \ll \hbar/\Delta E_a$, ce qui contredit la condition (3.5). Evidemment cela ne sera pas le cas, parce que ΔE_n peut être aussi positif que négatif, et de plus les expressions $(\psi_j, \mathfrak{P}[\varphi_n]\psi_i)$ auront de différentes phases.

La vraie situation dans des applications ordinaires sera probablement à peu près comme suit. Puisque N_a est extrêmement grand, il y aura un grand nombre (bien que $< N_a$) de fonctions propres $\varphi_n^{(l)}$ de H qui ont presque la même valeur de ΔE_n, soit ΔE_l. Dans ces conditions, la sommation dans (5.3) peut se faire en deux étapes:

$$\sum_l \Delta E_l \sum_n (\psi_j, \mathfrak{P}[\varphi_n^{(l)}]\psi_i) \tag{5.5}$$

$$= \sum_l \Delta E_l \sum_n (\psi_j, \xi_n^{(l)})(\xi_n^{(l)}, \psi_i) \tag{5.6}$$

où $\xi_n^{(l)}$ est la projection du vecteur $\varphi_n^{(l)}$ sur le sous-espace déterminé par ψ_i et ψ_j. En écrivant

$$\xi_n^{(l)} = r_n^{(l)}[\psi_i \exp(i\alpha_n^{(l)}) + \psi_j \exp(i\beta_n^{(l)})], \tag{5.7}$$

on obtient

$$\sum_n (\psi_j, \xi_n^{(l)})(\xi_n^{(l)}, \psi_i) = \sum_n (r_n^{(l)})^2 \exp(i\beta_n^{(l)} - i\alpha_n^{(l)}). \tag{5.8}$$

S'il y a beaucoup de $\varphi_n^{(l)}$ ayant presque la même valeur de $r_n^{(l)}$, on pourra s'attendre à ce que cette expression se détruise, ou au moins devienne extrêmement petite, à cause de la destruction mutuelle de différentes phases.

Pour cette raison, T_{ji} sera beaucoup plus petit que l'estimation pessimiste indiquée plus haut.

$$|T_{ji}|_{\max} \ll \Delta E_a. \tag{5.9}$$

Dans ces conditions, il est possible qu'un intervalle τ qui est plus grand que $\hbar/\Delta E_a$ puisse satisfaire à (5.1).

VI. PROBABILITÉ DE TRANSITION MACROSCOPIQUE PENDANT τ

En vue de déduire la probabilité de voie d'Onsager, nous allons d'abord obtenir la probabilité de transition au sens macroscopique, en nous servant des résultats des sections précédentes. Ecrivons la probabilité (4.11) dans la forme:

$$P(i \to \nu, \tau) = p_{\nu i}\tau, \qquad (i \in \mu \neq \nu), \tag{6.1}$$

avec

$$p_{\nu i} = |T_{ji}|^2_{j\in\nu} 2\pi\varrho_\nu/\hbar,$$

où $|T_{ji}|$ ne dépendra pas sensiblement de j à condition que (4.12) soit satisfaite. De même, pour les états finals ψ_j $(j \neq i)$ appartenant à la même cellule C_μ que ψ_i, on aura

$$\sum_{j\neq i}^{j\in\mu} P(i \to j, \tau) = p_{\mu i}\tau, \qquad (i \in \mu). \tag{6.2}$$

La probabilité totale pour que le système se trouve à l'instant $t+\tau$ dans le cellule C_μ (qui contient ψ_i) sera

$$P(i \to \mu, \tau) = (1-f_i\tau)+p_{\mu i}\tau, \qquad (i \in \mu), \tag{6.3}$$

avec

$$f_i = \sum_{\nu}^{\text{tous}} p_{\nu i}. \tag{6.4}$$

On peut unifier les équations (6.1) et (6.3) en une seule formule:

$$P(i \to \nu, \tau) = \delta_{\nu\mu}(1-f_i\tau)+p_{\nu i}\tau, \qquad (i \in \mu), \tag{6.5}$$

pour n'importe quelle cellule C_ν.

Si on donne le même poids à chacun des N_μ états contenus dans C_μ, on obtiendra la probabilité moyenne de transition de μ à ν pendant τ:

$$\bar{P}(\mu \to \nu, \tau) = (1/N_\mu) \sum_{i \subset \mu} P(i \to \nu, \tau) \tag{6.6}$$

$$= \delta_{\nu\mu}(1 - f_\mu \tau) + p_{\nu\mu}\tau \tag{6.7}$$

avec

$$p_{\nu\mu} = (1/N_\mu) \sum_{i \in \mu} p_{\nu i}, \qquad f_\mu = (1/N_\mu) \sum_{i \in \mu} f_i = \sum_{\nu} p_{\nu\mu}. \tag{6.8}$$

Si l'on a, pour une raison ou une autre, une connaissance probabiliste du poids w_i de chaque état ψ_i dans C_μ à l'instant t, on aura comme probabilité de transition de μ à ν

$$P(\mu \to \nu, \tau) = \bar{P}(\mu \to \nu, \tau) + \varepsilon_{\nu\mu}\tau, \tag{6.9}$$

avec

$$\varepsilon_{\nu\mu} = \sum_{i \in \mu} w_i \varepsilon_{\nu i}, \tag{6.10}^*$$

et

$$\varepsilon_{\nu i} = \delta_{\mu\nu}[-f_i + (1/N_\mu) \sum_{i \in \mu} f_i] + p_{\nu i} - (1/N_\mu) \sum_{i \in \mu} p_{\nu i}. \tag{6.11}^*$$

En général, on n'a pas la connaissance de w_i, et on doit considérer $\varepsilon_{\nu\mu}\tau$ comme une petite fluctuation imprévue autour de sa valeur moyenne qui est nulle:

$$\bar{\varepsilon}_{\nu\mu} = 0. \tag{6.12}$$

Dans la suite, on écrira, au lieu de (6.9),

$$P(\mu \to \nu, \tau) = \bar{P}(\mu \to \nu, \tau) + \varepsilon_{\nu\mu}\tau = \delta_{\nu\mu} - q_{\nu\mu}\tau + \varepsilon_{\nu\mu}\tau, \tag{6.13}$$

avec

$$q_{\nu\mu} = \delta_{\nu\mu} f_\mu - p_{\nu\mu}. \tag{6.14}$$

L'élément diagonal de $q_{\nu\mu}$ est toujours positif

$$q_{\mu\mu} = f_\mu - p_{\mu\mu} > 0, \tag{6.15}$$

car

$$f_\mu = \sum_{\nu}^{\text{tous}} p_{\nu\mu}. \tag{6.16}$$

La fluctuation $\varepsilon_{\nu\mu}\tau$ sera beaucoup plus petite que $\bar{P}(\mu \to \nu, \tau)$, si

* On trouvera plus tard dans cette section une discussion de cette sommation sur i.

$p_{\nu i}$ ne diffère pas sensiblement l'un de l'autre quand ψ_i est contenu dans la même cellule C_μ, c'est à dire, si la variation de $|T_{ji}|$ (quand on varie i dans C_μ) est beaucoup plus petite que la valeur moyenne de $|T_{ji}|(i \epsilon \mu)$. Si cela est le cas, la variation de $|T_{ji}|$ (quand on varie j dans C_ν) sera aussi beaucoup plus petite que la valeur moyenne de $|T_{ji}|$ $(j \epsilon C_\nu)$. Dans ces conditions, la restriction (4.12) imposée à τ ne sera plus nécessaire.

Il est intéressant à remarquer qu'on peut faire une sommation aussi sur ψ_i (au lieu de sur ψ_j) dans l'expression (4.1), et qu'on obtient

$$\sum_{i \epsilon \mu} P(i \to j, \tau) = N_\mu \bar{P}(\mu \to j, \tau) = |T_{ji}|_{i\epsilon\mu} 2\pi \varrho_\mu \tau/\hbar, \tag{6.17}$$

à condition que $|T_{ji}|$ soit à peu près constante en tant que i soit dans μ. En mettant $\varrho_\mu/\varrho_\nu = N_\mu/N_\nu$, on obtiendra

$$\bar{P}(\mu \to j, \tau) = (1/N_\nu)\, \bar{P}(\mu \to \nu, \tau) + \eta_{\nu\mu}\tau \tag{6.18}$$

où $\eta_{\nu\mu}\tau$ sera beaucoup plus petit que $(1/N_\nu)\bar{P}(\mu \to \nu, \tau)$. Le trait sur P sur le côté gauche signifie la valeur moyenne de P pour les différents états quantiques initiaux.

Dans les formules (6.6), (6.10) et (6.11), on a fait une sommation sur i, supposant un poids w_i à chaque état ψ_i dans la cellule C_μ. Ce procédé au fond suppose qu'on ait à l'instant initial un ensemble:

$$\sum_i w_i \mathfrak{P}[\psi_i]. \tag{6.19}$$

Voici la justification, probablement la plus simple, de cette représentation de l'état initial.

Si on fait une observation macroscopique à l'instant $t = 0$, et si on localise un système dans la cellule C_μ, le système sera dans un état quantique quelconque Ψ contenu dans C_μ. Cette fonction d'état Ψ ne coincidera pas en général avec une ou une autre des fonctions $\psi_i \epsilon C_\mu$ préalablement déterminées. S'il y a un grand nombre de cas, chaque vecteur Ψ dans le sous-espace C_μ sera représenté par un certain poids w. Parmi ces divers cas, prenons d'abord seulement les Ψ qui coincident avec une ou une autre des fonctions ψ_i préalablement déterminées. Pour cet ensemble limité, on aura certainement le droit d'employer l'expression (6.19).

Or, comme on a vu dans la Section II, le système de coordonnées ψ_i, en réalité, n'est déterminé que par la condition qu'il soit un des systèmes de coordonnées qu'on peut prendre dans le sous-espace C_μ. Soient ψ_i' les fonctions d'un autre système de coordonnées dans C_μ. En se servant de ce système ψ_i', on pourra envisager les cas où Ψ coincide avec une ou une autre de ces ψ_i. Cet ensemble sera représenté par un opérateur tel que $\sum_i w_i' \mathfrak{P}[\psi_i']$, et on obtiendra un résultat pareil à (6.9) pour ce système de coordonnées. Naturellement, la probabilité moyenne $\bar{P}(\mu \to \nu, \tau)$, (6.6), doit être calculée ici à l'aide du système ψ_i' au lieu du système ψ_i. Mais elle ne sera pas sensiblement différente de celle calculée à l'aide du système ψ_i. En se servant de tous les systèmes de coordonnées qu'on peut prendre dans le sous-espace C_μ, on pourra épuiser tous les cas initiaux possibles, et on aboutira après tout à la formule (6.9). Pour être rigoureux, la probabilité moyenne $\bar{P}(\mu \to \nu, \tau)$ sera non seulement la valeur moyenne par rapport à i dans un système particulier de coordonnées, mais aussi la valeur moyenne par rapport aux différents systèmes de coordonnées.

Avant de passer à la section prochaine, nous voulons remarquer une propriété très importante des probabilités de transition. En vertu de l'unitarité de la matrice de transition (ou bien en vertu de la réversibilité ou de l'inversibilité) on a toujours[2]

$$\sum_{j}^{\text{tous}} P(i \to j, \tau) = 1, \tag{6.20}$$

et

$$\sum_{i}^{\text{tous}} P(i \to j, \tau) = 1. \tag{6.21}$$

La première de ces relations a été toujours considérée dans notre définition de f_i ou de f_μ. La normalisation inverse (6.21) veut dire, en considération de (4.5),

$$\sum_{\mu} \sum_{i \in \mu} P(i \to \nu, \tau) = N_\nu. \tag{6.22}$$

Les formules (6.6) et (6.7) donnent alors

$$\sum_{\mu} N_\mu \bar{P}(\mu \to \nu, \tau) = N_\nu, \tag{6.23}$$

et

$$N_\nu f_\nu = \sum_{\mu} p_{\nu\mu} N_\mu. \tag{6.24}$$

En language de $q_{\nu\mu}$, la relation (6.24) se traduit

$$\sum_{\mu} q_{\nu\mu} N_\mu = 0. \tag{6.25}$$

La normalisation ordinaire (6.20) nous amène naturellement à $\sum_\nu q_{\nu\mu} = 0$.

En ce qui concerne $\varepsilon_{\nu i}$, on a, par définition,

$$\sum_i \varepsilon_{\nu i} = 0, \tag{6.26}$$

mais, en général, on n'a pas

$$\sum \varepsilon_{\nu\mu} N_\mu = 0, \tag{6.27}$$

à moins que w_i soit constant dans une cellule. Pour la sommation sur les états finals on a naturellement

$$\sum_\nu \varepsilon_{\nu\mu} = 0. \tag{6.28}$$

VII. PRINCIPE DE LA RÉALITÉ PHYSIQUE MACROSCOPIQUE

Nous allons démontrer dans cette section le théorème suivant:

$$\bar{P}(\mu_0 \to \mu_N, \sum_i^N \tau_i) = \sum_{\mu_{N-1}} \cdots \sum_{\mu_1} \bar{P}(\mu_0 \to \mu_1, \tau_1) \bar{P}(\mu_1 \to \mu_2, \tau_2) \cdots \bar{P}(\mu_{N-1} \to \mu_N, \tau_N), \tag{7.1}$$

où chaque τ_i est de l'ordre de grandeur déterminé aux sections précédentes pour τ. Il est naturellement entendu que $\bar{P}(\mu \to \nu, t)$ est une fonction déterminée uniquement par μ, ν et t. Si le théorème (7.1) se vérifie, on pourra parler d'une réalité physique macroscopique qui se développe avec le temps d'une façon presque continuelle, le concept de temps étant assujetti à une sorte de „quantification", qui divise le courant de temps en petites étapes de l'ordre de τ.

Pour prouver (7.1), nous allons nous servir de la méthode de l'induction mathématique par rapport à N, nombre d'intervalles. D'abord pour $N = 1$, le théorème est tautologique. En suite pour $N = 2$, on a en vertue de (6.13),

$$\begin{aligned} &\sum_{\mu_1} \bar{P}(\mu_0 \to \mu_1, \tau_1) \bar{P}(\mu_1 \to \mu_2, \tau_2) \\ &\qquad = \delta(\mu_2, \mu_0) - q(\mu_2, \mu_0)(\tau_1 + \tau_2) + \sum_{\mu_1} q(\mu_2, \mu_1) q(\mu_1, \mu_0) \tau_1 \tau_2. \end{aligned} \tag{7.2}$$

et, comme $\tau_1 + \tau_2$ est encore de l'ordre de τ,

$$\bar{P}(\mu_0 \to \mu_2, \tau_1 + \tau_2) = \delta(\mu_2, \mu_0) - q(\mu_2, \mu_0)(\tau_1 + \tau_2). \tag{7.3}$$

On aura donc le résultat voulu pour $N = 2$, si le troisième terme de

(7.2) est négligible. Ce sera vrai si, dans (6.13), la transition à d'autres cellules $\nu \neq \mu$ est très petite, c. à d., si

$$\sum_{\nu \neq \mu} |q_{\nu\mu}| \tau = q_{\mu\mu} \tau \ll 1. \tag{7.4}$$

Si l'on emploie l'expression (4.11), on obtiendra

$$\sum_{\nu} |q_{\nu\mu}| \tau \approx \sum_{\nu} |T_{ji}|^2_{i \in \mu, j \in \nu} 2\pi \varrho_\nu \tau/\hbar \approx |\overline{T_{ji}}|^2 2\pi\varrho\tau/\hbar, \tag{7.5}$$

où $|\overline{T_{ji}}|$ est une sorte de valeur moyenne de $|T_{ji}|$ pour $j \in G_a$, $i \in C_\mu$ et ϱ est la densité de niveaux dans la couche G_a. Si on met $\varrho \approx N_a/\Delta E_a$, on aura

$$\tau \ll \hbar \Delta E_a / |\overline{T_{ji}}|^2 N_a. \tag{7.6}$$

En tout cas, comme on verra plus tard, $q_{\mu\mu}$ est de l'ordre de la réciproque du temps de relaxation macroscopique, qui est vraisemblablement beaucoup plus grand que la limite inférieure de τ, qui est $\hbar/\Delta E_a$. Ainsi la relation (7.4) sera toujours satisfaite.

Allons maintenant démontrer le théorème (7.1) pour $N+1$, supposant qu'il soit vrai pour N et pour $(N-1)$, chaque τ_i n'étant sujet qu'à la condition par rapport à son ordre de grandeur. Ce qu'il faut démontrer alors est

$$\bar{P}(\mu_0 \to \mu_{N+1}, \sum_i^{N+1} \tau_i) = \sum_{\mu_N} \bar{P}(\mu_0 \to \mu_N, \sum_i^N \tau_i) \, \bar{P}(\mu_N \to \mu_{N+1}, \tau_{N+1}), \tag{7.7}$$

car $\bar{P}(\mu_0 \to \mu_N, \sum_i^N \tau_i)$ pourra se développer comme (7.1), si le théorème est vrai pour N.

On introduit maintenant un autre système de τ_i' (tout en satisfaisant la condition sur l'ordre de grandeur de τ) tel que

$$\sum_i^{N+1} \tau_i = \sum_i^N \tau_i', \qquad \sum_i^N \tau_i = \sum_i^{N-1} \tau_i', \qquad \tau_{N+1} = \tau_N', \tag{7.8}$$

ce qui revient à diviser $\sum_i^N \tau_i$ en $(N-1)$ intervalles de τ_i'. Par exemple, pour $N = 2$, on peut prendre $\tau_1 + \tau_2 = \tau_1'$, $\tau_3 = \tau_2'$. Pour un grand nombre N la différence entre τ_i et τ_i' sera très peu. Le côté gauche de (7.7) peut s'écrire

$$\bar{P}(\mu_0 \to \mu_{N+1}, \sum_i^{N+1} \tau_i) = \bar{P}(\mu_0 \to \mu_{N+1}, \sum_i^N \tau_i') \tag{7.9}$$

grâce à la définition même de $\bar{P}(\mu \to \nu, t)$.

En appliquant le théorème pour N au côté droit de (7.9), on obtiendra

$$\bar{P}(\mu_0 \to \mu_{N+1}, \sum_i^{N+1} \tau_i)$$
$$= \sum_{\nu_{N-1}} \cdots \sum_{\nu_1} \bar{P}(\mu_0 \to \nu_1, \tau_1') \cdots \bar{P}(\nu_{N-2} \to \nu_{N-1}, \tau_{N-1}') P(\nu_{N-1} \to \nu_N, \tau_N') \tag{7.10}$$

avec

$$\nu_N = \mu_{N+1}, \qquad \tau_N' = \tau_{N+1}. \tag{7.11}$$

Il y a N facteurs sur le côté droit de (7.10). En appliquant le théorème pour $(N-1)$ aux premiers $(N-1)$ facteurs, on obtiendra (7.7), le résultat voulu.

La propriété essentielle dont on s'est servi pour dériver le résultat voulu (7.1) est l'égalité (approximative)* de (7.2) et (7.3). On constate alors qu'en tant qu'il s'agit de cette propriété on peut inclure $\varepsilon_{\nu\mu}$ dans $q_{\nu\mu}$, et qu'on pourra obtenir (7.1), au moins formellement, pour $P(\mu \to \nu, t)$ sans trait sur P. Mais l'évaluation des fluctuations (c. à d. des écarts de P de $\bar{P}$) pour $t > \tau$ deviendra assez délicate. Voilà précisément le problème dont la théorie d'Onsager s'occupe principalement.

VIII. L'INTERVALLE ΔT QUI APPARAÎT DANS LE PRINCIPE D'ONSAGER ET LE TEMPS DE RELAXATION T_R

Si on fait une observation macroscopique sur un grand nombre de systèmes, leur état immédiatement après l'observation sera représenté par l'ensemble:

$$\sum_{\mu} \sum_{i \in \mu} w_i \mathfrak{P}[\psi_i]. \tag{8.1}$$

Comme on a vu, il faut considérer, pour être rigoureux, de divers systèmes de coordonnées, mais comme le résultat devient le même, on ne prendra qu'un seul système de coordonnées ψ_i bien fixe.

Pour un observateur macroscopique, chaque poids w_i est inobservable, bien que le poids macroscopique:

$$w_\mu = \sum_{i \in \mu} w_i \tag{8.2}$$

soit observable. La prédiction par un observateur macroscopique se

* Cette égalité n'est qu'approximative, car $q\tau$ ne peut être plus petit qu'une certaine limite. L'écart peut contribuer à la fluctuation dans le sens d'Onsager.

basera donc sur w_μ, c'est à dire, qu'il se servira de l'ensemble fictif

$$\sum_\mu (w_\mu/N_\mu)\,\mathfrak{P}[C_\mu] = \sum_\mu \sum_{i\in\mu} (w_\mu/N_\mu)\,\mathfrak{P}[\psi_i], \tag{8.3}$$

où N_μ est le nombre de dimensions de la cellule C_μ. La différence entre w_i et w_μ/N_μ sera traitée comme une fluctuation incontrôlable. Le remplacement de (8.1) par (8.3) correspond au remplacement de $P(i\to\nu, \tau)$ par $\bar{P}(\mu\to\nu, \tau)$.

Il faut aussi noter que si on a

$$w_\mu = w_{\mu 0}, \qquad \text{avec } w_{\mu 0} = N_\mu/N_\alpha, \tag{8.4}$$

l'ensemble (8.3) deviendra l'ensemble microcanonique. N_a est le nombre de dimensions de la couche d'énergie G_a.

Supposons qu'on ait à l'instant initial t un ensemble (8.1), que l'observateur macroscopique décrira par (8.3). S'il fait une seconde observation à l'instant $t+\tau$, il décrira son résultat par l'ensemble:

$$\sum_\nu [w_\nu(t+\tau)/N_\nu]\,\mathfrak{P}[C_\nu], \tag{8.5}$$

avec

$$w_\nu(t+\tau) = \sum_\mu w_\mu(t) P(\mu\to\nu, \tau), \tag{8.6}$$

qui devient, à l'aide de (6.13),

$$w_\nu(t+\tau) = w_\nu(t) - [qw(t)]_\nu \tau + [\varepsilon w(t)]_\nu \tau. \tag{8.7}$$

Introduisons une nouvelle variable v_μ définie par l'écart de w_μ de sa valeur dans l'ensemble microcanonique $w_{\mu 0}$:

$$v_\mu = w_\mu - w_{\mu 0} = w_\mu - (N_\mu/N_a). \tag{8.8}$$

L'équation (8.7) peut s'écrire alors, en vertu de la normalisation inverse (6.25),

$$v_\nu(t+\tau) = v_\nu(t) - [qv(t)]_\nu \tau + (\varepsilon v(t)]_\nu \tau + [\varepsilon w_0]_\nu \tau. \tag{8.9}$$

Notons que le dernier terme ne se detruit pas à cause de (6.27), tandis que $\sum_\mu q_{\nu\mu} w_{\mu 0} = 0$, à cause de (6.25).

Nous voulons maintenant représenter l'ensemble par les valeurs des grandeurs macroscopiques $\alpha_\varkappa$. Si on prend la valeur de α_k dans l'ensemble microcanonique comme origine de α_k, la valeur moyenne de α_k dans l'ensemble (8.3) sera

$$\langle\alpha_k\rangle = \sum_\mu a_{k\mu} v_\mu, \tag{8.10}$$

où $a_{k\mu}(1-w_{\mu 0})$ est la valeur dans C_μ de α_k, dont l'origine est ainsi fixée, voir (2.5). Puisque nous supposons que les w_μ puissent être déterminés par l'observation des $\langle\alpha_k\rangle$, il faut qu'on puisse soudre l'équation (8.10) pour v_μ:

$$v_\mu = \sum_k (a^{-1})_{\mu k} \langle\alpha_k\rangle. \tag{8.11}$$

Si on a les valeurs $\langle a_k(t)\rangle$ à l'instant t, les valeurs d'expectation des α_k à l'instant $t+\tau$ sera, d'après (8.9) et (8.10),

$$\langle\alpha_l(t+\tau)\rangle = \langle\alpha_l(t)\rangle - (aqa^{-1})_{lk}\langle\alpha_k(t)\rangle\tau + \varepsilon_l\tau \tag{8.12}$$

avec

$$\varepsilon_l = (a\varepsilon a^{-1})_{lk}\langle\alpha_k(t)\rangle + (a\varepsilon a^{-1})_{lk}\,\alpha_{k0}. \tag{8.13}$$

où α_{k0} est une constante:

$$\alpha_{k0} = \sum_\mu a_{k\mu} w_{\mu 0}. \tag{8.14}$$

Si l'écart v_μ dans (8.8) est petit comparé à $w_{\mu 0}$, le premier terme de (8.13) sera petit comparé au second terme, et ε_l peut être considéré comme une fluctuation dont l'ordre de grandeur est indépendant de $\langle\alpha_k\rangle$ et du temps. Naturellement, à cause de (6.12) ou (6.26), la valeur moyenne (par rapport aux états quantiques initiaux dans chaque cellule) de ε_l est nulle. Le dernier terme de (8.13) provient du fait que même si $\langle\alpha_k(t)\rangle = 0$, w_i peut être différent de sa valeur $1/N_a$ de l'ensemble microcanonique. En effet, si on a un véritable ensemble microcanonique ($w_i = 1/N_a$), il n'y aura pas de fluctuation, mais si on n'a que $\langle\alpha_k\rangle = 0$, le poids w_i ne sera sujet qu'à la condition

$$\sum_{i\in\mu} w_i = N_\mu/N_a, \tag{8.15}$$

et il y aura des fluctuations.

L'équation (8.12) peut s'écrire dans la forme d'une équation de Langevin

$$\langle\dot\alpha_l\rangle = -\sum_k \Gamma_{lk}\alpha_k + \varepsilon_l, \tag{8.16}$$

avec

$$\Gamma_{lk} = (aqa^{-1})_{lk} \tag{8.17}$$

Le point sur une grandeur dans (8.16) doit être interprété comme signifiant:

$$\dot f(t) = \frac{f(t+\tau)-f(t)}{\tau}. \tag{8.18}$$

Pour simplifier les formules, on va écrire $\langle \alpha_l \rangle$ et ε_l $(l = 1, 2, \ldots)$ comme vecteurs $\boldsymbol{\alpha}$ et $\boldsymbol{\varepsilon}$, et Γ_{kl} comme matrice $\boldsymbol{\Gamma}$. L'équation (8.16) sera dans ces symboles

$$\dot{\boldsymbol{\alpha}} = -\boldsymbol{\Gamma}\boldsymbol{\alpha} + \boldsymbol{\varepsilon}. \tag{8.19}$$

L'intégrale de cette équation est

$$\boldsymbol{\alpha}(t+N\tau) = e^{-\boldsymbol{\Gamma}N\tau}\boldsymbol{\alpha}(t) + \sum_{n=0}^{N-1} e^{-\boldsymbol{\Gamma}(N-n)\tau}\boldsymbol{\varepsilon}\tau. \tag{8.20}$$

Si les grandeurs α_k deviennent $\varrho_k \alpha_k$ $(\varrho_k = \pm 1)$ par l'inversion du temps, et que le système est sous l'influence des paramètres extérieurs p_i qui deviennent $\varrho_i p_i$ $(\varrho_i = \pm 1)$ par l'inversion du temps, il est aisé de voir que

$$\Gamma_{kl}(p_i) = \varrho_k \varrho_l \Gamma_{lk}(\varrho_i p_i), \tag{8.21}$$

pourvu que la réversibilité élémentaire règne le système. Pour simplifier notre dérivation, ne prenons que les cas où on a $\varrho_k \varrho_l = +1$, $\varrho_i = +1$, c. à d. que

$$\boldsymbol{\Gamma} = \tilde{\boldsymbol{\Gamma}}. \tag{8.22}$$

Dans ces conditions, on peut diagonaliser $\boldsymbol{\Gamma}$ par une transformation $\mathbf{O}$ réelle, orthogonale:

$$\tilde{\mathbf{O}} = \mathbf{O}^{-1}. \tag{8.23}$$

$\boldsymbol{\Gamma}'$ qui est donné par

$$\boldsymbol{\Gamma}' = \mathbf{O}\boldsymbol{\Gamma}\mathbf{O}^{-1} \tag{8.24}$$

peut devenir diagonal:

$$(\boldsymbol{\Gamma}')_{kl} = \delta_{kl}\Gamma'_k. \tag{8.25}$$

Les vecteurs $\boldsymbol{\alpha}$ et $\boldsymbol{\varepsilon}$ deviendront

$$\boldsymbol{\alpha}' = \mathbf{O}\boldsymbol{\alpha}, \qquad \boldsymbol{\varepsilon}' = \mathbf{O}\boldsymbol{\varepsilon}. \tag{8.26}$$

Dans la représentation où la matrice $\boldsymbol{\Gamma}'$ est diagonale, on peut écrire l'équation (8.20), en omettant $\langle\ \rangle$,

$$\alpha'_k(t+N\tau) = e^{-\Gamma'_k N\tau}\alpha'_k(t) + \sum_{n=0}^{N-1} e^{-\Gamma'_k(N-n)\tau}\varepsilon'_k\tau. \tag{8.27}$$

La durée de temps dont l'ordre de grandeur est donné par la réciproque de Γ'_k sera désormais appelée temps de relaxation:

$$T_R \approx 1/\Gamma'_k. \tag{8.28}$$

A cause de (8.17), on peut aussi écrire

$$T_R \approx 1/q_{\mu\mu} \approx 1/f_\mu. \tag{8.29}$$

En vue d'effectuer la sommation dans (8.27), il est utile de distinguer deux cas concernant la grandeur de N: (1) cas où $N\tau$ est plus petit que le temps de relaxation; (2) cas où $N\tau$ est de l'ordre du temps de relaxation ou plus grand.

Dans le premier cas, (8.27) peut s'écrire

$$\alpha'_k(t+\Delta T) = \alpha'_k(t) - \Gamma'_k \Delta T \alpha'_k(t) + \varepsilon'_k(\Delta T), \tag{8.30}$$

avec

$$\Delta T = N\tau < T_R \tag{8.31}$$

et

$$\varepsilon'_k(\Delta T) = \sum^{N} \varepsilon'_k \tau. \tag{8.32}$$

Dans le second cas, on a

$$\alpha'_k(t+N'\Delta T) = e^{-\Gamma'_k N'\Delta T} \alpha'_k(t) + \sum_{n=0}^{N'-1} e^{-\Gamma'_k(N'-n)\Delta T} \varepsilon'_k(\Delta T), \tag{8.33}$$

où

$$N'\Delta T = N'N\tau \gtrsim T_R. \tag{8.34}$$

On voit que, dans (8.32), $\varepsilon'_k(\Delta T)$ est la somme de N petites fluctuations inprévues du même ordre de grandeur $\varepsilon'_\varkappa \tau$. Par conséquent, on peut appliquer le théorème de la limite centrale, et le carré moyen de la fluctuation $\varepsilon'_k(\Delta T)$ sera proportionnel à N, c. à d. à ΔT. La probabilité conditionnelle que $\alpha'_k(t+\Delta T)$ soit $\alpha'^{(2)}_k$ lorsque $\alpha'_k(t)$ est $\alpha'^{(1)}_k$ sera donnée par

$$f_{\Delta T}(\boldsymbol{\alpha}'^{(2)}|\boldsymbol{\alpha}'^{(1)}) \sim \exp\left[-\sum_k \frac{(\alpha'^{(2)}_k - \alpha'^{(1)}_k + \Gamma'_k \Delta T \alpha'^{(1)}_k)^2 R'_k}{4\Delta T}\right]. \tag{8.35}$$

La racine carré moyen de la déviation de $\alpha'^{(2)}_k$ de $(\alpha'^{(1)}_k - \Gamma'_k \Delta T \alpha'^{(1)}_k)$ est

$$\sqrt{2\Delta T/R'_k}. \tag{8.36}$$

Pendant cette même durée de temps, la moyenne de $\alpha'_\varkappa$ change de

$$-\Gamma_k \Delta T \alpha'^{(1)}_k. \tag{8.37}$$

Si la fluctuation (8.36) est plus grande que cette grandeur-ci (8.37), il n'y aura pas lieu de parler d'un changement moyen de α'_k dans le temps, car celui-ci sera complètement "inondé" par celle-là. On obtient donc, comme Siegel a montré,[3] une nouvelle restriction sur ΔT:

$$\sqrt{2\Delta T/R'_k} \ll \Gamma'_k \Delta T \alpha'^{(1)}_k, \tag{8.38}$$

ou

$$\Delta T \gg 1/R'_k(\Gamma'_k \alpha'^{(1)}_k)^2. \tag{8.39}$$

En supposant maintenant la distribution (8.35) pour $\varepsilon'_k(\Delta T)$ dans (8.33), et en posant $N'\Delta T = T$, on obtient la probabilité pour que $\alpha'_k(t+T)$ soit $\alpha'^{(2)}_k$ lorsque $\alpha'_k(t)$ est $\alpha'^{(1)}_k$:

$$f_T(\boldsymbol{\alpha}'^{(2)}|\boldsymbol{\alpha}'^{(1)}) \sim \exp\left[-\sum_k \frac{[\alpha'^{(2)}_k - \exp(-\Gamma'_k T)\,\alpha'^{(1)}_k]^2 \Gamma'_k R'_k}{2[1-\exp(-2\Gamma'_k T)]}\right]. \tag{8.40}$$

En retournant à la représentation de $\boldsymbol{\alpha}$ (sans prime) par la transformation inverse de $\mathbf{O}$, on peut écrire (8.40) dans la forme

$$f_T(\boldsymbol{\alpha}^{(2)}|\boldsymbol{\alpha}^{(1)}) \sim \exp[(-\tfrac{1}{2}\{(\boldsymbol{\alpha}^{(2)} - e^{-\boldsymbol{\Gamma}T}\boldsymbol{\alpha}^{(1)}),\ \mathbf{B}(T)(\boldsymbol{\alpha}^{(2)} - e^{-\boldsymbol{\Gamma}T}\boldsymbol{\alpha}^{(1)})\}], \tag{8.41}$$

où les parenthèses $\{\boldsymbol{\alpha}, \boldsymbol{\beta}\}$ signifient le produit scalaire de $\boldsymbol{\alpha}$ et $\boldsymbol{\beta}$. Par exemple:

$$\{\boldsymbol{\alpha}, \mathbf{B}\boldsymbol{\alpha}\} = \sum_k \sum_l \alpha_k B_{kl} \alpha_l. \tag{8.42}$$

La matrice $\mathbf{B}(T)$ dans (8.41) est donnée par

$$\mathbf{B}(T) = \mathbf{O}^{-1}\mathbf{B}'(T)\,\mathbf{O}, \tag{8.43}$$

avec

$$[\mathbf{B}'(T)]_{kl} = \delta_{kl}\Gamma'_k R'_k/[1-\exp(-2\Gamma'_k T)]. \tag{8.44}$$

Pour les deux extrémités de T, on a alors

$$[\mathbf{B}(\Delta T)]_{kl} = (1/2\Delta T)\sum_m \mathbf{O}^{-1}_{km} R'_m \mathbf{O}_{ml} = (1/2\Delta T)\,\mathbf{R}_{kl} \tag{8.45}$$

et

$$[\mathbf{B}(\infty)]_{kl} = \sum_m \mathbf{O}^{-1}_{km}\Gamma'_m R'_m \mathbf{O}_{ml} = (\boldsymbol{\Gamma}\mathbf{R})_{kl} \tag{8.46}$$

où $\boldsymbol{\Gamma}$ et $\mathbf{R}$ commutent l'une avec l'autre, car elles commutent dans la représentation de $\boldsymbol{\alpha}'$ (avec prime).

Puisque $\mathbf{R}$ est diagonale simultanément avec $\boldsymbol{\Gamma}$ dans la représentation avec prime, elle doit être symétrique dans la représentation sans prime, dans laquelle $\boldsymbol{\Gamma}$ est symétrique.

$$\tilde{\mathbf{R}} = \mathbf{R}. \tag{8.47}$$

De même, $\mathbf{S}$ qui est definie par

$$\mathbf{S} = \mathbf{\Gamma R} = \mathbf{R\Gamma}, \tag{8.48}$$

sera symétrique dans la représentation sans prime:

$$\tilde{\mathbf{S}} = \mathbf{S}. \tag{8.49}$$

Si on laisse le temps couler indéfiniment, la probabilité (8.41) ne dépendra plus de $\boldsymbol{\alpha}^{(1)}$, et deviendra, en vertu de (8.46) et (8.48),

$$f_\infty(\boldsymbol{\alpha}^{(2)}) \sim \exp\left[-\tfrac{1}{2}\{\boldsymbol{\alpha}^{(2)}, \mathbf{S}\boldsymbol{\alpha}^{(2)}\}\right]. \tag{8.50}$$

Pour la durée ΔT, la probabilité (8.41) deviendra

$$f_{\Delta T}(\boldsymbol{\alpha}+\dot{\boldsymbol{\alpha}}\Delta T|\boldsymbol{\alpha}) \sim \exp\left[-(1/4)\{(\dot{\boldsymbol{\alpha}}+\mathbf{\Gamma}\boldsymbol{\alpha}), \mathbf{R}(\dot{\boldsymbol{\alpha}}+\mathbf{\Gamma}\boldsymbol{\alpha})\}\Delta T\right] \tag{8.51}$$

$$= \exp\left[-(1/4)(\{\dot{\boldsymbol{\alpha}}, \mathbf{R}\dot{\boldsymbol{\alpha}}\} + (d/dt)\{\boldsymbol{\alpha}, \mathbf{S}\boldsymbol{\alpha}\} + \{\mathbf{\Gamma}\boldsymbol{\alpha}, \mathbf{R\Gamma}\boldsymbol{\alpha}\})\Delta T\right] \tag{8.52}$$

où le point sur une grandeur quelconque $g(t)$ et (d/dt) appliqué sur $g(t)$ signifient en réalité

$$\frac{g(t+\Delta T) - g(t)}{\Delta T}. \tag{8.53}$$

La probabilité (8.50) donne la probabilité pour qu'un système, dont on n'a aucune information, ait $\boldsymbol{\alpha}^{(2)}$. Par conséquent, la probabilité jointe pour que le système ait $\boldsymbol{\alpha}^{(1)}$ à l'instant t et qu'il ait $\boldsymbol{\alpha}^{(2)}$ à l'instant $t+\Delta T$ sera donnée par

$$f_{\Delta T}(\boldsymbol{\alpha}^{(2)}, \boldsymbol{\alpha}^{(1)}) \sim \exp\left[\left(-\tfrac{1}{4}\{\boldsymbol{\alpha}^{(2)}, \mathbf{S}\boldsymbol{\alpha}^{(2)}\} - \tfrac{1}{4}\{\boldsymbol{\alpha}^{(1)}, \mathbf{S}\boldsymbol{\alpha}^{(1)}\}\right.\right.$$
$$\left.\left. - \tfrac{1}{4}\{\dot{\boldsymbol{\alpha}}^{(1)}, \mathbf{R}\dot{\boldsymbol{\alpha}}^{(1)}\} - \tfrac{1}{4}\{\mathbf{\Gamma}\boldsymbol{\alpha}^{(1)}, \mathbf{R\Gamma}\boldsymbol{\alpha}^{(1)}\}\right)\Delta T\right]. \tag{8.54}$$

Si on maintenant applique le principe de Boltzmann qui énonce

$$\text{probabilité} = \exp\left[\text{entropie}/k\right] = \exp\left[S(\boldsymbol{\alpha})/k\right], \tag{8.55}$$

à l'équation (8.50), on obtiendra

$$S(\boldsymbol{\alpha}) = S_0 - \frac{k}{2}\{\boldsymbol{\alpha}, \mathbf{S}\boldsymbol{\alpha}\} \tag{8.56}$$

où S_0 est l'entropie du cas: $\boldsymbol{\alpha} = 0$, c. à d., celle de l'ensemble microcanonique. Comme l'entropie est définie par les $\langle\alpha_k\rangle$, la différence entre l'ensemble microcanonique et l'ensemble $\langle\alpha_k\rangle = 0$, (8.15), n'intervient pas ici. Avec cette interprétation, les premiers deux termes de (8.54) deviennent

$$\frac{1}{2k}S(\boldsymbol{\alpha}^{(2)}) + \frac{1}{2k}S(\boldsymbol{\alpha}^{(1)}) - S_0. \tag{8.57}$$

Si l'on en suite introduit une nouvelle variable d'état $\mathbf{X}$ par

$$\mathbf{X} = \mathbf{S}\boldsymbol{\alpha} = \mathbf{R}\boldsymbol{\Gamma}\boldsymbol{\alpha}, \tag{8.58}$$

on peut écrire

$$\boldsymbol{\Gamma}\boldsymbol{\alpha} = \mathbf{R}^{-1}\mathbf{X}. \tag{8.59}$$

Par suite, le dernier terme de (8.54) devient, en vertu de (8.47),

$$(\mathbf{X}, \mathbf{R}^{-1}\mathbf{X}) = (\mathbf{X}, \mathbf{L}\mathbf{X}), \qquad \mathbf{L} = \mathbf{R}^{-1}. \tag{8.60}$$

Finalement, la probabilité jointe (8.54) devient

$$f_{\Delta T}(\boldsymbol{\alpha}^{(2)}, \boldsymbol{\alpha}^{(1)}) \sim \exp\left[-\left(\frac{1}{2k}S(\boldsymbol{\alpha}^{(2)}) + \frac{1}{2k}S(\boldsymbol{\alpha}^{(1)}) + \tfrac{1}{4}\{\dot{\boldsymbol{\alpha}}, \mathbf{R}\dot{\boldsymbol{\alpha}}\} + \tfrac{1}{4}\{\mathbf{X}, \mathbf{L}\mathbf{X}\}\right)\Delta T\right]. \tag{8.61}$$

Voilà la formule célèbre d'Onsager. L'équation "phenoménologique", ainsi que la relation réciproque, en suit. La relation (8.22) qu'on a utilisée dans la dérivation de (8.61) est essentiellement équivalente à la relation réciproque.

Si le nombre des grandeurs macroscopiques α_k n'est pas trop grand, on peut estimer l'ordre de grandeur de (8.39) de la façon suivante. En remplaçant Γ'_k par $1/T_R$, et $(\alpha'^{(1)}_k \Gamma'_k R'_k \alpha'^{(1)}_k)$ par

$$(\boldsymbol{\alpha}, \boldsymbol{\Gamma}\mathbf{R}\boldsymbol{\alpha}) \approx [S_0 - S(\boldsymbol{\alpha})]/k, \tag{8.62}$$

on obtient de (8.39):[3]

$$\Delta T \gg [k/(S_0 - S(\boldsymbol{\alpha}))]\,T_R. \tag{8.63}$$

Cette condition peut être interprétée aussi comme une condition imposée sur l'état macroscopique initial, à partir duquel on veut faire une prédiction par le théorème d'Onsager. Si l'écart de $S(\boldsymbol{\alpha})$ de sa valeur dans l'ensemble microcanonique s'approche, en décroissant, de l'ordre de la constante de Boltzmann, la condition (8.63) contredira l'autre condition (8.31)

En somme, ΔT est sujet à trois conditions, (8.31), (8.63) et

$$\Delta T \gg \tau, \tag{8.64}$$

celle-ci étant nécessaire à fin qu'on puisse appliquer le théorème de la limite centrale pour dériver (8.35).

IX. LA MÉMOIRE DU PASSÉ

Supposons qu'on fasse une observation à l'instant initial $t = 0$ sur un grand nombre de systèmes, et qu'on trouve une certaine fraction d'eux dans l'état macroscopique C_μ. Dépendant du passé des systèmes, le poids w_i de chaque état quantique $\psi_i \in C_\mu$ ne sera pas le même. Cet effet causera naturellement des fluctuations, qui ne sont pas determinées par le seul fait que les systèmes ont été dans C_μ à l'instant initial. Mais, même supposant que w_i soit le même dans C_μ à l'instant initial, les fluctuations ultérieures sont inévitables. En prenant un ensemble qui a été localisé dans C_μ à l'instant initial, et qui a des poids uniforme w_i, on fait une deuxième observation τ secondes plus tard. On trouvera une certaine fraction des systèmes dans C_ν. Mais parmi eux, les poids $w_j(\tau)$ des états quantiques $\psi_j \in C_\nu$ ne seront plus uniformes, car $|T_{ji}|$ n'est pas exactement le même pour de différents $\psi_j \in C_\nu$. Cette non-uniformité causera des fluctuations plus tard.

En général, les fluctuations sont inévitables, à moins qu'on ait un ensemble microcanonique à l'instant initial. Les valeurs des α_k ainsi montreront toujours des écarts des valeurs données par l'équation phénoménologique. Ainsi, même si on laisse l'ensemble longtemps à lui-même, l'entropie monterera des fluctuations au-dessous de sa valeur maximum. C'est au fond le résultat du parcours passé de chaque système individuel, incontrôlable par l'observation macroscopique. Mais, cette mémoire individuelle du passé est très faible, comme les fluctuations sont toujours petites.

Il est intéressant d'examiner le degré de persistance des fluctuations individuelles. Pour la durée de temps de l'ordre assigné à τ, les fluctuations sont proportionnelles à τ, comme on peut voir dans (6.9). Mais puisqu'il y a autant de fluctuations positives que des fluctuations négatives qui causent une interférence mutuelle, les fluctuations pour l'ordre de temps assigné à ΔT deviennent proportionnelles a $\sqrt{\Delta T}$, comme on voit dans (8.36) ou (8.45). Finalement, si la durée de temps devient plus grande que le temps de relaxation T_R, les fluctuations, qui ont lieu dans le passé plus loin que T_R commencent à s'effacer par l'effect de relaxation. Par suite, les fluctuations deviennent, dans leur ordre de grandeur, constantes, comme on peut voir dans (8.46) ou (8.50).

En ce qui concerne la prédiction, les éléments incontrôlables par une observation macroscopique actuelle se manifestent dans de petites fluctuations. Si l'on se propose de conjecturer (rétrodire) le parcours passé d'un système à partir des données actuelles d'une observation, on trouve que les éléments incontrôlables par cette observation sont beaucoup plus importants que dans une prédiction.[4] Complètement à part le fait que le système est trouvé à l'instant $t = 0$ dans C_μ, on doit avoir, et on a souvent, une probabilité a priori $w_\nu(-\tau)$ qu'on ratache à chaque cellule à l'instant $t = -\tau$. Si $w_\nu(-\tau)$ est proportionnelle à N_ν, le dimension de la cellule C_ν, ou plus précisément, si on peut se justifier à supposer a priori un ensemble microcanonique à l'instant $t = -\tau$, la probabilité (rétrodictive) pour que le système trouvé à $t = 0$ dans C_μ provenait de la cellule C_ν est donnée par

$$\begin{aligned}\bar{Q}_0(\nu \leftarrow \mu, -\tau) &= \sum_{i\varepsilon\mu} \sum_{j\varepsilon\nu} P(j \rightarrow i, \tau) / \sum_{i\varepsilon\mu} \sum_{j}^{\text{tous}} P(j \rightarrow i, \tau) \\ &= (N_\nu/N_\mu) \bar{P}(\nu \rightarrow \mu, \tau).\end{aligned} \tag{9.1}$$

Or, comme une cellule macroscopique, en général, contient un état quantique et son état renversé (c. à d. un état avec les vitesses renversées), on a, en vertu de la réversibilité élémentaire,

$$N_\nu \bar{P}(\nu \rightarrow \mu, \tau) = N_\mu \bar{P}(\mu \rightarrow \nu, \tau). \tag{9.2}$$

Il suit donc de (9.1)

$$\bar{Q}_0(\nu \leftarrow \mu, -\tau) = \bar{P}(\mu \rightarrow \nu, \tau) \tag{9.3}$$

Si l'on emploie cette probabilité rétrodictive (qu'on appelait probabilité aveugle), on aboutira à une conclusion exactement la même pour le passé que pour l'avenir. Mais cette rétrodiction n'est pas réaliste, car on a plus ou moins information (mémoire) ou conjecture justifiable sur le passé d'un système, a part le fait qu'il est trouvé dans C_μ à l'instant actuel. En général, on n'a pas $w_j(-\tau) =$ constante, ni même $w_\nu(-\tau) \sim N_\nu$. Si on a la probabilité a priori $w_\nu(-\tau)$ (mais qu'on n'a pas une information au regard de la distribution de probabilité dans une cellule), la probabilité rétrodictive deviendra[4]

$$\bar{Q}(\nu \leftarrow \mu, -\tau) - = \frac{(w_\nu(-\tau)/N_\nu) \bar{P}(\mu \rightarrow \nu, \tau)}{\sum_{\varkappa}^{\text{tous}} (w_\varkappa(-\tau)/N_\varkappa)\, \bar{P}(\mu \rightarrow \varkappa, \tau)}, \tag{9.4}$$

qui est tout à fait différente de la probabilité prédictive. L'écart de

(9.4) de (9.3) n'est pas une petite fluctuation. Le principe d'Onsager ne suit donc pas pour le passé.

Dans la représentation classique où chaque système est représenté par un point dans un espace de phase, chaque cas a une trajectoire bien définie dans cet espace. Ce qui a été expliqué en haut se traduit ici comme suit. Pour la prédiction, on peut remplacer un cas particulier qui se trouve à $t = 0$ dans C_μ par l'ensemble de tous les points dans C_μ avec un poids uniforme. L'erreur se manifeste comme une petite fluctuation. Pour la rétrodiction, on doit donner le poids $w_\nu(-\tau)/N_\nu$ à ceux des points dans C_μ qui provenaient de C_ν. La conclusion qui en résulte n'aura aucune ressemblance à l'équation phénoménologique. Voilà l'origine de l'asymétrie entre la passé et l'avenir.

Références

(1) L. Onsager, *Phys. Rev.*, **37**, 405 (1931); **38**, 2265 (1931).
L. Onsager et S. Machlup, *Phys. Rev.*, **91**, 1505 (1953).
N. Hashizume, *Progr. Theor. Phys.* (*Japan*), **8**, 461 (1952).

(2) S. Watanabé, *Rev. Mod. Phys.*, **27**, 26 (1955). Voir Sections 6 et 7.

(3) A. Siegel, *Phys. Rev.*, **102** 953 (1956).

(4) S Watanabé, *Rev. Mod. Phys.*, **27**, 179 (1955).

(5) J. von Neumann, *Z. Physik*, **57**, 30 (1929). J. von Neumann, *Mathematische Grundlagen der Quantenmechanik*, Springer, Berlin, 1932.

(6) N. G. van Kampen, *Physica*, **20**, 603 (1954).

A NOTE ON THE DOMAIN OF VALIDITY OF THE PRINCIPLE OF MINIMUM ENTROPY PRODUCTION

MARTIN J. KLEIN, *Department of Physics, Case Institute of Technology, Cleveland, Ohio*

I. INTRODUCTION

The principle of minimum entropy production says that the steady state of a system in which an irreversible process occurs is that state for which the rate of entropy production has the minimum value consistent with the constraints which prevent the system from reaching equilibrium.[1] This attractively simple criterion for the steady state is, unfortunately, not always valid. Some work has already been done on exploring the limits of validity of the principle,[2] and the present paper is a report of a modest investigation in this direction. The work described below deals with a very simple system for which detailed information has been obtained on both the steady state and the state of minimum entropy production.

The system considered is composed of N particles each of which has two energy states whose separation in energy is ε. This system is in contact with a heat bath at temperature T, and it absorbs monochromatic radiation whose frequency ν is equal to ε/h. The irreversible process which occurs is the conversion of the energy of this monochromatic radiation into thermal energy of the heat bath.

The exact conditions for a minimum in the rate of entropy production are determined and these are compared with the conditions for the steady state. Several interesting conclusions can be drawn from the work which is described below. The first is that the steady state may differ only slightly from the state of minimum entropy production even when these states are far from equilibrium. All previous analyses indicate that the principle of minimum entropy production should *not* hold under these circumstances. This result is of some interest in connection with the Overhauser nuclear polarization effect, whose equations are closely related to the model here considered.[3] The second result obtained is that the entropy production does not decrease monotonically with time in the approach to the steady state. This is to be expected when the principle does not apply.

II. MATHEMATICAL FORMULATION

We consider a system of N noninteracting particles each of which has two energy states whose energies are 0 and ε. Let p_1 and p_2 be the probabilities of finding a particle in the lower and upper states, respectively. The system is in contact with a heat bath at temperature T, and a particle can make a transition between its two states by exchanging energy ε with the heat bath. The system is subjected to radiation whose quanta have energy ε, and so a particle can also make a transition by exchanging this energy with the radiation. Consequently, the equation for the time variation of p_1 has the following form:

$$dp_1/dt = (a\alpha+b)p_2-(a+b)p_1\,. \tag{1}$$

In this equation a is the transition probability per unit time for a transition from the lower state to the upper due to coupling with the heat bath, b is the (symmetric) transition probability per unit time due to coupling to the radiation, and α is exp (ε/kT). We have used the fact that downward transitions are more probable than upward transitions by a factor α, when the transitions occur via exchange of energy with the heat bath.[4] It is not necessary to write out dp_2/dt; it must be the negative of dp_1/dt since we have the restriction

$$p_1+p_2 = 1. \tag{2}$$

The steady state of the system is found by setting dp_1/dt equal to zero. It is clear that in the steady state p_1 has the value $p_1^{(s)}$ given by

$$p_1^{(s)}=\frac{a\alpha+b}{a\alpha+a+2b}=\frac{\alpha+\beta}{\alpha+1+2\beta}, \tag{3}$$

where β is b/a, i.e., β is the ratio of the transition probability per unit time for radiation induced transitions to the corresponding quantity for transitions due to coupling with the heat bath.

The rate of entropy production is the sum of two terms, the entropy production in the system and the entropy production in the heat bath. For the system we obtain

$$\begin{aligned}\frac{ds}{dt} &= -Nk\frac{d}{dt}[p_1 \ln p_1 + p_2 \ln p_2] \\ &= -Nk[\ln (p_1/p_2)]\,[(a\alpha+b)p_2-(a+b)p_1].\end{aligned} \tag{4}$$

For the entropy production of the heat bath we obtain

$$\frac{ds_B}{dt}=\frac{N\varepsilon}{T}(a\alpha p_2-ap_1) \tag{5}$$

since the heat bath gains entropy ε/T for each downward transition of a particle and loses the same entropy for each upward transition.

The sum of Eqs. (4) and (5) gives the following expression for the total rate of entropy production dS/dt,

$$\frac{dS}{dt}=Nka\left[(\alpha p_2-p_1)\ln\left(\frac{\alpha p_2}{p_1}\right)+\beta(p_2-p_1)\ln\left(\frac{p_2}{p_1}\right)\right]. \tag{6}$$

The state of minimum entropy production is now obtained by minimizing dS/dt subject to the restriction expressed in Eq. (2). Straightforward differentiation leads to the equations

$$\ln(\alpha p_2/p_1)+\beta\ln(p_2/p_1)+[(\alpha+\beta)p_2-(1+\beta)p_1]/p_1=-\mu/a, \tag{7}$$

$$\alpha\ln(\alpha p_2/p_1)+\beta\ln(p_2/p_1)+[(\alpha+\beta)p_2-(1+\beta)p_1]/p_2=\mu/a, \tag{8}$$

where μ is the Lagrange multiplier for the constraint of Eq. (2).

Before we discuss the solution of these equations, there are two important remarks to be made. The first concerns the significance of the multiplier μ. As is usual in such problems the Lagrange multiplier has a physical interpretation. In this case μ is equal to the minimum entropy production itself. This is easily seen if $(-p_1)$ times Eq. (7) is added to (p_2) times Eq. (8). (It is worth noting that it can be shown that this result is not at all special to the particular problem under consideration.)

The second point is the nature of the minimizing procedure under consideration. The minimum of dS/dt determined by Eqs. (7) and (8) is the smallest value which dS/dt can have when the p's are subject to the equations of motion, Eq. (1). Our procedure does not correspond to the Hamiltonian formulation of mechanics where equations of motion are obtained from a variational principle. Instead we ask for the smallest value dS/dt can attain in the course of time, if the equations of motion are given, for any possible initial conditions. This last qualification is necessary, since for particular choices of the initial state dS/dt will never attain its minimum, e.g. if the initial conditions are those for the steady state itself.

III. DISCUSSION OF THE SOLUTION

The conditions for minimum entropy production which are expressed in Eqs. (7) and (8) simplify greatly under certain circumstances. If, in particular, both $\alpha p_2/p_1$ and p_2/p_1 differ from one by quantities whose square can be neglected, then it can readily be shown that Eqs. (7) and (8) have as their unique solution the steady state values of p_1 and p_2 given above in Eq. (3). In this case the principle of minimum entropy production holds; in this case, too, μ is zero, or more precisely the minimum rate of entropy production is of second order in the small quantities mentioned above. The circumstances just described are the usual ones for the validity of the principle of minimum entropy production.[5] It is clear that they will be satisfied if α is near one, i.e., at high temperatures, $(T \gg \varepsilon/k)$.

It is important to notice that the state of minimum entropy production determined by Eqs. (7) and (8) may be very close to the steady state even when the conditions discussed in the previous paragraph do not hold. To see this it is necessary to solve explicitly for the state of minimum entropy production. Even in our simple example, however, this must be done numerically. A convenient working equation is obtained by combining Eqs. (7) and (8) to obtain the equation

$$(1+\alpha+2\beta)\ln\left(\frac{1-p_1}{p_1}\right)+\frac{1}{p_1(1-p_1)}[\alpha+\beta-(1+\alpha+2\beta)p_1]+(1+\alpha)\ln\alpha=0 \tag{9}$$

Numerical solutions have been worked out for several cases in which the steady state differs from the equilibrium state by a considerable amount. The results are indicated in Table I, where values of p_1 are listed at equilibrium ($\beta = 0$), in the steady state, and in the state of minimum entropy production, for several values of the parameters α and β. Also listed are the values of dS/dt in the steady state and in the state of minimum entropy production for each case. (dS/dt is expressed in units of Nka.) It can be seen from Table I that the steady state and the state of minimum entropy production are different, but that their difference is never more than a few per cent. This remark also holds for the rates of entropy production in the two states. The parameter α ($= \exp(\varepsilon/kT)$) is equal to 10 in all cases, which means that the usual condition (discussed at the beginning of this section) for the validity of the principle is seriously violated. We note that β runs through a wide range of values, and that for large β the two states are almost identical.

TABLE I

Comparison of the Steady State and the State of Minimum Entropy Production

Parameters $\alpha = 10$	Occupation probability (p_1) Steady state	State of min. ent. prod.	Rate of entropy production Steady state	Min.
$\beta = 0$ (equil.)	0.909	0.909	0	0
$\beta = 1$	0.846	0.861	1.594	1.570
$\beta = 10$	0.645	0.670	6.685	6.601
$\beta = 100$	0.521	0.526	9.821	9.802

It is possible to determine analytically the condition for the behavior just described. If we set p_1 equal to $p_1^{(s)}+\xi$, where $p_1^{(s)}$ is the steady state solution given in Eq. (3), then we can solve Eq. (9) to first order in ξ. The result is

$$\xi = \frac{(1+\beta)(\alpha+\beta)}{2(1+\alpha+2\beta)^3}\left[(1+\alpha+2\beta)\ln\left(\frac{1+\beta}{\alpha+\beta}\right)+(1+\alpha)\ln\alpha\right] \qquad (10)$$

We note that ξ vanishes for $\beta = 0$ and for $\alpha = 1$, as expected. There are various ranges of the parameters for which ξ is a small correction to $p_1^{(s)}$. One interesting condition for small ξ is that β be large compared to $\alpha \ln \alpha$. This is the situation in the last row of Table I and it corresponds to saturation by the external radiation. It is possible that this last way of formulating the result may be of greater generality.

Another way of looking at the principle of minimum entropy production is to examine the manner in which dS/dt varies with time. This variation can be obtained from Eq. (6) if p_1 is known as a function of time. It is easy to integrate Eq. (1) after expressing p_2 in terms of p_1 with the help of Eq. (2) and to obtain the result

$$p_1(t) = p_1(0)e^{-\lambda t}+p_1^{(s)}(1-e^{-\lambda t}). \qquad (11)$$

In this equation $p_1(0)$ is the initial value of p_1, $p_1^{(s)}$ is the steady state value (see Eq. 3), and λ is equal to $(a+a\alpha+2b)$.

TABLE II

Rate of Entropy Production as Function of Time

($\alpha = 10, \quad \beta = 10$)

Tine (λt)	Occupation probability (p_1)	Entropy production dS/dt
0	0.909	18.839
0.4	0.822	10.598
0.8	0.764	7.995
1.2	0.725	7.056
1.6	0.698	6.723
2.0	0.681	6.619
2.4	0.669	6.601
2.8	0.661	6.611
3.0	0.658	6.619
4.0	0.650	6.655
8.0	0.645	6.684
10.0	0.645	6.685

In Table II we have given the values of dS/dt (in units of Nka) as a function of λt for the particular case $\alpha = 10$, $\beta = 10$ already considered above. The initial condition used was $p_1(0) = \alpha/(1+\alpha)$. (This value of $p_1(0)$ means that the system is initially in equilibrium with the heat bath at temperature T, and the radiation begins to act at $t = 0$.) It should be noticed that dS/dt does not decrease monotonically, but that it passes through its minimum en route to the steady state. With another choice of initial conditions this behavior would have a very different appearance, e.g. if $p_1(0)$ were the value of p_1 which minimizes dS/dt.

IV. CONCLUSION

In this final section we discuss several aspects of the work described above. The most significant conclusion to be drawn from this work is that the principle of minimum entropy production, while not valid in general, *may* provide a useful approximate criterion for the steady state even when the latter is very far from equilibrium.

It is interesting to ask whether the equations determining the steady state are the conditions that some function be a minimum. It is easy to show that this is the case for the function $\mathscr{W}$ defined by the equation

$$\mathscr{W} = a[(\beta+\alpha)p_2-(\beta+1)p_1] \ln \left[\frac{(\beta+\alpha)p_2}{(\beta+1)p_1}\right]. \tag{12}$$

That is, the condition that $\mathscr{W}$ is a minimum is precisely that dp_1/dt is equal to zero. We can write $\mathscr{W}$ in a more suggestive form as follows,

$$\begin{aligned}\mathscr{W} = \frac{d}{dt}[-p_1 \ln p_1 - p_2 \ln p_2 + p_1 \ln (b+a\alpha) + p_2 \ln (b+a)] \\ \equiv dW/dt,\end{aligned} \tag{13}$$

where the function W satisfies the equation

$$e^{-W} = \left(\frac{p_1}{p_1^{(s)}}\right)^{p_1} \left(\frac{p_2}{p_2^{(s)}}\right)^{p_2} \text{(constant)}. \tag{14}$$

The $p_1^{(s)}$, $p_2^{(s)}$ are the steady state values of Eq. (3).

The function $\mathscr{W}$ is the function whose minimum determines the steady state and $\mathscr{W}$ is the rate of "production" of W, which is a modification of the entropy. It can be proved[6] that for any system whose stochastic equations have the structure of Eq. (1) there is a minimum principle of the type just described, i.e., the steady state of the system is determined by the minimum of dW/dt, where W is defined by

$$e^{-W} = \prod_i (p_i/p_i^{(s)})^{p_i} \tag{15}$$

and where dp_i/dt is a suitable linear combination of the p_i, and the $p_i^{(s)}$ are the steady state values. Such a principle seems to be of little or no value since it cannot be formulated without a knowledge of the steady state.

It would be interesting to find a direct physical interpretation of the functions $\mathscr{W}$ and W.

The author would like to thank Mr. Burt M. Rosenbaum for a number of helpful discussions. The author would also like to thank the ONR and the Case Institute Research Fund for making it possible for him to attend this Colloquium.

References

(1) I. Prigogine, *Étude thermodynamique des phénomènes irréversibles*, Desoer, Liège, 1947, Chap. V. S. R. de Groot, *Thermodynamics of Irreversible Processes*, North-Holland, Amsterdam, Interscience, New York, 1951, Chap. X.

(2) M. J. Klein and P. H. E. Meijer, *Phys. Rev.* **96**, 250 (1954). M. J. Klein, *Phys. Rev.*, **98**, 1736 (1955). I. Prigogine, *Physica*, **15**, 272 (1949). I. Prigogine, in *Temperature, Its Measurement and Control*, Vol. II, ed. by H. C. Wolfe, Reinhold, New York, 1955, Chap. 14. K. G. Denbigh, *Trans. Faraday Soc.*, **48**, 389 (1952).

(3) See Klein (1955), ref. 2, and also A. W. Overhauser, *Phys. Rev.*, **92**, 411 (1953), and W. A. Barker and A. Mencher, *Phys. Rev.*, **102**, 1023 (1956).

(4) See the appendix in Klein and Meijer (1954), ref. 2 above, and also R. T. Cox, *Revs. Mod. Phys.*, **22**, 238 (1950).

(5) See the discussion in the first two papers of ref. 2 above.

(6) The study of the functions W and $\mathscr{W}$ has been carried out largely by Mr. Burt M. Rosenbaum.

ON THE DEFINITION OF ENTROPY IN MAGNETIC RESONANCE

PAUL H. E. MEIJER, *Catholic University of America, Washington, D. C.*

Abstract

If we deal with a system of magnetic spins which is slightly off temperature equilibrium, as a result of an oscillating magnetic field, some difficulty has arisen as to what the correct definition for the entropy would be. The usual definition does not give the entropy expression introduced by Wangsness. On the other hand his definition leads to consistent results. It is pointed out that the application of Casimir's considerations on even and odd variables leads to a restriction that confirms the Wangsness choice of the definition of entropy.

I. THE DESCRIPTION OF A SYSTEM

The state vector Ψ of a system is given by

$$\Psi = \sum_n a_n \varphi_n, \tag{1}$$

in which the φ_n form a complete set of eigenfunctions and a_n a set of stochastic variables. The matrix elements of the density matrix are given by

$$\varrho_{mn} = \langle a_m a_n^* \rangle_{\text{Av}} \tag{2}$$

and the entropy of this system is defined by the usual expression introduced by von Neumann:[1]

$$S/k = -\operatorname{trace} \varrho \ln \varrho. \tag{3}$$

This definition is a natural extension of the classical expression and fulfills the requirement of invariance under the change of representation.

In the equilibrium state the matrix elements can be expressed in terms of the energy, temperature, frequency, and volume. After substitution in Eq. (3) the entropy becomes a function of these macroscopic variables.

II. THE ENTROPY IN A NONEQUILIBRIUM SYSTEM

We will assume (3) still to hold in case the system is not completely in equilibrium, and we introduce the quantity ΔS as the difference between the equilibrium and nonequilibrium value of (3):

$$\Delta S/k = -\text{ trace } \varrho_{\text{eq}} \ln \varrho_{\text{eq}} + \text{trace } \varrho \ln \varrho = \frac{S_{\text{eq}} - S}{k}. \tag{4}$$

The representation of ϱ will generally speaking not be diagonal, contrary to ϱ_{eq} which is chosen that way. The logarithm of a matrix actually is only defined in the diagonal representation, but for large dimensionality this representation is impossible to obtain. As we will consider systems very near to equilibrium, the logarithm may be considered to be defined by its power series development.

A rather straightforward procedure gives the following result:

$$\begin{aligned} -S/k &= \text{trace } [\varrho \ln (\varrho_0 + \varrho_1)] \\ &= \text{trace } [\varrho \ln \{\varrho_0(1 + \varrho_0^{-1}\varrho_1)\}]. \end{aligned}$$

Here ϱ_0 is the diagonal part of the density matrix and ϱ_1 a matrix containing only off-diagonal elements. The second matrix is considered only up to the second order:

$$\begin{aligned} -S/k &= \text{trace } [\varrho \{\ln \varrho_0 + \varrho_0^{-1}\varrho_1 - \tfrac{1}{2}\varrho_0^{-1}\varrho_1\varrho_0^{-1}\varrho_1 \cdots\}] \\ &= \text{trace } \varrho_0 \ln \varrho_0 + \tfrac{1}{2} \text{ trace } \varrho_1\varrho_0^{-1}\varrho_1 \cdots \\ &= \text{trace } \varrho_0 \ln \varrho_0 + \tfrac{1}{2} \sum_{m \neq n} |\varrho_{nm}|^2/\varrho_{0nn}. \end{aligned} \tag{5}$$

The result is that ΔS contains two contributions, one from the diagonal terms, one from the nondiagonal terms,

$$-\Delta_1 S/k = \text{trace } \varrho_{\text{eq}} \ln \varrho_{\text{eq}} - \text{trace } \varrho_0 \ln \varrho_0 \tag{6a}$$

$$-\Delta_2 S/k = \tfrac{1}{2} \sum_{n \neq m} |\varrho_{nm}|^2/\varrho_{0nn}. \tag{6b}$$

We are interested in the second part of the entropy contribution, as these terms are closely related to those introduced by Wangsness.[2]

Before discussing this point it is necessary to make a clear distinction between microscopic and macroscopic considerations.

III. MACROSCOPIC AND MICROSCOPIC VARIABLES

As mentioned before the entropy is either a function of macroscopic or microscopic variables. In case we want to show the equivalence of the steady state with the state of minimum entropy production a proof is usually given in terms of macroscopic quantities. Assuming a linear dependence between fluxes and forces as well as the Onsager relations one shows easily that the fluxes, which belong to the forces that are not kept constant, adjust themselves according to the minimum entropy principle.[3]

Klein and Meijer[4] have shown that the minimum entropy production theorem holds also in a microscopic description in which the entropy is considered as a function of diagonal density matrix elements (the occupational probabilities of the levels) and minimized with respect to all these variables. Callen[5] has pointed out that this is a generalization of the first case. Instead of a few fluxes and forces we have now a very large number, viz. as many as there are energy levels.

Instead of constraining one or more macroscopic forces to a given value, we have to put certain expressions of the microscopic variables, representing the macroscopic forces, equal to a given value, all the other fluxes will adjust themselves according to the minimum principle. Callen showed that, assuming microscopic Onsager relations, a minimum principle could be established with respect to all the matrix elements of the density matrix.

IV. CASIMIR'S α AND β-VARIABLES

If we introduce the variables,

$$\alpha^i = x^i - x^i_0, \tag{7}$$

which are the deviations from the microscopic or macroscopic variables x^i from their equilibrium values x^i_0. The entropy of a system close to equilibrium can be expressed as a bilinear positive definite form:

$$\Delta S = -\tfrac{1}{2} \sum_{i,k} s_{ik}\, \alpha^i \alpha^k. \tag{8}$$

In Casimir's analysis a distinction is made between even and odd variables. The even variables, microscopic and macroscopic, have even parity under time reversal,

$$\overline{\alpha^i(t+\tau, H)} = \overline{\alpha^i(t-\tau, -H)}, \tag{9}$$

(all other α's kept constant). The time interval τ is large compared to the duration of the equilibrium-establishing process, but short compared to the time over which deviations from equilibrium lasts. The odd variables are characterized by

$$\overline{\beta^i(t+\tau, H)} = -\overline{\beta^i(t-\tau, -H)}. \tag{10}$$

As the entropy has to be an even function of the parameter τ the complete expression is

$$\Delta S = -\tfrac{1}{2}[\sum_{i,\kappa} s_{ik}\,\alpha^i\,\alpha^k + \sum_{\lambda,\nu} s_{\lambda\nu}\,\beta^\lambda\,\beta^\nu]. \tag{11}$$

If we express the fluxes as linear combinations of the forces, the Onsager relations between even and odd variables are

$$L^{i\lambda}(H) = -L^{\lambda i}(-H). \tag{12}$$

V. MAGNETIC RESONANCE

In case of a system of N nearly independent spin particles (we take $s = \frac{1}{2}$, but that is not a severe restriction), the density matrix can be reduced to N two by two density matrices, if we exclude the simultaneous transitions of two spins under the influence of the external rotating field.

Eq. (1) in a rotating coordinate system becomes

$$\Psi = \sum_m b_m(t)\, e^{im\omega t}\, u_m, \tag{13}$$

where u_m, are the eigenfunctions of the Z-component of the spin ($m = \pm\frac{1}{2}$). The density matrix elements in the laboratory system are:

$$\begin{aligned} \varrho_{++} &= \langle b_+ b_+^* \rangle = \tfrac{1}{2}+\varepsilon; \qquad & \varrho_{-+} &= \langle b_- b_+^* e^{-i\omega t} \rangle = \delta e^{-i\omega t}; \\ \varrho_{--} &= \langle b_- b_-^* \rangle = \tfrac{1}{2}-\varepsilon; \qquad & \varrho_{+-} &= \langle b_+ b_-^* e^{i\omega t} \rangle = \delta e^{i\omega t}. \end{aligned} \tag{14}$$

The b's are considered functions of $t = t'+\tau'$ and the average is taken both over t' and τ'. The first is the time (or ensemble) average over all possible initial situations. The second averaging process smoothes out the sudden change of the variables due to collisions and expresses b as a function of the average collision time τ.

The result for δ has been calculated by Wangsness (ref. 2, Eq. 8):

$$\begin{aligned} \delta = \{ & \Delta\omega_1 \tau^2 E + \tfrac{1}{2}(1+\omega_1^2\tau^2)\,(P+P^*) + \frac{P-P^*}{2} \\ & + i\omega_1 \tau E - i\Delta\tau P\} \frac{1}{1+\alpha^2\tau^2} \end{aligned} \tag{15}$$

ω is the frequency of the rotating coordinate system, $\omega_1/\gamma = H_1$, the amplitude of the oscillating magnetic field and $(\Delta+\omega)/\gamma = H_0$ the constant field. The deviation of the density matrix at time $t = t'$ (or $\tau' = 0$) is:

$$E = \langle b_+^0 b_+^{0*} \rangle - \tfrac{1}{2}; \qquad P = \langle b_+^{0*} b_-^0 \rangle.$$

The real and imaginary part of the function given in (15) is:

$$(1+\alpha^2\tau^2)\,\delta_{\text{real}} = \Delta\omega_1\tau^2 E + \tfrac{1}{2}(1+\omega_1^2\tau^2)(P+P^*) - i\Delta\tau\frac{P-P^*}{2},$$

$$(1+\alpha^2\tau^2)\,\delta_{\text{im}} = \tfrac{1}{2}(P-P^*) + i\omega_1\tau E - i\Delta\tau\frac{P+P^*}{2}.$$

The real part is an α-type of variable, as under the transformation $\tau \to -\tau$ and reversal of the magnetic field δ_{real} does not change sign. The reversal of the magnetic field transforms P into P^*.

The result is:

$$-\Delta S/k = 2\left\{\left(\frac{\delta+\delta^*}{2}\right)^2 + \left(\frac{\delta-\delta^*}{2}\right)^2\right\} = \delta^2+\delta^{*2}, \tag{16}$$

which corroborates the Wangsness choice definitely.* The factor 2 in front arises from the fact that the other off-diagonal element gives once more the same contribution.

A part of this work was done under Contract AF-18-(603)-120 of the Air Force Office of Scientific Research. The subject of this paper was conceived in the course of conversations with H. Callen and R. Wangsness, to both of whom I am very grateful.

References

(1) J. von Neumann, *Mathematische Grundlagen der Quantenmechanik*, Dover, New York, 1943.

(2) R. K. Wangsness, *Phys. Rev.*, **101**, 1, (1956), in particular Eq. (18).

(3) S. R. de Groot, *Thermodynamics of Irreversible Processes*, North-Holland, Amsterdam, Interscience, New York, 1951.

(4) M. J. Klein and P. H. E. Meijer, *Phys. Rev.*, **96**, 250 (1954).

(5) H. B. Callen, communication at this congress. Also published in: *Phys. Rev.*, **105**, 360 (1957).

* *Note added in proof*: The difference between the expression (16) and the usual definition $S = -k\delta\delta^*$ was pointed out by F. Lurcat, *Compt. rend.*, **242**, 1686 (1956).

ON THE PRINCIPLE OF LEAST DISSIPATION

H. WERGELAND, *Fysisk Institutt, Norges Tekniske Högskole, Trondheim, Norway*

The principle as given by Onsager[1] is: rate of entropy change minus dissipation equals a maximum with respect to variations in the rate of change of the state variables. This contains the linear phenomenological relations and their symmetry. Furthermore—as was indicated by Onsager 25 years ago[1] and proved recently[2, 3]—it contains all that is necessary to specify the stochastic process whose average or most probable path is the extremal of the variation principle. Since this links Onsager's theory with general Brownian motion, its relation to kinetic theory proper is traced back to the connection between Liouville's theorem, the Boltzmann equation, and the Fokker-Planck equation, whatever that connection may be.

Still one may ask whether a principle of minimum dissipation could determine molecular distribution laws, in particular for the stationary nonuniform state $\dot{S} = 0$. Before returning to that question I want to give a simple alternate form of the principle.

First of all we shall consider open systems in order for a steady non-equilibrium state to be possible. For such a system it was pointed out by Prigogine and Wiame[4] that:

(1) The dissipation → minimum compatible with external conditions.

(2) The entropy may tend to a minimum.

This can be illustrated very simply by the conduction of heat through a plate whose sides are kept at fixed temperatures. Expressing the dissipation by the products of forces and flows

$$2\Phi = \int d(\text{volume}) \sum \frac{\mathbf{X}_i \mathbf{J}_i}{T},$$

one has by the current procedure of quasithermodynamics:

$$\mathbf{X}_i = \mathbf{F}_i - T \operatorname{grad} (\mu_i/T),$$
$$\mathbf{X}_u = T \operatorname{grad} (1/T).$$

A mathematical formulation of Prigogine's assertion (1) now lies at hand. All one has to do is to write the linear relations

$$\mathbf{J}_i = \sum_k (L_{ik}/T)\, \mathbf{X}_k,$$

and accordingly the dissipation function, in the form

$$2\Phi = \int dV \sum_{i,k} L_{ik} \left[\frac{\mathbf{F}_i}{T} - \operatorname{grad}\frac{\mu_i}{T}\right]\left[\frac{\mathbf{F}_k}{T} - \operatorname{grad}\left(\frac{\mu_k}{T}\right)\right].$$

It is then seen that the variational derivatives with respect to the potentials are:

$$\frac{\delta\Phi}{\delta(\mu/T)} = \operatorname{div}\mathbf{J}_i,$$

$$\frac{\delta\Phi}{\delta(1/T)} = -\operatorname{div}\mathbf{J}_u + \mathbf{F}_i \cdot \mathbf{J}_i.$$

Hence the stationary state gives the minimum of dissipation when the local state T, μ_i, $\cdots$ is prescribed over the boundary of the system.

Now, returning to statistical mechanics: because of the arbitrariness of the linear phenomenological equations we have no theoretical basis for imposing minimum dissipation as a condition on the molecular distribution laws. On the other hand, microscopic reversibility, which is essential for the symmetry relations, is also fundamentally involved in the Boltzmann equation; and this may perhaps imply a variation principle for some functional of the distribution—beyond that of maximum entropy at equilibrium. In fact, it has been shown in a recent paper of S. Ono,[5] that the local dissipation—as calculated directly by the collision integral—is a maximum for the correct solution to the Boltzmann equation. That is to say, within the first approximation of Chapman and Enskog's method.

In this context I think mention should be made of an old attempt to deduce the distribution in a steady nonequilibrium state from a variation principle, viz. E. Einstein's doctoral thesis on radiometer forces.[6] The idea was to maximize the entropy locally, subject to a prescribed flow of heat, etc.

$$-k\int f \log f \, d\mathbf{v} = \text{max. with } (m/2)\int \mathbf{v}\, v^2 f \, d\mathbf{v} \text{ prescribed.}$$

If this had been feasible, one could in the next step adjust the spatial dependence to minimum dissipation, e.g. for the case in point

$$\lambda \int \left(\frac{\text{grad } T}{T}\right)^2 dx = \text{min.},$$

where

$$T = \frac{m}{3k} \int \mathbf{v}^2 f(\mathbf{v}, x)\, d\mathbf{v},$$

and so completely circumvent kinetic theory.

Unfortunately there are objections to this. In the first place it is not to be seen why a distribution thus obtained should approximately satisfy the Boltzmann equation. Second, the local auxiliary condition containing odd momenta of the velocity gives trouble with normalization.

References

(1) L. Onsager, *Phys. Rev.*, **38**, 2265 (1953).
(2) L. Onsager and S. Machlup, *Phys. Rev.*, **91**, 1505 (1931).
(3) N. Hashizume, *Progr. Theor. Phys.* (*Japan*), **8**, 461 (1952).
(4) I. Prigogine and J. H. Wiame, *Experientia*, **2**, 451 (1946).
(5) S. Ono, *Sci. Papers Coll. Gen. Educ. Univ. Tokyo*, **5**, 87 (1955).
(6) E. Einstein, *Ann. Physik*, **69**, 241 (1922).

ON THE PRINCIPLE OF MINIMUM ENTROPY PRODUCTION

HERBERT B. CALLEN, *Department of Physics, University of Pennsylvania, Philadelphia, Pennsylvania*

I. INTRODUCTION

The essential foundation of the theory of irreversible thermodynamics is the Onsager reciprocity theorem. Attempts have been made to rephrase the Onsager theorem in the hope that a statement with a greater appearance of generality might fortunately prove also to have a greater content of generality, or might at least suggest directions of possible generalizations of the theory. Accordingly Prigogine[1] showed that, in the steady state which is reached when certain affinities are constrained to have definite values, and in the absence of a magnetic field, all unconstrained affinities assume the values which minimize the entropy production function. Prigogine's reformulation did suggest a generalization, although this conjectured generalization does not appear to have been formulated explicitly in the literature. In particular, it was conjectured that, in the steady state in which one or more affinities are constrained, not only do the several remaining affinities assume values which minimize $\dot{S}$, but that every element of the microscopic density matrix also assumes a value which minimizes $\dot{S}$. The investigation of this conjecture was the underlying motivation of Klein and Meijer's[2] study of the flow of a gas between two pressure reservoirs, and of Klein's[3] study of the Overhauser effect. Setting up specific and tractable models they were able to compute explicitly the density matrix in the steady state, and thence to show that in these special cases the density matrix does indeed minimize the rate of entropy production. An analysis of magnetic resonance by Wangsness[4] suggests certain modifications necessary in this case of a nonzero magnetic field. We give a general proof of the theorem in the absence of a magnetic field.

II. THE KINETIC EQUATIONS

The interaction of a system with the irreducible fluctuations of the walls and of the vacuum induces an ergodic behavior and makes the wave function of the system a stochastic rather than a definite function. If the set of functions $\{\psi_n\}$ constitutes a complete orthonormal set spanning the Hilbert space of the system, and if we write the wave function of the system as

$$\Psi = \sum_n a_n \psi_n, \tag{1}$$

then the coefficients a_n are stochastic variables, with random moduli and random phases. The density matrix P has elements ϱ_{nm} which are the statistical averages of all pairs of coefficients:[5]

$$\varrho_{nm} = \langle a_n^* a_m \rangle. \tag{2}$$

The density matrix is a Hermitian matrix. Its elements are complex, but both the real and imaginary parts are average values of Hermitian operators.

The entropy of the system is defined in terms of the density matrix, by the definition:[6]

$$S = -k \operatorname{trace} [\mathsf{P} \cdot \ln \mathsf{P}]. \tag{3}$$

Although in equilibrium the quantities ϱ_{nm} are time-independent, in the course of an irreversible process they may depend explicitly on the time.

By Eq. (3), the entropy is a function of the parameters ϱ_{nm}. Associated with each matrix element ϱ_{nm} we define an affinity F_{nm} which vanishes in equilibrium:

$$F_{nm} = \partial S / \partial \varrho_{nm}. \tag{4}$$

We define a set of fluxes by

$$J_{nm} = \dot{\varrho}_{nm}, \tag{5}$$

and we note that the fluxes are functions of the affinities, such that the fluxes vanish if the affinities all vanish. For sufficiently small values of the affinities the fluxes are therefore linear homogeneous functions of the affinities, and we can therefore write:

$$J_{nm} = \sum_{r,s} L_{rs,\,nm} F_{rs}. \tag{6}$$

By repetition of the Onsager argument it is easily seen that the Onsager symmetry applies to the kinetic coefficients $L_{rs,\, nm}$, with the one reservation mentioned below.

III. MOMENTUM REVERSAL SYMMETRY

As Casimir has carefully pointed out,[7] the symmetry or antisymmetry of the fluctuating parameters under the momentum reversal operation is important in the Onsager proof. Whereas Casimir's observation is not usually of importance, because thermodynamic extensive parameters are always automatically symmetric under momentum inversion, our density matrix elements do not automatically have simple symmetry, and the Casimir observation now assumes a real significance. We therefore must so arrange our choice of basis functions $\{\psi_n\}$ as to insure a simple symmetry behavior in the density matrix elements.

All of the basis functions ψ_n of Eq. (1) may be chosen as eigenfunctions of the system Hamiltonian, with energy eigenvalues lying in an extremely narrow range of energy, in accordance with the microcanonical constraint on the energy. For convenience in discussion we shall assume that all the eigenvalues are nondegenerate. If wave functions are actually degenerate it is nevertheless possible to choose proper linear combinations so as to obtain the same symmetry properties as those obtained in the nondegenerate case, so that our assumption of nondegeneracy is purely a matter of analytic convenience.

The Hamiltonian which generates the basis functions $\{\psi_n\}$ is necessarily invariant under a reversal of all particle momenta, because the system is contained within fixed rigid walls. Since all the basis functions are nondegenerate it follows that each basis function is either symmetric or antisymmetric under the momentum reversal operator. We shall say that each basis function ψ_n has either even or odd "momentum parity."

The effect of the momentum reversal operator on the total wave function Ψ of Eq. (1) is to change the signs of the a_n corresponding to odd parity, and to leave unaltered the a_n corresponding to even parity. The parity of the product $a_n^* a_m$ is then the product of the parities of ψ_n and ψ_m. It therefore follows that the parity of the density matrix element ϱ_{nm} is the product of the parities of ψ_n and ψ_m. The diagonal elements of the density matrix all have even momentum parity, whereas the nondiagonal elements may have either even or odd momentum parity.

We identify each density matrix element of even parity as an "α-type variable" in Casimir's nomenclature, whereas each density matrix element of odd parity is a "β-type variable." We adopt Casimir's derivation to conclude that (in the absence of a magnetic field) the coefficients $L_{rs,\,nm}$ and $L_{nm,\,rs}$ are symmetric if ϱ_{rs} and ϱ_{nm} have like parity, and are antisymmetric if ϱ_{rs} and ϱ_{nm} have unlike parity.

IV. THE CASIMIR ANTISYMMETRY

The minimum entropy production theorem depends upon the kinetic coefficients being symmetric. We consequently wish to show that those kinetic coefficients which, by Casimir's argument, are ostensibly antisymmetric are actually zero.

The argument we use is essentially that which is ordinarily employed to show that those kinetic coefficients connecting fluxes of different vectorial character must vanish. Thus if J_1 corresponds to a (scalar) flux of energy from the electron "gas" to the lattice vibrations and if J_2 is an x-directed (vectorial) electrical current, then the kinetic coefficient L_{12} vanishes. This is true because all nonzero terms in the equation analogous to Eq. (6) must behave in the same way under the coordinate transformation $x \to -x$, $y \to -y$, $z \to -z$; both J_1 and F_1 are invariant under this transformation whereas F_2 is odd.

We consider for the moment that the basis functions in Eq. (1) are expressed in the momentum representation. Then the momentum inversion operation is equivalent to the coordinate transformation $x \to -x$, $y \to -y$, and $z \to -z$. The requirement that all terms in Eq. (6) behave in the same way under this coordinate transformation now implies that $L_{rs,\,nm} = 0$ if ϱ_{nm} and ϱ_{rs} have different parity. We thus conclude that Casimir's antisymmetry is not real, and that the matrix of the kinetic coefficients is necessarily symmetric in the absence of a magnetic field.

V. THE GENERALIZED MINIMUM ENTROPY PRODUCTION THEOREM

We consider the various density matrix element deviations $\Delta\varrho_{nm}$ to be components of a "vector" $\boldsymbol{\rho}$. The affinity vector $\mathbf{F}$ is related to $\boldsymbol{\rho}$ by the symmetric entropy matrix S

$$\mathbf{F} = \mathsf{S} \cdot \boldsymbol{\rho}. \tag{7}$$

The entropy deviation is, accordingly,

$$\Delta S = \tfrac{1}{2}\mathbf{F} \cdot \boldsymbol{\rho} = \tfrac{1}{2}\boldsymbol{\rho} \cdot \mathsf{S} \cdot \boldsymbol{\rho}. \tag{8}$$

The flux vector **J** is related to the affinity vector **F** by the symmetric kinetic matrix L:

$$\mathbf{J} \equiv \dot{\boldsymbol{\rho}} = \mathsf{L} \cdot \mathbf{F} = \mathsf{L} \cdot \mathsf{S} \cdot \boldsymbol{\rho}. \tag{9}$$

Finally, the entropy production function is defined by

$$\dot{S} = \mathbf{J} \cdot \mathbf{F} = \mathbf{F} \cdot \mathsf{L} \cdot \mathbf{F} = \boldsymbol{\rho} \cdot \mathsf{S} \cdot \mathsf{L} \cdot \mathsf{S} \cdot \boldsymbol{\rho}. \tag{10}$$

We now assume a set of imposed constraints of the form

$$\mathbf{b}^{(k)} \cdot \mathbf{F} = 1, \qquad k = 1, 2, \cdots, \varkappa \tag{11}$$

As a typical case we have a macroscopic affinity (such as a gradient of the inverse temperature) constrained to some constant value; as the macroscopic affinities are linear combination of our density affinities such a constraint is of the form (11).

The normalization condition on P requires that $\mathsf{1} \cdot \boldsymbol{\rho} = 0$, where $\mathsf{1}$ is a diagonal unit matrix. Inverting Eq. (7) to express $\boldsymbol{\rho}$ in terms of **F** the normalization condition can be written as

$$\mathbf{b}^{(\varkappa+1)} \cdot \mathbf{F} = (\mathsf{1} \cdot \mathsf{S}^{-1}) \cdot \mathbf{F} = 0. \tag{12}$$

We first note that it is always possible to replace the set of $\varkappa+1$ Eqs. (11) and (12) with an equivalent set

$$\mathbf{a}^{(k)} \cdot \mathbf{F} = A^{(k)}, \qquad k = 1, 2, \cdots, \varkappa+1, \tag{13}$$

where the $\mathbf{a}^{(k)}$ are orthogonal, the $A^{(k)}$ are constants, and $A^{(\varkappa+1)}$ is zero. We consider the coordinate transformation to the axes defined by the vectors $\mathbf{a}^{(k)}$. We define a transformed density vector:

$$\boldsymbol{\rho}' = \mathsf{a}^{-1} \cdot \boldsymbol{\rho}. \tag{14}$$

Inserting this into Eq. (8) we compute the entropy deviation:

$$\Delta S = \tfrac{1}{2}\boldsymbol{\rho} \cdot \mathsf{S} \cdot \boldsymbol{\rho} = \tfrac{1}{2}\boldsymbol{\rho}' \cdot \mathsf{a} \cdot \mathsf{S} \cdot \mathsf{a} \cdot \boldsymbol{\rho}'. \tag{15}$$

From this we can compute the transformed affinity vector, defined by

$$\Delta S = \tfrac{1}{2}\mathbf{F}' \cdot \boldsymbol{\rho}', \tag{16}$$

whence

$$\mathbf{F}' = \mathsf{a} \cdot \mathsf{S} \cdot \mathsf{a} \cdot \boldsymbol{\rho}' = \mathsf{a} \cdot \mathbf{F}. \tag{17}$$

From equations (14), (9), and (17) it follows that

$$\mathbf{J}' = \mathsf{a}^{-1} \cdot \mathbf{J} = \mathsf{a}^{-1} \cdot \mathsf{L} \cdot \mathsf{a}^{-1} \cdot \mathbf{F}'. \tag{18}$$

Finally, the entropy production is

$$\dot{S} = \mathbf{J} \cdot \mathbf{F} = (\mathsf{a} \cdot \mathbf{J}') \cdot (\mathsf{a}^{-1} \cdot \mathbf{F}') = \mathbf{J}' \cdot \mathbf{F}' = \mathbf{F}' \cdot \mathsf{a}^{-1} \cdot \mathsf{L} \cdot \mathsf{a}^{-1} \cdot \mathbf{F}',$$

and the conditions of constraint (13) become

$$\mathbf{F}' \cdot \boldsymbol{\delta}_k = A^{(k)}, \qquad k = 1, 2, \cdots, \varkappa+1, \tag{20}$$

where $\boldsymbol{\delta}_k$ is a unit vector along the kth axis of the primed coordinate system.

The actual steady state which will be realized with the constraints (20) is now trivial to compute. It is determined by the equations:

$$\mathbf{J}' \cdot \boldsymbol{\delta}_k = 0, \qquad k > \varkappa. \tag{21}$$

Eqs. (20) and (21) determine the solution. Writing each of these questions in terms of the $\boldsymbol{\rho}'$ vector we find:

$$\boldsymbol{\rho}' \cdot \mathsf{a} \cdot \mathsf{S} \cdot \mathsf{a} \cdot \boldsymbol{\delta}_k = A^{(k)}, \qquad k \leqq \varkappa, \tag{22}$$

$$\boldsymbol{\rho}' \cdot \mathsf{a} \cdot \mathsf{S} \cdot \mathsf{L} \cdot \mathsf{a}^{-1} \cdot \boldsymbol{\delta}_k = 0, \qquad k > \varkappa. \tag{23}$$

This set of simultaneous equations determines $\boldsymbol{\rho}'$ and hence $\boldsymbol{\rho}$ in the steady state.

We now show that this solution can also be obtained by minimizing $\dot{S}$. From Eq. (19) we find

$$\delta\dot{S} = 2\mathbf{F}' \cdot \mathsf{a}^{-1} \cdot \mathsf{L} \cdot \mathsf{a}^{-1} \cdot \delta\mathbf{F}' = 0, \tag{24}$$

where the variation $\delta\mathbf{F}'$ is to be taken subject to the constraint (20). But the only restriction implied by Eq. (20) is that $\delta\mathbf{F}'$ must be zero in the subspace $\leqq \varkappa$, and is completely arbitrary in the subspace $> \varkappa$. Thus Eq. (24) implies that the coefficient of $\delta\mathbf{F}'$ have no components in the subspace $> \varkappa$. That is,

$$\mathbf{F}' \cdot \mathsf{a}^{-1} \cdot \mathsf{L} \cdot \mathsf{a}^{-1} \cdot \boldsymbol{\delta}_k = 0, \qquad k > \varkappa. \tag{25}$$

Expressing $\mathbf{F}'$ in terms of $\boldsymbol{\rho}'$ by Eq. (17) gives:

$$\boldsymbol{\rho}' \cdot \mathsf{a} \cdot \mathsf{S} \cdot \mathsf{L} \cdot \mathsf{a}^{-1} \cdot \boldsymbol{\delta}_k = 0, \qquad k > \varkappa. \tag{26}$$

The fact that this equation is identical with (23) proves the theorem that, in the absence of a magnetic field, and subject to constraints of the form (11) and (12), the density matrix elements assume values which minimize the rate of entropy production.

This work was supported by the Office of Naval Research. Reproduction in whole or part is permitted for any purpose of the U. S. Government.

References

(1) I. Prigogine, *Étude thermodynamiques des phénomènes irréversibles*, Desoer, Liège, 1947.

(2) M. J. Klein and P. H. E. Meijer, *Phys. Rev.*, **96**, 250 (1954).

(3) M. J. Klein, *Phys. Rev.*, **98**, 1736 (1955).

(4) R. K. Wangsness, *Phys. Rev.*, **101**, 1 (1956).

(5) R. C. Tolman, *The Principles of Statistical Mechanics*, Oxford Univ. Press, Oxford, 1938, Chap. 9.

(6) J. von Neumann, *Mathematische Grundlagen der Quantenmechanik*, Dover, New York, 1943, p. 202. L. Landau and E. Lifshitz, *Statistical Physics*, Oxford Univ. Press, Oxford, 1938.

(7) H. B. G. Casimir, *Revs. Mod. Phys.*, **17**, 343 (1945).

FLUCTUATIONS AND IRREVERSIBLE THERMODYNAMICS

LASZLO TISZA and IRWIN MANNING,* *Department of Physics and Research Laboratory of Electronics, Massachusetts Institute of Technology, Cambridge, Massachusetts*

Abstract

The time-dependent theory of fluctuations is based on a combined application of the phenomenological theory of dissipation and the stochastic theory of random processes. The traditional method of joining these theories into a uniform scheme proceeds by adding a random perturbation to the differential equation of the phenomenological kinetic theory (Langevin-type equation). We have found that it is possible to approach the problem from an essentially statistical point of view. We deal with probability densities in function space (the manifold of fluctuation paths), and the role of the differential equation is to fix the form of the distribution function. The solutions of the equation constitute the most probable region in function space. The connection between the kinetic equation and the distribution function is stipulated by means of a postulate, the essential ingredient of which is the auxiliary functional recently introduced by Onsager and Machlup. Heuristically this postulate was suggested by the kinetic analog of Boltzmann's principle established by these authors. In the present logical structure it is sufficient to join this postulate to the standard assumptions of the kinetic and stochastic theories for the derivation of the entire time-dependent fluctuation theory. A number of statements usually postulated appear as theorems in this presentation. The reversible and irreversible aspects of time play an essential part in the argument.

I. INTRODUCTION

The theory of thermodynamic fluctuations has long been a subject of interest to many investigators not only for its own sake, but also because of the hope that fluctuation theory would shed light on the microscopic theory (statistical mechanics) of irreversible phenomena. The expectation has been that fluctuation effects, providing as they do a meeting ground for phenomenological and microscopic theories, would help in the construction of a partial bridge for obtaining information about the latter from a knowledge of the former.

* Present address: Physics Department, University of Wisconsin, Madison, Wisconsin.

Within this context, we feel that it would be of value to have as many different "pictures" or formulations of the thermodynamic theory of fluctuations as possible. In fact, what we wish to report here is just such a reformulation. Our contribution lies not so much in obtaining new results as in presenting known results from a different point of view. Most of the work for the one-variable case will appear in detail in a paper now being submitted for publication.

The thermodynamic theory of fluctuations deals with two types of problems. On a simpler level one considers the fluctuation of a quantity as registered at a single instant of time over an ensemble of systems. In problems of the second type one observes each member of the ensemble over a time interval rather than a single instant, yielding a fluctuation path $\alpha = \alpha(t)$ for each system; we are concerned with the distribution of these paths over an ensemble.

This classification of fluctuation problems corresponds closely with the division of phenomenological thermodynamics into *thermostatics* dealing with equilibrium and *irreversible thermodynamics*, or *kinetics*, devoted to the study of time-dependent dissipative processes. Whenever ambiguity might arise we shall qualify a fluctuation problem as "time-independent" or "thermostatic" on the one hand, and as "time-dependent" or "kinetic" on the other.

The time-independent theory is based on Einstein's[1, 8] interpretation of Boltzmann's principle. The definition of the entropy function is extended to a class of nonequilibrium states and used to establish a probability density function (p.d.f.).

Recently, Onsager and Machlup[2, 3] proved a theorem which is the kinetic analog of the Boltzmann-Einstein principle. They established a p.d.f. for fluctuation paths in terms of an auxiliary function (henceforth: the OM function), which in turn was defined by means of the phenomenological kinetic equation.

The Boltzmann principle plays a central role in the time-independent theory. It allows one to compute fluctuation moments and, more generally, serves as a point of departure for the theory of the generalized canonical ensembles. In this paper we embark on a program in which the Onsager-Machlup theorem is used as a similar organizing principle for the development of the time-dependent theory.

According to the central idea of this theory there is a close connection between fluctuation and dissipation phenomena.[2–5] In the usual approach, which we shall call the Langevin approach, this connection is accounted for by the method of stochastic differential equations. The phenomenological equations are augmented by a random term producing the correct amount of fluctuation.

We have shown that the same problem can be attacked from another point of view. Instead of focusing attention on differential equations, one utilizes a variational principle in considering the set of fluctuation paths and describes various physical situations in terms of appropriate distribution functions. The statistical point of view inherent in this approach is similar to the one taken in the time-independent fluctuation theory. However, the situation is complicated by the emergence of time as an independent variable. To clarify some of the problems connected with the role of time is one of the main purposes of our work.

II. PRELIMINARIES

For simplicity, we consider explicitly here systems which are capable of undergoing an irreversible process involving the redistribution of some extensive quantity between two subsystems. The phenomenological description of the irreversible process is by now standard.[6] The departure α of the extensive quantity from its equilibrium value is used as a measure of the departure of the composite system from equilibrium. We shall make the approximation of breaking off the Taylor expansion of the entropy function after the second term:

$$S(\alpha) = S_0 - \tfrac{1}{2}s\alpha^2, \tag{1}$$

where S_0 and s are constants, so that the thermodynamic force

$$X \equiv \partial S/\partial\alpha \tag{2}$$

becomes

$$X = -s\alpha. \tag{3}$$

We furthermore assume a linear relation between force and flux:

$$X = R\dot{\alpha}, \tag{4}$$

where the resistance R is independent of $\dot{\alpha}$.

We will be concerned with the statistics of the fluctuation paths $\alpha = \alpha(t)$ yielded by an ensemble of systems which have already reached equilibrium. In order to describe these fluctuation paths, we introduce the probability density function (p.d.f.)[2, 5]

$$W_p\begin{pmatrix}\alpha^{(1)} \ldots \alpha^{(p)} \\ t_1 \ \ldots t_p\end{pmatrix} \tag{5}$$

defined to be the probability that the path $\alpha(t)$ satisfy the p conditions

$$\alpha^{(k)} \leqq \alpha(t_k) \leqq \alpha^{(k)} + d\alpha^{(k)}, \qquad k = 1, \cdots, p, \tag{6}$$

where $t_1, \cdots, t_p$ are given instants of time and $\alpha^{(k)}$, $d\alpha^{(k)}$ are given numbers. We will also need the conditional p.d.f.

$$P_p\left(\begin{matrix}\alpha^{(1)} \\ t_1\end{matrix} \middle| \begin{matrix}\alpha^{(2)} \ldots \alpha^{(p)} \\ t_2 \ \ldots t_p\end{matrix}\right), \tag{7}$$

defined to be the probability that the path $\alpha(t)$ satisfy (6) for $k = 2, \cdots, p$, given that $\alpha(t_1) = \alpha^{(1)}$.

Along with the usual approach to the fluctuation theory[2, 5] we make the following additional assumptions about the process (postulates I—IV):

We assume that the process is stationary and Markoffian, that the fluctuations satisfy the principle of microscopic reversibility,[2, 7] and that the time-independent fluctuation theory is described by the Boltzmann-Einstein formula[1, 8]

$$W_1\begin{pmatrix}\alpha^{(1)} \\ t_1\end{pmatrix} \propto \exp\left(\frac{1}{k} S(\alpha^{(1)})\right). \tag{8}$$

III. FORMULATION OF THE FLUCTUATION THEORY

(a) Langevin Approach

The usual approach to the fluctuation theory[2, 5] is characterized by certain assumptions which we shall call the Langevin postulate, and which are added to the above postulates I—IV.

On a phenomenological level, we find from Eqs. (3) and (4)

$$R\dot{\alpha} + s\alpha = 0. \tag{9}$$

α in the above is to be interpreted as an ensemble average in the usual sense. The path $\alpha(t)$ for an ensemble member violates the above phenomenological equation, and the Langevin method "saves" the validity of this equation by adding to it a random perturbation

$$R\dot{\alpha} + s\alpha = \varepsilon(t). \tag{10}$$

Stochastic assumptions are made concerning the nature of the random force $\varepsilon(t)$: it is assumed to have a white Fourier spectrum with density adjusted to satisfy (8). We postpone until later further discussion of this method.

(b) Function-Space Approach

The point of view taken in this work calls for a shift of emphasis from the differential equation to the probability functions which describe the fluctuation paths. The Langevin postulate is replaced by a different postulate concerning the p.d.f., which we now describe.

The postulate is based on a variational principle due to Onsager and Machlup.[2] From inspection of Eqs. (3) and (4) one sees that the quantity

$$O \equiv (1/4R)(R\dot{\alpha}-X)^2 \tag{11}$$

is minimized by the phenomenological behavior (9), for which $O = 0$, and is positive otherwise. The essential idea is to admit all trial functions of the above variational principle as observable possibilities, and to use the above quantity as a measure for the departure of a particular ensemble member from phenomenological behavior. More specifically, we use the following quantity which we call the OM functional:

$$I = \int_0^{t_P} O\{\alpha(t)\}dt. \tag{12}$$

Postulate V which replaces the Langevin postulate states that the conditional p.d.f. (7) is some function of the above quantity,

$$P_p = P_p(I), \tag{13}$$

where, in evaluating I, one uses a particular path determined by the specifications (6).

The justification of the above postulate rests on its implications: On the basis of postulates I—V we derive all of the usual results of the fluctuation theory (including, of course, the Langevin postulate). However, a considerable amount can be said by way of motivating the above postulate V and showing its plausibility, and which will shed light on the structure of the fluctuation theory.

We have already seen that $I = 0$ for phenomenological behavior. It is interesting to note that if the time-reversed solution is inserted into (12) then I becomes equal to the change in entropy associated with this path. More generally, if a linear combination of forward and reversed paths is built up so as to satisfy the specifications (6) then the above OM functional exhibits a peculiar filtering property. It registers a nonzero value only for the reversed components of the path, and I becomes equal to the net entropy change associated with these components. The OM functional therefore looks like a measure for the departure of the specifications (6) from phenomenological behavior.

Further considerations having to do with time reversibility suggest that the irreversible behavior of an ensemble should be properly reflected in the conditional p.d.f. (7) rather than the quantity (5).

All of this is at least a partial motivation for the formulation of postulate V. In addition, the OM function can be given added significance within the framework of the purely phenomenological theory.

Equation (7) can be rewritten in the form

$$O = \tfrac{1}{2}[\phi(\dot{\alpha})+\psi(x)-\dot{S}], \tag{14}$$

where

$$\left.\begin{aligned} \phi &= \tfrac{1}{2}R\dot{\alpha}^2 \\ \psi &= \tfrac{1}{2}R^{-1}X^2 \end{aligned}\right\} \tag{15}$$

are the dissipation functions of Onsager.[2] The result for systems with several variables is quite similar. In order to see better the phenomenological significance of the above expression, we imagine that the kinetic equations (4) are no longer linear.[9] When we do this there emerge certain features of the dissipation functions which are obscured in the linear case. Having obtained these results we then return to the linear case with an added understanding of the structure of the above expression. We find that the dissipation functions play a role in irreversible thermodynamics parallel to that of the potential functions in thermostatics. Variational principles involving these dissipation functions can be formulated which yield stability conditions for steady state operation of the system under various boundary conditions . . . similar to the situation in thermostatics where variational principles for the thermodynamic potentials yield stability conditions for the equilibrium state for the system in contact with various combinations of reservoirs.

IV. DISCUSSION

The basic problem of the time-dependent theory of fluctuations is to combine the phenomenological thermodynamic theory and the stochastic theory of random processes into a consistent scheme. Our main contribution is to achieve this junction in a novel fashion.

The point of view we take calls for a shift in emphasis from the stochastic differential equation of the Langevin approach to the set of functions which describe the fluctuation paths. Concrete physical situations are accounted for in terms of distribution functions over this set of paths or, in other words, through p.d. functions for function space. These distributions are closely related to the phenomenological kinetic differential equation; the solutions of the latter constitute the most probable region in function space. The connection between the kinetic equation and the p.d.f. is stipulated by postulate V.

Heuristically, this postulate was suggested by the Onsager-Machlup distribution function derived synthetically from the Langevin postulate. In the present logical structure it is sufficient to join postulate V to the standard assumptions of the phenomenological and stochastic theories to develop the thermodynamic theory of fluctuations. As will shortly be described, this presentation is found to be equivalent to the one conventionally followed so far as results are concerned. However, we believe the present method has some appealing conceptual and formal features.

In the first place our formalism gives justice to both the reversible and irreversible aspects of time. The manifold of fluctuation paths is invariant with respect to time reversal, while bias in favor of the forward direction is introduced by means of the OM functional, which exhibits a peculiar selectivity with respect to the sense of time.

Although the Langevin theory is consistent with the microscopic reversibility of fluctuation paths, it fails to provide any formal counterpart to this principle. Thus, the regression of fluctuations is described by the phenomenological equation and the reverse process, the building up of fluctuations, is attributed to the random force.

Another advantage is, as already mentioned, that the statistical approach we take allows us to use the OM result as an organizing principle for the fluctuation theory, similar to the situation in thermostatics and the time-independent fluctuation theory. It must be pointed out that this analogy is severely limited by the fact that we restrict ourselves to the case of Gaussian distributions.

Another point we bring up in favor of the present approach is its economy. Our postulate V replaces the Langevin postulate and a number of others usually advanced without proofs. Thus, the Langevin postulate and also the Onsager hypothesis[4, 7] concerning the regression of fluctuations (which plays a key role in the proof of the Onsager reciprocal relations) appear as theorems in our presentation.

The economy appears also in the formal structure built on the above postulational basis. Due to limitations of time, this part of our work can be mentioned here only in passing.

Many of the results of the fluctuation theory have heretofore been arrived at without making use of the p.d.f.'s in function space by deducing stochastic properties of the solutions to the Langevin equation. One of our contributions is to point out that such calculations can frequently be performed more easily by starting directly from the p.d.f.'s.

Having found the expression W_p of (5), we go on to obtain also expressions for the distributions of the Fourier coefficients of the paths $\alpha(t)$. The possibility of performing calculations in either the time or the frequency domains provides considerable flexibility in approaching any particular calculation.

We have obtained most of the standard results of the time-dependent fluctuation theory starting directly from the distribution functions. Mentioning two isolated cases as examples here, we find:

(1) A not inconsiderable simplification in the derivation of the Callen-Greene fluctuation dissipation theorem.[10]

(2) Similarly, when the above is duly generalized[9] to include systems with several variables and systems with kinetic energy, a simplified derivation of a theorem due to Williams,[11] which has to do with the noise in a linear reactive electric network where the resistors may be at different temperatures.

This work is a development of the Ph. D. thesis submitted by Irwin Manning to the Department of Physics, M.I.T. The work was supported in part by the Army (Signal Corps), the Air Force (Office of Scientific Research, Air Research and Development Command), and the Navy (Office of Naval Research).

References

(1) A. Einstein, *Ann. Physik,* **33**, 1275 (1910).

(2) L. Onsager and S. Machlup, *Phys. Rev.*, **91**, 1505 (1953).

(3) S. Machlup and L. Onsager, *Phys. Rev.*, **91**, 1512 (1953).

(4) L. Onsager, *Phys. Rev.*, **37**, 405 (1931); **38**, 2265 (1931).

(5) M. C. Wang and G. E. Uhlenbeck, *Revs. Mod. Phys.*, **17**, 323 (1945).

(6) Cf., for instance, I. Prigogine, *Étude thermodynamique des phénomènes irréversibles,* Desoer, Liège, 1947.

(7) H. B. G. Casimir, *Revs. Mod. Phys.*, **17**, 343 (1945).

(8) R. F. Green and H. R. Callen, *Phys. Rev.*, **83**, 1231 (1951).

(9) I. Manning, Ph. D. thesis submitted to Dept. of Physics, Massachusetts Institute of Technology, Cambridge, Mass., 1955.

(10) H. B. Callen and R. F. Greene, *Phys. Rev.*, **86**, 702 (1952).

(11) F. C. Williams, *J. Inst. Elec. Engrs.* (*London*), **81**, 751 (1937).

CYCLIC PROCESSES IN IRREVERSIBLE THERMODYNAMICS

I. PRIGOGINE and R. BALESCU, *Faculté des Sciences, Université Libre de Bruxelles, Belgium*

In a previous work, Glansdorff and Prigogine[1] established the following theorem: Let the total differential of the entropy production P be written as

$$dP = d_X P + d_V P, \tag{1}$$

with

$$d_X P = \sum V_i dX_i \quad \text{and} \quad d_V P = \sum X_i dV_i \tag{2}$$

(V_i, X_i are rates and affinities of the irreversible processes).

Glansdorff and Prigogine have shown that, for time-independent boundary conditions,

$$d_X P \leqq 0 \tag{3}$$

along every path followed by the system during its evolution. The value 0 corresponds to the stationary state.

Although more general than the minimum entropy production principle, this theorem can, however, not be used as a variational principle because in general $d_X P$ is not integrable. Thermodynamics does not require the velocity field in affinity space to be irrotational. In a previous work[2] we have shown that, far from equilibrium, thermodynamics allows rotations about the stationary state. In this communication we shall briefly discuss an example of such a cyclic process, referring to the original paper[4] for a more general treatment.

In his classical book, *La théorie mathématique de la lutte pour la vie*, Volterra[3] studied the following model: Consider two biological species A and B coexisting in a given medium. Suppose the first one, if isolated, would multiply proportionally to the present number of individuals; on the other hand, B would die out in the absence of A. These assumptions are in agreement with observed facts if the two species are neither too numerous nor too dispersed.

Furthermore, B consumes A: every $A-B$ encounter is thus favorable to species B and unfavorable to species A. This model is contained in the following two kinetic equations:

$$\begin{aligned} \dot{A} &= \varepsilon_1 A - AB, \\ \dot{B} &= AB - \varepsilon_2 B, \end{aligned} \quad \varepsilon_1, \varepsilon_2 = \text{constants} > 0. \tag{4}$$

In order to understand clearly the thermodynamic features of the problem we shall consider a set of chemical reactions which lead to the same laws (4). These are

$$\begin{aligned} A+M &\rightleftharpoons 2A, \\ A+B &\rightleftharpoons 2B, \\ B+M &\rightleftharpoons M', \end{aligned} \tag{5}$$

with the following rates and affinities:

$$\begin{aligned} V_1 &= \varepsilon_1' MA - k_1 A^2, & X_1 &= \ln (\varepsilon_1' M/k_1 A), \\ V_2 &= AB - k_2 B^2, & X_2 &= \ln (A/k_2 B), \\ V_3 &= \varepsilon_2' MB - k_3 M', & X_3 &= \ln (\varepsilon_2' MB/k_3 M'). \end{aligned} \tag{6}$$

We shall assume that k_1, k_2, k_3 are very small and that we are in a region in which the quantities A, B, M' are not too large. Then, the second terms of the right-hand side of the kinetic equations can be neglected: reactions (5) are supposed to be practically irreversible.

Such a system can reach a stationary nonequilibrium state if one imposes a constant total affinity or, what amounts to the same, if one holds M, M' constant. Let us write $\varepsilon_1 = \varepsilon_1' M$, $\varepsilon_2 = \varepsilon_2' M$; these quantities are constant by constraint. One then easily sees that, with these assumptions, one finds for $\dot{A} = V_1 - V_2$ and $\dot{B} = V_2 - V_3$ Eqs. (4).

Now Eqs. (4) admit of a stationary state: $A = \varepsilon_2$, $B = \varepsilon_1$. The very existence of this stationary nonequilibrium state has been made possible by our constraint, which is interpreted as an invariable external medium (M, M' being all the external factors that influence the development of the two species). This condition is fulfilled in nature over not too long times.

Now the phenomenological matrix is antisymmetric; moreover, the system is very far from equilibrium (by our assumption of quasi-irreversibility); all the conditions leading to a cyclic process are thus fulfilled. Indeed, Volterra has shown that the trajectories of the system in A, B space are closed curves around the stationary state.

Let us calculate the quantity $d_X P/dt$

$$d_X P/dt = (B - \varepsilon_1)\dot{A} + (\varepsilon_2 - A)\dot{B} = -v \leqq 0. \tag{7}$$

This quantity is exactly the areal velocity (with changed sign) of the representative point of the system. Glansdorff and Prigogine's theorem requires a definite sign for this quantity. This amounts to imposing a certain sense of rotation around the stationary state.

It is interesting to compare this situation with a mechanical system. If such a system is rotating, the sense of rotation will be determined by the initial conditions. On the contrary, the irreversible rotations dealt with in this communication are characterized by a unique sense of rotation.

Further details on this problem of cyclic processes have been published by the authors.[4]

This work is part of a program on irreversible processes sponsored by the European Office of the Air Research and Development Command, USAF.

References

(1) P. Glansdorff and I. Prigogine, *Physica,* **20**, 773 (1954).

(2) I. Prigogine and R. Balescu, *Bull. classe sci. Acad. roy. Belg.*, **41**, 917 (1955).

(3) V. Volterra, *Théorie mathématique de la lutte pour la vie,* Gauthiers-Villars, Paris, 1931.

(4) I. Prigogine and R. Balescu, *Bull. classe sci. Acad. roy. Belg.*, **42**, 256 (1956).

Discussion XI

J. L. Lebowitz: In a somewhat different approach from that of Dr. de Groot and Dr. Mazur, Bergmann and I were able to prove the Onsager relations for a true steady state without any appeal to fluctuation theory.

Also (in a work to be published), we prove the Onsager relations without assuming detailed balance in equilibrium.

H. B. Callen (*to S. de Groot*): I would like to point out that the derivations given can be generalized in several ways. Most evident are the generalizations to odd variables (in the Casimir sense) and to magnetic fields. But I am principally interested in the generalization to the case in which the admittance matrix is not purely resistive. Or, stated differently, the phenomenological equations are higher than first order in the time derivatives. In connection with our fluctuation-dissipation theorem for multiple variables we have shown that every Fourier component of the admittance matrix satisfies a reciprocity relation. Proofs of this have been given both by your "equilibrium" and "nonequilibrium" methods.

S. de Groot (*to H. B. Callen*): The generalization to the case of odd variables, and also to the case in which a magnetic field is present, is straightforward. It is given explicitly in our paper.

H. Wergeland (*to H. B. Callen*): As the symmetry of the impedance matrix in a purely reactive network (or an undamped coupled mechanical system) is due to *dynamic* reciprocity (actio = reactio), should one perhaps not regard it as a generalization of the Onsager relations?

H. B. Callen (*to H. Wergeland*): The symmetry of the reactive portion of the admittance matrix follows in a trivial way as you say. But the restrictive portion (which depends upon the reactance in the system) is symmetric only by virtue of an extension of the Onsager approach.

R. Brout: Can the condition on detailed symmetry in the master equation be loosened up and Onsager's relation in terms of macroscopic variables still be derived?

S. de Groot (*to R. Brout*): This generalization has, to my knowledge, not been carried out. It could, however, very well be that, in the case you have in mind, the Onsager relations no longer hold.

J. L. Lebowitz (*to R. Brout*): This is the assumption which, as I mentioned earlier, we do not need in our proof (to be published).

N. G. van Kampen (*to S. Watanabé*): I do not understand the introduction of the additional ε terms to describe the fluctuations. Are the fluctuations not taken care of by the fact that the $P(\mu \to \nu, t)$ describe the evolution of the probability distribution of states (rather than the evolution of the system itself)?

S. Watanabé (*to N. G. van Kampen*): The fluctuation comes from the fact that each quantum state i contained in a given macroscopic cell μ has a slightly different transition probability to go into a macroscopic cell ν. Furthermore, deviation from the law of "macroscopic reality" (law of combination of transition probabilities) will contribute to the fluctuation.

I. Prigogine (*to S. Watanabé*): I wish to emphasize the fact that the justification of irreversible processes in classical mechanics is by no means simpler than in quantum mechanics. It is true that in classical mechanics you may introduce directly probabilities instead of probability amplitudes. However these probabilities satisfy the Liouville equation, which describes a unitary process. The transition from this equation to a Markoff chain presents about the same problem as the transition from the Schrödinger equation to a Markoff chain.

S. Watanabé (*to I. Prigogine*): I phrased carefully "macroscopic reality" all the way. As far as macroscopic probability is concerned, I believe Professor Prigogine will agree with me. Apart from this, it should be noted that existence of transition probability dependent only on the initial state is a very strict condition. It will be interesting to see how the transition probability proportional to the square of time can (or cannot) be reconciled with this condition and the "reality" condition for a very short time period. The "reality" condition means that there are two alternatives, namely a system *is* or *is not* in a state in *principle* (human ignorance is not in question).

N. G. van Kampen (*to S. Watanabé*): It all depends on what is called a "state" of the system. If the state is defined by means of a *complete* set of variables, the evolution of the state is always a Markoff process, by definition of "complete." This is the case for the macroscopic state, both in classical and in quantum mechanics. The problem of statistical mechanics is to understand the experimental fact that the *incomplete* macroscopic description of a system also constitutes a Markoff process.

S. Watanabé (*to N. G. van Kampen*): I consider only a complete set of states. Within this limit (which includes the cases I have in mind), what I said must be true.

I. Prigogine (*to H. B. Callen*): I think it is necessary to make a clear distinction between the theorem of minimum dissipation as derived by Onsager in 1931 and the theorem of minimum entropy production at the stationary state that I derived in 1945. In Onsager's theorem the velocity field is varied for a given field of affinities while in the second theorem the distribution of matter or energy is varied for given time-independent boundary conditions. Also, in Callen's example the theorem of minimum entropy production is directly connected with Onsager's reciprocity relations $L_{12} = L_{21}$. There are, however, many examples (see, for example, I. Prigogine, *Introduction to Thermodynamics of Irreversible Processes,* Thomas, 1955) where this theorem can also be applied to situations in which the different irreversible processes are independent and therefore the Onsager reciprocity is not used.

S. Machlup (*to I. Manning*): The function θ of Manning has an interesting variational property.

In the case of n variables, maximizing θ $(= 2S—\Phi—\Psi)$ and holding constant *any* set of n fluxes *or* affinities will yield the phenomenological equations.

M. Green (*to R. Balescu*): I wish to inquire if it is so that the circular trajectories you spoke of are not simply the limit cycles but the actual trajectories starting from arbitrary initial conditions.

R. Balescu (*to M. Green*): Yes.

H. Tompa (*to R. Balescu*): In view of the most unusual behavior of the model described I should like to ask the authors if actual systems have been observed whose behavior approaches that of the model, or is there somewhere a contradiction in the reaction scheme proposed which makes such a behavior impossible?

R. Balescu (*to H. Tompa*): There is no thermodynamic contradiction in the scheme proposed, and such cyclic processes are possible, in principle. Volterra's model has been verified by biological observations, with a good approximation. We have no knowledge of a chemical system showing this behavior.

I. Prigogine (*to H. Tompa*): The situation studied in our paper corresponds to a kind of limit. In general the approach to the stationary state corresponds to a spiral motion in the space of the generalized forces. Indeed, if the stationary state is far from equilibrium, the Onsager reciprocity relation no longer holds and we have antisymmetrical terms as well as symmetrical terms if we expand the phenomenological laws around the stationary state. In our example, we have considered the case in which only antisymmetrical terms exist.

PART XII

THEORY OF THE VIBRATIONAL RELAXATION OF DIATOMIC MOLECULES

ELLIOTT W. MONTROLL, *Institute for Fluid Dynamics and Applied Mathematics, University of Maryland, College Park, Maryland*

I. INTRODUCTION

Various physical situations arise in which the vibrational states of a system of polyatomic molecules are suddenly occupied in a nonequilibrium manner. A shock wave propagating through a polyatomic gas increases the translational and rotational energy of the gas molecules at the shock front, thus leaving a region of increased temperature behind.[1] Since the rate of conversion of translational energy and vibrational energy is slow, a lag is established between the passage of a shock front and the equilibration of vibrational and translational degrees of freedom. Some diatomic molecules are formed in excited states. For example the reactions[2]

$$O+NO_2 \rightarrow NO+O_2$$
$$O+Cl_2 \rightarrow ClO+O_2$$

yield oxygen in predominantly the eighth vibrational level while the OH radical resulting from[3]

$$H+O_3 \rightarrow OH+O_2$$

appears mainly in the ninth vibrational level. Some time is required for the subject diatomic molecules to relax to the Boltzmann distribution appropriate to the temperature of their surroundings.

The rates of certain monomolecular reactions are determined by the following two processes: The molecules are excited to a certain energy state (or to one of a special set of states). The energy is then redistributed so that a weak bond is broken. If the latter part of the process is sufficiently rapid the reaction rate is governed by the rate at which the molecules are excited to the required levels of excitation. The occupation numbers of these levels may never be those given by equilibrium statistical mechanics. Indeed these are probably a large number of chemical reactions whose rates cannot be estimated by equilibrium calculations.[4]

The object of this note is to review some recent results of Dr. K. E. Shuler and the author[5] on the relaxation of nonequilibrium states of a simple harmonic oscillator model of a diatomic molecule and to indicate the manner in which a study of the effect of anharmonicities on the relaxation might be made.

It is assumed throughout this paper that vibrational relaxation can be characterized by a set of differential equations

$$dx_n/dt = \sum_m (W_{nm}x_m - W_{mn}x_n), \qquad n = 0, 1, 2, \cdots, \quad (1)$$

$x_n(t)$ being the fractions of molecules in the nth energy state at time t. The transition probabilities W_{nm} are computed by time-dependent quantum mechanical perturbation theory. They are proportional to the squares of the absolute values of the matrix elements of the perturbation term in the molecular Hamiltonian which arises from the interaction with other molecules or the "heat bath" through collisions. The work of Landau and Teller[6] forms the basis of recent developments in this field.

We postulate our system of interest to be divided into two parts. The first is composed of the set of vibrational degrees of freedom which are out of equilibrium; the second is the remainder of the system which is assumed to contain many more degrees of freedom than the first and to remain at a temperature T at all times. We shall refer to the second part as a "heat bath."

Various interesting forms are possible for the heat bath. It may be (i) a monatomic gas which exchanges translational energy with vibrational energy of the polyatomic molecules, (ii) a gas composed of other polyatomic molecules of the same species as those in a nonequilibrium state but which are in both translational and vibrational equilibrium at a temperature T, or (iii) a radiation hohlraum at temperature T.

In case (i) the interaction of an atom with a diatomic molecule depends on the deviation of the atomic separation from its equilibrium value in the molecule. The perturbation Hamiltonian can be expanded as a power series in this deviation. Since deviations from equilibrium are small, only terms which are first order in it need be retained. This is the same form as the perturbation due to radiation, (iii), so that with the exception of the difference in certain proportionality constants the matrix elements of the perturbation in both of these cases are the same and are just those which arise in the theory of transitions between oscillator levels induced by electromagnetic fields. A review of the present status of the theory of the appropriate perturbation has been prepared by Herzfeld,[7] case (ii) is discussed as well as (i) and (iii) (see also ref. 5). Rubin and Shuler have discussed the effect of several of the above mechanisms operating together. In all cases the transport equations (1) appropriate for the harmonic oscillator model of a diatomic molecule have the same form, the specific nature of the process being reflected only in constants which characterize the time scale.

II. HARMONIC OSCILLATOR MODEL

A diatomic molecule can, as a first approximation, be represented as a harmonic oscillator with a natural frequency ν; the small vibrations of a polyatomic molecule can be decomposed into a set of independent normal modes of vibration each of which is dynamically equivalent to a harmonic oscillator. We now discuss the relaxation theory of a set of identical harmonic oscillators.

The energy of the nth vibrational state of the above model of a diatomic molecule is

$$E_n = (n+\tfrac{1}{2})h\nu, \qquad n = 0, 1, 2, \cdots. \tag{2}$$

The fraction of members of a system of such oscillators in the nth state when the system is at equilibrium at a temperature T is of course

$$x_n = (1-e^{-\theta})e^{-n\theta}, \qquad \theta = h\nu/kT. \tag{3}$$

If a harmonic oscillator in the nth state is perturbed through a linear interaction with a heat bath the matrix elements of the perturbation, $(n|H|m)$, vanish unless $m = n\pm 1$. Hence, the only transitions induced by the interaction are $n \to m\pm 1$. The well-known matrix elements lead to the transport equation of Landau and Teller[6] and Bethe and Teller:[1]

$$\begin{gathered} dx_n(t)/dt = \varkappa\{ne^{-\theta}x_{n-1}-[n+(n+1)e^{-\theta}]x_n+(n+1)x_{n+1}\}, \\ n = 0, 1, 2, \cdots \end{gathered} \tag{4}$$

with $\sum x_n(t) = 1$. The temperature-dependence of $\varkappa$ depends on the detailed mechanism of the heat bath interaction with the oscillator. A dimensionless time

$$\tau = \varkappa t(1-e^{-\theta}) \tag{5}$$

appears naturally in further developments.

The solution of the set (4) can be affected through the introduction of the generating function

$$G(z, t) = \sum_{n=0}^{\infty} z^n x_n(t). \tag{6}$$

This function satisfies a first-order partial differential equation whose solution[6] is

$$G(z, t) = \frac{e^{\theta}-1}{(z-1)e^{-\tau}-(z-e^{\theta})} G_0\left[\frac{(z-1)e^{-\tau}e^{\theta}-(z-e^{\theta})}{(z-1)e^{-\tau}-(z-e^{\theta})}\right] \tag{7a}$$

with

$$G_0(z) = G(z, 0) = \sum z^n x_n(0). \tag{7b}$$

The required fraction of molecules in the nth state at time t, $x_n(t)$ is then the coefficient of z^n in $G(z, t)$. Two initial $\{x_n(0)\}$'s, the Boltzmann and the δ-function distributions are of special interest.

An initial δ-distribution

$$x_n(0) = \delta_{nm} = \begin{cases} 1 \text{ when } n = m \\ 0 \text{ when } n \neq m \end{cases} \tag{8}$$

corresponds to a situation in which all molecules are found in the mth vibrational state at $t = 0$. One obtains

$$x_n(t) = \frac{(1-e^{\theta})e^{m\theta}}{e^{-\tau}-e^{\theta}} \left(\frac{e^{-\tau}-1}{e^{-\tau}-e^{\theta}}\right)^{n+m} F(-n, -m, 1; u^2) \tag{9}$$

with

$$u = \sinh \tfrac{1}{2}\theta / \sinh \tfrac{1}{2}\tau, \tag{10}$$

where F is a hypergeometric function. Since n and m are integers F can also be written as a polynomial so that

$$x_n(\tau) = \frac{(1-e^{\theta})e^{m\theta}\beta^m}{(e^{-\tau}-e^{\theta})} \sum_{i=1}^{\min[n, m]} \frac{m!\,n!\,\beta^{n-i}(\beta-\alpha)^i}{(m-i)!\,(n-i)!\,(i!)^2} \tag{11}$$

with

$$\beta = \frac{e^{-\tau}-1}{e^{-\tau}-e^{\theta}} \quad \text{and} \quad \alpha = \frac{e^{-\tau}-e^{-\theta}}{e^{-\tau}-1}. \tag{12}$$

The relaxation curves appropriate to the occupation of vibrational states of O_2 which result from the reaction $O+ClO_2 \rightarrow ClO+O_2$ (in which O_2 is formed in the 8th vibrational level) are plotted in Figure 1.

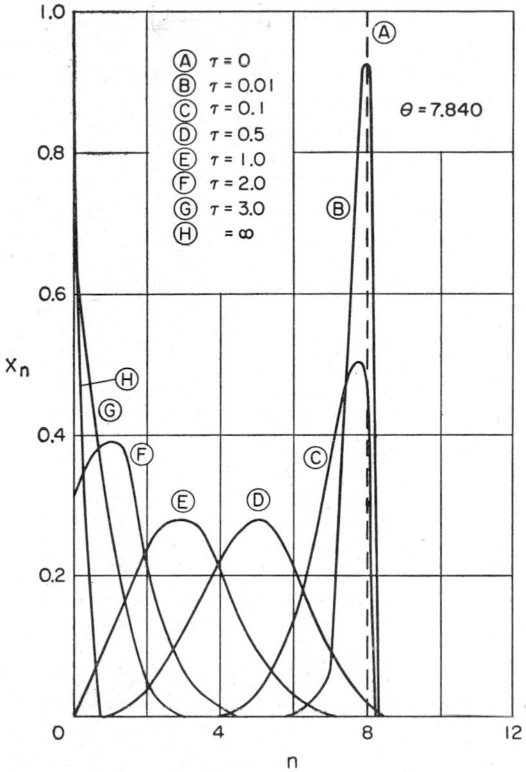

Fig. 1. Relaxation of O_2 formed in the 8th vibrational state by the reaction $O+ClO_2 \rightarrow ClO+O_2$. The relaxation of the initial distribution A to the equilibrium one H is brought about through collision with a heat bath of N_2 molecules at a temperature of 288°K.

The value $h\nu/k$ for O_2 is 2258°K. If the excited O_2 relaxes in an N_2 bath of temperature $T = 288°$ through collisions with N_2, $\theta = h\nu/kT = 7.84$. The graph plotted in Figure 1 by K. E. Shuler corresponds to these conditions.

The relaxation from any arbitrary initial distribution can be expressed as a linear combination of delta relaxations, for we note that the function $x_n(t)$ defined by (9) is exactly

$K_{nm}(\tau)$ = Prob {a molecule will be in the nth state at time τ after it was in mth state} (13)

Hence

$$x_n(\tau) = \sum_m K_{nm}(\tau) x_m(0). \tag{14}$$

We show in the next section that the matrix $K_0(\tau)$ whose elements are $K_{nm}(\tau)$ enters naturally into the perturbation theory of the anharmonic oscillator.

The relaxation of an initial Boltzmann distribution

$$x_n(0) = (1-e^{-\theta_0}) \exp[-n\theta_0] \tag{15}$$

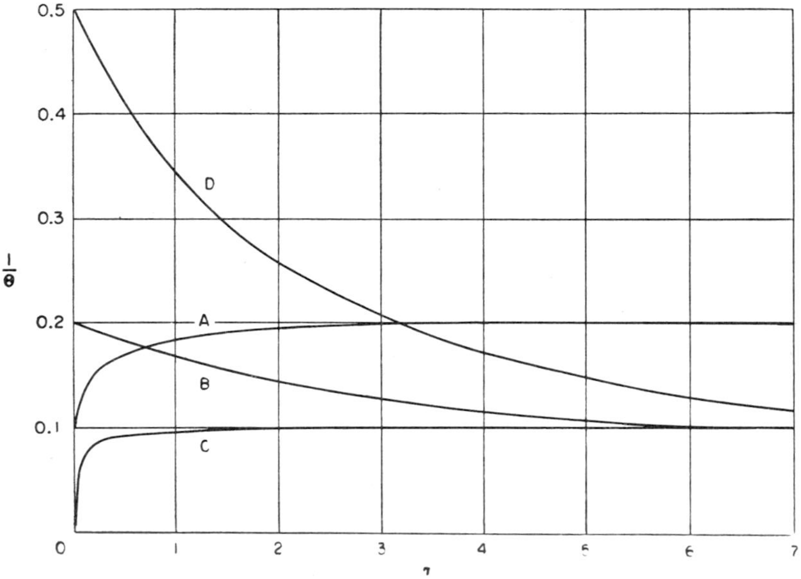

Fig. 2. The "temperature" $Tk/h\nu = \theta^{-1}$ as a function of time T for the relaxation of initial Boltzmann distributions. Initial and final values of θ are: Curve A: $\theta_0 = 10$, $\theta = 5$, $T = \frac{1}{2}T_0$; Curve B: $\theta_0 = 5$, $\theta = 10$, $T_0 = 2T$. Curve C: $\theta_0 = 20$, $\theta = 10$, $T_0 = \frac{1}{2}T$. Curve D: $\theta_0 = 2$, $\theta = 10$, $T_0 = 5T$

has the unique property of being invariant in form. At time τ

$$x_n(\tau) = [1-e^{-\Theta(\tau)}] \exp[-n\Theta(\tau)], \tag{16}$$

where

$$\exp\left[-\Theta(\tau)\right] = \frac{e^{-\tau}(1-e^{\theta-\theta_0})-(1-e^{-\theta_0})}{e^{-\tau}(1-e^{\theta-\theta_0})-e^{\theta}(1-e^{-\theta_0})}. \tag{17}$$

An effective time-dependent temperature $\mathscr{T}(\tau)$ can be defined such that

$$\Theta(\tau) = h\nu/k\mathscr{T}(\tau). \tag{18}$$

We have plotted $\mathscr{T}(\tau) = h\nu/k\Theta$ as a function of time in Figure 2 for various initial and final temperatures $T_0 = h\nu/k\theta_0$ and $T = h\nu/k\theta$.

III. PERTURBATION THEORY OF KINETICS EQUATION WITH ANHARMONICITIES

If our molecular model is complicated through the addition of anharmonicities or by introducing a tighter coupling between oscillator and heat bath the kinetic equation (4) can no longer be solved in a simple manner through the aid of generating functions. Hence, we shall summarize a standard perturbation procedure which can be applied to these cases.

Let $x(t)$ be a vector whose jth component, $x_j(t)$, is the fraction of molecules in the jth state at time τ. Then

$$\partial x(t)/\partial t-(A+\varepsilon B)x(t) = 0, \tag{19}$$

where A is the transition matrix associated with our harmonic oscillator model and εB is the perturbation due to anharmonicity. There exists a transition probability matrix $K(t-\tau)$ such that

$$x(t) = K(t-\tau)x(\tau) \quad \text{for } t \geqq \tau. \tag{20}$$

Clearly as $t \to 0$

$$K(t) \to I, \tag{21}$$

I being the identity matrix. It is convenient to define $K(t)$ such that

$$K(t) = 0 \qquad \text{if } t < 0. \tag{22}$$

Then, if $\tau_0 > 0$ and $\tau_0 \to 0$, $K(t) = IH(t)$ for $t < \tau_0$, where $H(t)$ is the Heaviside step function:

$$H(t) = \begin{cases} 1 & \text{if } t \geqq 0 \\ 0 & \text{if } t < 0. \end{cases}$$

Since $\partial H/\partial t = \delta(t)$ it is clear that for all t

$$\frac{\partial K(t-\tau)}{\partial t}-(A+\varepsilon B)K(t-\tau) = I\delta(t-\tau). \tag{23}$$

Now suppose $K_0(t-\tau)$ is the transition probability matrix of the harmonic oscillator (and whose elements are given by (9)). Then

$$\frac{\partial K_0(t-\tau)}{\partial t}-AK_0(t-\tau) = I\delta(t-\tau). \tag{24}$$

If we let

$$K(t) = K_0(t)+K'(t), \tag{25}$$

then $K'(t)$ satisfies

$$\frac{\partial K'(t-\tau)}{\partial t}-AK'(t-\tau) = \varepsilon BK(t-\tau), \tag{26a}$$

which is easily verified to be equivalent to

$$K'(t) = \varepsilon\int_{-\infty}^{\infty} K_0(t-\tau)BK(\tau)d\tau, \tag{26b}$$

for application of $(\partial/\partial t-A)$ yields

$$\varepsilon BK(t) = \varepsilon\int_{-\infty}^{\infty} I\delta(t-\tau)BK(\tau)d\tau = \varepsilon BK(t).$$

Hence

$$K(t) = K_0(t)+\varepsilon\int_{-\infty}^{\infty} K_0(t-\tau)B(\tau)K(\tau)d\tau. \tag{27}$$

Since $K_0(t)$ is a known function, $K(\tau)$ is the solution of the Fredholm-type integral equation with a kernel $K_0(t-\tau)B(\tau)$. The iteration solution

$$K(t) = K_0(t)+\varepsilon\int_{-\infty}^{\infty} K_0(t-\tau)B(\tau)K_0(\tau)d\tau$$
$$+\varepsilon^2\iint_{-\infty}^{\infty} K_0(t-\tau)B(\tau)K_0(\tau-\lambda)B(\lambda)K_0(\lambda)d\tau\, d\lambda + \cdots. \tag{28}$$

is a power series in ε and will serve as the basis of our perturbation calculation.

The vector $x(t)$ is then expressible as

$$x(t) = [K_0(t)+\varepsilon\int_0^t K_0(t-\tau)B(\tau)K_0(\tau)d\tau + \cdots]x(0), \quad t \geqq 0. \tag{29}$$

The generalization of (4), which is appropiate for a slightly anharmonic oscillation with small anharmonicity coefficient ε (the nth energy level being given by $E(n) = h\nu(\frac{1}{2}+n-\varepsilon n^2)$, is

$$\begin{aligned}\frac{1}{K}\frac{dx_n}{dt} &= ne^{-\theta}x_{n-1}-[(n+1)e^{-\theta}+n]x_n+x_{n+1}(n+1)\\ &+\varepsilon\{\tfrac{1}{4}n(n-1)e^{-2\theta}x_{n-2}+n[n+\theta(2n-1)]e^{-\theta}x_{n-1}\\ &-x_n[n^2+\tfrac{1}{4}n(n-1)+\tfrac{1}{4}(n+1)(n+2)e^{-2\theta}\\ &+(n+1)e^{-\theta}(n+1+\theta[2n+1])+(n+1)^2x_{n+1}+\tfrac{1}{4}x_{n+2}(n+1)(n+2)\}\end{aligned} \tag{30}$$

The derivation of this equation and its perturbation solution will be presented and discussed in a paper by K. E. Shuler, N. Bazley, and E. W. Montroll.

IV. CHEMICAL KINETICS AND THE RANDOM WALK

Let the vibrational states of a diatomic molecule be represented by 0, 1, 2, 3, $\cdots$ and suppose that when it is excited to the $N+1$st state it decomposes or changes its structure in some way so that a "chemical reaction" occurs. If the reaction is very fast after the $N+1$st state is achieved the rate of the reaction is determined by the rate at which molecules are excited by the heat bath from their initial states to the $N+1$st state. A molecule initially at the nth state wanders at random (with transition probabilities determined in the manner described in Section I) from one energy level to its neighbors either up or down until it finally reaches the Nth level, where it "dies" as the reaction occurs. In the language of the theory of stochastic process the level is an absorbing barrier. On the basis of our harmonic oscillator model, the equations governing the reaction rate are given below. It is to be noted that our model is the quantum mechanical analog of that of Kramers.[9]

Since the $N+1$st level is a point of no return in the "random walk" between levels all transitions go from $N \to N+1$ and none in the opposite direction. Hence

$$dx_{N+1}/dt = \varkappa(N+1)e^{-\theta}x_N. \tag{31a}$$

Again, in view of the impossibility of the transition $N+1 \to N$, dx_N/dt has no term proportional to x_{N+1} so that

$$dx_N/dt = \varkappa\{Ne^{-\theta}x_{N-1}-[N+(N+1)e^{-\theta}]x_N\}, \tag{31b}$$

while for $n = 0, 1, \cdots, N-1$ Eq. (4) still remains valid.

The solution of (4) with top condition (31b) can be shown to be

$$x_n(t) = \sum_{j=0}^{N} a_j l_n(u_j) \exp\{-t\varkappa u_j(1-e^{-\theta})\}, \tag{32}$$

where the coefficients a_j are given in terms of the initial distribution $x_n(0)$ through

$$a_j = \sum_{n=0}^{N} x_n(0)\, l_n(u_j) e^{n\theta} / \sum_{m=0}^{N} l_m^2(u_j) e^{m\theta}, \tag{33}$$

the quantity $l_n(u)$ is the Gottlieb polynomial which is defined by

$$l_n(u) = e^{-n\theta} \sum_{\nu=0}^{n} (1-e^{\theta})^{\nu} \binom{n}{\nu} \binom{u}{\nu} \tag{34}$$

and the u_j's are zeros of $l_{N+1}(u)$:

$$l_{N+1}(u_j) = 0. \tag{35}$$

Since the derivation of this solution of (4) is somewhat lengthy and since a discussion of its consequences is even more so, these topics will be presented in a forthcoming paper by K. E. Shuler and the author.

The state of a complex molecule with several degrees of freedom is characterized by several vibrational quantum numbers $n^{(1)}, n^{(2)}, \cdots$, each referring to a normal mode of vibration of the molecule. The state of a molecule can then be represented as a lattice point in multidimensional space and the relaxation from an initial state is equivalent to a multiple dimensional random walk with absorbing barriers at those points which yield a chemical change in the molecule. Such multidimensional walks are difficult to discuss analytically, but are ideal processes for elucidation through Monte Carlo techniques on high-speed computing machines.

The author is indebted to Dr. K. E. Shuler for many interesting discussions on the topics touched upon in this paper.

References

(1) H. Bethe and E. Teller, *Deviations from Thermal Equilibrium in Shock Waves*, Ballistic Research Laboratory Report X-117 (1941).

(2) F. J. Lipscomb, R. G. W. Norrish, and B. A. Thrush, *Proc. Roy. Soc. (London)*, **A233**, 455 (1956).

(3) A. B. Meinel, *J. Astrophys*, **111**, 207, 433, 555 (1950).

(4) K. E. Shuler, *Fifth Symposium on Combustion*, Reinhold, 1955, p. 56.

(5) E. W. Montroll and K. E. Shuler, *J. Chem. Phys.*, **25**, 454 (1957).

(6) L. Landau and E. Teller, *Physik. Z. Sowjetunion,* **10**, 34 (1936).
(7) K. E. Herzfeld, *Handbook of High Speed Aerodynamics*, Princeton Univ. Press, Vol. I, Section H, 1953.
(8) R. J. Rubin and K. E. Shuler, *J. Chem. Phys.*, **25**, 59, 68 (1956).
(9) H. A. Kramers, *Physics,* **7**, 284 (1940).

Discussion XII

H. L. Frisch: Certain further conclusions concerning Poincaré recurrences and similar questions can be obtained by a modification of the theorems of Weyl and others alluded to by Professor Montroll in his talk today. Thus if we restrict ourselves to multiply periodic systems fairly precise estimates of Poincaré recurrence time $\bar{t}(\varepsilon)$ can be found. Introducing action and angle variables for such a system with a time-independent Hamiltonian we can find the characteristic frequencies ν_i, $i = 1, 2, \cdots, N$ of our system from the energy E, i.e., $\partial E/\partial J_i = \nu_i$, with J_i the ith action variable. By hypothesis our system is such that there exist a set of canonical variables p_i, q_i such that the q_i can be written in the form

$$q_i = \sum_{n_k} c_{n_k} \exp\{2\pi i n_k \nu_k t\}.$$

One can show that the recurrence time $\bar{t}(\varepsilon)$ for such systems is given (Frisch, *Phys. Rev.*, **109,** 22(1958)) by

$$\tilde{t} \sim C_N \tau/\varepsilon^N$$

where $2\pi\varepsilon$ is the error of the ν_i $(0 < \varepsilon < 1)$ which we allow in specification of the recurrent initial states. $1/\tau = \max \nu_i$ $(i = 1, \cdots, N)$ and C_N is a constant of the order of unity as would be expected intuitively. What is interesting about this result is that the time required for the recurrence of a given initial state is independent of the location in phase space of this state. It is of interest to ask whether only such multiply periodic systems share this property or whether there exists a more general class of mechanical systems for which this is true. Furthermore, for such more general mechanical systems one would expect that possibly the recurrence time itself would be time-dependent.

Perhaps a physically more interesting question in connection with heat theory is what is the fraction of the time that a system spends in an initially recurrent state? For this question an exact result can be found directly from Weyl's theorem, namely if $t_k - t_{k-1}$ $(k = 1, 2, \cdots)$ represent time intervals during which such a multiply periodic system is under observation and $N_1(\varepsilon, t_k)$ represents the sum of the time intervals during which the system is undergoing a recurrence to a given initial state then, provided only that $\lim_{k\to\infty} t_k = \infty$,

$$F = \lim_{k\to\infty} \frac{N_1(\varepsilon, t_k)}{t_k} = \varepsilon^N ,$$

or, more generally, if the error specification of ν_i is ε_i, then

$$F = \prod_{i=1} \varepsilon_i .$$

In turn this result suggests that the fraction of the time such a system starting from a given initial state disobeys a strong version of the second law of thermodynamics is equal to or less than F.

J. L. Lebowitz: I would like to remark that Bergmann and I have been able to show for the general type of problem about which Professor Montroll talked, i.e., the behavior of a system in contact with a (infinite) reservoir, whose distribution function obeys the type of equation given by Montroll (or more generally in Γ-space of the system)

$$\frac{\partial\mu(\mathbf{x})}{\partial t} + (\mu, H) = \int_\pi [K(\mathbf{x}, \mathbf{x}')\,\mu(\mathbf{x}') - K(\mathbf{x}', \mathbf{x})\,\mu(\mathbf{x})]d\mathbf{x}'.$$

If there exists a stationary distribution

$$(\mu_s(\mathbf{x}), H) \equiv \int d\mathbf{x}'\{K(\mathbf{x}, \mathbf{x}')\,\mu(\mathbf{x}') - K(\mathbf{x}', \mathbf{x})\,\mu(\mathbf{x})\}$$

then under very general conditions

$$\lim_{t\to\infty} \mu(\mathbf{x}, t) = \mu_\varrho(\mathbf{x}) \qquad \text{for any } \mu(\mathbf{x}, 0)$$

when $\mu_\varrho(\mathbf{x}) = e^{-H(x)/kT}/z$ (as in Montroll's case) the free energy decreases monotonically until equilibrium is reached. In general

$$\frac{d}{dt}\left\langle \ln\left(\frac{\mu}{\mu_\varrho}\right)\right\rangle \leqq 0$$

and $\langle \mu/\mu_\varrho \rangle$ is a minimum in the stationary state.

PART XIII

VISCOSITY AND HEAT CONDUCTION OF GASES (AND LIQUIDS) IN THE NEIGHBORHOOD OF THE CONDENSATION REGION

A. MICHELS, *Van der Waals-laboratorium, Gemeente Universiteit, Amsterdam, The Netherlands*

In a dilute gas, transport of energy and momentum is due only to the motion of the molecules. In a dense gas, however, the influence of molecular interaction upon transport properties becomes very important. In the case of thermal conductivity the work done by the intermolecular forces will give a contribution to the transport of energy. Likewise, the transport of momentum is composed of a kinetic and a potential part: while the pure kinetic contribution to the transport of energy and of momentum is dominant in dilute gases, in a dense gas most of the transport results from molecular interaction.

For a gas whose molecules are rigid spheres a fairly complete theory has been given by Enskog.[1] In this case the assumption of binary encounters between the molecules holds also at higher densities. It is obvious that such a theory will break down for real molecules, for it does not account at all for the attractive forces between molecules; also, the rigid sphere model gives only an approximate representation of the repulsive part of the intermolecular potential. Therefore, it is to be expected that the influence of intermolecular forces upon the transport phenomena will give deviations from the theory of Enskog.

An experimental investigation of transport coefficients in the gas and liquid state, in particular at densities near the critical density, can give some indication of the influence of intermolecular attraction upon these transport coefficients. Thermal conductivity has been measured with a plane parallel plate method[2] and viscosity by a transpiration method.[3] As a background to the behavior of the transport phenomena near the critical region first λ and η are shown as a function of pressure and of density at temperatures far above critical[3,4] (Figs. 1, 2, 3, and 4). Both the transport coefficients show the same general trend. The curves against pressure have a region where the isotherms intersect and $(\partial\lambda/\partial T)_p$ and $(\partial\eta/\partial T)_p$, respectively, change sign. As a function of

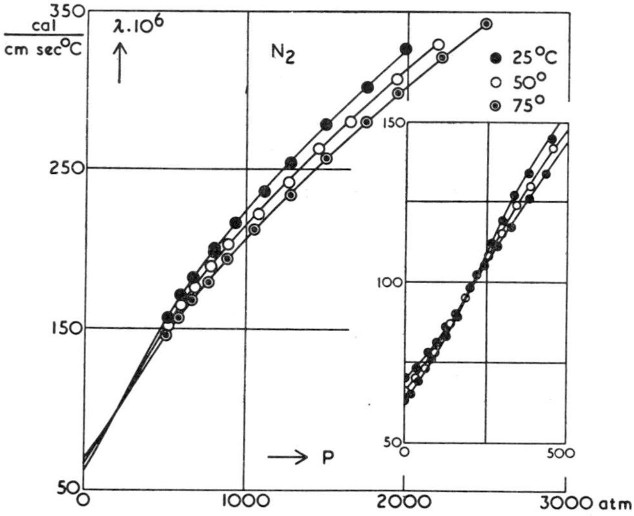

Fig. 1. Thermal conductivity of nitrogen vs. pressure.

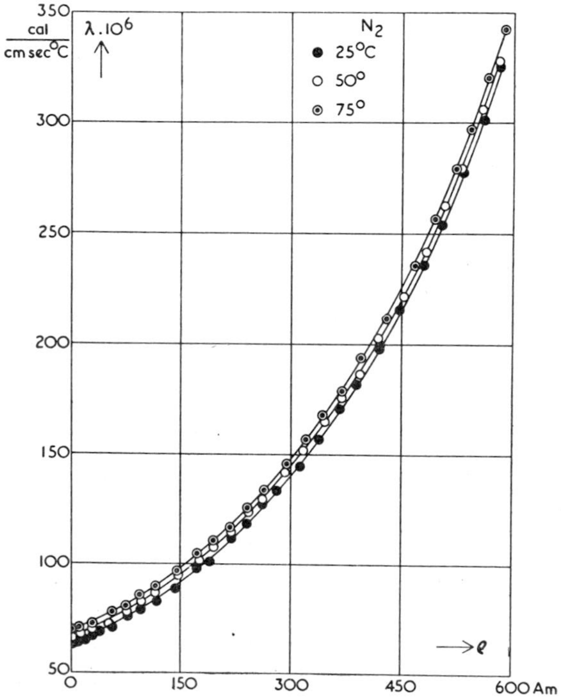

Fig. 2. Thermal conductivity of nitrogen vs. density.

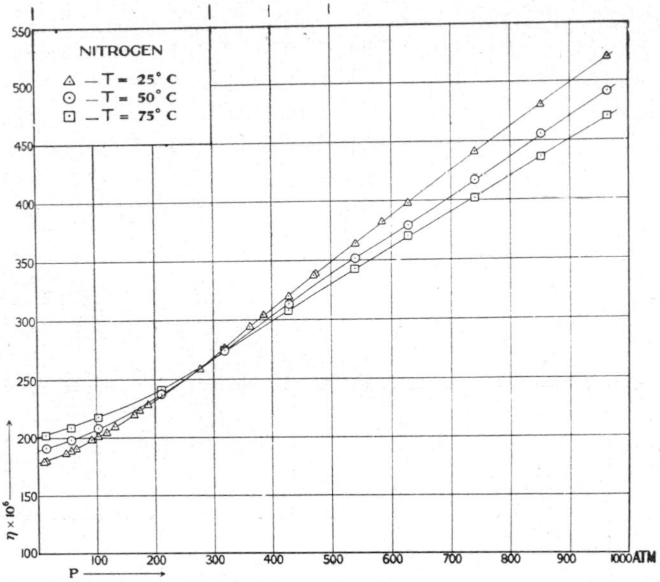

Fig. 3. Viscosity of nitrogen vs. pressure.

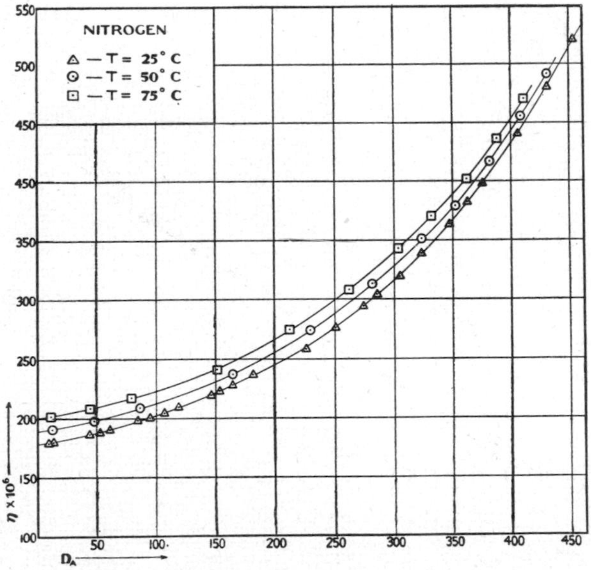

Fig. 4. Viscosity of nitrogen vs. density.

density the λ- and η-isotherms run more or less parallel. For the η of hydrogen and deuterium we obtain similar graphs.[5] For the application of the formulae of the theory of Enskog the parameters are calculated by fitting the experimental pvT data to the theoretical equation of state derived on the same basis by Enskog. This leads to an effective molecular diameter which depends upon temperature. It appears that the theoretical data agree reasonably well with the experimental coef-

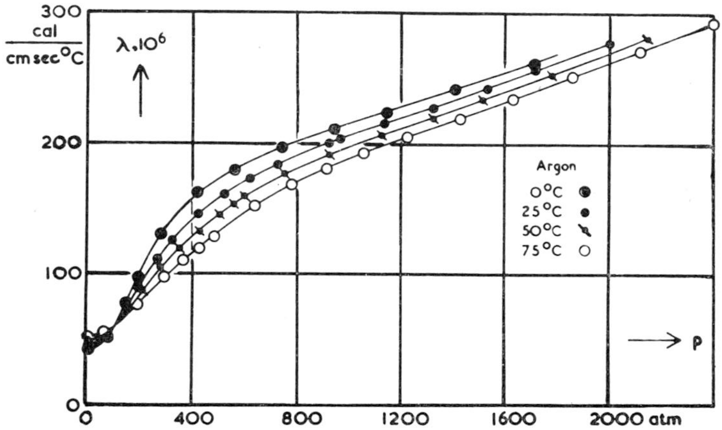

Fig. 5. Thermal conductivity of argon vs. pressure.

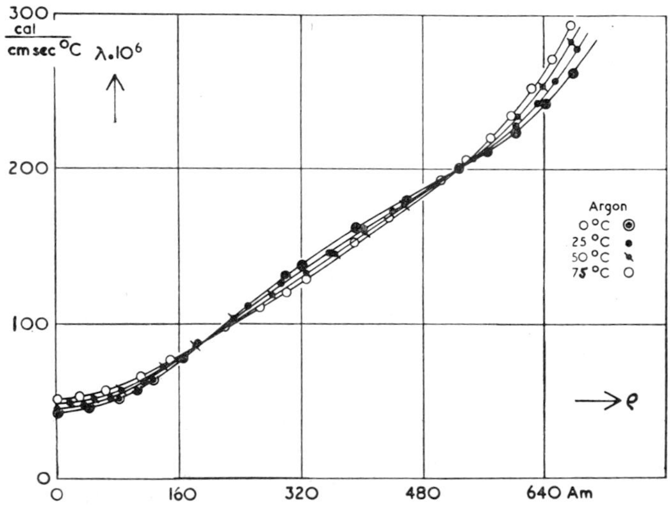

Fig. 6. Thermal conductivity of argon vs. density.

ficients. For nitrogen the discrepancy at the highest experimental pressures is of the order of 10 %.

Deviations from the theory of Enskog become more apparent in the case of argon. In Figures 5 and 6 the experimental data of λ are shown.[6] The pressure-dependence of these λ-isotherms is similar to that for nitrogen, but the dependence on density appears to be quite different. It is seen that the λ-isotherms as a function of density have two intersections where $(\partial\lambda/\partial T)_\varrho$ changes sign. These λ-curves have something like a maximum in the neighborhood of the critical density ($\varrho_c = 286$ Amagat). This maximum is most pronounced at the lowest temperature of 0°C. This suggests that the critical region has something to do with this phenomenon. A similar indication is obtained by considering the experimental data for C_p, best shown in Figure 7, where $C_p - C_v$ is plotted vs. density for the temperatures for which the thermal conductivity has been measured.

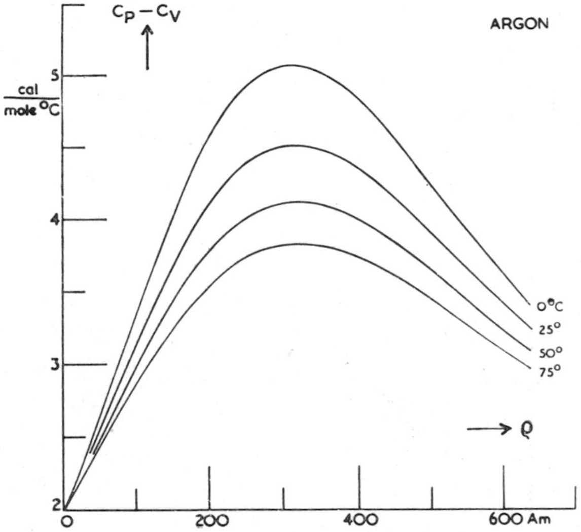

Fig. 7. $C_p - C_v$ of argon as a function of density.

One may ask whether the same result is not found for the λ of nitrogen. At first we find that for nitrogen these temperatures are higher relative to the critical temperature (for N_2 $t_c = -147.1$°C and for A $t_c = -122.4$°C). Moreover, this is supported by comparison of specific heat data for nitrogen and argon, where for argon a more pronounced maximum exists at the same temperatures. Therefore, for nitrogen the same phenomenon is expected for λ at lower temperatures.

It is plausible that, near the critical region, the contribution to transport of energy and momentum from the attractive forces, which are not taken into account in the theory of Enskog, becomes important. Perhaps one could think of a description of the transport phenomena in terms of molecular clusters. On the other hand, one could look for a relation between transport phenomena, in particular thermal conduction, and the equilibrium thermal quantities that take account work done against the attractive forces. Usually λ is related to C_v; but, although no convincing theoretical arguments for this have been developed, it is interesting to compare λ also with C_p, which includes the work done against the intermolecular forces and the external pressure as the temperature is raised, whereas C_v does not. This is illustrated in Figures 8 and 9. In Figure 10, λ is compared with the quantity $C_p - p(\partial V/\partial T)_p$, in which only the work done against intermolecular forces is taken into account.

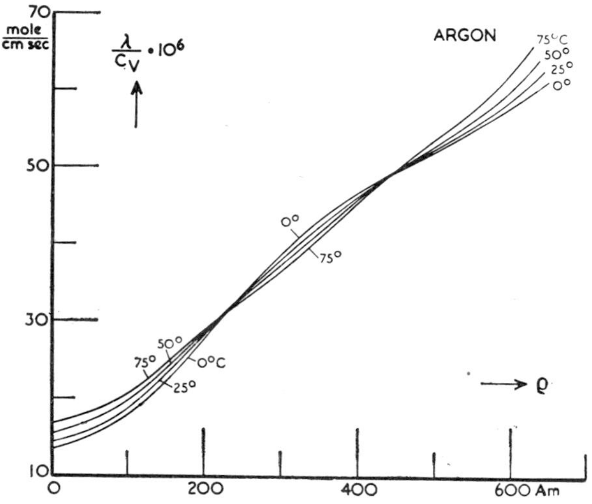

Fig. 8. λ/C_v of argon as a function of density.

From the η of argon at the same temperatures an influence of the critical region is much less apparent.[7] The η-isotherms of argon given in Figure 12 do not show such intersections as in the case of the thermal conductivity. Nevertheless there is also in this instance a large dis-

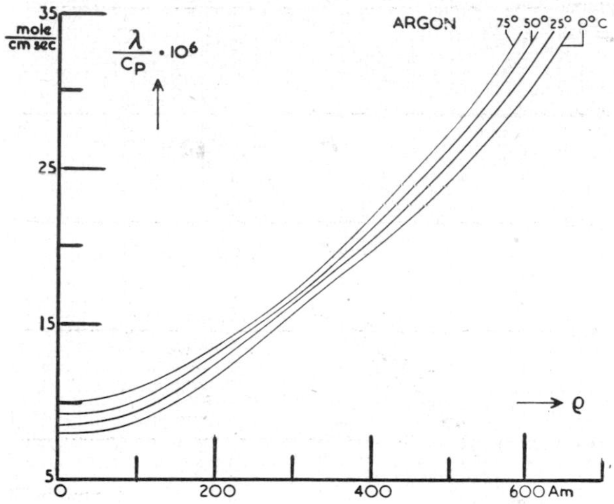

Fig. 9. λ/C_p of argon as a function of density.

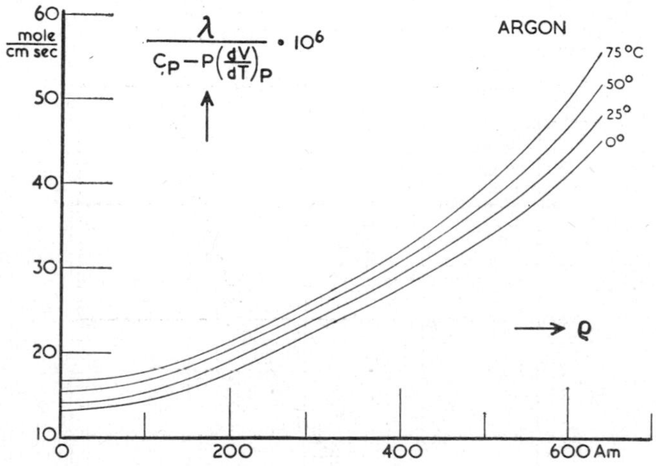

Fig. 10. $\lambda/[C_p - p(\partial V/\partial T)_p]$ of argon as a function of density

crepancy with Enskog's theory (up to 100 % at the highest densities).

The question now arises as to whether the viscosity will show deviations similar to thermal conductivity at lower temperatures. Therefore, to obtain further information about the transport phenomena nearer to the critical region, carbon dioxide was taken because it has a rather high critical temperature ($t_c = 31.04$°C).[8] It can be seen from Figure 13

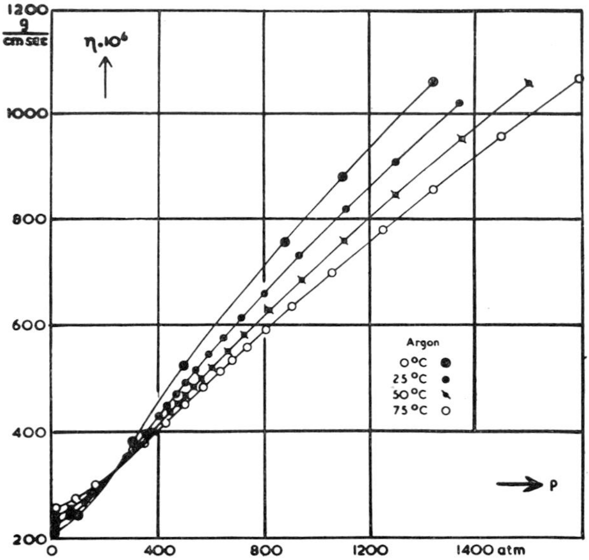

Fig. 11. Viscosity of argon vs. pressure.

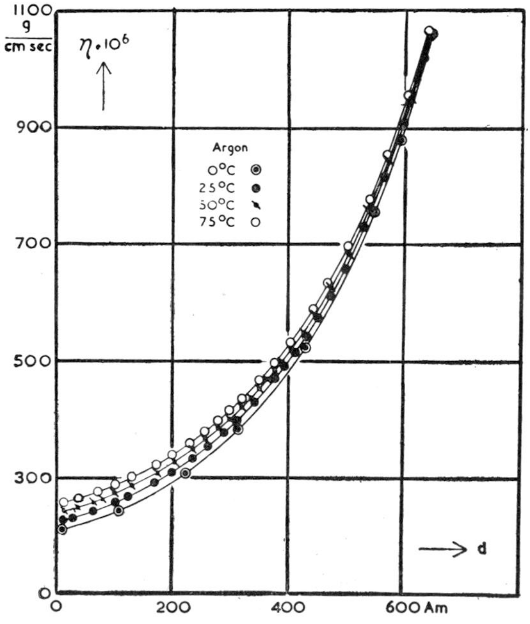

Fig. 12. Viscosity of argon vs. density.

that at temperatures just above critical the curves have a maximum near the critical density ($\varrho_c = 237$ Am.). This is more pronounced in the density-dependence (Fig. 14). This phenomenon is more evident at 31.10°, 32.20°, and 34.60°C and less at 40°C. Although the maxima in the η-isotherms occur only very near the critical temperature, the behavior is similar to the λ vs. density curves of argon. In the critical region, however, little precision can be ascribed to the viscosity data, a consequence of the large density gradient in the capillary during

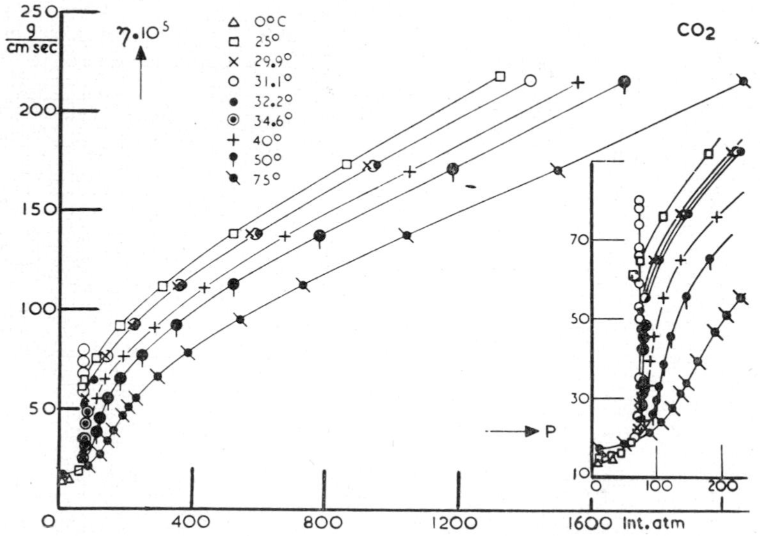

Fig. 13. Viscosity of carbon dioxide vs. pressure.

measurement due to the pressure difference which causes the gas flow through the capillary. Nevertheless, there is no doubt that the experiments give an increase of viscosity in this region. Evidently these effects are connected with the attractive forces between molecules, forces which are responsible for the occurrence of the critical point.

At the moment, measurements of the thermal conductivity of carbon dioxide in the same temperature and density region are in progress. Definite results cannot yet be reported but preliminary measurements confirm that λ increases rapidly at densities near the coexistence region. From these experiments it may be concluded that the influence of the proximity of the critical region results in an increase in the transport coefficients. Comparison of thermal conductivity and viscosity data of argon at the same temperature indicates that this influence upon λ is greater than upon η, in accordance with the relation of λ both with η and specific heat, which itself goes through a maximum in the mentioned region. This may illustrate the importance of the present ex-

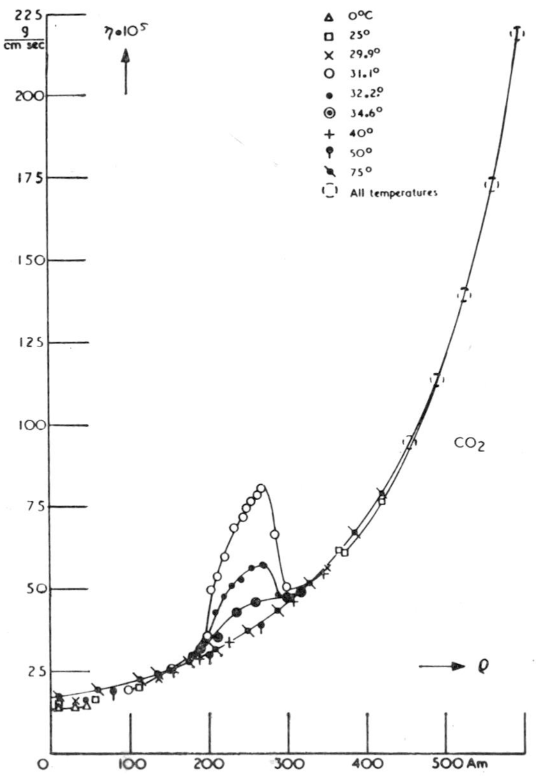

Fig. 14. Viscosity of carbon dioxide vs. density.

periments on the thermal conductivity of carbon dioxide and of other gases near their critical point.

Further research will give more information about the dependence of transport properties upon the gas state. This may lead to a better understanding of the contribution of the different modes of transfer in relation to the state of the gas.

References

(1) S. Chapman and T. C. Cowling, *The Mathematical Theory of Non-uniform Gases*, Cambridge Univ. Press, London, 1939.

(2) A. Michels and A. Botzen, *Physica*, **18**, 605 (1952).

(3) A. Michels and R. O. Gibson, *Proc. Roy. Soc.* (*London*), **A134**, 288 (1931).

(4) A. Michels and A. Botzen, *Physica*, **19**, 585 (1953).

(5) A. Michels, A. C. J. Schipper and W. H. Rintoul, *Physica*, **19**, 1011 (1953).

(6) A. Michels, A. Botzen, A. S. Friedman and J. V. Sengers, *Physica*, **22**, 121 (1956).

(7) A. Michels, A. Botzen and W. Schuurman, *Physica*, **20** 1141 (1954).

(8) A. Michels, A. Botzen, and W. Schuurman, *Physica*, **23**, 95 (1957).

APPLICATION OF KIRKWOOD'S FORMALISM TO HEAT CONDUCTION IN COMPRESSED ARGON

J. V. SENGERS and S. MACHLUP, *Van der Waals-laboratorium, Gemeente Universiteit, Amsterdam, The Netherlands*

Abstract

Kirkwood's theory for the transport properties of fluids [1] gives a formula for calculating transport coefficients if one knows (1) the radial distribution function $g(r)$ and (2) the friction constant ζ which appears in the "Brownian movement" description of molecular motion. The heat conductivity λ can be expressed as a sum of a pure kinetic energy transport term λ_K and a potential energy term λ_V which takes account of transport due to intermolecular forces. Using published radial distribution functions [2] and an approximation for the friction constant, λ has been calculated for argon at densities up to 770 Amagat at 0° and 75° C. At temperatures so high above critical only the first maximum in $g(r)$ turns out to be important, so that the approximation in which $g(r)$ is an exponential function of the form $g(r_0)$ exp $[-V(r)/kT]$ introduces little error.

The resulting λ's differ greatly from experimental heat conductivities; they are too low by as much as a factor 3. To investigate whether this discrepancy is due to a fundamental inadequacy of the theory or simply to a bad estimate of ζ, the ratio $\lambda_K/(\lambda_K+\lambda_V)$ (which is independent of ζ) has been compared with the same ratio calculated on the basis of the Chapman-Enskog theory [3] at low densities. Another possibility of eliminating direct calculation of the friction constant is offered by comparison with viscosity.

The purpose of this communication is, first, to present some results of calculations of heat conductivity using the Kirkwood theory. We shall see that they disagree with experiment, and shall discuss attempts to find the source of the discrepancy. It should be remarked that this is a preliminary report; some of these calculations are still in progress.

The statistical mechanical theory of transport processes in fluids due to Professor Kirkwood and his co-workers is a theory intended for high densities. Transport equations are derived from pure statistical mechanics; i.e., self-contained equations for the lower order distribution functions, equations analogous to the Fokker-Planck equation in the theory of the Brownian motion, are derived from the Liouville equation. The derivation rests on approximations which one expects to be bad at low densities.

If each molecule is considered as performing Brownian motion due to interaction with its neighbors, it will obey the Langevin equation:

$$\frac{d\mathbf{p}}{dt} + \frac{\zeta}{m}\mathbf{p} = \mathbf{G}.$$

G is the fluctuating force due to the other molecules. Note that the damping force on the left is proportional to the velocity: The existence of a friction constant ζ which is independent of the velocity is one of the simplifying assumptions of the theory.

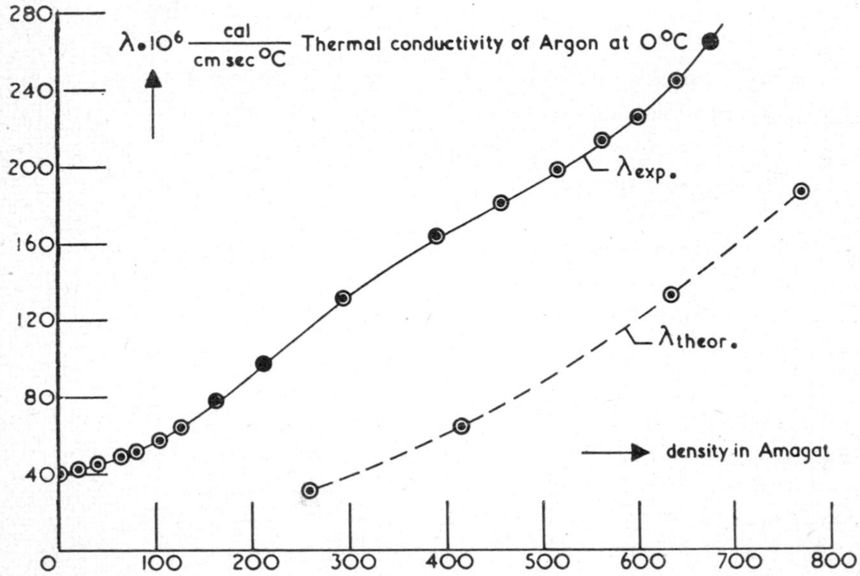

Fig. 1.

Another simplifying assumption even more fundamental to the theory is also connected with the existence of the friction constant: ζ is expressed in terms of molecular variables as an integral over a time interval τ. This integral must possess a plateau value for τ long enough so that there is negligible correlation between the fluctuating forces **G** separated by a time interval τ. The existence of such a plateau value for the friction constant ζ is a fundamental assumption of the theory. Furthermore, there is the assumption that the friction tensor of a pair of molecules can be written in terms of the scalar friction constant for one molecule.

More and more experimental data are becoming available on heat conductivity in gases at high densities. In the preceding paper, Professor Michels reported some of these results. However, at the densities and temperatures for which we have calculated heat conductivity, the data do not agree well with experiment.

Figure 1 shows the results for argon. The critical density of argon is 286 Amagat, the critical temperature 150°K. So we are in the range of liquid densities, but far above liquid temperatures. The heat conductivity has been calculated at four densities, at both 0° (shown) and 75°C. The calculated values are between 1/3 and 1/2 of the experimental ones. It should be mentioned that we were not looking for the detailed structure; our calculations were not that accurate. For example, we neglected the secondary maxima of the radial distribution function. However, the results are not very sensitive to changes in the radial distribution function. The terms we have neglected might change the results by about 2 %.

The question now arises as whether the theory is invalid in this range, or whether it is only our friction constant ζ that is poorly calculated. The weakest part of the calculation is the evaluation of ζ: two different approximations give results differing by factors of 2.* Therefore it may be useful to check that part of the theory which is independent of the *values* of the friction constant. As an attempt in this direction we have investigated an expression that is independent of ζ: the *fraction* of the heat conductivity which is purely kinetic energy transport.

If one writes the pure statistical mechanical expression for heat transport, it separates naturally into two parts that we may call "kinetic" and "potential," so that we write thermal conductivity λ as $\lambda = \lambda_K + \lambda_V$. On the one hand, as a molecule moves, it carries its kinetic energy with it, giving the contribution λ_K. On the other hand, the interactions between molecules also provide a mechanism for heat conduction, giving the contribution λ_V. The second mechanism is, of course, the dominant one in solids—the phonon mechanism—whereas the pure kinetic contribution is dominant in dilute gases.

In dense gases both are needed. At the critical density and above, the potential contribution λ_V is more important. The following are the

* We used the formula given by Kirkwood, Buff, and Green, *J. Chem. Phys.*, **17**, 988 (1949), Eq. (40).

Kirkwood theory expressions for λ_K and λ_V. Note that they are both inversely proportional to the friction constant ζ:

$$\lambda_K = \frac{kT}{\zeta}\frac{Nk}{2v}\left[1+\frac{T}{3v}\left(\frac{\partial v}{\partial T}\right)_p\right],$$

$$\lambda_V = \frac{kT}{\zeta}\frac{\pi N^2}{3v^2}\left[\int_0^\infty r^3\left(r\frac{dV}{dr}-V\right)g\frac{d}{dr}\left(\frac{\partial \ln g}{\partial T}\right)_p dr\right.$$
$$\left.+\int_0^\infty r^3\left(3V-r\frac{dV}{dr}\right)\left(\frac{\partial g}{\partial T}\right)_p dr\right].$$

The thermal expansion coefficient needed for λ_K is obtained directly from the compressibility isotherms, as are the parameters in λ_V. The pair distribution function $g(r)$ comes in only in λ_V (and, of course, into the evaluation of the friction constant). For a Lennard-Jones potential, $g(r)$ has been calculated by Kirkwood, Lewinson, and Alder.[2] It is an oscillatory function, with one large maximum at a distance corresponding roughly to the molecular diameter and smaller maxima further out, indicating short-range order. At temperatures much above critical only the first maximum gives an appreciable contribution to the integral, so that we were able to use an approximation which is good near the molecular diameter r_0:

$$g(r) = g(r_0)\exp[-V(r)/kT].$$

The value of $g(r_0)$ we took from Kirkwood, Lewinson, and Alder, while the potential $V(r)$ is the Lennard-Jones 6—12 potential with the proper constants for argon. As mentioned above, this approximation introduces an error of about 2 %.

To obtain an expression independent of ζ, we have plotted the ratio of the kinetic part of heat conductivity to the total, and compared this ratio with the results of the Enskog theory (Fig. 2).

The Enskog theory for dense gases is just the kinetics of hard spheres. It is reasonably good at low densities and quite bad at high. To compare the two theories we have split the Enskog λ into kinetic and potential contributions:

$$\lambda_K = (\lambda_0/\chi)(1+0.6\,b\varrho\chi),$$
$$\lambda_V = (\lambda_0/\chi)(0.6b\varrho\chi+0.7574b^2\varrho^2\chi^2).$$

Both theories, of course, have to give unity at low densities, where λ

is entirely kinetic. The curve of the ratio $\lambda_K/(\lambda_K+\lambda_V)$ calculated using the Kirkwood theory is certainly much steeper at low densities than physical intuition leads us to expect. Possibly the regions of validity of the two theories do not overlap at all.

$$\frac{\lambda_k}{\lambda_k+\lambda_v} \text{ Fraction of pure kinetic thermal conductivity} \qquad \text{Argon } 0^{\circ}\text{C}$$

$$\text{Formulas of Enskog:} \quad \lambda_k = \frac{\lambda_o}{x}\left(1 + 0.6\,b\rho x\right)$$

$$\lambda_v = \frac{\lambda_o}{x}\left(0.6\,b\rho x + 0.7574\,b^2\rho^2 x^2\right)$$

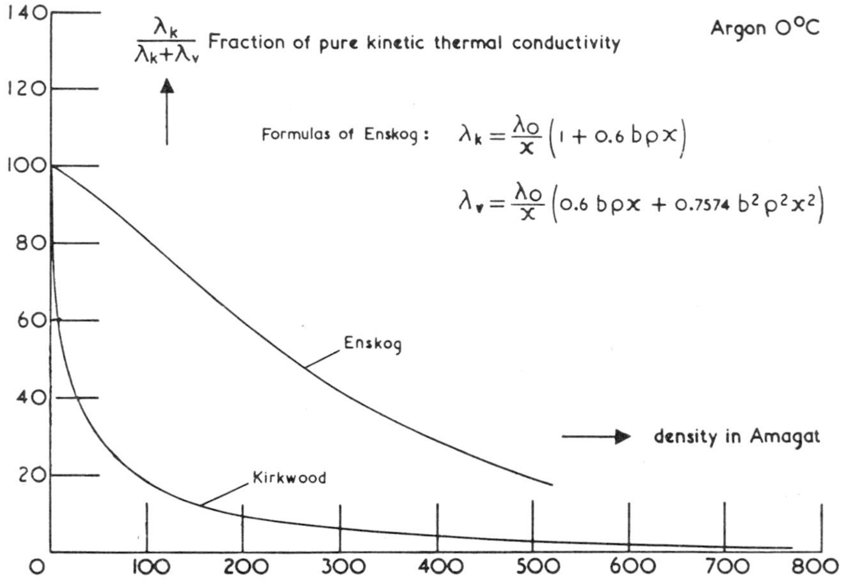

Fig. 2.

Another way of eliminating the friction constant is to compare the Kirkwood theory results for heat conductivity with those for viscosity. In heat conductivity, the friction constant came in as a pure proportionality constant. In viscosity, it enters in the form

$$\eta = (A/\zeta)+B\zeta,$$

that is, in the denominator in the kinetic term and in the numerator in the potential term.

Comparing the expressions for heat conductivity and viscosity gives a relation between the two quantities which is independent of the friction constant ζ, and which can be compared directly with experiment. This may lead to a clearer understanding of the source of the inadequacy. These calculations are now in progress.

We should like to express our gratitude to Dr. C. A. ten Seldam for his helpful advice in this investigation.

References

(1) J. G. Kirkwood, *J. Chem. Phys.*, **14**, 180, 347 (1946).
R. W. Zwanzig, J. G. Kirkwood, I. Oppenheim, and B. J. Alder, *J. Chem. Phys.*, **22**, 783 (1954).

(2) J. G. Kirkwood, V. A. Lewinson, and B. J. Alder, *J. Chem. Phys.*, **20**, 929 (1952).

(3) S. Chapman and T. C. Cowling, *The Mathematical Theory of Non-uniform Gases*, Cambridge Univ. Press, London, 1939.

THE THERMAL CONDUCTIVITY OF IMPERFECT GASES

F. G. WAELBROECK, *Laboratoire de Chimie-Physique, Université Libre de Bruxelles, and Institut Belge des Hautes Pressions, Belgium*

Abstract

It is not possible, by any existing theory, to predict the variation of the thermal conductivity coefficient λ with pressure in the whole temperature range. Reasonably simple models may be used in two limiting cases: (1) At "high" temperatures (above the Boyle point), the attractive intermolecular forces may be neglected; the molecules may be treated as hard spheres, as was done by Enskog. (2) At "low" temperatures (boiling point and below), the attractive intermolecular forces predominate; the gas is practically a mixture of monomers and dimers, and one may use the thermodynamics of irreversible phenomena to calculate the increase of λ resulting from this dissociation reaction. Waelbroeck, Lafleur, and Prigogine have considered this case, and attempted to evaluate roughly the contribution of the attractive forces at higher temperatures and pressures. A short discussion of their results is given.

The elementary kinetic theory of gases predicts that the thermal conductivity coefficient λ should be independent of pressure.* It is well known that this is only a first approximation, and that λ increases slowly with pressure. Enskog[1, 2] has shown that this variation should be expected, even in a hard sphere gas (with purely repulsive interactions). His result depends on a single parameter, the equivalent hard sphere diameter of the molecule, which can be evaluated from other experimental data (equation of state, viscosity). At relatively high temperatures (above the Boyle point), the depth of the minimum in the intermolecular potential curve is much smaller than the energy of thermal agitation kT, and the intermolecular forces are essentially repulsive. In this region, the increase of λ predicted by the Enskog equation agrees remarkably well with the experimental values, up to very high densities.[3]

At lower temperatures, the observed variations[4] do not agree with the prediction of Enskog. It has generally been stated that this is due

* We assume that the pressure is sufficiently high and that the effects characteristic of the Knudsen domain may be neglected.

to the attractive intermolecular forces, but, as far as we know, the order of magnitude of this possible effect has not been evaluated. We wish to discuss here the results of some rough calculations[5] that have been carried out to determine this order of magnitude.

In a dissociated gas (N_2O_4, I_2),[6] when the chemical reaction rate is not too slow, the concentrations of the dissociated (monomers) and undissociated (dimers) particles tend toward equilibrium along the temperature gradient. This leads to diffusion of the dimers from the cold to the hot parts of the apparatus, where they dissociate, absorbing the heat of dissociation, and of the monomers toward the cold parts, where they recombine with a liberation of energy. This "circulation" effect increases the heat flux and thermal conductivity. In the case of N_2O_4 about 50 % dissociated, the circulation effect is calculated[6] and observed[7] to be approximately 10 times larger than the normal (kinetic, rotational, and vibrational energy exchange) heat transfer.

At sufficiently low temperatures (boiling point and lower), we can think of a real gas as a perfect mixture of monomers and dimers in chemical equilibrium (trimers and larger complexes may be neglected, since their concentration is negligible even in the vicinity of the condensation pressure). In this first approximation, we may use the equation which has been deduced by the thermodynamics of irreversible phenomena[6c] for the heat transferred by the relative circulation of dimers and monomers:

$$\lambda_r' = Dk\left(\frac{r_{pT}^{(0)}}{kT}\right)^2 \frac{n_1 n_2 (n_1+n_2)}{(n_1+2n_2)^2} \tag{1}$$

where D is the diffusion coefficient, k is the Boltzmann constant, r_{pT}^0 is the heat of the dissociation reaction, at constant temperature and pressure, and n_1 and n_2 are the molecular concentrations of monomers and dimers.

If we use the equation of state to evaluate the molecular concentrations n_1 and n_2 of the monomers and dimers, and assume that the energy of reaction is equal to the depth of the minimum in the Lennard-Jones 6—12 interaction curve, we calculate[5] by means of Eq. (1) that the circulation effect λ_r represents about 6 % of λ for argon at its boiling point, whereas the Enskog effect is of the order of 1 %.

If, at constant average density, the temperature is increased, the Enskog effect is hardly modified, whereas the contribution of the circulation effect decreases sharply (both n_2 and $(r_{pT}/kT)^2$ decrease). At atmospheric pressure, the two effects should be approximately equal at the critical temperature, and the circulation effect should be vanishingly small at the Boyle temperature and above.

When the pressure is increased in the neighborhood of the critical temperature, the contributions of the trimers and of the larger aggregates become important. If one assumes[5] (i) that the evolution equation for the distribution function f_γ of a γ-mer ($\gamma = 1, 2, 3, \cdots, n$) can be written $Df_\gamma/Dt = -(f_\gamma - f_\gamma^0)/\tau_\gamma$, where f_γ^0 is the equilibrium distribution function of the γ-mer, D/Dt is the hydrodynamic time derivative and τ_γ is a characteristic time (relaxation time), (ii) that the stationary state is established and that there are no external forces acting on the molecules, (iii) that the deviations from local equilibrium are small, and (iv) that the relaxation times of the various γ-mers are approximately equal, one obtains

$$\lambda_r = \frac{\tau}{mT}\left[\sum_\gamma \frac{n_\gamma r_{pT}^{(\gamma)2}}{\gamma} - \frac{1}{n}\left(\sum_\gamma n_\gamma r_{pT}^{(\gamma)}\right)^2\right], \tag{2}$$

where n_γ and $r_{pT}^{(\gamma)}$ are the molecular concentration and heat of formation of a complex of γ particles and $n = n_1 + n_2 + n_3 + \cdots + n_\gamma$ is the total number of particles in a cubic centimeter.

It appears (Eq. (2)) that the contribution to λ_r of the γ species is roughly proportional to its concentration and to the square of its heat of formation. Thus small quantities of rather large complexes, whose contribution to the equation of state would be negligible, may contribute appreciably to the thermal conductivity because of a large heat of formation. Moreover, the energy carried by a γ-mer depends on its shape: for example, a triangular trimer, with three internal links, carries a much larger energy than a linear trimer, with but two bonds. The additional thermal conductivity λ_r thus depends strongly on the assumed representation of the gas, and about the only conclusion which we can draw from our calculations, based on various rough models, is that the circulation effect must lead, in the critical region, to an increase of λ with pressure which is of the same order of magnitude as the Enskog effect.

It seems worth while to make a few remarks concerning the validity of the procedure we have followed:

(1) We have considered the gas as a perfect mixture of stable mono-,

di-, tri-, · · ·, γ-mers in equilibrium with each other. This assumption is roughly valid when the depth of the minimum in the interaction curve is larger than kT.[8] At the ebullition temperature of argon, ε/kT is only about 1.3. We expect that a rather important part (but not all) of the gaseous imperfections is due to the existence of physically stable dimers. As the temperature is raised, the model breaks down, particularly when only dimers are considered, since the part of the cluster integral due to the physically stable dimers becomes less important. At these temperatures, the contributions to λ of the attractive forces could be split into two parts: the first is the circulation of the energy of formation of the stable dimers which has been discussed above; the second results from the imperfections of the thus defined mixture of monomers and stable dimers: whenever a particle crosses over from the hot to the cold region, or *vice versa*, both its kinetic and potential energy change.

(2) At higher pressures and temperatures, another difficulty arises through the definition of the "stable" trimers and larger aggregates. There is no ambiguity in the definition of a stable dimer which is composed of two monomers which cannot separate without the intervention of a third body; but a trimer could have an appreciable life time, although its total energy (spread on the various internal bonds) might be larger than the energy of dissociation of one of these bonds. A rigorous calculation should thus take into account the mechanisms of dissociation of the various γ-mer species.

(3) As a first approximation, we have considered that the Enskog and circulation effects are additive. This seems justified, since the combination of two molecules to give a dimer is, most probably, a ternary collision phenomenon, i.e., a rather rare occurrence, whereas practically every other (binary) collision is quasi-elastic, and should contribute to the Enskog effect.

References

(1) D. Enskog, *Kgl. Svenska Vetenskapsakad. Handl.*, **63**, No. 4 (1922).

(2) Cf. also J. O. Hirshfelder, C. F. Curtiss, and R. B. Bird, *Molecular Theory of Gases and Liquids*, Wiley, New York, 1954.

(3) A. Michels and A. Botzen, *Physica*, **19**, 585 (1953).

(4) A. Uhlir, *J. Chem. Phys.*, **20**, 463 (1952), A. Michels, A. Botzen, A. S. Friedman and J. Sengers, *Physica*, **22**, 121 (1956).

(5) F. Waelbroeck, S. Lafleur, and I. Prigogine, *Physica*, **21**, 667 (1955).

(6) (a) W. Nernst, *Boltzmann Festschrift,* 504 (1904).
(b) P. A. M. Dirac, *Proc. Cambridge Phil. Soc.*, **22**, 132 (1924).
(c) I. Prigogine and R. Buess, *Bull. classe sci. Acad. roy. Belg.*, **38**, 711, 852 (1952).
(d) J. Meixner, *Z. Naturforsch.*, **7A**, 553 (1952).
(e) E. U. Franck, *Z. physik. Chem.*, **201**, 16 (1952).
(f) J. O. Hirshfelder, University of Wisconsin WIS. ONR. 18; WIS. ONR. 22; and University of Wisconsin C.M. 880 (1956).
(7) Magnanini and Malagnini, *Nuovo cimento,* **6**, 352 (1897).
(8) T. L. Hill, *J. Chem. Phys.*, **23**, 617 (1955).

MEASUREMENTS ON THERMAL DIFFUSION COMBINED WITH ORDINARY DIFFUSION IN GAS MIXTURES

A. VAN ITTERBEEK, *Physical Laboratory, Louvain, Belgium Centre d'Études Scientifiques du Froid, Louvain, Belgium*

Résumé

Des mesures ont été faites sur la thermodiffusion des mélanges gazeux H_2—He, H_2—O_2 et H_2—N_2. La variation de la concentration est déterminée à partir des mesures sur la vitesse du son. Partant d'une méthode formulée par Jones et Furry des mesures ont été faites sur la variation de la vitesse du son en fonction du temps, causée par suite de la variation de la concentration. Nous sommes parvenus à déterminer ainsi le coefficient de diffusion D_{12} pour les différents mélanges en fonction de la température. Un bon accord est obtenu avec les valeurs calculées à partir des équations publiées dans le livre de Hirschfelder.

During our earlier work[1] with gas mixtures at low temperatures we were interested mainly in pure thermal diffusion, and therefore determined change in concentration ($\Delta\gamma$) as a function of concentration (γ) at a fixed temperature interval. We also determined change of $\Delta\gamma$ as a function of temperature. From these experiments and using the equations

$$\Delta\gamma = k_T \ln (T_1/T_2) \tag{1}$$

or

$$\Delta\gamma = R_T \gamma \cdot (1-\gamma) \cdot \ln (T_1/T_2) \tag{2}$$

we could obtain values for the thermal diffusion ratio $k_T = D_T/D_{12}$, and compare these with the results of theoretical calculations. The experimental procedure consisted in measuring change in concentration from measurements of change in the viscosity coefficient, as represented in Figure 1. The viscosity apparatus was at room temperature (T_1) and the large volume at low temperatures (T_2). A handicap in this kind of measurement is that we do not obtain separate values for the thermal diffusion coefficient and the ordinary diffusion coefficient. Because of the experimental equipment used, the method is, rather, a static one

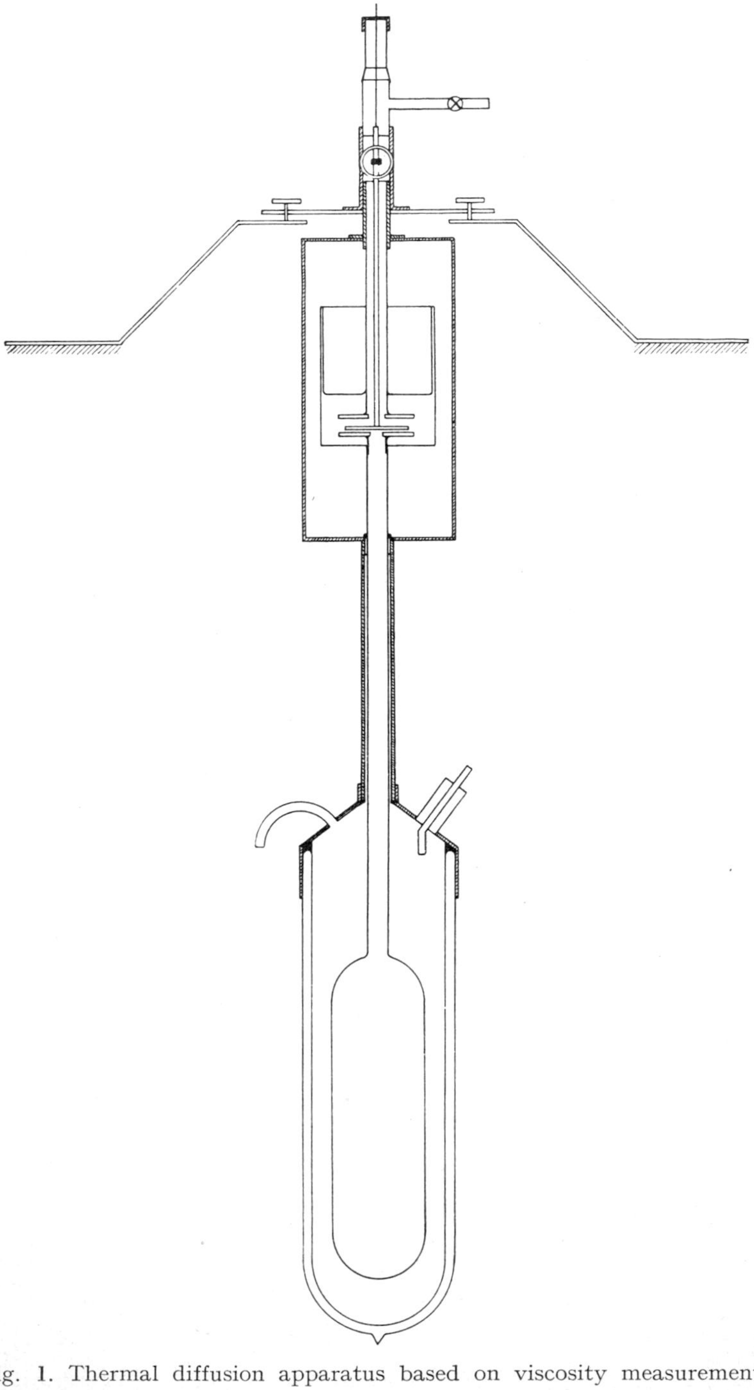

Fig. 1. Thermal diffusion apparatus based on viscosity measurements.

which only permits determining $\Delta\gamma$ (for $t = \infty$) and not $(\Delta\gamma)_t$ as a function of time.

For a few years now we have succeeded in seriously improving our accuracy by making use of ultrasonics (velocity of sound measurements) to determine the variation in concentration. The velocity of sound W in a gas mixture is given by means of the equation:

$$W^2 = \frac{C_p^{(1)} \cdot \gamma + C_p^{(2)}(1-\gamma)}{C_v^{(1)} \cdot \gamma + C_v^{(2)}(1-\gamma)} \cdot \frac{R_M T}{M_1 \cdot \gamma + M_2(1-\gamma)}.$$

Velocity can be determined with great accuracy, and the concentration can be determined with the same accuracy. In the new apparatus the viscosity cell used earlier is replaced by an acoustical interferometer, as can be seen from Figure 2.

The new experimental method also has a second advantage: because the velocity can be measured very quickly, the change in concentration can be measured practically instantaneously and the variation followed as a function of time. As is well known from this kind of experiment the ordinary diffusion coefficient can be determined. The theory of this method has been indicated by Clark Jones and Furry[2] and is based on the following equation

$$(\Delta\gamma)_t = \Delta\gamma_{t=\infty}(1-e^{-t/\tau}), \tag{2}$$

$(\Delta\gamma)_t$ being the instantaneous change in concentration at moment t and τ being the relaxation time. For τ we have

$$\tau = \frac{N_1 N_2}{N_1+N_2} \cdot \frac{L}{n \cdot D_{12} \cdot S} \cdot \frac{T_2}{\Delta T} \ln \frac{T_1}{T_2}, \tag{3}$$

N_1 and N_2 being, respectively, the numbers of molecules, in volumes V_1 and V_2 and n being the molecular density in volume V_2.

Eq. (3) can also be written as

$$\tau = \frac{V_1 V_2}{T_1} \cdot \left(\frac{V_1}{T_1} + \frac{V_2}{T_2}\right)^{-1} \cdot \frac{L}{D_{12}} \cdot \frac{T_2}{S \cdot \Delta T} \cdot \ln \frac{T_1}{T_2}, \tag{4}$$

where L and S length and section of the connecting tube between volumes V_1 and V_2, $\Delta T = T_1 - T_2$, and D_{12} = ordinary diffusion coefficient corresponding to the average temperature:

$$\bar{T} = \frac{T_1 \cdot T_2}{T_1+T_2} \ln \frac{T_2}{T_1}.$$

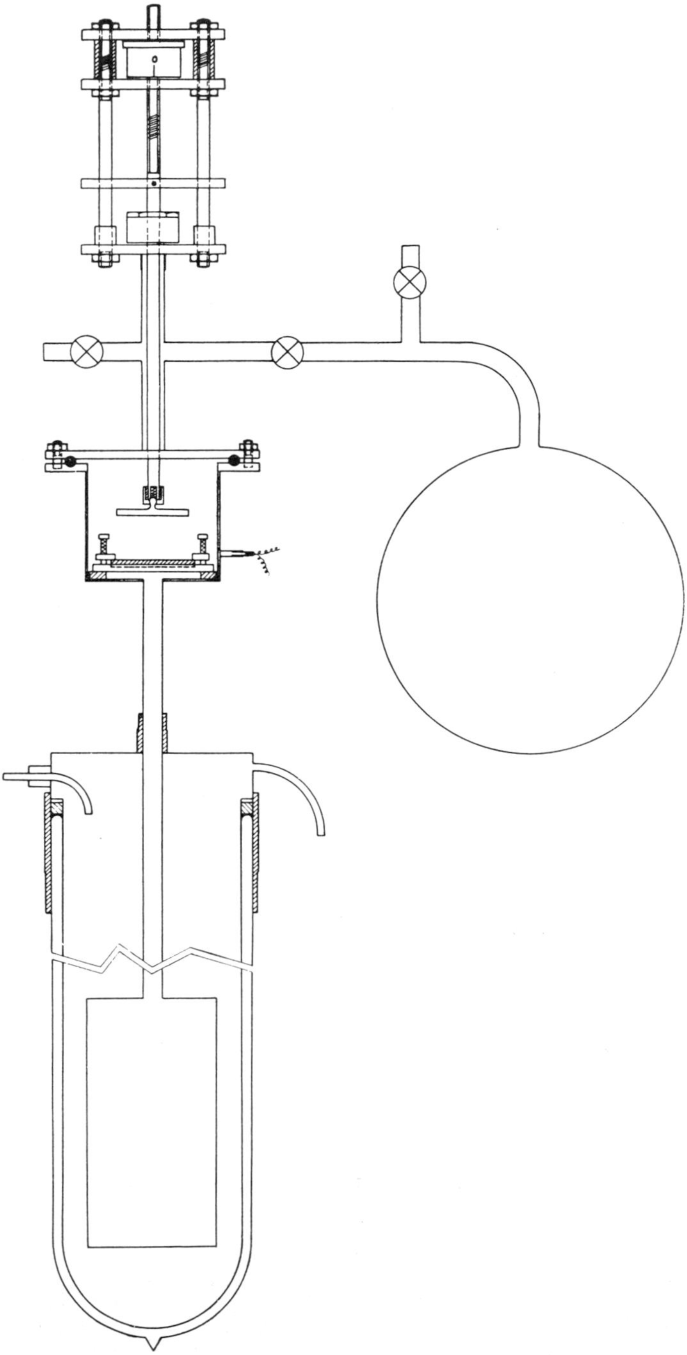

Fig. 2. Thermal diffusion apparatus based on ultrasonic measurements.

Measurements were carried out on H_2—He, H_2—N_2, and H_2—O_2 at a concentration of approximately 50 %.

In Figure 3, an example is given of our measurements in H_2—He mixture. In this figure three curves are drawn together: curve (1) represents the change in velocity as a function of t; curve (2) represents $\Delta\gamma$ as a function of time; and curve (3) gives $\ln [1-(\Delta\gamma/\Delta\gamma_\infty)]$ as a function of time. From this figure we see that for curve (3) a straight line is obtained which agrees with the Clark Jones and Furry theory.

The results of our measurements together with our calculations are given in Table I.

TABLE I

Mixtures	(T_1, low temp.) T_2 °K	$\bar{T}$, °K	$\tau \times 10^{-3}$, sec	D_{12} (exp.) cm²/sec	(D_{12}) (theor.) cm²/sec
H_2—He (50 %)	90.1	153	8.36	0.421	0.518
	77.3	137	8.84	0.343	0.429
	20.3	58	9.48	0.093	0.098
	17.1	52	9.52	0.076	0.078
H_2—He (35 %)	77.3	137	8.77	0.346	0.429
H_2—N_2 (50 %)	90.1	153	17.0	0.207	0.237
	90.1	153	16.8	0.209	0.237
	90.1	153	16.9	0.208	0.237
	77.3	137	19.6	0.173	0.194
H_2—O_2 (50 %)	90.1	153	16.4	0.215	0.250
	80.1	142	18.2	0.174	0.218

In the last column of this table are given the values of the ordinary diffusion coefficient D_{12}, which we calculated using the equations and the empirical data given in Hirschfelder's book. A comparison between experimental and calculated values shows that the agreement is not so bad.

The measurements will now be continued for other mixtures.

We take this opportunity to express our thanks to the Belgian Ministry of Education for financial aid during these experiments.

We also express our thanks to Mr. J. Nihoul for his help with the measurements.

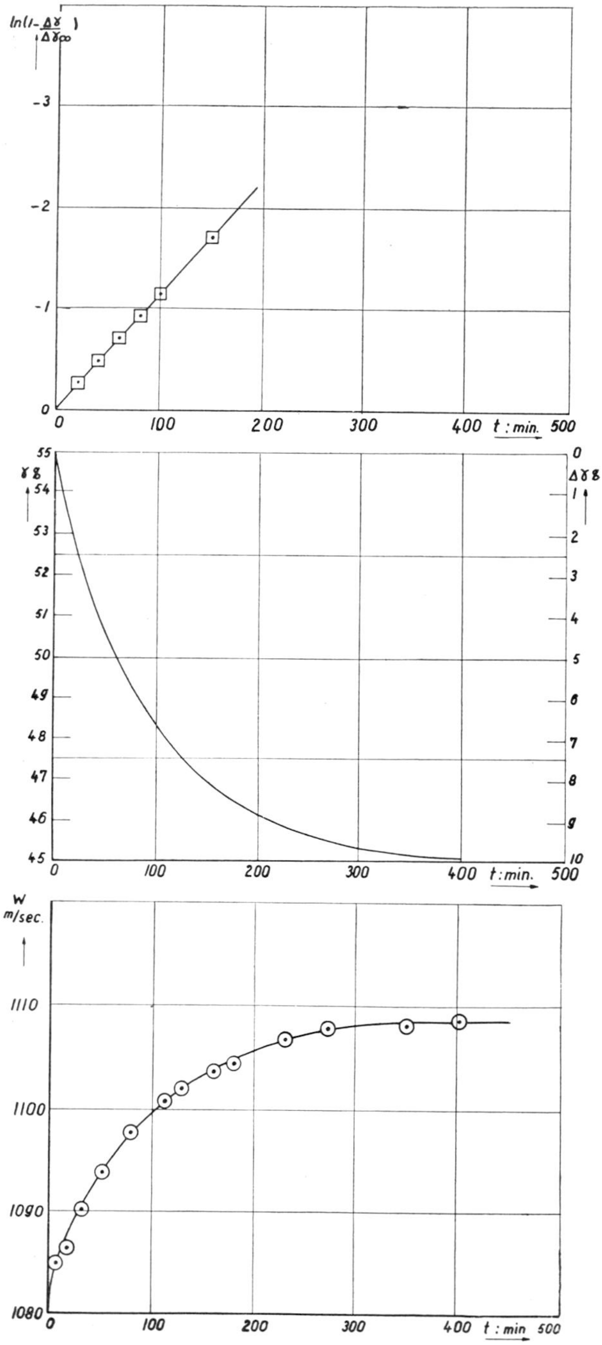

Fig. 3. Thermal diffusion in H_2—He mixtures ($T_2 = 20°K$; $= 55\%$ He).

References

(1) A. van Itterbeek, O. van Paemel, and J. van Lierde, *Physica,* **13**, 231 (1947). A. van Itterbeek and A. de Troyer, *Physica, II,* 329 (1950). A. de Troyer, A. van Itterbeek, and G. J. van den Berg, *Physica,* **16**, 669 (1950). A. van Itterbeek, G. Forrez and P. Mariens, *Physica,* **19**, 525 (1953).

(2) R. Clark Jones and W. H. Furry, *Revs. Mod. Phys.,* **18**, 151 (1941).

Discussion XIII

R. Haase: I think it can be shown that C_p—C_V (as well as C_p) tends toward infinity if one approaches the critical point.

M. Fierz (*to A. Michels*): Near the critical point one has long-range correlated density fluctuations. Could one not guess from this fact that the conduction of heat must become big near the critical point?

L. Van Hove (*to M. Fierz*): Since critical fluctuations are not effective in transporting energy, one does not see how they would make the heat conduction infinite under critical conditions. It further deserves mention that the energy transfer in very slow neutron scattering by a liquid or gas near critical conditions is strongly influenced by the mechanism of heat transport; one might eventually find there another experimental approach to this problem.

I. Prigogine (*to A. Michels*): I wish to draw attention to the simple model which has been developed by Dr. Waelbroeck in which the attractive forces are taken into account in a rough but perhaps not unreasonable way by the circulation of molecular clusters. Using such a model, one can at least qualitatively understand the abnormal behavior of thermal conditions near the critical temperature. The behavior of viscosity is more mysterious. It may be that one should take into account the bulk viscosity of the molecular clusters.

A. van Itterbeek: We carried out in Leiden measurements on the viscosity of helium gas as a function of pressure at the boiling point of liquid helium. If there is a pressure-dependency this must be very small ($\pm$ 1 %). On the other hand we measured the change in heat conductivity as a function of pressure and found a change of $\pm$ 5 %, so that we can not very well understand these measurements.

M. Green (*to J. G. Kirkwood*): I would like to point out that λ/c_v can be considered to be the diffusion constant for energy transport. If λ is finite at the critical point, this means that $\langle \Delta x^2 \rangle$ is no longer proportional to Δt, where Δx is the fluctuation of quantity of energy in time Δt.

J. G. Kirkwood (*to J. V. Sengers*): The decrepancy between theory and experiment in the heat conductivity of argon is precisely what would be expected at intermediate densities. The Brownian motion approximation must be inaccurate at low densities, but becomes increasingly adequate at high densities, as is evident in Sengers' calculations.

J. V. Sengers (*to J. G. Kirkwood*): In applying the equations of Enskog for transport coefficients to a real gas one can use a molecular diameter σ and a factor χ, accounting for the change of the collision probability obtained by different methods. Attention may be drawn to the fact that such methods give different results, so that at least at intermediate densities one cannot decide whether the theory of Enskog predicts values larger or smaller than the experimental coefficients.

J. E. Mayer (*to F. Waelbroeck*): I would like to ask Mr. Waelbroeck if he has not really discussed this contribution to heat conduction in terms of dimers and polymers rather than in terms of clusters of two and higher? I mean my question in the sense that it is sometimes convenient to reserve the terms "number of pair clusters" for the number of pairs close together minus the number which could be close in a random distribution, whereas the number of dimers would be the total number of pairs closer than some arbitrary chosen distance. The distinction between higher clusters and the corresponding polymers is similar. If, as I believe, Mr. Waelbroeck has used the concept of physical dimers and polymers, rather than clusters, in the above sense, I would like to ask if he has contemplated the possibility of translating the concept into clusters? This would have the advantage that the clusters do behave like a perfect gas mixture, and that the necessary integrals are determinable in principle, at least, from the equation of state of the gas.

F. Waelbroeck (*to J. E. Mayer*): The cluster theory should certainly give a more accurate prediction of the "circulation" effect λ_r. One must, however, consider the fact that the stable and unstable clusters contribute to λ_r by two different mechanisms: the stable clusters "circulate," whereas the unstable clusters lead to gaseous imperfections, which also affect the thermal conductivity. Large clusters, however, are mostly metastable (i.e., their total internal energy, spread out on the various bonds, is larger than the dissociation energy of one of the bonds), and an accurate prediction of λ_r at higher pressures, by the cluster theory, or by any theory, requires an evaluation of the life time of these clusters, to decide which of them should be considered as stable, and which unstable.

S. Machlup (*to G. Careri*): With reference to calculations of activation energies such as Dr. Nardi is engaged in, do you have suggestions for a suitable interatomic potential?

G. Careri (*to S. Machlup*): It is difficult in a liquid metal to calculate the activation energy accurately enough, due to the incertitude on the central forces one should assume.

D. K. C. MacDonald (*to G. Careri*): I recall a paper, presented by Nachtrieb of Chicago at the Gordon Research Conference on Metals last year, on self-diffusion in solid + liquid sodium. My recollection was that in that case he was able to put forward an explanation for the *apparently* large change in diffusion activation energy on melting in terms of the relatively large fraction of vacancies generated at melting (a few per cent, I believe). However, I do not remember any details off hand.

G. Careri (*to D. K. C. MacDonald*): Nachtrieb has worked with a small temperature range, so he could not detect any curvature. I remember his explanation was only in terms of the Stokes-Einstein equation.

J. G. Kirkwood: Wang and Corbett at Yale have recently measured the self-diffusion coefficient of argon at 90°K and a pressure of several atmospheres. Their value of 2.1×10^{-5} cm^2/sec is in good agreement with the theoretical value of Kirkwood, 2.6×10^{-5} cm^2/sec.

A. van Itterbeek (*to J. Chanu*): Est-ce que vous n'avez pas pensé à utiliser la méthode de Byr-Jean pour la détermination de la vitesse du son par voie optique? La séparation serait terriblement simplifiée. La méthode expérimentale serait aussi plus simple.

R. Haase (*to J. Chanu*): (1) The formula for the difference in final potentials for two thermal cells containing two salts with a common ion was derived in 1953 (R. Haase, *Trans. Faraday Soc.* **49,** 724(1953)). I am very happy that the simplest possible solution of the problem has been verified: the heat of transport of a given ion, at a given concentration, is approximately independent of the nature of the other ion. (2) Our own measurements (not yet published) on aqueous solutions of KCl show that, in the concentration-dependent part of the heats of transfer, there is a term proportional to $\sqrt{m}$ and a term proportional to m (m being the molarity of the electrolyte), as occurs in the case of activity coefficients. The measurements also show that—at least in this particular system—the terms containing the various entropies of transport (in the sense of Holtan) approximately cancel the terms containing hydration effects, so that the potential difference (per unit temperature gradient) can be calculated from purely thermodynamic quantities. A similar, but not identical statement has already been made by Holtan.

J. Chanu (*to R. Haase and R. Defay*): Nous avons fait des mesures comparatives du potentiel de thermodiffusion stationnaire dans divers chlorures. En particulier le coefficient d'électrode σ dans chaque expérience était le même.

G. Careri (*to K. Compaan*): Do your analyses apply to results of the Urbana (Ill.) group on ionic crystals?

K. Compaan (*to G. Careri*): Very little experimental data have been available to date for a comparison of diffusivity with conductivity in the same crystal; only then can one expect unique results.

DIFFUSION IN A QUASI-CRYSTALLINE LIQUID

G. CARERI* and A. PAOLETTI, *Istituto di Fisica, Università di Roma, Italy*

1. This laboratory has been interested in the experimental determination of the self-diffusion coefficient in some liquid metals, like tin and indium,[1] and in the system 1 % lead in indium.[2] The purpose of this work has been to obtain data for some elements which have been investigated also in the solid state, in order to compare the mechanisms which operate in the two states. The technique consists mainly in the investigation of the penetration rate of the active material in a capillary one-half of which was initially full of active and the remaining one-half of inactive material. From the profile of the penetration curve and the time-dependence, one can determine if the diffusion equation is satisfied and then derive the diffusion coefficient, or if some convection

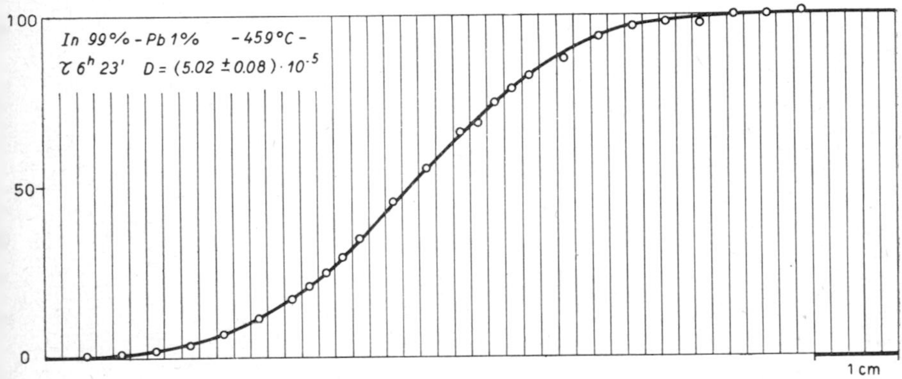

Fig. 1. A typical penetration curve for active lead diffusing in an alloy of 1 % Pb and 99 % In. The ordinates represent activity and the abscissae the position of the section of the capillary.

was superimposed on the molecular diffusion. Since the technique has already been described, no details will be given here. A typical run for active lead diffusing in a 1% Pb-In alloy is shown in Figure 1. The two

* Present address: Istituto di Fisica, Università di Padova.

main differences between the liquid and solid state experiments can be summarized as follows:

(*1*) The apparent activation energy of the liquid is much smaller than that of the solid.

(*2*) In the liquid, there is a small departure from the simple Arrhenius law, which holds well for the solid.

2. These two properties can be used to describe a mechanism of diffusion in the liquid if one accepts a quasi-crystalline model of the liquid state. This model describes well many equilibrium properties of simple liquids, but it is questionable how one may find in this ordered picture of the liquid atom movements which lead to the diffusion of matter more effectively by than in the solid state. It is sound to believe that local microscopic fluctuations of density are possible in the liquid state, due to the easier relaxation of the local structure, which allows movement of one or more atoms. Certainly there is not a unique mechanism for these movements, which can be applied to any liquid under any condition. However for "monatomic" liquids, which are close enough to their melting point to be described fairly well as a blurred copy of the solid, one may hope to use the same treatment as has been applied to the crystal (to the quasi-crystal which represents well the local ordered liquid). In this case, the two basic mechanisms for atom movements are the vacancies and the ring displacements.

If we describe diffusion in the quasi-crystal as a random walk process, and denote by "a" the lattice distance τ the mean time of stay between jumps, and γ a geometric factor, we can use the familiar expression

$$D = \gamma a^2/\tau.$$

Expressions for τ have been derived for simple molecular models which describe a direct interchange of two neighboring atoms, and the jump of one atom into the vacant lattice site. For the sake of brevity we will not give here these expressions and the analysis of the experimental data; but we do call attention to the complete failure of the vacancy mechanism, on the one hand, and to the success of the interchange mechanism, on the other, to describe our experimental data. For the latter mechanism all the experimental points can be obtained by help of only one parameter, this being the height of the potential barrier.

3. A similar analysis has been applied to the new data of the lead-indium system, and the good agreement of the direct interchange mechanism is still preserved; details will soon be published for this and other mixtures which are at present being investigated.

A few words, however, are needed to make clear what this agreement means. We are dealing here with liquids of a particular structure, which are so far removed from their critical point as to make a quasi-crystalline picture of them quite reasonable. It is only for these "ordered" liquids that a simple mechanism like the direct interchange of two neighbors can be thought of as a rough approximation for the many atom movements responsible for the transport of matter in condensed systems.

References

(1) G. Careri and A. Paoletti, *Nuovo cimento,* **2**, 574 (1955).
(2) G. Careri and A. Paoletti, unpublished results.

MESURE DE L'EFFET SORET DANS LES SOLUTIONS IONIQUES

J. CHANU, *Laboratoire de Physique Appliquée du Muséum National d'Histoire Naturelle, Paris, France*

Parmi tous les problèmes que pose l'étude des solutions électrolytiques, ceux qui traitent des phénomènes de diffusion, semblent se situer parmi les plus intéressants quant aux conclusions susceptibles d'en résulter.

La diffusion isotherme, celle qui consiste en des déplacements de matières sous la seule influence d'inégalités de concentration, apparaît dès à présent comme assez confortablement explorée, bien que dans ce cas comme dans tant d'autres, rien de définitif ne saurait être acquis. Certes les premières manifestations de ces phénomènes sont connues de longue date, mais ce n'est que récemment, au prix de difficultés techniques souvent considérables, que l'expérimentation a conduit à un ensemble déjà important de résultats.

Les phénomènes de diffusion thermique sont aussi anciennement connus. On a coutume de leur donner le nom d'Effet Ludwig-Soret (C. Ludwig, 1856, et Ch. Soret, 1879) quand on s'adresse aux phases condensées et ils désignent les migrations de matière provoquées par inégalités de température. Dans ce domaine les données expérimentales sont incontestablement plus lacunaires que dans le précédent.[1–5] En outre, nous avons à faire ici à des phénomènes certainement beaucoup plus complexes puisqu'à la variable titre des solutions vient s'adjoindre la variable thermodynamique fondamentale: la température.

Aussi bien, la thermodynamique classique, encore à l'aise dans les processus isothermes de diffusion (quoique irreversibles), avait les plus grandes difficultés à envisager les phénomènes où, outre leurs autres causes d'irreversibilité venait s'ajouter celle due à l'inégalité de température.[6, 7]

Bien qu'ayant pour but, dans ce qui va suivre, de nous limiter strictement à des résultats expérimentaux que nous nous venons d'obtenir, nous voudrions signaler qu'en accord avec une thermodynamique de l'irreversibilité (valable dans un domaine où les "déplacements" sont petits vis à vis de l'équilibre) nous avons fait apparaître les phénomènes de diffusion isotherme et de thermodiffusion dans la production irreversible positive d'entropie ($dS > 0$) du système que constitue une solution d'électrolyte.[8, 9]

I. L'EFFET SORET DANS LES SOLUTIONS

Dans une solution initialement homogène en titre et température, un gradient thermique local créera des différences de densités, donc des flux de convection. Si on utilise un appareil qui permette le blocage rapide de ces flux, alors au sein de la solution s'instituere une situation compétitive entre la diffusion thermique et la diffusion ordinaire résultant du gradient de concentration formé, jusqu'à l'obtention d'un équilibre dit équilibre Soret. C'est du moins sous cet aspect très sommaire que l'on peut concevoir "l'Effet Soret pur." C'est l'Effet Soret pur que nous avons cherché à étudier expérimentalement. La réalisation d'un tel dispositif est connu: la solution en expérience est maintenue entre 2 plans horizontaux dont le supérieur est amené à une température homogène plus élevée que celui du bas. Notons que le succès de telles expériences réside essentiellement dans la qualité des définitions géométriques, mécaniques et thermiques de l'appareil.

La méthode de l'Effet Soret pur n'est certes pas la seule utilisable dans l'étude expérimentale de ce phénomène. D'autres techniques, telles le procédé thermogravitionnel, ont permis des applications pratiques très importantes. Dans ce cas c'est la convection elle-même qui est utilisée pour amplifier l'effet prévu.[9]

II. MÉTHODES EXPÉRIMENTALES

Dans l'étude expérimentale où nous nous confinons volontairement ici, nous avons cherché à recueillir le maximum d'informations sur les effets thermodiffusionnels dans les solutions ioniques.

C'est pourquoi il nous a paru intéressant d'effectuer des mesures simultanées de l'Effet Soret par deux méthodes indépendantes. Alors, les constantes physiques de l'appareil, identiques pour chacune d'elles, ne pouvaient que rendre les résultats plus directement comparables.

Il est à noter que, si l'on s'en tient à un formalisme classique dont nous donnons un schéma très bref un peu plus loin, l'on ne devait pas s'attendre à voir lever définitivement les indéterminations qui entourent certaines grandeurs telles que les chaleurs de transfert, car au fond, quelle que soit l'expérience en cause, on utilise toujours la même relation fondamentale. Dans un premier stade la confrontation des résultats doit donc surtout rechercher à fonder certaines hypothèses faites lors des calculs théoriques.

Nous avons utilisé une cellule à diffusion du type classique à gradient vertical dans laquelle à l'instant t l'état de la solution peut être considéré comme uniforme dans tout plan horizontal donné (Fig. 1). Un

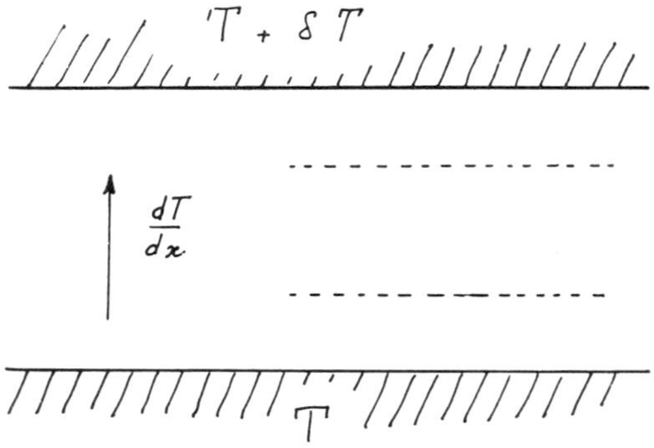

Figure 1

montage interférométrique basé sur le principe des franges d'Young permettait de suivre, par le défilement de franges, la variation de la différence de concentration aux niveaux de pinceaux lumineux interférents,[5] tandis que 2 électrodes horizontales, placées dans des plans différents, constituaient une pile thermique dont la f.e.m. était mesurée par une méthode classique d'opposition.

Nous avons choisi des sels pour lesquels l'Effet Soret était d'un signe tel qu'il ne risquait pas de compromettre l'équilibre gravitationnel obtenu lors de l'établissement du gradient de température. De plus l'emploi d'électrodes à Ag/ClAg très maniables nous a conduit à étudier jusqu'ici quelques chlorures alcalins et alcalino-terreux.

La Figure 2 montre à titre d'exemple les résultats d'une expérience où l'Effet Soret apparaît en nombre de franges et en microvolts en fonction du temps en minutes et correspond pour une solution de Cl_2 Ba à 1 N à un gradient de 10.94°C cm^{-1} avec une température moyenne de 25.02°C.

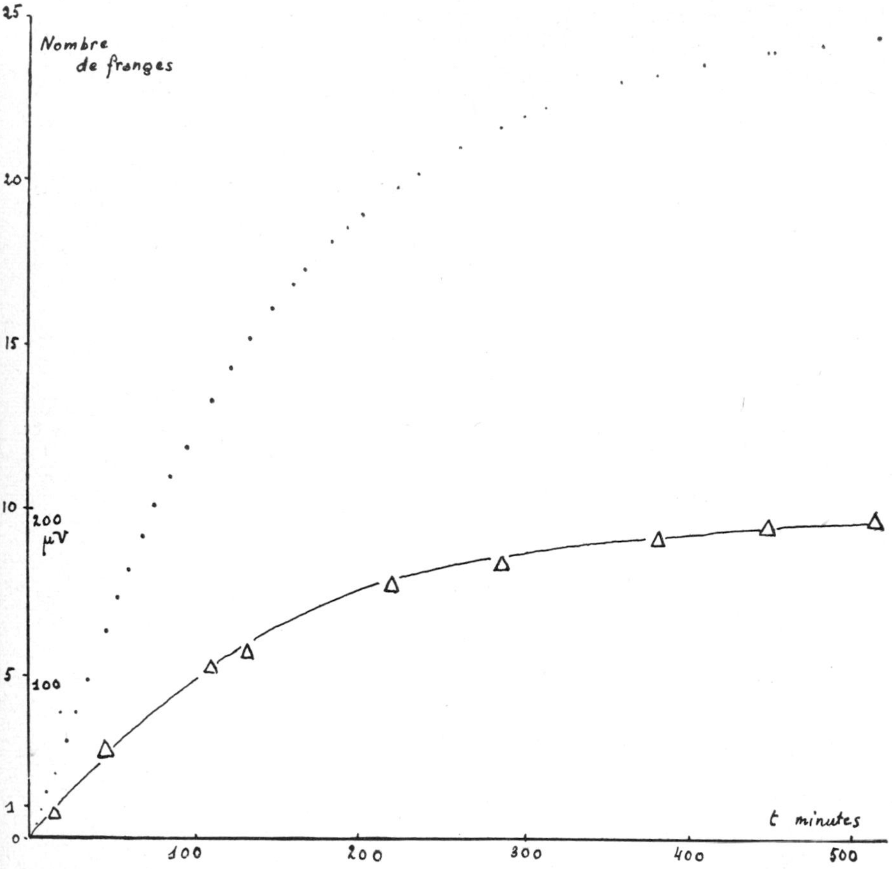

Figure 2

Remarques. I. La loi exponentielle $x_t = x_\infty\{1 - \exp(-t/\Theta)\}$ prévue par la théorie[9] semble une fois de plus recevoir confirmation tant dans la mesure de la variation d'indice que dans celle de la variation du potentiel. *II.* Les solutions mises en oeuvre ont été préparées dans une gamme de concentration assez vaste, en particulier les solutions de sels alcalins pour lesquels la méthode interférentielle s'est révélée peu sensible sauf aux fortes concentrations.

III. RÉSULTATS

Nous nous contenterons de donner quelques relations générales afin de mieux situer les résultats expérimentaux obtenus.

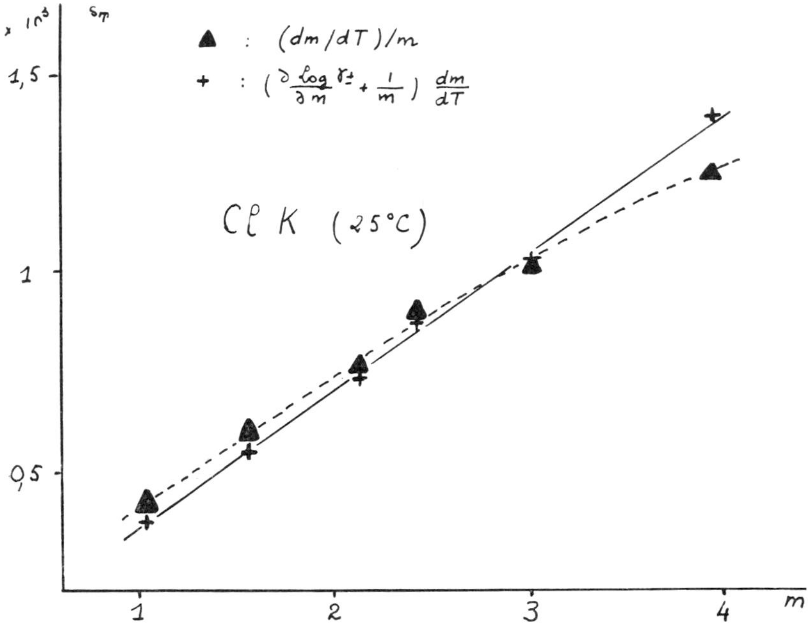

Figure 3

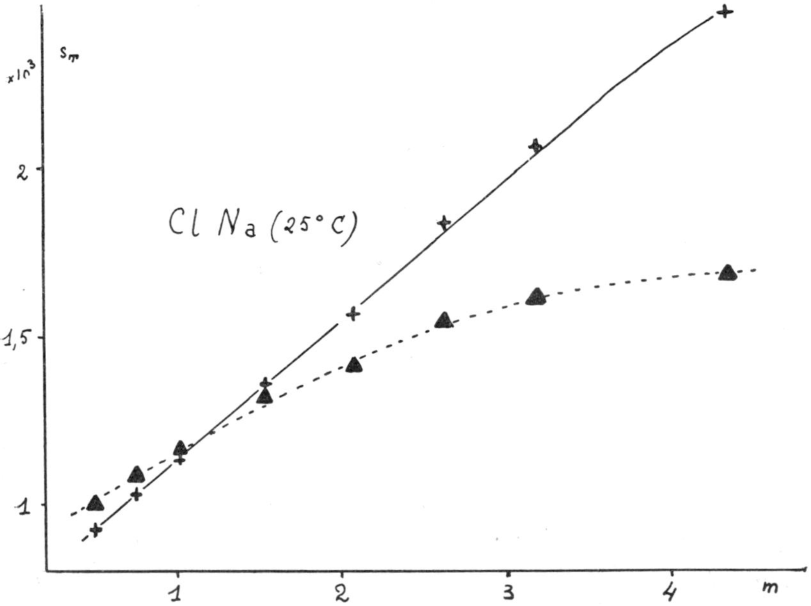

Figure 4

Toutefois il ne saurait être question de fournir ici une discussion détaillée de ceux-ci. Trop de questions complexes, telle la solvatation, sont volontairement passées sous silence pour que les grandeurs définies ultérieurement puissent faire illusion et que leur contenu soit immédiatement interprétable. De plus on doit garder en mémoire que l'expérimentation présente s'est adressée à des solutions généralement très concentrées.

Le traitement devenu classique de la production d'entropie conduit à des relations linéarisées qui,[8, 9] dans le cas d'un électrolyte binaire, s'écrivent, sous réserve de certaines hypothèses simplificatrices, pour l'équilibre Soret:[10]

$$\left.\begin{aligned} z_1 F d\phi + (\partial\mu_1/\partial m)dm + S_1 dT &= 0 \\ z_2 F d\phi + (\partial\mu_2/\partial m)dm + S_2 dT &= 0 \end{aligned}\right\}, \tag{1}$$

où l'indice 1 désignera le cation de valence (z_1), l'indice 2 l'anion de valence (z_2), μ_i les potentials chimiques, S_i les entropies de transfert au sens d'Eastman, ϕ le potentiel électrique et m la molalité de la solution:

$$m_1 = \nu_1 m, \qquad m_2 = \nu_2 m, \qquad m_i = \text{molalités ioniques.}$$

L'équilibre Soret se définira donc par la quantité

$$\frac{\partial\mu(m)}{\partial m}\frac{dm}{dT} = -(\nu_1 S_1 + \nu_2 S_2) \tag{2}$$

voir par

$$\left(\frac{\partial \log \gamma_\pm}{\partial m} + \frac{1}{m}\right)\frac{dm}{dT} = -\frac{\nu_1 S_1 + \nu_2 S_2}{\nu RT} \tag{2'}$$

avec

$$\nu = \nu_1 + \nu_2, \qquad \mu(m) = \nu_1\mu_1 + \nu_2\mu_2.$$

Dans les Figures 3, 4, 5, et 6 nous avons représenté la variation de cette expression vis à vis de la concentration et comparé à l'expression classique de l'Effet Soret $(1/m)(dm/dT)$. Ces valeurs ont été calculées à partir des mesures interférométriques.

Dans le calcul du potentiel électrique, il est bon de faire apparaître la quantité réellement mesurée entre les bornes des électrodes supposées à la même température.

Nous avons mesuré évidemment le potentiel initial $(d\phi/dT)_0$ qui existe au moment de l'établissement du gradient de température

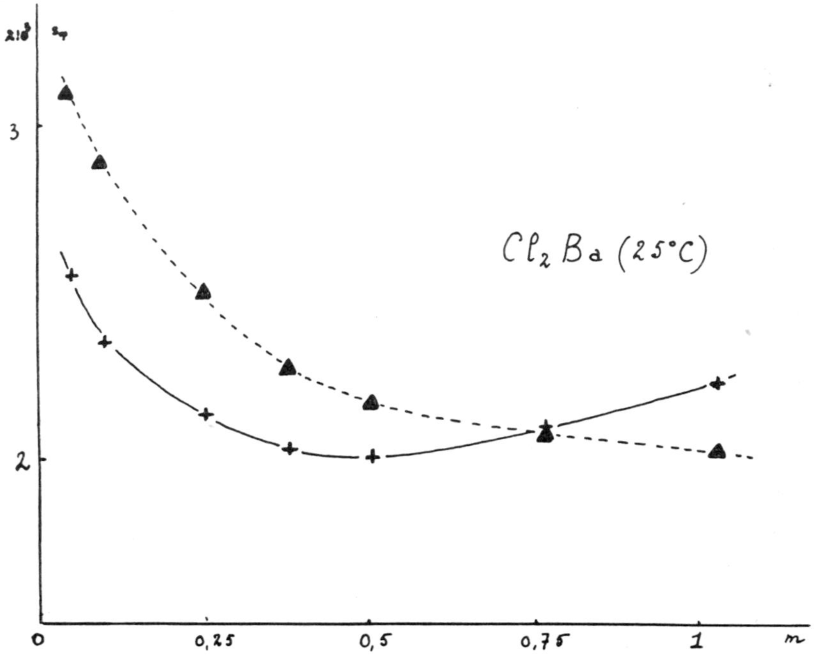

Figure 5

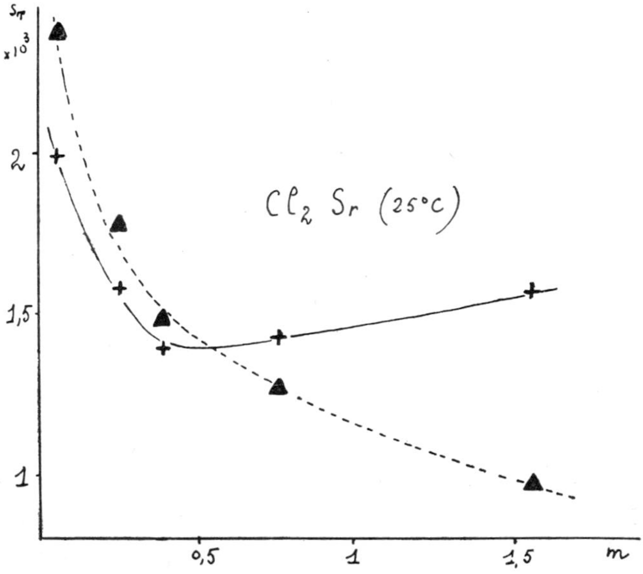

Figure 6

c'est à dire avant l'intervention de l'Effet Soret, puis le potentiel $(d\phi/dT)_\infty$ présent au moment de l'équilibre.

Le calcul de ces expressions a déjà été présenté à plusieurs reprises d'une façon plus ou moins complète.[11–15]

Nous obtenons ainsi par exemple:

$$\left(\frac{d\phi}{dT}\right)_0 = -\frac{1}{F}\left\{\sigma + \frac{\partial \mu_2}{\partial T} + \frac{t_1}{z_1} S_1 + \frac{t_2}{z_2} S_2\right\}, \tag{3}$$

où (t_i) sont les nombres de transport, et σ un coefficient caractéristique des électrodes utilisées, qui, en principe, n'a rien à voir avec les solutions expérimentées.

Les entropies de transfert (S_i) au sens d'Eastman sont liées aux entropies de transfert (S_i^0) dites souvent entropies absolues de transfert par:

$$S_i^0 = S_i + s_i = S_i - \partial\mu_i/\partial T, \tag{4}$$

où μ_i est le potentiel chimique de l'ion.

Par une transformation simple,[16] analogue à celle utilisée dans le calcul de la f.e.m. d'une pile de concentration avec transport, Lepoutre a montré que:

$$\left(\frac{d\phi}{dT}\right)_0 = -\frac{1}{F}\left\{\sigma + \frac{t_1}{\nu_1\nu_2}\frac{\partial \mu(m)}{\partial T} + \frac{t_1}{z_1} S_1^0 + \frac{t_2}{z_2} S_2^0\right\} \tag{3'}$$

où $\mu(m) = \nu_1\mu_1 + \nu_2\mu_2$ est le potentiel chimique du sel expérimenté.

L'intérêt de cette transformation prend tout son sens quand on envisage l'expression de $(d\phi/dT)_\infty$.

Il vient alors:

$$\left(\frac{d\phi}{dT}\right)_\infty = -\frac{1}{F}\left\{\sigma + \frac{S_2^0}{z_2}\right\}.^{*} \tag{5}$$

Fait particulièrement remarquable, le potentiel d'équilibre que nous avons mesuré devrait être indépendant de l'électrolyte. Il ne dépendrait donc que de l'ion réversible (ion Cl^-) commun à tous les sels étudiés.

Dans cette optique, les courbes de Figure 7 représentant la variation

* Cette relation particulièrement simple a déjà été présentée par Tenkin et Charosin.[14]

de $(d\phi/dT)_\infty$ avec la concentration devraient être, pour le moins, identiques pour les 4 sels. Ce n'est qu'une approximation.

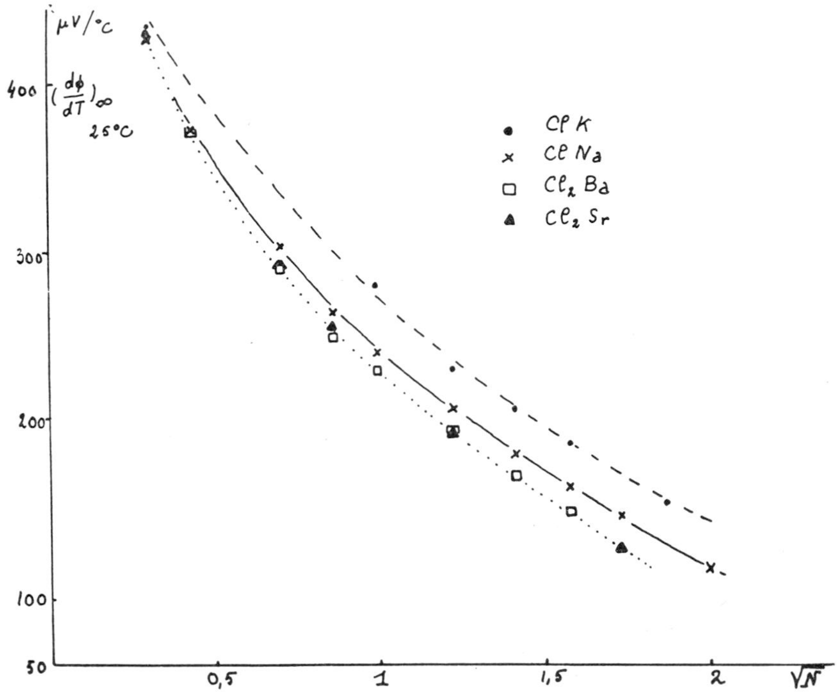

Figure 7

De plus pour chacune d'elles, cette variation montre à quel point la quantité ($S^0_{Cl^-}$) qui traduit globalement certaines propriétés thermoélectriques de transfert de l'ion Cl^- dans son contexte aqueux est une fonction complexe de la concentration.

IV. CONCLUSION

Les considérations qui précèdent semblent nous inviter, pour des études de cette sorte, à utiliser une expérimentation aussi variée que possible.

On ne pouvait songer ici à présenter une discussion complète des résultats expérimentaux que nous avons obtenus. Nous nous sommes contentés de montrer un des aspects intéressants parmi les plus simples que l'on peut tirer du type d'expérimentation auquel nous nous sommes attachés.

Références

(1) Th. Wereide, *Ann. phys.*, **2**, 67 (1914).
(2) J. Chipman, *J' Am. Chem. Soc.*, **48**, 2577 (1926).
(3) C. C. Tanner, *Trans. Faraday Soc.*, **23**, 75 (1927); **49**, 611 (1953).
(4) J. N. Agar and W. G. Bruk, *Nature*, **175**, 298 (1955).
(5) J. Chanu et J. Lenoble, *J. chim. phys.*, **53**, 30 (1956).
(6) E. D. Eastman, *J. Am. Chem. Soc.*, **48**, 1482 (1926); **50**, 292 (1928).
(7) C. Wagner, *Ann. Physik.*, **3** 629 (1929); **6**, 670 (1930).
(8) I. Prigogine, *Étude thermodynamique des phénomènes irreversibles*, Desoer, Liège, 1947.
(9) S. R. de Groot, *L'Effet Soret*, Thèse, Amsterdam, 1945.
(10) R. Haase, *Trans. Faraday Soc.*, **49**, 724 (1953).
(11a) H. J. V. Tyrell and G. L. Hollis, *Trans, Faraday Soc.*, **45**, 411 (1949).
(11b) H. J. V. Tyrrell and R. Colledge, *Trans. Faraday Soc.*, **50**, 1056 (1954).
(12) H. Holtan Jr., (Thèse, Utrecht, 1953.
(13) J. Chanu, *J. chim. phys.*, **51**, 390 (1954).
(14) M. I. Tenkin et A. V. Charosin, *Zhur. Fiz. Khim.*, **26**, 773 (1952).
(15) Z. G. Szabo, *Z. physik. Chem.*, **181**, 169 (1938).
(16a) Ch. Moreau et G. Lepoutre, *J. chim. phys.*, **52**, 498 (1955).
(16b) H. Holtan, P. Mazur, et S. R. de Groot, *Physica*, **19**, 1109 (1953).

THERMODIFFUSION PRÈS DU POINT CRITIQUE DE DÈMIXTION

G. THOMAES, *Faculté des Sciences, Université Libre de Bruxelles, Belgium*

Nous avons tenté de mettre en évidence le caractère thermodynamique du coefficient de diffusion isotherme. La thermodynamique des phénomènes irréversibles[1, 2] montre que le coefficient de diffusion D contient le facteur thermodynamique $\partial\mu_i/\partial x_i$ (dans lequel μ_i est le potentiel chimique et x_i le titre), alors que le coefficient de thermodiffusion D' est purement cinétique. Une forte dépendance du potentiel chimique avec le titre doit donc se traduire par une variation importante du coefficient de diffusion isotherme D et par conséquent du coefficient de Soret D'/D contrairement à ce que l'on observe généralement.

En thermodiffusion, la production d'entropie peut s'exprimer sous la forme

$$T\sigma[s] = -J_1 \left(\frac{\partial\mu_1}{\partial x_1} - \frac{\partial\mu_2}{\partial x_2}\right)_{Tp} \operatorname{grad} x_1 - \frac{w}{T} \operatorname{grad} T,$$

avec $\sigma[s]$ = source d'entropie, J_1 = flux de matière et w = flux calorifique réduit $= W - \Sigma_\gamma h_\gamma J_\gamma$.

Les relations phénomènologiques liant les flux de matière aux gradients sont donc en première approximation:

$$J_1 = -a_{11}\left[\frac{\partial\mu_1}{\partial y} - \frac{\partial\mu_2}{\partial y}\right]_{Tp} - \frac{a_{1q}}{T}\frac{dT}{dy}, \quad y = \text{coordonnée de l'espace.}$$

En comparant avec l'expression phénomènologique bien connue,

$$J_1 = -D'\varrho x_1(1-x_1)\frac{dT}{dy} - D\varrho\frac{\partial x_1}{\partial y},$$

on obtient les expressions des coefficients D et D':

$$\varrho D = a_{11}\frac{(\bar{M})^3}{(M_1 M_2)^2 x_2}\cdot\left(\frac{\partial\mu_1}{\partial x_1}\right)_{pT}, \quad \varrho D' = \frac{a_{1q}}{T}\frac{\bar{M}^2}{M_1 M_2 x_1 x_2},$$

avec M = masse de la particule et $\bar{M} = \Sigma_\gamma x_\gamma M_\gamma$.

D'autre part, les conditions de stabilité thermodynamique de diffusion indiquent[3] que le point critique ("critical solution point") se caractérise par

$$\frac{\partial \mu_1}{\partial x_1} = \frac{\partial^2 \mu_1}{\partial x_1^2} = 0.$$

On voit qu'au point de démixtion, si D' reste constant, le coefficient D'/D doit être infini. L'approche immédiat de ce point doit se traduire par une brusque augmentation du coefficient de Soret. C'est effectivement ce que l'on observe, quand on fait varier la température moyenne de l'expérience. Nous avons étudié le système *n*-hexane nitrobenzène, point de démixtion supérieur, t°C $= 19{,}8$, $x = 0.5$, dans un domaine de température allant de 31° à 21°C. Les valeurs obtenues vont de $D'/D = 2 \times 10^{-2}$ pour t°C $= 32$ à $D'/D = 49 \times 10^{-2}$ pour 21°C. (Ces résultats sont réunis dans le *Journal of Chemical Physics*, July, 1956). La variation observée semble confirmer les prévisions tirées de la thermodynamique des phénomènes irréversibles. L'appareil dans lequel ont été réalisées ces mesures est constitué par deux plaques distantes de 0,2 mm environ entre lesquelles circule le liquide à la vitesse moyenne de 10 cm à l'heure. A la sortie de l'appareil un dispositif scinde le flux laminaire en deux autres que l'on dose séparément. L'appareillage est décrit dans le *Journal de chimie physique*, p. 407 (1956).

Références

(1) I. Prigogine, *Étude thermodynamique des phénomènes irréversibles*, Desoer, Paris, 1947. *Introduction to Thermodynamics of Irreversible Processes*, C. C. Thomas, Springfield, Illinois, 1954.

(2) S. R. de Groot, *Thermodynamics of Irreversible Processes*, North-Holland, Amsterdam, 1951; Interscience, New York.

(3) I. Prigogine et R. Defay, *Chemical Thermodynamics*, Longmans, Green, 1954.

DIFFUSION OF TRACERS THROUGH SOLIDS

K. COMPAAN and Y. HAVEN, *Philips Research Laboratories, N.V. Philips' Gloeilampenfabrieken, Eindhoven, The Netherlands*

Several methods exist for calculating diffusion coefficients from molecular data (jump-frequencies, lattice constants, etc.). For diffusion through solids a well-known method is the lattice planes method, a method founded on the assumption that the diffusing particles move in a random way. If one is interested, however, in the mechanism of diffusion and wishes to draw certain conclusions from experimental data about that mechanism, one must use a different method of calculation, one that takes into account the nonrandomness of the particle movements, the so-called correlation.

For ionic crystals an experimental procedure exists that compares the data for the self-diffusion coefficient (measured with the help of tracers) with ionic conductivity, leading to a kind of Einstein relation. As an example, the case of interstitial diffusion of Ag through AgCl will be treated here.[1]

In Figure 1a Ag and Cl ions are shown, and also the surrounding interstitial sites. If in P there is an interstitial Ag ion, several possibilities of interstitial diffusion mechanisms exist for the Ag ions. Two will be discussed here. In the well-known "direct" interstitial mechanism, the Ag ion moves along the cubic lattice of interstitial sites (e.g. from P to T, etc.). The second mechanism, the "indirect" interstitial mechanism, is denoted by the heavy lines. The interstitial ion at P jumps to lattice site Q and pushes the ion occupying that site to a neighboring interstitial site. For simplicity we take only the forward direction $Q \rightarrow S$, from which this ion may again jump in one of the four possible directions, again pushing a silver ion into the next interstitial site, etc. If the ions are undistinguishable, there results a random motion of *an* interstitial silver ion (the diffusing entity) along the diamond lattice of heavy lines. The electric charge will move in the same way.

For the first mechanism, the direct one, one must expect the following relation between diffusivity and ionic conductivity

$$D_{tr}/\sigma = kT/Ne^2, \tag{1}$$

where N = the number of Ag ions per cc, σ is the ionic conductivity of Ag, and D_{tr} is the (self-) diffusion coefficient of Ag, measured with

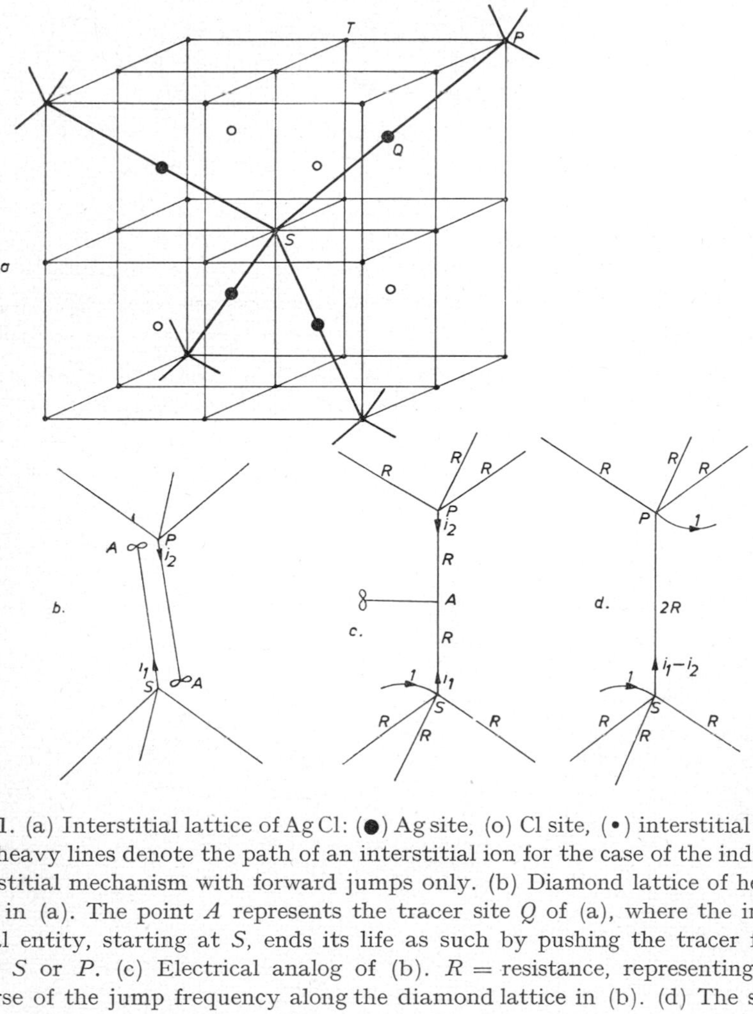

Fig. 1. (a) Interstitial lattice of Ag Cl: (●) Ag site, (o) Cl site, (•) interstitial site. The heavy lines denote the path of an interstitial ion for the case of the indirect interstitial mechanism with forward jumps only. (b) Diamond lattice of heavy lines in (a). The point A represents the tracer site Q of (a), where the interstitial entity, starting at S, ends its life as such by pushing the tracer from Q to S or P. (c) Electrical analog of (b). R = resistance, representing the inverse of the jump frequency along the diamond lattice in (b). (d) The same as (c), but with an extra current of magnitude -1 in P.

the help of radioactive Ag isotopes, the so-called tracers, and by applying a tracer concentration gradient.

The second mechanism gives a slightly altered relation:

$$\frac{D_{\mathrm{tr}}}{\sigma} = \frac{kT}{Ne^2} \tfrac{1}{2} f. \tag{2}$$

The factor $\frac{1}{2}$ occurs because of the fact that, at each tracer step, the electric charge moves twice the distance ($PS = 2PQ$). In many problems this factor does not occur, and then the only difference between the mechanisms must be found in the factor f. This "correlation factor" f arises from the fact that the tracers in the second case, the indirect mechanism, no longer move in a random way, but in a correlated way.

If there is in P an Ag tracer ion, we shall then see that the movement of this tracer is a correlated one. The jump from interstitial (P) to normal site (e.g. Q) is still random, because the four possible directions have equal probability. But, arrived at the normal site Q, it must wait for the next step until some interstitial ion comes to one of the neighboring interstitial sites. However, if the concentration of interstitials is low, it is almost certain that the same entity comes back that starts at S, to where the tracer on Q has just pushed it. The probability of returning after some time from the left ($S \rightarrow Q$) will be greater than from the right ($P \rightarrow Q$). Therefore, if we measure the diffusion coefficient of these tracers with the help of a tracer concentration gradient, we shall find relation (2) with the factor f, which can be calculated in this case from

$$f = 1 - (i_1 - i_2), \tag{3}$$

where i_1 is the probability that the interstitial entity, starting at S, arrives at Q along SQ without ever having passed Q before, and the same for i_2 along PQ. Because $i_1 > i_2$ one has $f < 1$.

In Figure 1b the situation is given schematically. If the particle has passed the tracer branch ($S \rightarrow Q$ or $P \rightarrow Q$), it is taken out of the lattice so as to be sure that it passes there for the first time. The values of i_1 and i_2 can be measured in an electrical network (Fig. 1c) because it can be shown that the probabilities of passing in Figure 1b are equal to the currents in Figure 1c, if the starting of the entity at S is translated by the input of a current of magnitude 1. The branches must all have the same resistance R and the ends A (representing Q) must be connected with "infinity." Now the problem is to find $(i_1 - i_2)$, which can be done more easily in Figure 1d by putting in a second current of -1

at point P. The connection with infinity then becomes superfluous, because the potentials of A and infinity are equal.

Figure 2c is equal to Figure 1d, and is also equivalent to the circuit of Figure 2d. Here Z represents the resistance of the lattice, parallel

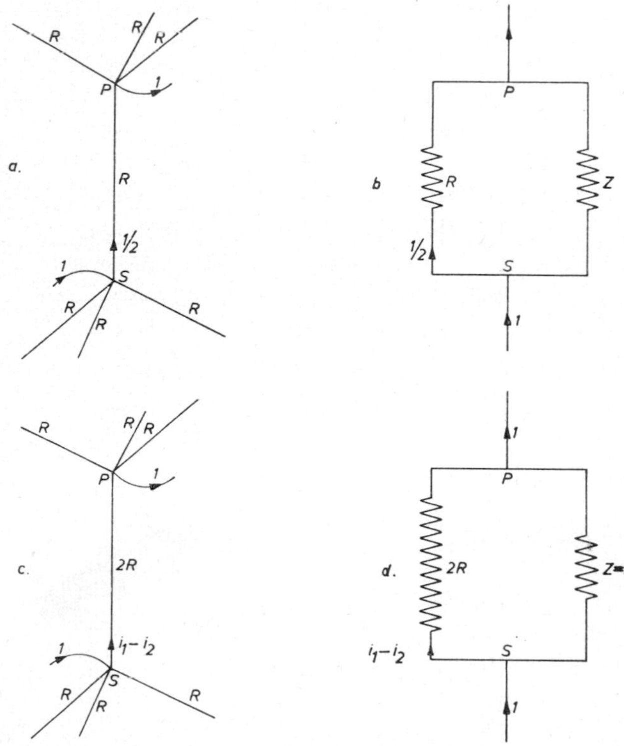

Fig. 2. (a) The diamond lattice with equal resistance R in every branch. (b) The equivalent circuit of (a). (c) Identical with Fig. 1d. (d) The equivalent circuit of (c).

to the resistance $2R$ between P and S. In Figure 2a one knows the current along SP, the "tracer branch," namely $\frac{1}{4}$ caused by the current 1 in S, because of symmetry around S, and again $\frac{1}{4}$ caused by the current -1 in P for the same reason. Therefore $\frac{1}{2}$ goes along SP and $\frac{1}{2}$ must go round about through the lattice. It follows that the parallel resistance Z in Figure 2b, the equivalent of Figure 2a, must be equal to R. And so it follows from Figure 2d that

$$i_1 - i_2 = \tfrac{1}{3}. \tag{4}$$

From (3) we find for the factor occurring in (2):

$$\tfrac{1}{2}f = \tfrac{1}{2}(1-\tfrac{1}{3}) = \tfrac{1}{3}. \tag{5}$$

From experiments done by Compton[2] on AgCl, one can deduce a value of $\frac{1}{2}f \approx 0.55$. The discrepancy can be shown to be caused by the assumption of only forward jumps PQS. The value of (5) will increase appreciably by allowing only for a small possibility of side jumps.

From this example two conclusions may be drawn:

(1) As f is dependent both on the special type of lattice and on the special type of diffusion mechanism, a comparison of the experimentally measured f with the theoretical values for various possibilities may give some information about the underlying mechanism.

(2) Many problems of both correlated and uncorrelated random walk along a fixed lattice can be simplified by translating them into problems in electrical networks, the electrical language being the richer of the two.

References

(1) C. W. McCombie and A. B. Lidiard, *Phys. Rev.*, **101**, 1210 (1956).
(2) W. D. Compton, *Phys. Rev.*, **101**, 1208 (1956).

THE SORET EFFECT. PART 3. DEMONSTRATION OF POSITIVE SORET COEFFICIENTS IN AQUEOUS SOLUTIONS OF SOME ELECTROLYTES

C. C. TANNER, *Imperial Chemical Industries Ltd., Jealott's Hill Research Station, Bracknell, Berkshire, England.*

Abstract

It seemed unlikely that measurements would be possible for systems in which the Soret coefficient was positive because of the consequent risk of density instability in the solutions. From earlier work, examples were known of systems possessing Soret coefficients apparently very close to zero. It has been possible to show that some of those systems have positive Soret coefficients, though the positive effect is relatively small. A margin for limited thermal diffusion change, without mixing, exists in the slight density gradient that is brought about at once when the temperature gradient is imposed. Until the density gradient is nullified by thermal diffusion of solute up the temperature gradient (positive Soret coefficient) thermal diffusion can go on, and has been observed in a few cases.

I. INTRODUCTION

The method of approach was that given in earlier published papers.[1,2] The solution was confined as a shallow horizontal layer between metal surfaces that were brought to the same temperature initially and then quickly changed to different temperatures to establish the temperature gradient.

Exploration of resulting changes in the solution, for all horizontal levels in the cell, was essential, and was secured by the improved optical method, some details of which have already been published.[2]

II. THE CELL

The cell shown in Figure 1 had optically plane walls of thin glass in the path of the beam of light and thicker glass walls elsewhere. The thermal conductivity of glass is but little different from that of the solutions under examination.

To minimize end effects, the cell was made long in relation to its height; a ratio of 10 : 1 was convenient. To avoid convectional mixing of the contents it had to be absolutely level. To insure reasonably quick attainment of a steady state concentration gradient, the vertical height of the cell was made small, about 1 cm. To establish a steady temperature gradient as rapidly as possible after disturbing the system from its initial, isothermal state, the upper surface was heated and the lower surface cooled simultaneously. The isothermal temperature was 30°C, the upper temperature 35°C, and the lower temperature 25°C. By thus moving from an isothermal state at the mean temperature, equilibrium in temperature distribution was established four times as quickly as it would have been had the cell been held initially at the lower temperature of 25°C. Temperatures were nearly steady in one minute, and readings could be taken after two to four minutes from the start of an experiment. For most aqueous solutions the subsequent time required for a 50 % approach to Soret equilibrium was between thirty and ninety minutes, and an experiment was allowed to run for a fivefold multiple of that period, the necessary time being determined from the experimental figures as they came to hand. To insure a uniform temperature distribution across the solution only insulating materials were used to fasten together the two metal parts and the glass walls, and symmetry was observed as far as possible in the cell design. The metal of choice for the upper and lower surfaces was silver, noncorrodible and possessing high thermal conductivity.

Temperatures were measured by calibrated, solid stem mercury-in-glass thermometers, with their bulbs placed in cavities in the metal just above and just below the plane surfaces in contact with the solution in the cell. It was necessary to use a liquid conductor, such as glycerin, to make efficient contact between the thermometer bulb and the metal; otherwise the thermometers responded more slowly than the cell contents.

Thermostats of unusually large capacity were employed so as to suffer minimum disturbance when the diffusion cell, virtually a thermal short-circuit, came on load. Large capacity pumps and short, wide-bore leads were used for water circulation. The hollow silver vessels comprising the upper and lower parts of the cell were also made as small and light as possible to reduce their heat capacity and thus to insure rapid attainment of uniform temperatures. To the same end, the water passages in the cell were baffled internally, the water leads from the thermostats were of thin-walled rubber tubing lightly lagged with layers of aluminum foil, and the cell was not lagged but protected from draughts by a Perspex screen. The diffusion laboratory was a small, isolated room and was thermostated.

Thus for the cell and arrangements shown in Figure 2. A number of compromises had to be struck to give an optimum combination.

Fig. 1. The cell.

Fig. 2. The apparatus.

III. OPTICAL ANALYSIS

In the optical method of analysis, also, it was necessary to compromise. For example, to explore a long cell a horizontal beam of monochromatic light had to be used. So it was necessary to accept, not a sharp image of the slit, but a shadow image, with a bright central line and alternating dark and light interference fringes of rapidly decreasing intensity. At the best, the shadow image was only moderately good. To sharpen it would have required increasing the width of the slit responsible for giving the line beam, but a limit was set by the height of the cell: the slit width has always to be much less than the cell height. If the cell height had been increased, to permit the use of a wider slit and a sharper image, the experiment would have taken an undue length of time, the extreme temperatures would have had to be set wider apart to give the same numerical temperature gradient, and the time required for establishing the temperature gradient would have lengthened by reason of the bulkier cell and contents.

The measurement of changes in concentration at any level in the cell was based on the displacement of that element of the beam of initially horizontal light that passed through it. But if the light was deviated, some elements hit the base of the cell and failed to emerge, while those elements near the top of the cell traversed layers lower and lower down, on the average, as the extent of deviation increased. Allowance could be made, if required, for the latter, second-order, effect, but the first could at best be minimized by insuring that the deviations were small.

While a photographic recording method had advantages, and was in fact adopted for some of the initial work in 1924—27, it had also several disadvantages. The presence of the bands of interference fringes, bordering the central bright line, gave overlapping images when successive exposures were taken on the same plate, unless marginal exposure times were adopted. Another restriction was the finite width of the central, bright line. It was necessary to insure that lines photographed in succession on the same plate could be separately resolved and identified, since each had to be assigned to an appropriate time, measured from the start of an experiment. A further and more serious defect was the inability to control an experiment on the basis of the extent to which diffusion had already proceeded; exposures literally had to be taken "in the dark." For these reasons, when work was taken up in 1952—53, and later, direct visual measurement was preferred, though it was more laborious to carry out. At a given time, readings were taken of the position of the shadow image of the slit on a suitably graduated graticule. The sharpest elements in the line were the two dark bands adjacent to the central, bright one, and one of them was selected for reference. From time to time, as the image of the slit swept across the graticule, a set of ten readings along its length was made in the course of a minute, during which time general displacement of the line was negligible.

So much for the technique of measurement. Again, it is quite evident that compromises were necessary.

IV. RESULTS

With the latest experimental apparatus some sixty experiments were completed and the value of the improvements in minor matters of technique fully demonstrated.

In the earlier work of 1924—27 no measurable displacements of the image had been found in twenty-four hours for solutions of LiCl, $MgCl_2$, $CaCl_2$, Li_2SO_4, and NH_4Cl. Hence these substances were regarded as having zero Soret coefficients. Examination of the photographic slides did show, however, especially for LiCl and $MgCl_2$ solutions, that the extremities of the deviated beam, taken soon after the temperature gradient was uniform, appeared to tip upward, which was the reverse of the usual direction.

When the more sensitive apparatus became available it was considered worth-while to reexamine some of those solutions. The sensitivity of the improved method, governed by the minimum displacement of the beam of light that could be measured with certainty on the graticule, was about 0.00001 in terms of refractive index, corresponding to a figure in the fifth decimal place for the Soret coefficients of the solutions under test. As most aqueous solutions of electrolytes have Soret coefficients of about -0.001, there was good scope for showing any small effect that might be present.

The results of some experiments with aqueous solutions of LiCl, $MgCl_2$, and $CaCl_2$ are given in Table I.

It became clear in the course of the work from the small shifts of the beam in an upward, as opposed to the normal downward direction, following the initial rapid downward dip when the temperature grad-

TABLE I

Soret Coefficient, $\frac{1}{m}\frac{dm}{dT}$, deg^{-1}

	Mole fraction, m	Soret coeff.
Cell height, 1.105 cm; T_c, 25° C; T_h, 35° C		
Lithium chloride	0.01817	+0.00027
	0.03631	+0.00010
	0.07405	+0.00005
Magnesium chloride	0.00963	+0.00004
	0.01796	+0.00005
	0.03643	+0.00003
Calcium chloride	0.0099	−0.00009
	0.0192	−0.00003
	0.0384	+0.00001
	0.0384	+0.00002
Cell height, 0.978 cm; T_c, 25° C; T_h, 35° C.		
Lithium chloride	0.03631	+0.00006
	0.07405	+0.00005

ient was applied, that these electrolytes were diffusing up the temperature gradient. Some measurements of a colleague, Mr. Chapman, working with the same apparatus for Mr. Tyrrell, showed that $LiNO_3$ solutions also had a small, positive coefficient. In all cases the effects were not much greater than the measure of experimental uncertainty, so that the original findings that the coefficients were close to zero still stand. But the weight of evidence is that these solutions have small, positive coefficients, and these facts, together with a recital of the experimental details involved in the latest approach to the problem of measuring Soret coefficients, are presented for interest.

The author wishes to express his thanks to Imperial Chemical Industries Limited for a grant covering the purchase of apparatus which made possible the continuation of the work.

References

(1) C. C. Tanner, *Trans. Faraday Soc.*, **23**, 75 (1927).
(2) C. C. Tanner, *Trans. Faraday* Soc., **49**, 611 (1953).

AUTHOR INDEX

Italic items refer to pages on which references occur.

SUBJECT INDEX